MARK TWAIN'S
WHICH
WAS
THE DREAM?

and Other Symbolic Writings of the Later Years

Edited with an Introduction by
John S. Tuckey

Mark Twain

UNIVERSITY OF CALIFORNIA PRESS
Berkeley and Los Angeles 1967

CENTER FOR EDITIONS OF
AMERICAN AUTHORS

AN APPROVED TEXT

MODERN LANGUAGE
ASSOCIATION OF AMERICA

UNIVERSITY OF CALIFORNIA PRESS
Berkeley and Los Angeles, California

CAMBRIDGE UNIVERSITY PRESS
London, England

© 1966 The Mark Twain Company
Library of Congress Catalog Number: 66–19100

Designed by Adrian Wilson
Manufactured in the United States of America

THE MARK TWAIN PAPERS

To Mother

Acknowledgments

Some five years ago Henry Nash Smith gave me exceedingly valuable counsel and encouraged my following of a line of inquiry that led into a fascinating area of study—that of Mark Twain's later writings. During my work in the Mark Twain Papers at the University of California, Berkeley, Frederick Anderson, the present literary editor of the Papers, has been extremely helpful in more ways than I could even begin to suggest without turning this section into a chapter. I am also greatly indebted to Albert Bigelow Paine, Mark Twain's biographer and first literary editor, and to Bernard DeVoto, who pioneered in studying the unpublished later writings—especially the "Great Dark Manuscripts" that appear in this volume. Valuable and much appreciated suggestions have been contributed by Paul Baender, Howard Baetzhold, Walter Blair, James M. Cox, Franklin R. Rogers, and Albert E. Stone, Jr. The works of a good many other scholars have also been used, in ways acknowledged in the notes; to them I here express my heartfelt thanks. The American Philosophical Society and the Purdue Research Foundation have provided generous and timely grants to make possible my working in the Papers. My wife Irene was a true helpmate in typing most of the manuscript for this book —after being wonderfully gracious about my leaving her and Janis and Alan at home while I was at Berkeley. I am most grateful to all of the persons and organizations that have in so many ways helped me study and prepare for publication the manuscripts here presented. I am also deeply grateful to the Mark Twain Estate for permission to publish these materials.

John S. Tuckey

November 1965

Contents

Abbreviations

MTP   Mark Twain Papers, University of California, Berkeley

LE   *Letters from the Earth,* ed. Bernard DeVoto (New York, 1962)

LLMT   *The Love Letters of Mark Twain,* ed. Dixon Wecter (New York, 1949)

MT & HF   Walter Blair, *Mark Twain & Huck Finn* (Berkeley, 1960)

MTA   *Mark Twain's Autobiography,* ed. Albert Bigelow Paine (New York, 1924)

MTB   Albert Bigelow Paine, *Mark Twain: A Biography* (New York, 1923)

MTE   *Mark Twain in Eruption,* ed. Bernard DeVoto (New York, 1940)

MTHL   *Mark Twain-Howells Letters,* ed. Henry Nash Smith and William M. Gibson (Cambridge, 1960)

MTL   *Mark Twain's Letters,* ed. Albert Bigelow Paine (New York, 1923)

MTN   *Mark Twain's Notebook,* ed. Albert Bigelow Paine (New York, 1935)

MTSatan   John S. Tuckey, *Mark Twain and Little Satan* (West Lafayette, Ind., 1963)

Writings   *The Writings of Mark Twain* (New York, 1922–1925) 37 vols.

Introduction

T HESE SELECTED later writings of Samuel L. Clemens—Mark
Twain—are here published for the first time, with but two excep-
tions: "The Great Dark" appeared in *Letters from the Earth*, as
edited by Bernard DeVoto; [1] and a 5,000-word excerpt from "Three
Thousand Years Among the Microbes" was published by Albert
Bigelow Paine in his biography.[2]

THE BIOGRAPHICAL BACKGROUND

All of the selections in this volume were composed between 1896
and 1905. Mark Twain wrote them after the disasters of the early
and middle nineties that had included the decline into bankruptcy
of his publishing business, the failure of a typesetting machine in
which he had invested heavily, and the death of his daughter Susy.
Their principal fable is that of a man who has been long favored by
luck while pursuing a dream of success that has seemed about to
turn into reality. Sudden reverses occur and he experiences a
nightmarish time of failure. He clutches at what may be a saving

---

[1] *Letters from the Earth* (New York: Harper & Row, 1962)—hereafter
designated as *LE*, pp. 235–286. An excerpt from "The Great Dark" was published
in Bernard DeVoto, *Mark Twain at Work* (Cambridge, Mass.: Harvard
University Press, 1942), pp. 133–140. The present edition provides substantively
different readings of several passages in the text; these are discussed in the notes
on "The Great Dark." A major variant, "The Mad Passenger," which DeVoto
did not publish, is included in the Appendix.

[2] *Mark Twain: A Biography* (New York: Gabriel Wells, 1923—hereafter
MTB), 4 vols., IV, 1663–1670.

1

thought: perhaps he is indeed living in a nightmare from which he will awaken to his former felicity. But there is also the possibility that what seems a dream of disaster may be the actuality of his life. The question is the one asked by the titles that he gave to two of his manuscripts: "Which Was the Dream?"[3] and "Which Was It?"[4] He had posed a similar question in 1893: "I dreamed I was born, and grew up, and was a pilot on the Mississippi, and a miner and journalist . . . and had a wife and children . . . and this dream goes on and on and *on,* and sometimes seems so real that I almost believe it *is* real. I wonder if it is?"[5] Behind this naïve query was his strong interest in conscious and unconscious levels of mental experience, which were then being explored by the new psychology.[6]

Prominent among the dream-like events of Mark Twain's life were his experiences with the typesetter. He had first seen an early model in 1880 and had then met its gifted but eccentric inventor, James W. Paige. A few years later, after his imagination had become fired with the idea of developing and marketing the device, Paige offered him a substantial interest, and on 6 February 1886, he entered into a contract that he expected would make him one of the richest men in the world.[7] But the typesetter was never perfected. Its failure must already have been apparent in 1891 when, summarizing his life, he wrote that he had "watched over one dear project . . . for years, spent a fortune on it, and failed to make it go" and that "the history of that would make a large book in which a million men would see themselves as in a mirror" and would "cast dust upon their heads, cursing and blaspheming."[8] Yet

---

[3] The holograph is designated as DV 301 in the Mark Twain Papers, General Library, University of California, Berkeley (hereafter MTP).

[4] DV 302, MTP.

[5] Mark Twain to Susan Crane, 19 March 1893; copy in MTP. This letter is quoted in part, with changes, in *Mark Twain's Letters,* ed. Albert Bigelow Paine (New York: Gabriel Wells, 1923—hereafter *MTL*), II, 581.

[6] He expressed the question in a slightly more sophisticated way in a letter to Sir John Adams, quoted in the latter's *Everyman's Psychology* (New York: Doubleday, Doran, 1929), p. 203: "Meantime *which is I and which is my mind?* Are we two or are we one?"

[7] *MTB,* III, 905–906.

[8] *MTL,* II, 542–543

even as late as 1894, the year in which his publishing firm, Webster & Company, went into bankruptcy, he lived from week to week in the hope that the machine was at last to be marketed and that he would quickly make a financial recovery. One of his notebook entries of the last week of January 1894 reads: "2 *p.m.*, *Mr. Rogers's offices.* The great Paige Compositor Scheme consummated. At 2:15 cabled Livy, Paris: 'A ship visible on the horizon coming down under a cloud of canvas.'"[9] On 2 February, believing that his hopes were in fact realized, he sent his wife another cablegram, "to be put on her breakfast plate this morning (our 24th anniversary): 'Wedding-news: *Our ship is safe in port.*'"[10] But ten days later, still using the ship as the figure for his dream of a fortune to be made from the machine, he was sending her this rueful message: "Ships that Pass in the Night."[11] The scheme had miscarried. Late in that same year Henry H. Rogers, his able business advisor, made it clear that the typesetter had almost no commercial value. Mark Twain replied in a letter of 22 December 1894: "It hit me like a thunder-clap. . . . I went flying here and there . . . , only one clearly defined thought standing up visible and substantial out of the crazy storm-drift—that my dream of ten years was in desperate peril."[12] On the same day he wrote to Bram Stoker that there was in his "machine-enterprise" a "hitch so serious as to make it take to itself the aspect of a dissolved dream."[13] It was at this time that he wrote "The Derelict," a set of verses that are purportedly the mutterings of a mindless almshouse inmate who thinks of himself as a storm-beaten hulk adrift on the sea, "friendless, forlorn, and forgotten."[14] The ship of fortune had become an abandoned wreck that would never make port.

---

[9] These memoranda are available in the holographic notebooks and in full typescript copies in MTP. See Typescript 27, p. 51. This entry regarding the cablegram has been published with some inaccuracies in *Mark Twain's Notebook*, ed. Albert Bigelow Paine (New York: Harper & Brothers, 1935—hereafter *MTN*), pp. 235–236.

[10] Typescript 27, p. 51; *MTN*, p. 236.

[11] Typescript 27, p. 53; *MTN*, p. 236.

[12] *MTL*, II, 617.

[13] *MTL*, II, 620.

[14] DV 225, MTP.

Probably it was at about this time that he first planned the dream-of-disaster story. On 2 January 1895, he wrote a most revealing letter to Rogers:

> There's one thing which makes it difficult for me to soberly realize that my ten year dream is actually dissolved; and that is, that it reverses my horoscope. The proverb says, "Born lucky, *always* lucky," and I am very superstitious. . . . And so I have felt entirely certain that that machine would turn up trumps eventually. It disappointed me lots of times, but I couldn't shake off the confidence of a life-time in my luck.
>
> Well, whatever I get out of the wreckage will be due to good luck —the good luck of getting you into the scheme—for, but for that, there wouldn't be any wreckage; it would *be* total loss.
>
> I wish you had been in at the beginning. Then we should have had the good luck to step promptly ashore.
>
> Miss Harrison [15] has had a dream which promises me a large bank account, and I want her to go ahead and dream it twice more, so as to make the prediction sure to be fulfilled.
>
> I've got a first rate subject for a book. It kept me awake all night, and I began it and completed it in my mind. The minute I finish Joan I will take it up.[16]

In the themes here touched upon—the man of great fortune whose luck deserts him, the dream extending over a period of years, the voyage of disaster—there are portents of much that is to be found in Mark Twain's writings of the following period. In all probability the book planned at just this time was to contain such elements. And apparently it was this "first rate subject for a book" that he confided to William Dean Howells after returning to the United States in the next month, and that he later identified in a letter to Howells of 16 August 1898: in that letter he spoke of being again at work on a version of the story that he had "mapped out in Paris three or four years ago" and had thereafter told him about "in New York under seal of confidence . . . the story to be called 'Which

---

[15] Miss Katharine I. Harrison, Henry H. Rogers's secretary.
[16] *MTL*, II, 621–622. Paine published this letter without a date; a dated copy is in MTP.

Was the Dream?' " [17] It will be seen presently that he used this name in referring to several planned drafts of the tale of a calamitous voyage, which he thought of as variants of "Which Was the Dream?"

Although he had intended to take up his planned story directly after finishing *Joan of Arc,* he found little opportunity for further composition after completing that book in the spring of 1895. He was ill much of the time and was also increasingly occupied with preparations for the lecture tour around the world by which he would earn the money to pay his debts.[18] Yet he was gathering impressions that would later find a place in the dream tale. When business took him to Hartford on 19 March (Susy's birthday), he visited the great house that had been the Clemens residence during seventeen more prosperous years but had been closed since 1891.[19] The place had lately been rented to John and Alice Day. His letter of 20 March to his wife Olivia, who was still in Paris, tells of the impression that he received upon entering the house:

> [I]t seemed as if I had burst awake out of a hellish dream, & had never been away, & that you would come drifting down out of those dainty upper regions with the little children tagging after you.
>
> Your rocking chair (formerly Mother's) was in its place, & Mrs. Alice tried to say something about it but broke down.[20]

This homecoming fantasy became the story frame for the tale of disaster, in which the husband living happily at home with his wife and children would have a dream, lasting only a moment but seemingly filled with the tragic events of many years, after which he would awaken to find himself still at home with his family. The

---

[17] *Mark Twain—Howells Letters,* ed. Henry Nash Smith and William M. Gibson with the assistance of Frederick Anderson (Cambridge, Mass.: Harvard University Press, 1960—hereafter *MTHL*), II, 675.

[18] On 14 April 1895, he wrote to Henry H. Rogers, "I am tired to death all the time, and my head is tired and clogged, too, and the mill refuses to go. It comes of depression of spirits, I think, caused by the impending horror of the platform." A copy of this letter is in MTP.

[19] See *MTB,* III, 920.

[20] *The Love Letters of Mark Twain,* ed. Dixon Wecter (New York: Harper & Brothers, 1949—hereafter *LLMT*), p. 312.

ending as he planned it in several groups of working notes was to
feature such an incident as the one in which "Mrs. Alice" had
figured—and significantly the narrator's wife is named Alice or
Alison in several of the drafts. In "The Great Dark," for example,
the husband's narrative was to conclude, "It is midnight—Alice
and the children come to say good-night. I think them dreams.
Think I am back home *in a dream*." [21] The extent to which this
fantasy had taken hold of his imagination is further indicated in
the same letter of 20 March—which is headed "At Home,
Hartford": "I was siezed with a furious desire to have us all in this
house again & right away, & never go outside the grounds any
more forever—certainly never again to Europe." [22] His desire
became a sustained resolve. In a postscript added on the next day
he said, "I have made up my mind to one thing: if we go around
the world we will move into our house when we get back." [23] "At
Home" was, moreover, the title that he gave to the platform address
that he was soon delivering again and again; he carried the dream
of homecoming around the world with him. But when he had
nearly completed the long tour—he had reached London and was
planning to bring the family together there—he received word of
the death of Susy, of meningitis, on 18 August 1896. She had died
in the Hartford home, where she had remained with "Mrs. Alice."
Susy and he had been extremely close, and to lose her was a
catastrophe. And it is worth noting in what terms he later spoke of
what her death meant to him:

> A man's house burns down. The smoking wreckage represents only a
> ruined home that was dear through years of use and pleasant
> associations. By and by, as the days and weeks go on, first he misses
> this, then that, then the other thing. . . . Always it is an *essential*—
> there was but one of its kind. . . . It will be years before the tale of
> lost essentials is complete, and not till then can he truly know the
> magnitude of his disaster.
>   The 18th of August brought me the awful tidings.[24]

---

[21] Notes for "The Great Dark," DV 91, bb-4, MTP.
[22] *LLMT*, p. 312.
[23] *LLMT*, p. 313
[24] *Mark Twain's Autobiography*, ed. Albert Bigelow Paine (New York:
Gabriel Wells, 1924—hereafter *MTA*), II, 34.

Susy's death had meant a ruined home. And after that terrible August it must have seemed to him that the house itself was likely to be destroyed. On 23 September he sent his business agent F. G. Whitmore a postcard of seven words: "Keep house insured. My luck is down." [25] Such forebodings were to find their way into the story that he now more than ever had reason to write. It is with the burning of the family home that the nightmare of disaster begins in both "Which Was the Dream?" and "Which Was It?" Before writing those manuscripts, however, he wrote two story fragments in which a burning ship figures as an alternate symbol for the loss of fortune—and of family.

"THE ENCHANTED SEA-WILDERNESS"

In "The Passenger's Story," which was probably written in the fall of 1896, a vessel is becalmed on the Indian Ocean. On board is a splendid St. Bernard dog, "just a darling" and "the pet of the whole crew." When the ship catches fire one night, the dog rouses the sleeping deck-watch just before the flames reach some powder kegs. The lifeboat is quickly manned and all hands are saved—but not the dog. The captain has tied him to the mainmast, saying, "He'd be more in the way than a family of *children*—and he can *eat* as much as a family of children, *too*." [26] In the other fragment, "The Enchanted Sea-Wilderness," the same incident is given fuller development. Again the darling and almost humanly intelligent dog rescues the ship's company but is left by the captain to burn; again—copied verbatim from the earlier draft—there is the captain's statement that the dog would have been as much in the way and would have eaten as much as a family of children. Susy, who had died of brain fever during an August heat wave, had almost literally burned up in the Hartford house; in the incident of the abandoned dog, he may have been projecting his sense of guilt for having left her behind while he traveled. "The Enchanted Sea-

[25] Copy in MTP.
[26] DV 37a, MTP, p. 6.

Wilderness" begins with the ship "becalmed, away down south, dead summer time, middle of December, 1853," as a result of "a judgment on the captain" for letting the dog perish. The captain has "had an idea that he was born lucky," and for a time he refuses to believe that his luck has changed—until the ship is caught "in the whirl and suck of the Devil's Race-Track" and carried farther southward into a kind of Sargasso sea of the Antarctic called "The Everlasting Sunday," a graveyard for sailing vessels.[27]

"The Enchanted Sea-Wilderness" was written while Mark Twain was at an early stage of his composition of *Following the Equator*, which he began on 24 October 1896; [28] it was, in fact, written as a part of Chapter Four of the first volume and afterward omitted. Since he worked rather steadily on the travel book, he probably reached this point well before the end of 1896. That he continued to hold in mind the situation of the derelict vessels as one of great personal significance is suggested by what he wrote to his friend Joseph H. Twichell on 19 January 1897: "You have seen our whole voyage. You have seen us go to sea, a cloud of sail, and the flag at the peak; and you see us now, chartless, adrift—derelicts; battered, water-logged, our sails a ruck of rags, our pride gone." [29] A notebook entry of March 1897 is also of interest: he planned to use in a "Dream-tale" an incident concerning a "man . . . in deep trouble, busted, breaking for Australia in despair," who an hour after sailing would find that he had someone else's satchel, containing a fortune in banknotes.[30]

"Which Was the Dream?"

After he had at last finished the writing of *Following the Equator* on 18 May, he made within the next five days some notes for the long-postponed story. He first sketched the beginning and ending frame:

---

[27] DV 37, MTP, pp. 162–180.
[28] See *MTN*, p. 306.
[29] *MTL*, II, 640.
[30] Typescript 32a (I), p. 15.

1853

"I smell smoke. . . . Why, bless my soul, the house is burning down!"

1870

"It is 17 years since I wrote that last sentence. I will finish."

She. When he wrote said "last sentence" I was behind him—he nodded for an instant—possibly 15 seconds, but I think not more—it merely gave me time to pick up his cigarette, hold it under his nose a moment, then put it down—he started violently, but immediately began to write again. I peeped over his shoulder and saw him write the 3 first words "I smell smoke," then I slipped out charmed with the idea that he had known of my presence and was going to insert some pretty fancy about it.

I sat for 3 hours where I could see him writing. Then the nurse brought the children to say goodnight—we entered, and he said "O my God, who are you!" [31]

The story was to conclude with the homecoming fantasy that he had held in mind since his visit to the Hartford house in March 1895; however, the narrator's terrible dream, which he would believe to have lasted for seventeen years, was to make him a stranger in his own household at the moment of awakening. Other notes following those for the story frame gave the marriage date of the man and wife as 1846 and listed birth years for several children: two designated as "S" and "C" (suggesting Mark Twain's daughters Susy and Clara), born in 1847 and 1849; a third for whom the date was "ostensibly 1855." The latter child was to be only imaginary, a part of the husband's fifteen-second dream. Further notes were for the sea-voyage portion of the dream: "Steve and little Ward, sailors"; "Paige Captain"; "Whitmore, supercargo (should be captain's equal, is snubbed and insulted by him)." F. G. Whitmore had warned at the time of the contract with Paige that its terms regarding the typesetter could bankrupt Mark Twain. Presumably the story as planned at this time was to include a voyage that would symbolically represent the experiences of his ill-starred business venture.

---

[31] Typescript 32a (I), pp. 25–26.

Immediately following these notes Mark Twain recorded, *"May 23/97. Wrote first chapter of above story today."* [32] What he had begun was almost certainly the manuscript which bears his title "Which Was the Dream?" [33] The part that he then wrote may be found in the existing manuscript, in which it was incorporated, with some revisions, when he continued his composition several months later.[34] Under the heading "1853," as he had also begun his notebook entry, he started with the narrative of the husband, who had decided to please his wife Alice—"short for Alison"—by writing in shorthand the simple events of their lives. After recalling the time when they had been childhood sweethearts, aged five and eleven, he closed his chapter with the remark that their love "had stayed until this day and date, March 1, 1854. . . ." He took up the story again after locating for the summer at Weggis, beside Lake Lucerne in the Swiss Alps. At this time he preceded the husband's beginning with a statement "From Mrs. Alison X'.s Diary," starting with the date to which the tale had already been carried: *"March 1, 1854, morning.—*It will be a busy day." After showing the family at home, with preparations going forward for fancy dances and for a play to be presented by the children, he brought in the incident planned in the notes of 18–23 May. The wife, watching her husband at work with the pen, observed that "he fell asleep for a second and his nodding head drooped gradually down till his nose was right over the ascending film of cigar smoke. It woke him with a violent start and a sneeze, and he went straight on with his work again." [35] The first several chapters of the narrative of "Major General X" are to be understood as having

---

[32] Typescript 32a (I), p. 26.

[33] Apparently Bernard DeVoto was not aware of the existence of this manuscript at the time that he composed his "Editor's Notes" for *LE,* in which he stated, p. 293, that "no manuscript called 'Which Was the Dream?' is among the Mark Twain Papers." The holograph is now in MTP and was at some time catalogued by DeVoto as DV 301.

[34] He deleted the first two paragraphs of the previously written part, no longer needed as an introduction. That part which he had written in May is on the kind of paper that he had been using for the manuscript of *Following the Equator;* the rest of "Which Was the Dream?" is on a cross-barred paper that he used extensively during the stay at Weggis during July, August, and September 1897.

[35] DV 301, p. 5.

been written by him before his nodding and his dream of the fire and other disasters. He tells of happy years at West Point and of distinction in war, followed by still further "favors of fortune": election to the Senate; the friendship of famous men; the clear prospect of being elected to the Presidency. Again his happy home life is stressed as he writes of his daughters, now called Jessie and Bessie. Most of his reminiscences are of the gifted Bessie; in effect, this part of the manuscript is a barely fictional memorial to Susy, one that parallels Mark Twain's eulogy in his *Autobiography*.[36] Thereafter the dream begins; the house is found to be burning. Other disasters follow. It is discovered that the house was not insured and is a total loss. A trusted associate has been systematically robbing "X," who is forced into bankruptcy. When "X" is charged with forgery, the shock of the experience causes him to lose consciousness. He afterward finds himself living with his family in an "unimaginably inexpensive log house" that has a huge fireplace; this dwelling was described in part from Mark Twain's remembrances of the farm home of his Uncle John Quarles near Hannibal, Missouri.[37] "X" learns that he has been in a coma for a year and a half. He hears of the hardships met by his family during that time—and then the manuscript ends, incomplete.

The draft was thus abandoned before the dream-voyage part had been reached. However, extensive notes made on 22 August 1897 represent further planning of such a part of *Which Was the Dream?* They are phrased as the further narration of the fallen general, who is a passenger on a "new sailing vessel laden with imperishable provisions for Australia." He is believed by the others to have committed crimes, which are ignored because of his rank, making him feel secretly ashamed: "Thus my disgrace soon passes from the children's memories . . . (Bessie in delirium is proud that certain distinctions are shown to 'the General's daughter')." But at least he is in a position of superior knowledge: of those aboard, only he and his family are no longer pursuing some vain dream of success. "Everybody but us is full to the lips of this world's ambitions (and the best and holiest of them are sordid and mean)."

[36] *MTA*, II, 33–64.
[37] See *MTA*, I, 96–97.

The plan was still to have the ship get into the Devil's Race-Track, as in "The Enchanted Sea-Wilderness," and be led into the trap of the Everlasting Sunday. One note reads, "Ballet troupe, pretty girls —manager wildly enthusiastic—going to storm Australia—practices them in full costume even after they get in the Race, so hard it is for him to give up his splendid dream." [38] The hopes of all were at length to give way to despair, followed by madness and finally by death: "The *usual* death in this ship is suicide. And they hunt up new and insane ways to do it." [39]

FURTHER BOOK PLANNING

The date of these entries marks a time of major planning for the group of intended books that Mark Twain was to work upon intermittently during the next few years. The first anniversary of Susy's death had come on 18 August, and his thoughts were full of that tragedy when on the morning of 22 August he wrote to Wayne MacVeagh, "Four days ago the anniversary of our unspeakable disaster came, and trailed its black shadow over us"; the calamity, he said, still seemed "not a reality, but a dream, which will pass,—*must* pass." He reported that he had just finished correcting proof for *Following the Equator* and was ready for other work: "I have mapped out four books this morning, and will begin an emancipated life this afternoon, and shift back and forth among them." [40] Another letter of the same day is even more explicit: "I have begun four books; and by shifting from one to another of them according to the impulse of the day, I shall expect them to keep me entertained and recreated for the next three or four years. I don't mean to finish more than one per twelvemonth. There are five of them, in fact, but two of them are not for publication in my lifetime." [41] The two works then intended for posthumous publica-

[38] Typescript 32b (I), pp. 29–30.
[39] Typescript 32b (I), p. 33.
[40] MTP.
[41] Mark Twain to Mr. Skrine, 22 August 1897. Copy in MTP.

tion were probably *The Mysterious Stranger* and *What Is Man?*
One of the other books was obviously the dream-of-disaster tale for
which he made notes on the same day. Either at that time or shortly
afterward he also noted, "The Microscope and the Diatom"; "The
Whale and the Infusoria"; "The General and the Cholera microbes." [42] Although these memoranda are without predication,
they suggest that he may then have thought of using a microcosmic
setting for the dream voyage. They look toward "The Great Dark,"
written in the following year, which features a whaling ship and
crew of microscopic proportions, sailing in a drop of water that is
their ocean. The reference to cholera microbes may also be one hint
of some early planning of "Three Thousand Years Among the
Microbes," in which the narrator is a cholera germ. Another entry
made soon after the ones of 22 August 1897 more directly
anticipates the story situation of that book: "The globe is a living
creature, and the little stinking human race and the other animals
are the vermin that infest it—the microbes." [43]

As he had announced that he would do, he shifted back and
forth in working upon his planned writings, as well as upon other
incidental literary projects. He was still planning to write the
dream-voyage story, for on 26 November 1897 he added to his
notebook, "Remember the case of the bridegroom . . . leaning
over the taffrail a black and stormy night (friends present) when
the bowsprit of a passing vessel picked him off and he disappeared
in the dark with a shriek? . . . Add it to 'Which Was the
Dream?'" [44] On that same day, he was witnessing the historic
uprising on the floor of the Austrian parliament, the Reichsrath,
and recording impressions which afterward influenced the writing
of *The Mysterious Stranger*. Near the end of 1897 he composed
the first four and one-half chapters of the "Eseldorf" draft of *The
Mysterious Stranger*, presenting the boy-angel Philip Traum, an
unfallen nephew of Satan, as the sardonic observer of the crimes
and follies of mankind. He thus began *The Mysterious Stranger* as

[42] Typescript 32b (I), p. 35–36.
[43] Typescript 32b (I), p. 37.
[44] Typescript 32b (II), p. 48–49.

his first major creative effort after the book plannings of 22 August. After carrying the "Eseldorf" version to a length of some 12,000 words, he put it aside at about the time that he reported making "a shift into dramatic work"—in the middle of January 1898.[45]

"An Adventure in Remote Seas"

A close comparison of the papers and inks that he was using for various manuscripts during the rest of the year indicates that it was probably late in the spring that he was again at work upon a version of the sea-voyage tale—this time one that he called "An Adventure in Remote Seas." [46] Again the ship was carried far south, into forbidding Antarctic seas; again there was a dream of fortune that was to turn into a nightmare of disaster: after finding a great treasure of gold coins upon a barren island, the crew were to learn that their ship had been carried away in a storm; that they were trapped on the island with no hope of escape; that their gold had no more real value than a phantom hoard. Mark Twain did not carry the manuscript very far, but in what he wrote one can find, in addition to some now outdated arguments for free silver coinage, elements of the conventional sea romance: a remote, treasure-laden island; a marooned crew. Probably it was after dropping work upon "An Adventure in Remote Seas" that he planned a draft of "Which Was the Dream?" that would have brought such elements into that story: "In Which Was the Dream? they find an island all of virgin gold. It is [illegible] yds long and 100 feet high. Many dead . . .

---

[45] See John S. Tuckey, *Mark Twain and Little Satan: The Writing of "The Mysterious Stranger"* (Lafayette: Purdue University Studies, 1963—hereafter *MTSatan*), pp. 16–39. The texts of the three existing versions of *The Mysterious Stranger* (the holographs are in MTP) will be published in another volume of the Mark Twain Papers Series.

[46] DV 59, MTP. An eight-page holograph, "A Word to Exiles" (Paine No. 229, MTP), dated by Mark Twain 24 May 1898, matches DV 59 as exactly as possible in paper, ink, fineness and smoothness of penpoint, and style of handwriting—all of which vary markedly in the later writings. DV 235, MTP, a fragment about the servants of the household, dated 4 June Kaltenleutgeben [1898], is an equally close match. These manuscripts are written in black ink with a medium pen on wove paper, buff, size $5\frac{11}{16}$" x $8\frac{13}{16}$".

preserved by the cold and purity—had quarreled and fought before they knew they were prisoners for life. . . ." [47]

"The Great Dark"

When Mark Twain used romantic themes, the urge to burlesque them was usually not far behind. He knew the books of W. Clark Russell, then one of the most successful writers of romantic sea novels. Several years earlier, in a fragmentary essay styled "Studies in Literary Criticism, Lecture IV, *The Wreck of the Grosvenor*," he had touched upon the melodramatic aspects of Russell's fiction: "The crew rise and kill the captain and mate and take possession of the ship. Their leader is the carpenter, a treacherous and malignant rascal." [48] Such a carpenter leads an attempted mutiny in "The Great Dark." And it appears that Mark Twain was led into the writing of that story by way of attempts to burlesque Russell's writings. Parodying the latter's *Sailor's Language*,[49] he composed a comic "Glossary of Sea Terms," containing such ludicrous definitions as *"Stuns'l boom.* Sound made by the stuns'l when it is functioning in rough weather." All the listings had, he claimed, been "carefully examined by Mr. W. Clark Russell the best living expert in sea terminology." [50] Another fragment, written in the summer of 1898, presents a young mate who spews burlesque sea language in telling a tale that seems "taken detail by detail from one of Russell's enchanting descriptions." [51] In still another abortive draft, "Statement of Captain Murchison," one Samuel L. Clemens ships aboard a sailing vessel as mate and promptly astonishes the

---

[47] DV 91b, MTP. These notes are faintly written in pencil on a manila envelope. Other inscriptions on the face of the envelope show that it was used sometime as a container for materials relating to an early draft of *The Mysterious Stranger* and for a version of *What Is Man?*

[48] DV 6, MTP, p. 5. The holograph is on a paper watermarked "Victoria Regina" that he was using in 1895.

[49] *Sailor's Language: A Collection of Sea-terms and Their Definitions* (London: Sampson, Marston, Searle, and Rivington, 1883).

[50] DV 332a, MTP. This fragment includes some comic sea-language that Mark Twain transcribed verbatim when he composed "The Great Dark."

[51] DV 331, MTP, p. 2.

captain with his sea talk. He doesn't know a binnacle from a booby hatch but fancies himself an expert on nautical terminology and reveals that he is preparing a dictionary of it; he provides examples, taken from the glossary.[52] "The Great Dark," [53] which presents the "Statement of Mr. Edwards" and includes much comic sea language, was probably begun not long after the writing of "Statement of Captain Murchison."

The experience that most immediately prompted Mark Twain to begin "The Great Dark" was—if a notebook entry of 10 August 1898 can be taken literally—his own dream during the preceding night "of a whaling cruise in a drop of water." [54] The already mentioned letter of 16 August 1898 to Howells reveals that he had lately reread the story "mapped out in Paris . . . to be called 'Which Was the Dream?' " and had then hit upon a better plan; also, that he had been at work upon the new version for about a week—or from about the time that he had had his dream:

> A week ago I examined that MS—10,000 words—& saw that the plan was a totally impossible one—for *me;* but a new plan suggested itself, & straightway the tale began to slide from the pen with ease & confidence. I think I've struck the right one this time. I have already put 12,000 words of it on paper. . . . I feel sure that all of the first half of the story—& I hope three-fourths—will be comedy; but by the former plan the whole of it (except the first 3 chapters) would have been tragedy & unendurable, almost. I think I can carry the reader a long way before he suspects that I am laying a tragedy-trap.[55]

After using a story frame similar to the one for "Which Was the Dream?" he did play for humorous effects in "The Great Dark." His narrator speaks of the "mizzen foretop halyards" (rather like referring to a basement penthouse), describes one sailor as "asleep on the binnacle" and another as "bending on a scuttle-butt," confuses "Top-sail haul" with "Topsails all," and commits numerous other blunders. Then there is the mate's story of the captain

---

[52] DV 332, MTP.
[53] DV 91, MTP.
[54] *MTN*, p. 365.
[55] *MTHL*, II, 675–676.

who took the pledge just before a long, cold voyage and was thereby restrained from the use of warming spirits, even though his mouth watered for them so much that his "every cuss word come out damp, and froze solid as it fell." There is also the episode in which the mate Turner is a butt for the practical jokes of the invisible Superintendent of Dreams, who keeps drinking his coffee.

After writing these comic episodes, Mark Twain then turned to the question of the role and function of the dream mind. In writing to Howells of the new version that was to be half or three-fourths comedy, he had also commented, "If you should see a little short story in a magazine in the autumn called 'My Platonic Sweetheart' (written 3 weeks ago), *that* is not this one. It may have been a suggester, though." No doubt it was, for the "story" was in part a layman's treatise on the psychology of dreams; he later decided to withhold it from publication because it was "neither fish, flesh nor fowl." [56] He was particularly interested in the relationship of the conscious and the unconscious levels of the mind, which he personified as the waking self and the dream self. His reading on the subject had included William James's *The Principles of Psychology,* Sir John Adams's *Herbartian Psychology,* [57] and Georg Christoph Lichtenberg's writings on dreams. The views of Lichtenberg must especially have interested him, for that eighteenth-century mathematician and psychologist believed that a dream of a moment's duration might appear to last for many years; he also regarded dream experiences as real events, in the sense of their being "also a life and a world." [58] Moreover, he held that "a man can really never know whether he isn't sitting in a madhouse." [59] In his working notes Mark Twain planned to have his narrator quote Lichtenberg to convince his wife of the possibility of confusing dream and reality. Conceivably, the ideas of Lichtenberg also

[56] Mark Twain to Henry Rogers, 2 November 1898. MTP. The 51-page holograph of "My Platonic Sweetheart" is Paine No. 111, MTP. In an abridged form it was published posthumously, in *Harper's Magazine* (December 1912).
[57] *The Herbartian Psychology Applied to Education* (London, 1898).
[58] *Lichtenberg: A Doctrine of Scattered Occasions,* ed. P. P. Stern (Bloomington: Indiana University Press, 1959), p. 232.
[59] *Lichtenberg: A Doctrine of Scattered Occasions,* p. 232.

prompted him to introduce a character called "The Mad Passenger" a few pages before the end of Book I; he wrote twenty-five manuscript pages concerning him but later cut them out of the story (see "The Mad Passenger" in the Appendix).

To account for the Mad Passenger's presence, he made use of the incident of the man snatched from the taffrail of his ship by the bowsprit of another vessel, which he had noted during November 1897 as material to be added to "Which Was the Dream?" Its appearance in a variant of "The Great Dark" confirms that he thought of this later narrative as another draft of the earlier one. And another of the notes, one on page 74 *verso* of the holograph, indicates that he thought of "The Passenger's Story" and "The Enchanted Sea-Wilderness" also as precursors of the same story: there is a reference to the time "2 years ago when the Dog-Tale Man had his accident" and a remark that "he and 2 or 3 others are still of this crew, but believed to be a shingle off." The Dog-Tale Man presumably was the sailor who had told of the heroic dog left on the burning ship. Probably Mark Twain regarded all of the drafts of the voyage-of-disaster tale as his successive attempts to bring to completion one literary work.

After cutting out the Mad Passenger episode, he made revisions in the earlier part of "The Great Dark," working out the inversion of dream and reality in terms of the narrator's own mental processes rather than those of another character. By the new plan Edwards's remembrances of life on earth were to be fading impressions of dream visits to an unreal place, whereas the recollections of his shipboard life were to remain strong and convincing. Some further changes were made to work out a way of having his wife share his dream memories. The Superintendent of Dreams was to have taken her to the dream place of earth on many occasions. As the story stands with these revisions, Alice remembers their home in Springport, the story equivalent of the Hartford residence, but only as a dream home; before revision, she had not remembered it at all. Apparently Mark Twain decided to make such changes when he was about at the point of finishing Book I.

In Book II he began to move toward the intended tragic outcome. But although he had a horrendous kraken-like monster attack the ship and so frighten the crew that they became ready to mutiny, he never actually wrote the tragedy that he had planned in his notes. At the time of the most determined attempt of the mutineers to take over the ship, the captain, who in Book I has been a rather weak man, suddenly becomes a forceful leader of the type of Captain Ned Wakeman—Mark Twain's Captain Stormfield.[60] After subduing the rebellious crewmen, he makes a moving speech to them, ending on a note of high courage:

> Are we rational men, manly men, men who can stand up and face hard luck and a big difficulty that has been brought about by nobody's fault, and say live or die, survive or perish, we are in for it, for good or bad, and we'll stand by the ship if she goes to hell! . . . If it is God's will that we pull through, we pull through—otherwise not. We haven't had an observation for four months, but we are going ahead, and do our best to fetch up somewhere.[61]

With this Odyssean speech (which has also an echoing of Huckleberry Finn's strong "All right, then, I'll *go* to hell!" [62]), the manuscript breaks off. The last part of "The Great Dark," as written, expresses strength and hope, rather than futility and despair.

His latest intention for a tragic finale is probably represented in a notebook passage of 21–22 September 1898, which is discussed in another section of this volume—in a note on the text of "The Great Dark." After a series of disasters, including the death of two of the Edwards children, the concluding part of the narrative frame was to be used at the time of the husband's awakening: "Looks up—is at home—his wife and the children coming to say goodnight. His hair is white." [63] There is no indication that he ever did any more work upon the story after making these notes. About two months later he was at work upon another draft of *The Mysterious*

---

[60] See Ray B. Browne, "Mark Twain and Captain Wakeman," *American Literature*, XXXIII (November 1961), 320–329.

[61] DV 91, MTP, pp. 134–135; 139 (pagination skips 136–138).

[62] *The Adventures of Huckleberry Finn*, Definitive Edition, XIII, 297. The edition, used for this and subsequent references to the published works unless otherwise noted, is *The Writings of Mark Twain* (New York: Gabriel Wells, 1922–1925), 37 vols., hereafter cited as *Writings*.

[63] Typescript 32 (II), p. 46.

Stranger. In the earlier "Eseldorf" version he had used an Austrian locale; he now laid the scene in Hannibal. This attempt too he abandoned, after writing about 15,000 words.[64]

"Which Was It?"

Thereafter, probably in the spring of the following year, he started a new version of the dream-of-disaster story in which the dream events were to take place not on a voyage but in a village resembling Hannibal. It will be recalled that before dropping work upon "Which Was the Dream?" he had introduced such a setting. This time the locale was to be a midwestern hamlet named Indiantown. The writing of the long manuscript "Which Was It?" —a loosely constructed, partly finished novel that used the Indiantown setting—occupied him from time to time between 1899 and 1903. He wrote much of the first 215 pages while staying in Sanna, Sweden, where his daughter Jean was in 1899 undergoing osteopathic therapy for epilepsy. The family went to Sanna in July of that year. Mark Twain made occasional business trips to London, and it is possible to identify parts of the manuscript that he very likely wrote at those times—on a kind of paper used for other writing done in London but quite different from what he was regularly using at Sanna. A preliminary sketch of the setting and characters for "Which Was It?" is on the London paper and was probably written there (it refers to conditions "in London to-day" and also mentions the Thames). This manuscript, "Indiantown," includes some pages of an earlier pencil draft and also some penciled notes that read, "Fairfax. He saves and protects Pomp"; "Boy-quarrel (?) with George"; "Fight with Ferguson." [65] An incident involving Fairfax and Ferguson is described in the *Autobiography*: the aristocratic Lord Fairfax, a friend of the Clemenses of the southern branch of the family, had one day been insulted by a "pestilent creature named Ferguson" and had knocked him down:

---

[64] See *MTSatan,* pp. 41–43.
[65] DV 302g, p. 16a.

Ferguson gathered himself up and went off, mumbling threats. Fairfax carried no arms, and refused to carry any now, though his friends warned him that Ferguson was of a treacherous disposition and would be sure to take revenge by base means, sooner or later. Nothing happened for several days; then Ferguson took the earl by surprise and snapped a revolver at his breast. Fairfax wrenched the pistol from him and was going to shoot him, but the man fell on his knees and begged, and said: *"Don't* kill me. I have a wife and children." Fairfax was in a towering passion, but the appeal reached his heart, and he said, *"They* have done me no harm," and he let the rascal go.[66]

The pencil draft shows that he was beginning to make fiction of this incident. And in "Which Was It?" Squire Fairfax horsewhips the surly, revenge-minded Jake Bleeker after the latter has accosted him on the street in an insolent manner. The episode initiates the main sequence of actions, leading to the murder of Bleeker by the highly respected George Harrison—under circumstances that make the squire appear guilty of the crime. Harrison, having robbed and then killed in attempting to get money to save the family estate, maintains an anguished silence when Fairfax is accused. As the narrator, he tells the story of his own cowardice. Mark Twain had long intended writing such a story. In 1879 he jotted in his notebook this idea: "The Autobiography of a Coward. Make him hideously but unconsciously base and pitiful and contemptible."[67] And in a letter to his brother Orion Clemens written on 26 February 1880 he spoke of two books he had long intended to write, "The Autobiography of a Coward" and "Confessions of a Life That Was a Failure." One plan, he said, would be to "tell the story of an abject coward who is *unconscious* that he is a coward."[68] Significantly, in an early set of working notes for "Which Was It?" he wrote, "George is always unconsciously illustrating Self[ishness]."[69] A weak man tempted beyond his limit, Harrison furnishes by his evasions and rationalizations an extended exemplum for a

---

[66] *MTA*, I, 82.

[67] Typescript 14, p. 16.

[68] *Mark Twain, Business Man*, ed. Samuel Charles Webster (Boston: Little, Brown, and Co., 1946), pp. 142–144.

[69] DV 302b—Al, MTP, p. 1.

text on cowardly selfishness: his story is in part a fictional analogue of *What Is Man?*

The greater part of the manuscript was written between 1900 and 1902. The paper of this part of over 400 pages is that of the "Par Value" tablet stock Clemens used from the time of his return to the United States in the fall of 1900 until about the middle of 1904. The initial story frame, which again is similar to the one he had devised for "Which Was the Dream?," is on this paper and probably was not added to the manuscript until he took it up again —after having written the first 215 pages. By 1902 he had carried the book far enough to be thinking of marketing it. In August of that year he noted "Which Was It?" as a work "to be serialized in a weekly" [70] and then brought out as a book. But he did not go on to complete the story. Had he done so, the outcome would have been much as he had planned it for the dream tale in earlier versions. When he was far along in his composition, he noted regarding Harrison and his wife Alison (who had been together in their beautiful mansion before his momentary dream and his narrative):

> They will not meet again till midnight—then his book of 32,000 words will be done, and when she comes he will be gray and old, and will think he is in a dream and they are apparitions of his dead.
>
> He will pick up her MS and groan. It has been by him 4 hours, but *he* thinks 15 years. [71]

He did not reach this ending, in which the husband would have found himself "at home." He probably did a little more work on the manuscript in 1903; at least, his notation of 30 May 1903 on a typescript copy shows that he looked over what he had thus far written.

HOMECOMING: FANTASY AND REALITY

It was also in the spring of 1903 that the Hartford home, which had been the focus of Mark Twain's homecoming fantasy, was

---

[70] Typescript 35, p. 24.
[71] DV 302b, MTP, p. 3.

sold. The dream of living there again as a family could never be realized—and perhaps could not be written. Yet even in 1904, in the final weeks and days and moments of Olivia's life, the dream of home was in their thoughts and on their lips. Her death came on June 5, in Florence, where they had located for her health in the preceding fall. Three days later he wrote to Twichell that, at Olivia's urging, they had been "hunting for a villa," and "always with an option to *buy*," for "she wanted a *home*—a home of her own; . . . was tired and wanted rest, and could not rest and be in comfort and peace while she was homeless." [72] Later in the year he recalled the last moments spent with his wife:

> Yes, I told her the long search was over and the villa found; it would be her own property at once, and she would have her heart's desire—she would live in her own home, she would be a wanderer no more. [73]

After a "glad half-hour," he said, there came "the most perfect expression of her love for me within my whole knowledge of her." [74] The dream of homecoming must have seemed almost a reality to Mark Twain as well as to Livy at that moment, but it was, of course, a fantasy. The homelessness was the reality. About two weeks later, on 19 June, he described himself as "a man without a country," explaining, "Wherever Livy was, that was my country. And now she is gone." [75]

It was at about this time that he composed the concluding chapter for *The Mysterious Stranger*, in which the narrator finds at the last that he is but "a homeless thought, wandering forlorn among the empty eternities!" [76] In this conclusion there is a negation of the idea of homecoming that he had been associating with the dream tale, for there is to be no awakening from the dream. The dream, for all of its nightmarish content, is all there is: "*Life itself is only a vision, a dream.*" [77] What could now offer

---

[72] Mark Twain to Joseph H. Twichell, 8 June 1904. Copy in MTP.
[73] Mark Twain to Muriel Pears, 24 October 1904. Copy in MTP.
[74] *Ibid.*
[75] Mark Twain to Charles Langdon, 19 June 1904. Copy in MTP.
[76] *Writings*, XXVII, 140. The evidence regarding the time of his writing of this chapter is considered in *MTSatan*, pp. 62–65.
[77] *Writings*, XXVII, 138.

solace was not the thought of an awakening from the fantasy of disaster to the reality of family joys, but the idea that there were no realities. On 28 July 1904 he wrote to Twichell, who had, he remembered, been asking how "life and the world—the past and the future" were looking to him; he replied:

> (A *part* of each day—or night) as they have been looking to me the past 7 years: as being NON-EXISTENT. That is, that there is *nothing*. That there is no God and no universe; that there is only empty space, and in it a lost and homeless and wandering and companionless and indestructible *Thought*. And that I am that thought. And God, and the Universe, and Time, and Life, and Death, and Joy and Sorrow and Pain only a grotesque and brutal *dream*, evolved from the frantic imagination of that insane Thought. . . .
>
> And so, a part of each day Livy is a dream, and has never existed. The rest of it she is real, and is gone. Then comes the ache. . . .[78]

"THREE THOUSAND YEARS AMONG THE MICROBES"

In 1905, having returned to America after Livy's death, he spent a lonely spring and summer at Dublin, New Hampshire, filling the days by dictating his autobiography and by writing. The book that he began shortly after reaching Dublin on 20 May was "Three Thousand Years Among the Microbes," in which he presented a satirical view of the human situation that had been in his thoughts for many years. In August 1884 he had written, "I think we are only the microscopic trichina concealed in the blood of some vast creature's veins, and it is that vast creature whom God concerns Himself about and not us." [79] Some twelve years later, he expressed a similar concept in *Following the Equator*:

> In Sydney I had a large dream. . . . I dreamed that the visible universe is the physical person of God; that the vast worlds that we

---

[78] Copy in MTP.
[79] *MTN*, p. 170.

see twinkling millions of miles apart in the fields of space are the blood-corpuscles in His veins; and that we and the other creatures are the microbes that charge with multitudinous life the corpuscles.[80]

It has been mentioned that in the summer of 1897 he made some memoranda relevant to the "microbe story" that he had probably begun to plan. Similarly, in the fall of 1898, following the notebook entries of 21–22 September for the ending of "The Great Dark," he wrote, "The Microbe-God," and, after that phrase, "bacillus dream." [81] At that time he perhaps considered adapting such matter to his dream tale, in which—as he had recently been writing it —things were already on a microscopic scale. When he finally came to the writing of "Three Thousand Years Among the Microbes," however, he did not present it as the narrator's dream, from which he was later to awaken. Rather, the narrator has at the beginning awakened into another existence. Although he sometimes dreams of his human past, he knows that outside of dreams there can be no return to his former life. It is, as Mark Twain's biographer Albert Bigelow Paine described it, a "fantastic tale . . . , the autobiography of a microbe that had been once a man, and through a failure in a biological experiment transformed into a cholera germ when the experimenter was trying to turn him into a bird. His habitat was the person of a disreputable tramp named Blitzowski, a human continent of vast areas, with seething microbic nations. . . ." [82]

In this bizarre narrative Mark Twain was still attempting to use his early recollections of Hannibal which had for so long served as the matrix of his creative work. But these Hannibalesque aspects are in some instances curiously disguised or transformed. For example, the narrator, whose microbic name is *Bkshp,* eventually becomes known by the nickname "Huck"; this "buried" identification is made only after the story is well in progress.[83] And there is a further, hidden tie between the names "Huck" and *Bkshp.* The

---

[80] *Writings,* XX, 114.
[81] Typescript 32 (II), p. 46a.
[82] *MTB,* III, 1238.
[83] The narrator takes the nickname "Huck" on p. 110 of the holograph, DV 347, MTP.

latter name is represented to be the narrator's earthly name rendered into "microbic orthography." Actually, *Bkshp* appears to be a coding of "Blankenship," the name of the Hannibal boy who was a childhood acquaintance of Samuel Clemens and who later served as the real-life model for Huckleberry Finn: "In *Huckleberry Finn* I have drawn Tom Blankenship exactly as he was," [84] Mark Twain has stated in the *Autobiography*. That *Bkshp* indeed signifies "Blankenship" appears the more probable when the name as spelled in the text is collated with the variant form that appears in a preliminary draft of the title page: *"Blkshp."* Moreover, the drunken tramp who is the planet of the microbes contains "rivers (veins and arteries)" that "make the Mississippi . . . trifling . . . by comparison." [85] "Huck" *Bkshp,* who exists within Blitzowski, is in circumstances like those described in the note of August 1884: he is a germ *"concealed* in the blood of some vast creature's veins." [86] That note, incidentally, was made during the time that Mark Twain was preparing *Huckleberry Finn* for publication.[87] It is interesting to find this hint that a character such as Blitzowski, the cosmic Pap Finn in whose Mississippi-like veins a Huckian germ would one day be hidden, had in effect been conceived at that time.

"Huck" has, like Huckleberry Finn, the imagination of disaster: reflecting that "D. T. will fetch Blitzy" before long, bringing about the destruction of the microbes' world and of its inhabitants, he asks, "My molecules would scatter all around and take up new quarters . . . , but where should *I* be?" Facing the prospect of his own dissolution, he muses upon what it will be like to lie helplessly watching his "faculties decay and depart, one by one, like lights which burn low, and flicker, and perish," then exclaims, "oh, away, away with these horrors, and let me think of something wholesomer!" [88] This fantasy of disaster is, however, but one part of

---

[84] *MTA,* II, 174.

[85] DV 347, MTP, p. 11.

[86] The italics are the editor's.

[87] During August 1884, he was reading the proofs. See Walter Blair, *Mark Twain & Huck Finn* (Berkeley: University of California Press, 1960—hereafter *MT&HF*), p. 360.

[88] DV 347, pp. 58–60.

a very loosely plotted story that is a vehicle for Mark Twain's views on many subjects.

His letters reveal that by June 11 he had reached page 240 of the manuscript and that he continued his writing until about 23 June.[89] Soon afterward he shifted to further work upon the "Print Shop" version of *The Mysterious Stranger,* and there is no indication that he ever did any further work on the microbe story.

SUMMATIONS

During the summer of 1906 he was again at Dublin but did much less work with the pen. In his autobiographical dictation of 30 August 1906 he spoke of the books which he had left incomplete. It had, he said, been four years since he had last taken up work upon "Which Was It?"; he could, he felt sure, "take up that book and write the other half of it without a break or any lapse of interest," but he would not do so: "The pen is irksome to me. . . . I am quite sure I shall never touch a pen again; therefore that book will remain unfinished—a pity, too, for the idea of it is (actually) new and would spring a handsome surprise upon the reader at the end." [90] He did not describe the surprise that he had in mind, but went on to speak of his other incomplete manuscripts:

> There is another unfinished book, which I should probably entitle "The Refuge of the Derelicts." It is half finished, and will remain so. There is still another one, entitled "The Adventures of a Microbe During Three Thousand Years—by a Microbe." It is half finished and will remain so. . . . These several tanks are full now, and those books would go gaily along and complete themselves if I would hold the pen, but I am tired of the pen.[91]

---

[89] Mark Twain to Clara Clemens, 11 June 1905. Copy in MTP. See also his memoranda regarding his literary work of 1905 in *MTL,* II, 783, and his letter to Joseph H. Twichell dated "St. John's Day [24 June], 1905"; copy in MTP.

[90] *Mark Twain in Eruption,* ed. Bernard DeVoto (New York: Grosset & Dunlap, 1940—hereafter *MTE*), p. 198.

[91] *MTE,* pp. 198–199.

"The Refuge of the Derelicts" was probably the title that he would have given to the voyage-of-disaster book if he had completed it. The other books are clearly identified, and it is evident that he was losing his intention of completing them. His last available word upon the matter may be his memorandum of 30 April 1909: referring to "four or five novels on hand at present in a half-finished condition," he said, "[I]t is more than three years since I have looked at any of them. I have no intention of finishing them." [92]

It should not be assumed that he regarded the work upon these unfinished drafts as wasted effort. During his world tour, he had told a reporter for the Bombay *Gazette*, "I like literary work for its own sake, and I am sorry that I did not make time to write, and not to publish. I should like to have half-a-dozen works in manuscript just for the pleasure of writing them." [93] He made these comments in January 1896. Within the next ten years, or for as long as he still enjoyed work with the pen, he did find time "to write, and not to publish." The books that he left incomplete represent a substantial fulfillment of one of his latest literary aspirations. He wrote them to please, first of all, himself, but they will also be of interest to both the scholar and the general reader. Although they were dreamed in the wake of disaster, they were written by a Mark Twain who even in a time of declining powers had, as Howells knew, almost the best talk in the world still in him.

The texts here presented have been transcribed from the holographs which are in the Mark Twain Papers at the General Library of the University of California at Berkeley. The aim has been to provide a reliable and readable text which represents Mark Twain's final intention insofar as it can be determined. For several of the selections there are typescripts which were revised by him in whole or in part; these have been taken into consideration. Further discussion of the times of composition of the manuscripts, sources

---

[92] *MTL*, II, 487. See, however, Paine's account of Mark Twain's discussion, on "a day in 1909," of the possibility of finishing *The Mysterious Stranger*, in *MTN*, p. 369. See also *MTSatan*, pp. 13–14, 71–75.

[93] Bombay *Gazette*, 23 January 1896. A copy of the article containing these quoted words of Mark Twain is in a file of newspaper clippings in MTP.

used by Mark Twain, and other relevant matters will be found in the editor's headnotes for the selections. Major variants have been presented in an Appendix. Important cancellations and insertions are discussed in the notes; in keeping with the editorial policy for the Mark Twain Papers series, there has been no attempt to record all minor changes, which would have clogged the volume with matter of little value even to specialists. Misspellings have been corrected, except when they are intentional, as in representing dialectal speech. Idiosyncratic spellings such as "to-day" and British spellings such as "centre" have, if consistently used, been retained. Ampersands have been spelled out as "and." Because Mark Twain's handwriting sometimes makes no clear distinction between capital and small letters, the normal usage of his period has been followed. A few indecisive punctuation marks—for example, dashes at the ends of sentences—have been regularized. Otherwise, his punctuation has been closely followed, for he expected as much. He once wrote of a proofreader who had taken the liberty of changing many of his marks, "Conceive of this tumble-bug interesting himself in my punctuation." [94] Although Mark Twain may not now be among the living, his editors can afford to be careful.

---

[94] Mark Twain to "C & W" [Chatto and Windus, London publishers], 25 July 1897. Copy in MTP.

Which Was the Dream?

"WHICH WAS THE DREAM?" was planned at the beginning of 1895 but was not written until 1897. The first twelve manuscript pages of the husband's narrative were written on 23 May, five days after Mark Twain had finished his composition of *Following the Equator*. For this initial chapter he drew upon his early memories of Hannibal in sketching the Tom-Sawyer-and-Becky-Thatcher-like courtship of Major General "X" and Alison Sedgewick. The rest of the incomplete draft was written during August 1897, the month in which there came the first anniversary of the death of Susy Clemens. It is hardly surprising to find many recollections of Susy—or to find some lack of coherence in what he then wrote. After the month had passed, he wrote, "[T]here will never be an August day, perhaps, in which I shall be sane. It is our terrible month." [1]

In representing the honor and greatness of "X" before his fall, he probably had in mind the military career of General Ulysses S. Grant, even though another character is more explicitly identified with him— the "young man named Grant" whose actions at the time of the fire save the assembly from panic and further tragedies. Mark Twain's own reverses, as well as those attributed to Major General "X" in the story, closely resemble those which he said in his *Autobiography* that Grant had suffered. The great general and President had after his retirement been forced into bankruptcy; had been unable to keep his houses or live in them; had been swindled by business associates; had in good faith written checks that "came back upon his hands dishonored." [2] A similar program of indignities, culminating in a charge of forgery,

[1] Mark Twain to Mr. Skrine, [9?] September 1897; copy in MTP.
[2] *MTA*, I, 27–48.

31

causes "X" to lose consciousness. In a discarded passage that originally followed at this point, his wife overhears the charge and then makes an impassioned defense of her husband. "Which Was the Dream?" is in part a fictional account of what Mark Twain had endured at the time of his business failure in 1894.

In this piece and in subsequent selections throughout this volume, occasional words have been supplied in square brackets to clarify Mark Twain's meaning. Unconscious abbreviations have been expanded ("straightford" to "straightforward"). Misspellings for which there is no contemporary or standard authority have been corrected but Mark Twain's consistently idiosyncratic spelling has been preserved. Inserted material has been moved into the text according to the author's instructions or evident intention, with punctuation corrected to integrate the insertions.

Like other texts here printed, this working manuscript presents a remarkably clear text in which cancellations average no more than one or two to a typical page and generally represent only an effort to achieve precision or conciseness and were chiefly made at the time of initial writing. Thus Mark Twain altered "happiness which had gone before" to "previous happiness," "full of admiration" to "bursting with admiration," and "a million and more" to "a million or two." He deleted an entire sentence when he discovered he could improve its phrasing later in the same paragraph. For example, on page 34 Clemens cancelled "Presidents do not break down the barriers of etiquette for persons of his sex." Occasional changes of intention are represented by the alteration of the General's name from "George" to "Tom" and his native state from "Ohio" to "Kentucky." Most other cancellations represent such routine changes as the substitution of "courageous" for "honest," "he" for "Sedgewick," and "a good many" for "a number of,"

Which Was the Dream?

FROM MRS. ALISON X.'S DIARY.

M ARCH *1, 1854, morning.*—It will be a busy day. Tom
and the servants and a carpenter or two have already begun to set
up the stage and scenery in the north end of the picture gallery *

* We call it the picture gallery because it isn't. It is the ball room.

for Bessie's play—first dress rehearsal to-night. There will be two
more before the great occasion—Bessie's eighth birthday—the
19th. The scenery and costumes have cost a great sum, and are very
beautiful. It will be a fine show to see that company of pretty children clothed in those rich habits. Tom tried to design Bessie's costume himself; dear man, he is daft about the child; about both of
them, indeed. He is vain of the play, and says it is wonderful; and
it is, perhaps, for a child of eight to have conjured out of her small
head. It lacks coherence, of course, and it has some rather startling
feats in it, even for magicians and fairies to do; still it is a remarkable little play, all things considered, and is adorably naïve and
quaint.

Tom has often promised me to write a little sketch of his life for
the children to have when we are gone, but has always put it off
and put it off; but as soon as I suggested that he write it in honor of
Bessie's birth-day, that was quite another matter and he was full of
it at once. I think I ought to be jealous; anything that Bessie wants,
Bessie can have, but poor mamma has to put up with a kiss and a
postponement. Of course Tom would find some opportunity in the

matter to show Bessie off. He will write the sketch in shorthand
tonight, and between this and the birthday Bessie will turn it into
long hand, with a little of my help, and then, on the birthnight,
after the ball and the play, she—

Mid-afternoon. Dear me, these interruptions! It is a busy day,
sure enough. I don't get time to turn around or get a moment's rest,
they keep after me so with their How shall we do this? and how
shall we do that? and so on. Tom is going to be tired out before
night, the way he is working. But he says he won't. And he has
devised a surprise of some kind or other for the end of the evening.
As soon as the night's rehearsals of the fancy dances and the play
are over I am to bring Bessie and Jessie to his study, and then he—

8 p.m. What a darling flock it is! They have all arrived at last,
with their troop of mothers. It is going to be a beautiful sight. The
gallery never looked so brilliant before, nor so grand and spacious;
and it will look finer than ever on the birth-night, with five
hundred handsome people in it and all the military and naval
uniforms, and the Diplomatic Body in their showy clothes. Washington is a good place for clothes. . . .

I went to the study, and looked in through the glass door. Tom
was at his task—since how long, I don't know. He was drowsy, I
could see that; I knew he would be tired. But his pen was going.
His cigar was lying on the table, and while I looked he fell asleep
for a second and his nodding head drooped gradually down till his
nose was right over the ascending film of cigar smoke. It woke him
with a violent start and a sneeze, and he went straight on with his
work again, and I hurried away, amused, to my room, to get a
moment's rest before beginning my long task of superintending the
costuming of the little people and directing the series of rehearsals. . . . A note—from the White House. The President
invites himself for this evening! This *is* an honor. And it is all for
Bessie, none of it for Tom. This it is, to be a Chief Magistrate's
small sweetheart. Someday it will make the child proud to be able
to say that once a President of the United States broke the laws of
etiquette that hedge his station for love of her. If he—"Coming!" I
am getting tired of that word.

MAJOR GENERAL X.'S STORY.

ALICE (short for Alison) Sedgewick and I (Thomas X.,) were born in the little town of Pawpaw Corners, in the State of Kentucky, I in 1820, she in 1826. When she was five and I eleven, we became engaged. I remember it very well, and so does she. It was the first time we had ever met; for it was only just then that her family had moved into our neighborhood from the other side of the town. We met on the way to school, on a pleasant morning in the early summer time—April, I should say; perhaps toward the end of it. It would be about that time I think, for it was warm enough for even boys connected with "quality" families to begin to hope for leave to go barefoot. The damp was stewing out of the ground, the grass was springing briskly, the wild flowers were thick, and in the woods on Murray Hill early in the mornings there was a musical riot of bird-song in place of the stillness that had reigned there so long. All the common boys had been barefoot for as much as a week already, and were beginning to mock at us for "Miss Nancys," and make fun of us for being under our mother's thumbs and obliged to be unmanly and take care of our health like girls. I had been begging my mother for leave, but she would not give it. She said we were as good blood as the best in the town—good old Virginian stock, like the Sedgewicks and the Dents—and she would not allow her boy to take second place to any offshoot of theirs. She said that I could come out barefoot when Billy Dent and Jeff Sedgewick did, and not a day before. Billy Dent was the county Judge's son, and Mr. Sedgewick was the principal lawyer and had run for Congress once. Mr. Sedgewick was Alice's father and Jeff's uncle, and had a large farm in the country, and owned more negroes than any other man in the town; and Jeff was a playmate of mine, although I had never seen his cousin until now.

I had my new summer suit on, that morning—yellow nankeens

—and was proud; proud of the clothes, but prouder still because I was barefoot; the first "quality" boy in the town to be "out." I had been showing off before Jeff and Billy, and making them green with envy: for they had supposed it was by my mother's permission that I was barefoot—supposed it from something I had said, I think. But I knew where my shoes were, and could find them when I wanted to go home.

The schoolhouse stood on a small bare hill, and at that time there was a thicket at the bottom of it, with a clear stream rippling through it; and it was just there that I came upon Alison. She was the dearest and prettiest little thing I had ever seen, and I loved her from that very moment. She had a broad leghorn hat on, with a wide red satin ribbon around it, the long ends dangling down behind; and her little short frock was of thin white summer stuff, and a piece of that same ribbon was tied around her waist for a belt. In one hand she had a Webster spelling-book and first reader, and in the other she had the last winter-apple that was left over.

I wanted to speak to her, but I was all in a quiver and did not know how to begin. She looked timidly up at me out of her brown eyes, then dropped them, and stood there before me silent. I had a marble in my hand—it was a white alley that I had just got in a trade for a China that was so worn that you could hardly see the stripes on it—and my excitement made my hand tremble, and it fell on the ground near by. It was precious property, but I would not take my eyes off that pretty little creature long enough to pick it up; but worked my right foot toward it and closed my toes over it and took it in their grip. That interested her, and broke the ice. She said—

"I didn't know anybody could do that but my cousin Jeff and our Jake. Can you walk with it so? They can."

"Oh, yes—it's easy; anybody can do it."

I made a step or two. Then with my foot I threw up the marble and caught it in my hand.

She was bursting with admiration, and tried to clap her hands, but they were too full of things. She cried out—

"Oh, do it again—do it again!"

I said—

"Shucks, that's nothing—look at this."

I gripped the marble in the toes of my right foot, balanced myself on my left, swung my right forward once or twice, to get impulse, then violently upward and backward, and sent the marble well up into the air above our heads, then made a spring and caught it as it came down.

She was mine! I saw it in her eyes. Her look was the concentrated look which Europe cast upon Napoleon after Austerlitz. She impulsively reached out the apple to me and said—

"There. You may have it all for your own."

I said—

"No, not all of it—we'll have it together. First, you'll take a bite, and then I'll take a bite, and then you'll take a bite, and then—"

I held it to her mouth, she took her bite, then I took mine, and munching we sauntered into the thicket, along the worn path, I holding her by her left hand. And by the stream we sat down together, and took bites turn about, and contentedly munched and talked. I told her my name, she told me hers, and the name of her kitten and its mother's, and some of their habits and preferences and qualities, and I told her how to dig fishing-worms, and how to make a pin-hook, and what to do to keep awake in church, and the best way to catch flies; and at last I asked her if she was engaged, and explained it to her; and when she said she was not, I said I was glad, and said I was not; and she said she was glad; and by this time we had munched down to the core, and I said now we could find out if everything was going to come out right and we get married. So then I took out the apple-seeds one by one and laid them in her small palm, and she listened with deep interest and grave earnestness while I delivered the fateful word that belonged with each:

"One I love, two I love, three I love I say;

Four I love with all my heart, and five I cast away;

Six *he* loves—"

"And *do* you, Tom?"

"Yes. Are you glad?"

"Yes, Tom. Go on."

"Seven *she* loves—*do* you, Alice?"

"Yes, Tom. Go on."

"Eight they *both* love—and they do, *don't* we, Alice?"

"Yes, Tom. Keep on."

"Nine he comes, ten he tarries—"

"What is tarries, Tom?"

"Oh, never mind—t'isn't so, anyway—eleven he courts, and twelve he marries! There, that settles it! It's the very last seed, Alice, dear, and we are going to get married, sure; nothing can ever prevent it."

"I'm *so* glad, Tom. *Now* what do we have to do?"

"Nothing but just kiss. There—another—and one more. Now it's fixed. And it'll stay forever. You'll see, dearie."

And it did stay forever. At least it has stayed until this day and date, March 1, 1854; and that is twenty-three years.[3]

I will skip a good many years, now. They were filled to the brim with the care-free joys of boyhood, and were followed by four happy years of young manhood, spent at the Military Academy of West Point, whence I was graduated in the summer of 1841, aged 21 years. All those years were a part of my life, it is true, yet I do not count them so. By my count they were merely a preparation for my life—which began in 1845 with my marriage. That was my supreme event; that was happiness which made all previous happinesses of little moment; it was so deep and real that it made those others seem shallow and artificial; so gracious and so divine that it exposed them as being earthy and poor and common. We two were one. For all functions but the physical, one heart would have answered for us both. Our days were a dream, we lived in a world of enchantment. We were obscure, we were but indifferently well off, as to money, but if these were lacks we did not know it, at least did not feel it.

---

[3] At this point ends the part of the narrative of "X" that was written in May 1897. The holograph of this part, paginated 1–12, is in black ink on olive paper 5″ x 8″, with vertical water-mark lines spaced 1⅛₆″. The remaining parts, paginated respectively 1–6 (Mrs. X.'s statement) and 1–97 (the rest of X.'s narrative) are in black ink on buff sheets 5⅜″ x 8⁵⁄₁₆″ with a cross-barred pattern of lines—a paper that Clemens used at Weggis in August 1897.

In 1846 our little Bessie was born—the second great event in my life. A month later, my wife's father died; within the week afterward coal was discovered on his land and our poverty—to exaggerate the term a little—disappeared in a night. Presently came the war, and through a film of proud tears my Alison, holding our little Bessie up to look, saw her late unnoted 2^d lieutenant, U.S.A., march for Mexico, colonel of a regiment of volunteers. In a little while she began to see his name in the war news, among the crowd of other names; then she saw it gradually and steadily separate itself from the crowd and grow more and more isolated, conspicuous, distinguished; and finally saw it hoisted aloft among the great head-lines, with Scott's and Taylor's for sole company; and in these days it was become as common as theirs upon the world's tongue, and it could be uttered in any assemblage in the land and be depended upon to explode a mine of enthusiasm. She was a proud woman, and glad; and learned to practice deceit, to protect her modesty and save the exultation in her heart from showing in her face—pretending not to hear, when she passed along, and there was a sudden stir upon the pavement, and whispers of, "There—look—the wife of the boy General!" For I was by many years the youngest of that rank in our armies.

And more was to come; the favors of fortune were not exhausted yet. There came a stately addition to that remark—"wife of the boy General—United States Senator—the youngest that was ever elected." It was true. The brief war over, I learned the news from the papers while I was on my way home.

And Alice was a proud woman again when her late obscure 2^d lieutenant entered our village and drove, at the Governor's side, through the massed country multitudes, under triumphal arches, in a rain of rockets, and glare of Greek fire, and storm of cannon-blasts, and crash of bands and huzzahs, to the banquet prepared in his honor; and proud once more when he rose at her side, there, and she saw the house rise at him and fill the air with a snow-tempest of waving napkins and a roar of welcoming voices long continued; and proud yet once more when he made his speech, and carried the house with him, sentence by sentence to the stirring close, and sat down with a dazzling new reputation made. (Her own dear words, and a pardonable over-statement of the facts.)

Those were memorable days, marvelous days for us. More than ever we seemed to be living in a world of enchantment. It all seemed so strange, indeed so splendidly impossible, that these bounties, usually reserved for age, should be actually ours, and we so young; for she was but 22 and I but 28. Every morning one or the other of us laughed and said, "Another day gone, and it isn't a dream *yet!*" For we had the same thought, and it was a natural one: that the night might rob us, some time or other, and we should wake bereaved.

We built a costly and beautiful house in Washington, and furnished it luxuriously. Then began a life which was full of charm for both of us. We did not have to labor our way into society with arts and diplomacies, our position was already established and our place ready for us when we came. We did not need to court, we were courted. We entertained freely, and our house was the meeting ground for all who had done anything, for all who were distinguished in letters, the arts, in politics and fashion, and it was almost the common home of Clay, Webster, Benton, Scott, and some of the other men of conspicuous fame. Alison's beauty and youth attracted all comers to her, and her sterling character and fine mind made them her friends.

And she was the gratefulest creature that ever was. Often she would take my face between her hands, and look into my eyes, and say—

"How dear you are! and it is you that have given me all this wonderful life. But for you I should be nothing—nothing at all. I am so proud of you; so proud, and so glad that you are mine, all mine."

It was her wealth that made this choice life possible; but she always put her hand on my lips when I said that, and would not listen; and said my fame and deeds would have been sufficient.

We are happy, we are satisfied. Fortune has done all for me that was in her power. She would have added the last possible distinction, but was defeated by the Constitution. I should be President and First Citizen of the United States now, if I were of lawful age. It is not I that say this immodest thing—ask your mother. It seems decreed, past all doubt, that I shall ascend to that high post three years hence, but we will not talk of that now, dear; there is no hurry.

POSTSCRIPT.

THERE—my sketch is done, I have made my promise good. There is enough of it for the purpose. For further particulars, Bessie dear, see the four Biographies. Your mamma is going to give them to you on your birthday morning. And let me whisper to you, Craig's is the best, because it flatters me.

Now I will go on and write something for the mamma. That will be easier work than that which I have just finished—so easy that it will write itself if I merely hold the pen and leave it free, for the text is so inspiring—The Children.

Our Jessie was born in the year of the Californian gold-rush, a cunning black-headed mite that weighed just four pounds, and was as welcome as if she had weighed a hundred. She is above five years old, now, a practical, decisive, courageous, adventurous little soldier, charged to the chin with tireless activities, and never still except when asleep. She is the embodied spirit of cheerfulness; everything that happens to her is somehow convertible into entertainment; and that is what results, no matter what the hap is. This has made it difficult to punish her. Even the dark closet was a failure. It missed her, and merely punished her mother, who kept her shut up a quarter of an hour and then could endure the thought of the little prisoner's sufferings no longer, and so went there to give her the boon of the blessed light again; but found her charmed with the novelty of the darkness and the mystery of the place and anxious to stay and experiment further.

She bears pain with a rare fortitude, for a child—or for an adult. Last summer her forefinger got a pinch which burst the fat front of the main joint, but she cried only a moment, then sat in her

mother's lap and uttered no sound while the doctor sewed the
ragged edges together—sat, and winced at the proper times, and
watched the operation through with a charmed and eager interest,
then ran off to her play again, quite ready for any more novelties
that might come her way. Tobogganing, last winter in the north,
the toboggan ran into a tree, and her ancle was sprained and some
of the small bones of her foot broken; but she did not cry—she
only whimpered a moment, that was all; and then had as good a
time in bed for a week or two as she could have had anywhere.

The other day she was taken to the dentist to have a tooth
drawn. Seeing how little she was, the dentist proposed to give her
an anaesthetic and make the operation painless, but her mother
said it would not be necessary. Alison stepped into the next room,
not wishing to see. Presently she heard the dentist say, "There, that
one is out, but here is another one that ought to come;" so she
stepped in and said, "Here is another handkerchief for you, dear,"
but [J]essie said, "Never mind, I brought two, mamma, I thought
there might be two teeth." She always had a thoughtful business
head from the beginning. And she is an orderly little scrap, too.
Her end of the nursery is always ship-shape; but poor Bessie's end
of it is an exaggeration of chaos.

For Bessie is a thinker—a poet—a dreamer; a creature made up
of intellect, imagination, feeling. She is an exquisite little sensitive
plant, shrinking and timorous in the matter of pain, and is full of
worshiping admiration of Jessie's adventurous ways and manly
audacities. Privately we call Bessie "Poetry," and Jessie "Romance"
—because in the one case the name fits, and in the other it doesn't.
The children could not pronounce these large names in the
beginning, therefore they shortened them to Potie and Romie, and
so they remain.

Bessie is a sort of little woman, now; and being a thinker, she is
learning to put a few modifying restraints upon herself here and
there in spots—and they were needed. To start with, she was a dear
little baby, with a temper made all of alternating bursts of storm
and sunshine, without any detectable intervals between these
changes of weather. She was a most sudden creature; always
brimming with life, always boiling with enthusiasm, always ready

to fly off on the opposite tack without any notice. Her approval was passionate, her disapproval the same, and the delivery of her verdict was prompt in both cases. Her volcano was seldom quiet. When it was, it was only getting ready for an irruption; and no one could tell beforehand whether it was going to illuminate a landscape or bury a city. Fortunately for herself and for us, her exaltations of joy were much more common than her ecstasies of anger. It took both to make her thoroughly interesting; and she was that. And keep us busy; and she did that.

The foundation of her nature is *intensity*. This characteristic is prominently present in her affections. From her babyhood she has made an idol of her mother. She and her mother are sweethearts, lovers, intimate comrades and confidants, and prodigal of endearments and caresses for each other. Nobody but the mother can govern her. She does it by love, by inalterable firmness, by perfect fairness, by perfect justice. While she was still in the cradle Bessie learned that her mother's word could always be depended upon; and that whatever promise her mother made her—whether of punishment, or a holiday, or a gratification, or a benevolence— would be kept, to the letter. She also learned that she must always obey her mother's commands; and not reluctantly and half-heartedly, but promptly, and without complaint. She knew the formula, "Do this, Bessie; do that, Bessie;" but she never had experience of the addition, "If you will, I will give you something nice." She was never hired to obey, in any instance. She early learned that her mother's commands would always be delivered gently and respectfully, never rudely or with show of temper, and that they must be obeyed straightway, and willingly. The child soon learned that her mother was not a tyrant, but her thoughtful and considerate friend —her loving friend, her best friend, her always courteous friend, who had no disposition in her heart or tongue to wound her childish self-respect. And so, this little whirlwind was brought under government; brought under obedience; thorough obedience, instant obedience, willing obedience. Did that save the child something? I think so. If a child—or a soldier—learns to obey promptly and willingly, there is no sting in it, no hardship, no unhappiness. The mother who coaxes or hires her child to obey, is providing unhappiness for it; and for herself as well. And particularly because the mother who coaxes and hires does not always coax and hire, but is in all cases a weak creature, an ill-balanced creature, who now and then delivers herself up to autocratic exhibitions of authority, wherein she uses compulsion—usually in a hot and insulting temper—and so the child never knows just how to take her.

It is a shameful thing to insult a little child. It has its feelings, it has its small dignity; and since it cannot defend them, it is surely an ignoble act to injure them. Bessie was accustomed to polite treatment from her mother; but once when she was still a very little creature she suffered a discourtesy at her hands. Alison and Senator Walker's wife were talking earnestly in the library; and Bessie, who was playing about the floor, interrupted them several times; finally Alice said pretty sharply, "Bessie, if you interrupt again, I will send you at once to the nursery." Five minutes later, Alice saw Mrs. W. to the door. On her way back through the main hall she saw Bessie on the stairs—halfway up, pawing her course laboriously, a step at a time. Alice said—

"Where are you going, Potie?"

"To the nursery, mamma."

"What are you going up there for, dear—don't you want to stay with me in the library?"

Bessie was tempted—but only for a moment. Then she said, with a gentle dignity which carried its own reproach—

"You didn't speak to me right, mamma."

She had been humiliated in the presence of an outsider. Alice felt condemned. She carried Bessie to the library and took her on her lap and argued the matter with her. Bessie hadn't a fault to find with the justice of the rebuke, but she held out steadily against the *manner* of it, saying gently, once or twice, "but you didn't speak to me *right*, mamma." She won her cause. Her mother had to confess that she *hadn't* spoken to her "right."

We require courteous speech from the children at all times and in all circumstances; we owe them the same courtesy in return; and when we fail of it we deserve correction.

These are lovely days that we are living in this pleasant home of ours in Washington, with these busy little tykes for comrades. I have my share of the fun with them. We are great hunters, we. The library is our jungle, and there we hunt the tiger and the lion. I am the elephant, and go on all fours, and the children ride on my back, astride. We hunt Jake. Jake is the colored butler. He belonged to Alison's estate, and is the same Jake whom she mentioned in our engagement-conversation when she was five years old. We brought him and his sister Maria from Kentucky when we first came to Washington. Both are free, by grace of Alice. Jake is thirty-two years old, now; a fine, large, nobly-proportioned man, very black, and as handsome as any man in the city, white or black, I think, and fully twice as good as he is handsome, notwithstanding he is a bigoted Methodist, a deacon in his church, and an incurable gambler on horse-races and prize fights. He is our prey, and we hunt him all over the library and the drawing rooms. He is lion; also tiger; preferably tiger, because as lion his roaring is too competent for Bessie's nerves. Bessie has a passion for hunting the tiger, but as soon as he gives notice that he is going to turn himself into a lion she climbs down and gets behind a chair and Jessie hunts him to his lair alone.

Bessie's mind is my pride, and I am building high hopes upon it. I have said that she is a thinker, and she is; and deep and capable. She has the penetrating mind, the analytical mind—and with it, naturally, precision of speech, intuitive aptitude in seizing upon the right word. Even when she was littler than she is now she often surprised me by the happy ingenuity she showed in choosing the word which would make her meaning clear. For instance. All of us who have labored at a foreign language by *book,* know how hard it is to get rid of the disposition to separate the words and deliver them with over-exactness of enunciation, instead of running them together and making them flow liquidly along, as a person does who has acquired the language by ear in strenuous fun and frolic and quarrel—in the nursery, for example. One day a couple of years ago I was playing with the children, and Bessie glibly—and as I thought, loosely—fluttered off a little German stanza about the

"Vöglein." Then I read it from the *book,* with care and emphasis, to correct her pronunciation, whereupon Jessie corrected *me.* I said I had read it correctly, and asked Bessie if I hadn't. She said—

"Yes, papa, you did—but you read it so '*stinctly* that it 'fused Romie."

It would be difficult to better that, for precision in the choice of the right word for the occasion. At five Bessie was busy enlarging her vocabulary. Some pretty large words got into it, and once she adopted one which presently met with an accident. She told a visitor she was never at church but once—"the time Romie was crucified." Meaning christened.

Bessie has always been dropping her plummet into the deeps of thought, always trying to reason out the problems of life, always searching for light. One day Alison said to her, "There, there, child, you must not cry for little things." A couple of days later Bessie came up out of a deep reverie with the formidable question—

"Mamma, what *is* LITTLE things?"

No one can answer that, for nothing that grieves us can be called little: by the eternal laws of proportion a child's loss of a doll and a king's loss of a crown are events of the same size. Alice was not able to furnish a sufficient answer. But Bessie did not give the matter up. She worked at the problem several days. Then, when Alice was about to drive down town—one of her errands being the purchase of a promised toy watch for Bessie—the child said, "If you should forget the watch, mamma, would that be a little thing?"

Yet she was not concerned about the watch, for she knew it would not be forgotten; what the struggling mind was after was the getting a satisfactory grip upon that elusive and indefinite question.

Like most people, Bessie is pestered with recurrent dreams. Her stock dream is that she is being eaten up by bears. It is the main horror of her life. Last night she had that dream again. This morning, after telling it, she stood apart some time looking vacantly at the floor, absorbed in meditation. At last she looked up, and with the pathos of one who feels that he has not been dealt by with even-handed fairness, said—

"But mamma, the trouble is, that I am never the *bear* but always the *person eaten.*"

It would not occur to everybody that there might be an advantage in being the eater, now and then, seeing that it was nothing but a dream, after all, but there *is* an advantage, for while you are *in* a dream it *isn't* a dream—it is reality, and the bear-bite hurts; hurts in a perfectly real way. In the surprise which I am providing for the children to-night, Bessie will see that her persecuting dream can be turned into something quite romantically and picturesquely delightful when a person of her papa's high capacities in the way of invention puts his mind to work upon it.

Bessie has the gift of concentration. This makes her a good listener, a good audience, for she keeps close track of what is said. And remembers the details, too,—which sometimes makes trouble for me; for I forget my details, and then am brought to book. Every evening I have to tell the children a story after they are in their cribs and their prayers accomplished—and the story has to be invented on the spot; neither of them will put up with any second-hand contributions. Now in all these inventions of mine, from away back, I have had one serious difficulty to contend with, owing to Alison's influence—*nobody in my tale must lie,* not even the villain of the piece. This hampers me a good deal. The blacker and bloodier I paint the villain the more the children delight in him, until he makes the mistake of telling a lie—then down he goes, in their estimation. Nothing can resurrect him again; he has to pack up and go; his character is damaged beyond help, they won't have him around any longer.

Sometimes I try to cover up, or slide over, or explain away, one of these lies which I have blundered into, but it is lost time. One evening during one of our European vacations I was in the middle of the fifth night of a continued story which I intended should last a year and make things easy for my invention-mill; and was gliding along like this—

"But the moment the giant invited him, the grasshopper whispered in Johnny's ear that the food was poisoned; so, Johnny said very politely, 'I am very much obliged to you indeed, sir, but I am not hungry, and—' "

"Why, *papa!* he told a lie!"

(I said to myself, I have made a blunder; Johnny is compromised; I must try to get him out of this scrape.) "Well, you see, Bessie, I reckon he didn't think what he was saying, and—"

"But papa, it couldn't *be;* because he had just said, that very minute, that he was *so* hungry."

"Ye-s, I believe that is true. Yes, that *is* true. Well, I think perhaps he was heedless, and just came out with the first thing that happened in his mind, and—"

"Oh, no, papa, he wasn't ever a heedless boy; it wasn't like him to be heedless; you know how wise and thoughtful he always was. Why, night before last, when all those fairies and enchanted creatures tried their very best, a whole day, to catch him in some little carelessness so they could get power over him, they never *could.* No, papa, all through this story, there never was such a wise boy—he *couldn't* be heedless, papa."

"Well, Potie, I reckon he was so weary, so kind of tired out—"

"Why, papa, he *rode* all the way, on the eagle, and he had been sound asleep all the whole day in the gold-and-ivory bed, with his two lions watching him and taking care of him—why how *could* he be tired, papa, and he so strong? You know the other night when his whale took him to Africa he went ashore and walked all day and all night and wasn't a bit tired; and you know that other time when—"

"Yes, yes, you are right, Bessie, and I was wrong; he couldn't have been tired—but he never intended any wrong; I'm sure he didn't mean what he said; for—"

"Then it *was* a lie, papa, if he didn't mean what he said."

Johnny's days of usefulness were over. He was hard aground, and I had to leave him there. He was a most unprincipled and bloody rascal, and if he could have avoided his one vice he might still be with us, nights, to this day, and as limitlessly happy as we are, ourselves. Romie once said this handsome thing about him—however, I will put that in further along, when I sketch out Romie's little history. I have a little more to say about her sister, yet.

Of instances of Bessie's delicate intuitions there are many in my mind. Here is one which is pleasant to me, and its original sweetness is in no way impaired by my often thinking of it. Last Christmas Eve Alice brought home a variety of presents, and allowed Bessie to see those which were to be sent to the coachman's family. Among these was an unusually handsome and valuable sled for Jimmy. On it a stag was painted, and also the sled's name in showy gilt capitals, "DEER." Bessie was joyously enthusiastic over everything until she came to this sled; then she became sober and silent. Yet this sled was the very thing she was expected to be most eloquent over, for it was the jewel of the lot. Alice was surprised; also disappointed; and said—

"Why Potie, doesn't it please you? Isn't it fine?"

Bessie hesitated; plainly she did not like to have to say the thing that was in her mind; but being pressed, she got it out—haltingly:

"Well, mamma, it *is* fine, and of course it *did* cost a good deal—but—why should that be mentioned?"

Seeing she was not understood, she pointed to that word "deer!" Poor chap, her heart was in the right place, but her orthography wasn't. There is not a coarse fibre in Bessie; she is as fine as gossamer.

From her earliest babyhood her religious training has gone on steadily at her mother's knee, and she has been a willing and interested pupil. But not a slavish one. She has always been searching on her own account, always thinking. There have been abundant evidences of that. I will set down one instance.

For some months, now, the governess has been instructing her about the American Indians. One day, a few weeks ago, Alice, with a smitten conscience, said—

"Potie, I have been so busy that I haven't been in at night, lately, to hear you say your prayers. Maybe I can come in tonight. Shall I?"

Bessie hesitated, waited for her thought to formulate itself, then brought it out—

"Mamma, I don't pray as much as I used to—and I don't pray in the same way. Maybe you would not be pleased with the way I pray now."

"Tell me about it, Potie."

"Well, mamma, I don't know that I can make you understand. But you know, the Indians thought they knew—and they had a great many gods. We know, now, that they were wrong. By and by maybe it will be found out that *we* are wrong, too. So now I only pray *that there may be a God*—and a heaven—OR SOMETHING BETTER."

It is the garnered doubt—and hope—of all the centuries, compacted into a sentence. And by a child.

She is a great treasure to us. Indeed we couldn't do without Bessie. Life would be flat, without her stimulating presence. She is not clay. She is a spirit. Generally in motion, seldom still—a sort of glimpse of frolicking sea-waves flashing in the sun; seldom a cloud-shadow drifting over them in these later times. She is all life, and soap-bubbles, and rainbows, and fireworks—and anything else that has spring and sparkle and energy and intensity for its make-up. She never talks much. I mean, in her sleep.

Now for Jessie—now for the busy brunette. The first day that ever Jessie—

CHAPTER

I DID NOT get a chance to finish the sentence. A shriek rang through the house, followed by a confusion of excited cries, and I ran to see what the matter was. The house was on fire. All the upper part of it was burning briskly before the calamity was discovered, for everybody was below, absorbed in the rehearsals.

For a moment the crowd of fifty children and thirty mothers had been in great danger—not from the fire, but from the perils inseparable from panic. There would have been manglings and crushings, if no man had been present. But fortunately, and by a mere chance, there was a man there; and by a still happier chance he was a soldier; a soldier of the best sort, the sort that is coolest in circumstances which make other people lose their heads. This was a young man named Grant, who was a third class man at West Point when I was a first. He had come to see me about something, and entered the ball room only a moment before the alarm was given. He was by the door, and took his place in front of it at once. The mob of women and children were paralyzed with fright for a moment; the next moment they would have made their fatal rush; but Grant did not wait for that. He spoke up in the calm and confident voice which stills troubled human waters by some subtle magic not explicable by the hearer but which compels his obedience, and said—

"Stand as you are! Do not move till I speak. There is no hurry, and there is no danger. Now then, you, madam, take two children by the hands, and move forward; you next, madam—do the same. Next—next—next."

And so on. In orderly procession the column fell in and filed out like a battalion leaving the field on dress parade.

But for West Point's presence there, I should be setting down a pathetic tragedy now. Lieutenant Grant had served under me for a while in the beginning of the Mexican war, and lately he had come to Washington on a business visit from his home in the West, and we had renewed our acquaintanceship. I think he had in him the stuff for a General, or certainly a Colonel; I do not know why he achieved no distinction in the war—but then, such things go a good deal by luck and opportunity. From what he had been telling me about his later fortunes, I judged that he was not born to luck. He remarked upon his Mexican nickname, "Useless," and said the old saying was true, in his case, that fun-nicknames are unwitting disguises of grave fact; for that if ever there was a useless man in the world, and one for whom there was plainly no place and no necessity, he was the one. Before the month was out I had sorrowful occasion to recal this talk of ours. With the Mexican war, his only chance for success in this world passed away; he recognized that, and I recognized it also, and was sorry for him. He was a good fellow, a sterling fellow, and should not have been wasted at West Point in the acquiring of a useless trade. But unfortunately none of us can see far ahead; prophecy is not for us. Hence the paucity of suicides.

We were overwhelmed with kindnesses by our friends; shelter in their houses was freely offered, but it seemed best, on the whole, to take quarters in the hotel, and this we did. The firemen saved the main part of the contents of the ground floor of our house, but nothing from the upper floors—the floors where we had lived, and where every detail was a treasure and precious, because hallowed by association with our intimate and private home life. This was a bitter hardship for us. A battered toy from the nursery would have been worth more to us than all the costly rubbish that was saved from the drawing rooms. Those dumb artificialities could be replaced, but not the historic toys.

The last of our hospitable friends left us at about two in the morning, and then we went to bed, tired out with the labors of the day and the excitements of the night. Alice said—

"I suppose you will rebuild the house just as it was before, Tom?"

"Yes. Jeff can begin tomorrow." That name reminded me of something, and I said, "Why, Alice, I did not see Jeff at the fire—did you?"

"No. And he has not been here in the hotel since we arrived, so far as I know."

"That is very strange. When did you see him last?"

"He left the house about five minutes before the fire alarm, and said he should be back within a quarter of an hour. He must have come back, of course; still, I did not see him."

"Alice! Could he have gone up to his room to save valuables, and got cut off and burned up?"

"He had no valuables in his room."

"No, not of his own, I know, but ours."

"Give yourself no trouble. Jeff Sedgewick has not risked his skin to save valuables of ours. He is not that sort of a man."

"Alice, you do not like your cousin."

"Tom, I have never accused myself of it."

Then we went to sleep. In the morning, still no Jeff Sedgewick. The forenoon wore away, and still he did not come. Everything was at a standstill. There was nobody to make contracts for the rebuilding of the house. Jeff was my business man and confidential secretary. He had begun as my secretary merely, when we first came east; but I knew nothing of business and had an aversion for it, and so, all my matters of that sort gradually drifted into his hands; for he was fond of business, and seemed made for it. In the beginning I franked my public documents myself—a wearisome job; one night I left half the documents unfranked; in the morning they lay in a confused pile, *all* franked. Jeff said—

"I finished the franking myself. Examine the pile, and see if you can tell the genuine signature from the imitation."

I couldn't. I was glad to let him do all the franking after that. In the beginning he wrote my letters from dictation, and I signed them. Later he wrote and signed a letter himself, without dictation, and I saw that he had caught my style exactly, and my hand. After that I was glad to let him do all my letters for me—in "autograph," and out of his own head. Soon he was signing and endorsing checks in "autograph." By and by all of my business was in his hands, every detail of it, and I was a free man and happy. Then came the full power of attorney, quite naturally, and thenceforth I was saved from even the bother of consulting and confirming.

In the very beginning Alice had begged me not to take Jeff to Washington.

"But Alice, he is an old friend, a schoolmate, he is poor and needs help, we are prosperous, we are fortunate, he is smart and capable, I am not, and I need such a person badly."

"But Tom, he is bad; bad to the marrow, and will do you an ill turn some day—the worst turn he can invent. He is envious, malicious, deceitful. He envies you your fame and prosperity, and hates you for it, privately. Every kindness you do him, every step you advance him, he will make record of and charge up against you, and when his opportunity comes he will take his revenge."

I laughed, at the time, at these unreasoning prejudices, and never thought for a moment that a young and inexperienced country girl like Alice could have an opinion that was valuable upon matters like these. I know, now, that her judgment of character was fatally and unfailingly accurate, but I did not find it out as early as I ought to have done.

She did not persecute me with her warnings; it was not her way;

but now and then at intervals she used to drop them when there seemed opportunity to accomplish something by them. Once in the early Washington days Jeff came in arrayed in what he thought was the finest and latest thing in New York fashion. And perhaps it was the finest and latest thing in the Bowery. He was as pleased as a child, with his vulgar outfit. I have never had any tact; and that is why I said—

"I thought the Independent Order of the Fantastics had been disbanded years ago. When are they going to parade?"

He looked ignorantly embarrassed—like one who suspects that an offence has been intended him, but is not certain. He said—

"I believe I don't quite get your meaning."

"Isn't that a uniform?"

He went out without saying anything, and did not appear any more in those clothes. I spoke to Alice of the incident in the evening. It troubled her, and she said—

"I wish you hadn't done it, Tom. You laugh at it, but it is not matter for laughing. He is a vulgar, vain fool, and you have hurt him in a tender place. He will not forget it, nor forgive it. Do get rid of him, Tom."

Although Jeff had held the power of attorney for years, Alice never found it out till a month before the fire—for I was too often unfaithful to her in my business affairs. I hid things from her that I was ashamed of. Secrecy is the natural refuge of people who are doubtful about their conduct. She was appalled when I told her the matter of the power of attorney. She said—

"Oh, Tom, what have you done!" and begged me to abrogate it, and said Jeff would make beggars of us.

I was able to triumph, this time, and said—

"On the contrary, dear, he has doubled our fortune. Come, now, you must be just to him at last, and take back some of the hard judgments you have passed upon him in the bygone times."

She was doubtful still, that was plain; and she asked for particulars. But I said—

"Wait one month, then you will see."

She sighed and said—

"I will wait, Tom, since you ask it, but even if he should

quadruple the fortune, I should still never be easy until we were rid of him."

I had no fears. I was preparing a pleasant surprise for Alice, and was sure I could spring it upon her in a few weeks. Jeff had made some brilliant speculations for me, of late years, and my confidence in his wisdom and shrewdness had grown in consequence until now they were boundless. He had sold out Alice's estate and invested her fortune in a Californian gold mine; for many months the mine had been swallowing money wholesale, but recent reports from its chief engineer showed that it was now on the point of paying back the fortune, with a hundred per cent interest. I had never liked the name of it—the "Golden Fleece"—but that was Jeff's taste; he named it.

Next morning we created a parlor and an office by having the beds cleared out of a couple of large chambers, and furniture proper to their new functions put in. In our house, Sedgewick's office had been on the ground floor, consequently all my business books and papers were saved. Alice soon arranged these in our new quarters. It was common for people whose houses had been burned down to send the firemen a donation and a word or two of compliment and gratitude, therefore in deference to this custom Alice asked me to draw a check for her to forward to the fire marshal. It was customary to disproportion the donation to the service rendered; therefore at Alice's request I made the check large. At least I considered it large; it was for $3,000. But then it was to help the company buy a new engine and build a new engine house.

Before Alice could finish writing her note of compliment and gratitude—she did not expect me to do any clerical work that could be shifted to somebody else—company began to pour in again. The stream continued until mid-day; then dinner interrupted it for an hour and a half; then the flow was resumed. About mid-afternoon or a little later Alice stole a moment and wrote the note, and sent it to the marshal by Jake. Still no Jeff appeared. Alice knew I was uneasy, for she knew the signs of all my moods, and with her native generous forbearance she left Jeff unmentioned. She never made a sore place of mine worse by meddling with it at the inopportune time. This is a beautiful trait; indeed it may be called a noble trait; and we all know it to be a rare one. I was never able to learn it, never able to make it a possession of mine. By taking thought I could *practice* it, momentarily, at wide intervals, but that was all. It was a *part of* Alice, and she did not have to think about it; but it refused to become a part of me. I was born small and selfish; Alice and the children were not. In nine cases in ten, when Alice had a sore place, I hastened with an insane eagerness to bruise it, and grieve her heart—and yet I loved her so, and had such a deep reverence for her beautiful character. I hurried to bruise it, knowing, when I did it, that when I saw the wounded look in her eyes I should be blistered with remorse and shame, and would give anything if I had not done it. But I could not help it, for deep down in the very web and woof of my nature I was ignoble and ungenerous.

How little the world knows us; indeed how little any except our nearest friends know us. You who are reading these lines—your world loves you and honors you. But suppose it knew you as you know yourself? Be humbly thankful that it does not.

Supper. Still no Jeff. My uneasiness was steadily growing.

I had not been out, all day. In fact, I had even kept away from the windows, I did not know why. I knew I should see a crowd of waiting strangers from different regions of the Union on the opposite sidewalk. I was used to it, had been used to it ever since I came back from Mexico with my military glories upon me; and had always been pleased with it, happy in it. But the thought of it troubled me, now. I was accustomed to driving or walking, every day, and accustomed to be flocked after and cheered, as I went along, and no more minded it than did the stately General Scott; in fact dearly liked it and enjoyed it, as he did. But to-day, for some reason, I shrank from the thought of it. There was a vague, indefinable, oppressive sense of impending trouble in the air.

After supper came the marine band—a serenade. The idea of it, to take friendly notice of our little mishap. I was in the room which had been set apart as a nursery, and was employed as usual at that hour of the evening—inventing a blood-curdling story for the children; a child seated on each arm of my chair, their feet in my lap, their elbows on their knees, their chins crutched in their plump hands, their eyes burning duskily through their falling cataracts of yellow hair and black. For ten minutes I had been wandering with these two in a land far from this world; in the golden land of Romance, where all things are beautiful, and existence is a splendid dream, and care cannot come. Then came that bray of the brazen horns, and the vision vanished away; we were prisoners in this dull planet again. I was for ignoring the serenade, and getting back to that shining land with my story, and Jessie was for supporting me in that impropriety; but Bessie had inherited higher instincts than we, and larger principles; and she said—

"No, no, papa, mamma would not approve. You must go, papa."

"And make a speech? Somehow it seems impossible to-night."

"Oh, no it isn't, papa. It is nothing. Don't be afraid. Make the same speech you always make. Everybody says it is a good one. Mr. Pierce likes it better every time; he says so his own self."

Out of the unconscious lips of babes and sucklings are we satirized. I walked slowly away into my banishment, leaving happiness behind me. For I left a dispute behind me; and where no care is, that is joy. I heard Bessie say—

"Papa didn't say that. He *couldn't* say it, because there's no sense in it. You've got two things mixed up, Romie."

"I haven't. He did say it. I heard him; I heard the very words. He said it is foolish to kill the goose that lays the golden calf."

It would have been a joy to me—an old and familiar and beloved joy—to go back and take a solemn hand in the discussion and mix it all up till the puzzled little rascals could make neither head nor tail of it, but this boon was not for me. From outside went up a crashing cheer which lifted my spirits away up into the sunshine, and set my pulses to leaping, and for a moment I was myself again. But for a moment only. Then at the door a bank president touched me on the shoulder and whispered—

"Senator, can I have a word with you presently?"

"Yes," and I passed on. But there was something in his manner which blotted out my sunshine and made my heart cold. I stepped out on the balcony, and gazed out, dazed and hardly conscious, over the wide sea of flaring torches and uplifted faces; and the explosions of welcome which went up sounded muffled and far away in my dulled ears. I made my speech—no, it made itself, automatically; and it was as if it was some one else talking, and I scarce noting what was said. Then the cheers burst out again, as in a dream, and I—as in a dream—bowed, and went my way.

I took the bank president into my office, closed the door, and said—

"What is it?"

He answered, apologetically—

"I am sorry to disturb you with such a matter, Senator, but the fire marshal handed in a check just as we were closing the bank, and—and—"

"Very well. Go on."

"And—and—well, the fact is, Senator, your account is overdrawn."

What a load it lifted off my breast. And what a relief it was, to hear myself laugh once more; it had seemed to me that I had forgotten how.

"Oh, dear me," I said, "is that all? What of it? It isn't uncommon."

But he did not laugh. He remained ominously grave. He was silent a moment, gathering courage for a disagreeable duty, then he spoke out and named the amount of the overdraft.

I staggered as I have seen a soldier do when hit in the breast with a spent ball. After a little I rallied, and said, "I am amazed. I never could have imagined this. I don't know what Sedgewick can have been thinking of. Let us square up at once; and pray don't ever let this happen again—by his authority or any one else's." I sat down at the desk and said, "I will give you a check on Riggs's."

Nothing but a deadly silence followed this remark. I turned in my chair. My guest said, reluctantly—

"I am sorry, but it would do no good."

"Oh, what *do* you mean?"

"We bankers have been together this evening to look over the situation, and unfortunately we find—we find—"

"Well, well, you find—what do you find?"

"That you are heavily overdrawn all around."

He told me the several amounts. It made my head swim, for a moment. Then I pulled myself together, and said—

"After all, Simmons, it is merely embarrassing, not serious; and in no sense alarming. By good luck our house has burned down; the insurance-money will far more than pay you gentlemen, and henceforth I shall keep clear of this kind of thing. Even if I owed a million or two I should still be solvent, by grace of my Californian mining venture."

The banker asked me if I would mind telling him, in confidence, something about the Golden Fleece. I said I should be very glad to tell him *all* about it; that there was no occasion for concealment. So I got out the mining manager's long series of carefully detailed reports, and we examined them patiently from the first one to the last. Mr. Simmons was very much pleased, indeed. He said the reports were remarkably clear, orderly and candid, and that I was fortunate in having a manager who was courageous enough to put in the bad news as well as the good. He conceded that I was demonstrably worth above a million and a half, and prospectively worth indefinitely more. Then he confessed that when Sedgewick began to overdraw rather heavily, sometime back, and had spoken mysteriously of the wonders of the Golden Fleece, he had felt a little uneasy and had written his brother, a banker in Grass Valley for particulars concerning the mine. He had had no answer as yet, but he could forsee, now, that it would be a satisfactory one when it came.

Then a letter was brought up which completed my comfort. It was from the lost Sedgewick. I read it aloud. It said—

"No doubt you have wondered what was become of me. When I returned and found that the house was doomed, I hurried to the station and caught the midnight train for New York; for there was an informality in one of the insurance policies which—however I will explain how it happened when I get back. As to $102,000 of the insurance, there will be no trouble. I think there will be none about the rest—$38,000—but I shall stay here two or three days and see. Meantime, through the luck of coming here just a[t] this time I am likely to bring back, from another source, $80,000 which I had long ago given up as an irremediable loss. Indeed it is not merely likely, I feel that I may regard it as sure."

Mr. Simmons and I parted on very pleasant terms, and I went to bed a serene and contented man.

CHAPTER . . .

Next day I presided, for half an hour, at a session of the Committee on Military Affairs, then went back to Willard's, and Alice and I excused ourselves to callers and spent the whole happy day planning little improvements in the proposed new house, the architect helping and suggesting. Alice, who was conservative, wanted the cost kept within the former house's figure, but I said we could afford a more expensive one; and I talked her out of her reluctances and gained my point. She had been used to money all her life, therefore the possession of it did not turn her head or incline her to vain shows and display; but I was a kind of beggar on horseback, and had no sense of financial proportion, no just notion of values, and—but you know the kind of man I was. We did not get through until midnight; then the architect went away with a house in his pocket which charmed him and me, and made Alice shudder.

Two or three more days went pleasantly by, then came Mr. Simmons, Mr. Riggs, and Mr. Fulton, bankers, and with them a Mr. Collins from New York. Their manner was a warning; it spread a frost over the summer that was teeming in my heart, and the chill of it invaded my spirits. Trouble was coming; I felt it. They wished to see me in my private office. Arrived there, they sat down, and there was a moment or two of silence; then one said to another, with solemnity—

"Will you begin?"

"No, you, if you prefer."

"Perhaps it will be best that Mr. Simmons open the matter."

It was so agreed. Every face there was hard and set, every eye frankly unfriendly. Mr. Simmons cleared his throat and said—

"General X., you will pardon me if I ask you one or two blunt questions."

"Go on, sir."

"What property do you own, aside from the Golden Fleece?"

"None."

The men glanced at each other; Riggs and Fulton twisted nervously in their chairs.

"Has your wife any property other than the Golden Fleece?"

"None."

The color left the faces of Riggs and Fulton at that, then came back in a purple flush, and Fulton put up his hand and loosened his collar.

"One more question, Senator X." This in a slightly rising voice. "When you showed me the reports of your mining manager, was it your purpose to deceive me?"

I flushed, but said, with as much calmness as I could command—

"Mr. Simmons, have a care. I must remind you that you are going too far."

"I am, am I?" said he, excitedly. "My brother's letter has arrived from Grass Valley. Read it!"

I read it. Read it again; and still again, not able to believe my eyes. There was one italicized line in it which seemed written in fire, it glared so, and burnt me so: *"There is no such mine as the Golden Fleece."* The life was all gone out of me, and I said—

"I am a ruined man, gentlemen. I realize it—absolutely ruined. But my destruction does not injure you. The insurance-money will more than pay everything I owe."

"That is your whole resource, then?"

"Yes."

"Are you certain that your house was insured?"

"Certain of it? Of course. It has always been insured, from the first; and in the same companies. Here is the record. The last entry, as you see, is of date a year ago, and insures the house for three years."

"Mr. Collins is the agent through whom your policies were always taken out. Mr. Collins, will you speak?"

Collins addressed himself to me, and said—

"You may remember, sir, that something more than a year ago, I wrote you two personal letters. In the first one I reminded you; in the second I urged you, to renew your insurance, for that I was not able to get Mr. Sedgewick's attention. My letters were confidential, as I did not wish to get your representative's ill will. You remember my letters?"

"Quite well. In the case of the first one I asked Sedgewick to answer you and re-insure; in the second I gave him a peremptory order to do it."

"Have you your policies there?"

"Yes."

"Last year's, too?"

"I suppose so. I will see. N-no. Not last year's."

"It is because that last-year entry is fraudulent. Your house was not insured. The loss is total."

My God, the words went through me like a bullet. If they were true, they meant that I was not merely and only a pauper, but a hundred times worse than that—*in debt*. For a time, no one spoke. The stillness was oppressive, smothering. All were waiting for me; but I was dumb, I could not find my voice. When it came back to me at last, I said—

"I am to blame. I am to blame, I confess it freely. I trusted Sedgewick as no human being ought to be trusted, and I have my reward. He has destroyed me."

There was no word of response. I was ashamed. I had expected at least a recognition of my remark, the mere courtesy of a comment of some kind or other; I was used to this much deference—and entitled to it. My dignity was wounded. I glanced up at the faces about me, and was cut to the heart; for if I could read what was written there, it was contempt! It seemed unbelievable, it had been so many years since any face had delivered me a message like that. I gathered my pride together, and said—

"Do not mistranslate me, gentlemen; I was not begging for sympathy."

Simmons made a gesture of impatience, and said—

"This is not a time for womanish sentimentalities, General X., with these strange facts—shall I say, these suspicious facts?—before us. You must see it yourself."

"What do you mean, sir?" I said with some little heat—I could not keep it all down. "Please explain yourself."

He amended his manner, then, leaving nothing of discourtesy in it or in his tones. But his words were knives.

"I ought not to forget, and I do not, that of the three or four men of towering eminence in the Union, you are one; that your great services deserve the country's gratitude and have it; and that until now your public and private conduct has been above the reach of suspicion; but—but—" He stopped for a moment, troubled as to how to go on; then added reluctantly, and with the manner of one who is saying a thing which he does not want to say, but which he does not know how to get around, "but these insurance-entries, which are—I hate to use the word—fraudulent—why did you make them?"

"*I* make them! *I* didn't make them."

The kindness faded out of the banker's face, and stupefaction took its place—stupefaction, mixed with surprise and unbelief; and he said with offended severity—

"I beg your pardon. I know your hand well."

For the first time, I saw my whole peril. The earth seemed to be opening under me, and said in a voice which made my words sound like a lie even to me, so sapped of force were they by my despairing conviction that I was not going to be believed—

"I give you my word of honor—oh, more, I give you my oath—that I never wrote—"

"*Don't!* Stop where you are, for God's sake!"

"I implore you to believe me! Gentlemen, I call God to wit—"

"Stop where you are! Do not make it worse than it already is. Remember what you are. Go on, and say what you can in palliation of this unfortunate act—even in plausible explanation of it, if such a thing may be possible—but for your own pride's sake leave out denials backed by oaths."

I went back to the beginning of my connection with Sedgewick, and told the tale all down to date; told them the simple truth, the plain, straightfor[war]d, humiliating facts—burning up with self-contempt while I did it, and watching those marveling and incredulous faces for any relenting sign, as wistfully as ever a prisoner on trial for his life watched the faces of the jury.

The sign never came. When I finished, the group looked at each other and said, plainly, though without words, "It is pitiable to see an illustrious man degrade himself to the manufacture of such trash as this." I read the words in their faces, and knew that my good name was gone, now, as well as my bread. After a considerable silence, Mr. Fulton said, with chill deliberation—

"As I understand it, sir, you ask credit for these several most extraordinary asseverations, to-wit, that you, an educated man, a man of the world, a general of the army, a statesman, a grown person, put yourself, body and soul, together with your wife's whole property and your own, unreservedly into the hands of a man—*any* man—empowering him to originate and write letters for you in your own handwriting, sign and endorse your name upon checks, notes, contracts, in your own hand, and speculate in anything he pleased, with the family's money—and all without even your casual supervision of what he was doing, or inquiry into it? Am I right?"

Detailed, item by item, in that cold direct fashion, it seemed incredible, impossible, even to me. And yet it was true, every shameful detail of it; and I said so. Mr. Fuller spoke out with what sounded like an almost generous enthusiasm—

"For the honor I bear your great name I will do you the reverence to believe not one damned word of it!"

I fought, and fought long, and the best I could, to save some shred of that name, but it was a lost battle. These men *could* not believe me. To them, it was impossible that a full grown man could be the fool I had professed myself to be. Their minds were soon made up that Sedgewick and I were partnership swindlers—pals.

They almost used that word; I was sure of it. From that conviction no arguments of mine were able to move them. They summed our affairs concisely up in this way: we had speculated in New York stocks and lost money and been obliged to sell Alice's estate; we had speculated further, and gotten deeper in; we had invented the Golden Fleece to postpone the crash and gain time to recoup; we continued to go from bad to worse; when the house burned, I had seen that the game was up, and had hurried Sedgewick off to scrape up what money he might for our joint benefit before the exposure should fall, and take it to some far country, leaving me to put all the irregularities upon him—he not minding that, since it could not hurt his pocket.

I said that my own statement of my conduct—if true—proved me a fool; but that this new solution of it—if true—proved me insane. I urged that a General of the Army, Senator, and prospective President of the United States could not by any possibility commit the crimes imputed to me unless he were insane, and that the gentlemen here present must know this themselves. I felt a hopeful glow at the heart for a moment, for I said to myself, *that* is an argument which will spike their guns; it is unanswerable.

But how little I knew the religion of commerce and its god. The argument fell flat; more—it was received with disdain—disdain of the sort evoked when a person intrudes a triviality into a serious discussion. Mr. Simmons brushed it aside as indifferently as if he were squelching the ignorant prattle of a schoolboy—

"Men will do anything for money."

From the moment that those men arrived at the conviction that I was a swindler and Sedgewick my tool and partner, my reasonings went for nothing. It untangled every tangle, it laid bare the core of every mystery, it explained and accounted for every move in the odious game that had been played.

If I said that *I* couldn't know that the mining reports exhibited to me as coming from Grass Valley were manufactured in Washington,—why, true,—yes, quite so—etc., etc.; which being translated, meant that my word, as to that, was not valuable, in the circumstances.

If I referred to Sedgewick's letter from New York (about the insurance) as having been received by me in perfect and unsuspecting good faith, the comment I got was merely noddings of the head which meant "Oh, certainly, certainly, quite so—pray do not think we doubt it."

I started, once, to inquire how *I* was to be benefited by making false entries in my insurance-list, and—

But they interrupted me impatiently, with a "There, it isn't worth while to go into *that* again," meaning, "Oh, it is quite simple —part of the game, dear sir, part of the game—any one can understand it."

I had tried all things, said all things, that might help me; there was nothing more that I could do, nothing more that I could say. I was lost. There was no help for me. The consciousness of this settled down upon me and wrapped me as in a darkness. There was a long silence. Then I broke it.

"Gentlemen, I comprehend that I am a ruined man—bankrupt in purse, and, in your belief, in character also. It may be that I shall never be able to retrieve myself financially, though I shall try my best while I live to do that and clear away the debts put upon me by a trusted subordinate; but I am *not* a dishonest man, whatever you may think, and I will bring that man before the courts and fasten all these swindles upon him, where they belong."

"When?" asked Mr. Collins.

"When? Why, at once."

"He sailed for the other side of the world the day he wrote you the letter; a friend of mine saw him go." Then he could not deny himself the pleasure of adding—as if to himself, and not intended for me to hear, "But it may be that this is not news."

Anybody could insult me now, with impunity—even that poor thing. Being pleased with himself for his boldness in kicking the dead lion, and detecting condescending approval in the faces of the bankers, he thought he saw his opportunity to ingratiate himself further with these high deities of his heaven; so he jauntily covered himself. But Mr. Riggs said, angrily—

"Uncover! Have you no shame? Respect what he *was*."

What he *was*! It lit up my whole vast ruin, from horizon to horizon; it compacted my colossal disaster into a single phrase. I knew that those words were burnt in; that no lapse of time, no mental decay, would ever rid my memory of them.

But why were these men still waiting? Was there more? More! The idea was almost able to make *me* smile. More? Was not Pelion piled upon my Ossa? More, indeed! The possibilities had been exhausted. I stirred in my chair, to indicate that I was ready for the interview to terminate if they were. Nobody moved. Then I said—

"I suppose we have finished, gentlemen." Still, nobody moved. The situation was embarrassing; and so, with a groping idea of relieving it, I added in a wan and sickly attempt at playfulness, "I seem to have committed about all the crimes there are; still, if by chance one has been overlooked, let us complete the tale. Pray bring it out."

Mr. Riggs began to wash his hands nervously; Simmons glanced at me, and dropped his eyes; Fulton, without passion or even emphasis, spat out the word—

"Forgery!"

I sprang at him—and remembered no more.

CHAPTER

WHEN I CAME to myself I had the feeling of one who has slept heavily, is lazily comfortable, but not greatly refreshed, and is still drowsy. My mind was empty of thought, and indifferent. My eyelids began to droop slumbrously, and I was drifting pleasantly toward unconsciousness, when I heard Jake's voice cry out—apparently in the next room—

"No indeed it ain't, honey—it's a jay-bird. Wait till I come. Don't make a noise; you'll scare him."

My eyes came open, and then there was a surprise. I was stretched upon a bed, in a log cabin. The sharp March weather was gone, summer was in the air. The floor was of earth, packed hard and clean swept; at one end was a vast fire-place, built of undressed

stones; in it a couple of great smouldering logs six or seven feet
long; swinging above them, from an iron chimney-hook, a large
iron pot; on rude unpainted shelves, on one side, some old but
brightly polished tin pans, plates, pint cups, candle-sticks and a
coffee pot, some bone-handled knives and forks, some tin cans,
some wooden and pasteboard boxes such as candles and groceries
come in, and some brown paper parcels; against the logs on that
side, under a small square window, a coverless deal table that had
paper and pens on it and half a dozen old books; for sole ornament,
a crippled tumbler containing a bouquet of fresh wild flowers;
against the logs, beside the window, was fastened a diamond-
shaped piece of looking-glass, and under it was a shelf with cheap
combs and brushes on it. On the other side of the fireplace, by the
door, was a small wooden bench, with a piece of bar soap on it in a
common white saucer, a tin wash-basin inverted, and a wooden pail
of water with a tin dipper in it; under the ceiling, above the bench,
hung half of a side of bacon; on the floor on that side was an open
sack of flour, and another of navy beans. Nailed to the wall opposite the bed was a deep long stretch of curtain calico which bulged,
and I knew by that sign that it was the wardrobe. Along the wall,
above the bed, four cheap lithographs were tacked to the logs—the
Battle of Buena Vista, the storming of San Juan d'Ulloa, (I took
part in both), and portraits of Scott and Taylor in uniform. Overhead was a ceiling made of flour-sacks sewed together; it was a
frescoed ceiling, so to speak, for the sacks bore the names and addresses of the mills, loudly stenciled in blue capitals. Across the
room, past the head of the bed, ran a flour-sack partition, also frescoed. It was the picture gallery; against it was pinned a number of
steel engravings from Godey's Lady's Book.

Everything about the place was beautifully neat and clean and
trim—and unimaginably inexpensive. I examined the bedstead. It
was made of small poles—only tolerably straight, and the bark still
on—laid close together along a frame supported by posts—the bark
still on—driven into the ground. There was but one mattrass; it
was filled with straw; there were pillows, filled with something or
other; their cases and the sheets were of coarse white cotton; a
cheap white blanket completed the bed.

I had on an old pair of blue jeans breeches and a private soldier's blue army shirt.

Where was I? I had no idea.

A glory of sunny hair appeared in the open door, now, and with it a bright young face—Bessie's.

"Come here, dear," I said, "and read me this riddle."

"Why, *papa!*"

She came cautiously in, and slowly approached, her eyes big with glad wonder—and doubt. She hesitated, then stopped, in the middle of the little room, four feet from me, and said wistfully—

"Papa—do you know me?"

"Do I *know* you? Why, Bessie, what—"

With a spring she was in my arms and covering my face with frantic kisses. Presently she had flashed away again, with the suddenness of a ray of light, and I heard her calling—outside—excitedly:

"Run here—run—run!"

Then she came flying back and stood, expectant, in the middle of the room, her eyes and cheeks glowing; and in a moment or two more Jessie was at her side, a speaking picture of childish interest and curiosity. Bessie put her mouth close to Jessie's ear, whispered a word, then stepped back to observe the effect. Jessie looked startled, but said promptly—

"I don't believe it."

The effect seemed to be all that could have been desired, for Bessie clapped her hands like a gratified showman and said—

"I knew you wouldn't. Now you'll see. Papa, who is this?"

"Come, what kind of game are you little rascals playing? Do you suppose I don't know Romie?"

And now they were both in my arms, and for some reason or other seemed to be mad with delight. Presently I said—

"It's a charming piece, and I am playing my part of it as well as I can, but I am in the dark, you know. Why am I in jeans and army shirt? And why are you two in these little linsey-woolsey frocks, and why are you barefooted? And why are we in this log cabin? Is it all in the piece? And how much do we get for it? But first of all, where *are* we?"

The children looked troubled and disappointed, and a little apprehensive, and Bessie said—

"But papa, I thought you would know *everything*, now. Don't you?"

"Dear me, no, apparently I don't. I am reveling in mysteries. Really, I don't seem to know much of anything."

Jessie said, as one who is trying to offer encouragement—

"Oh, no, papa, you mustn't say that. You know *us*—you know you do."

"Oh indeed, yes, if that is large learning, I am not at the foot of the class yet. I can say my lesson. You are Bessie and Jessie, and I am Thomas X."

Their soft hands covered my mouth at once, and they said in a frightened way—

" 'sh! papa! You mustn't say that!"

"Mustn't say it? Why?"

"Because it isn't your name. You've got another name, now. Don't you know your other name?"

"Oh, you mean my stage name. No, I don't know what it is. What is it?"

"Jacobs—Edward Jacobs; and you mustn't forget it, papa; you mustn't *ever* forget it. Promise."

"All right, I promise. Jacob Edwards—it's a very pretty name, too."

"No, no—Edward *Jacobs*. Say it again, papa; and keep saying it till you learn it good."

"All right, I'll begin now. Are you ready?"

"Yes, papa—and do be careful; and don't hurry."

And they fixed their grave eyes upon me; eyes charged with hope, hope just touched with a pathetic shade of doubt. I couldn't help toying with it.

"Yes, I will be very careful, because always it is best to get a thing right in the first place, then after that it comes easier. And in the case of a difficult name like Jacob Edwards—"

"Oh, papa!"—this with a sort of anguish; and the tears sprang into their eyes.

I gathered the abused pair to my breast and cried out—

"Bless your hearts I was only fooling. I didn't know it was any matter to you. I won't do it any more. I wasn't in earnest, upon my word I wasn't. I can say it without any trouble; listen: Edward Jacobs, Edward Jacobs, Edward Jacobs—"

The sunshine was come again, and I thought I would not play any more treacheries like that for the present. I said—

"But come. You know you haven't told me where we are."

"Why, we are in a town, papa."

"No we are not, Potie, we are only in the edge of it."

"Well, in the edge of it, then—it's all the same. And its name—don't you know its name, papa?"

"I think I can tell better when I hear it. What is it, Bessie?"

She hesitated, and said—

"Mamma only just calls it *the town;* and so that is what we call it, too; but the people—they—well, the people call it—"

"Hell's Delight," said Jessie, gravely.

It nearly startled me out of my army shirt, for it suggested some tremendous possibilities. My breath came short and quick, now, and in insufficient quantity for a person who was full of questions and in a hurry to ask them; but I got them out, and as fast as I could:

"Are we in California?"

"Yes, papa."

"What time of the year is it?"

"The middle of August."

"How old are you, Bessie?"

"Nearly nine and a half, papa."

"This is amazing. I have been asleep eighteen months! Amazing —incredible—impossible. And how you children have grown—I was supposing it was your mean disguises that were deceiving my eyes. What—"

"Mamma's come, mamma's come! Oh, mamma, he's in his right mind!"

We two had been separated just an hour—by the clock—but in the *true* sense a whole year and a half. What the meeting was like, there is no art to tell. The ignorant cannot imagine it, but only such as have lived it.

CHAPTER . . .

W HEN A PERSON has been absent from the planet a year and a half, there is much news to hear when he gets back. It took Alison many hours to tell me her story. She had had a hard life of it, and heavy work and sharp privations, and this had aged her body a little, but not her spirit. Her spirit was [as] it had always been; its courage, its hopefulness, its generosities, its magnanimities had suffered no impairment, her troubles had not soured its native sweetness nor embittered its judgments of men and the world. She had no complaints to make about her poverty; and as for upbraiding me for causing it, she never thought of such a thing. It shamed me to see this, knowing how quick I should be to upbraid her if our places had been changed, and how meanly prone to keep her reminded of it—and sincerely repent, in sackcloth and ashes for it —and then do it again the next day, and the next, and the next, and all the days.

She told me her tale. When she found that we were ruined and in debt she left the hotel at once and got three cheap rooms and a kitchen on the fourth floor of a tenement house, and discharged Jake and Maria. They declined the discharge. Maria remained and did the housework, and Jake went out to service and made her take and use almost all the money he earned. It helped to save us alive, in those first days before Alice had found work for herself. She presently got copying to do; and so great was the sympathy which her calamities excited that she was soon overrun with this kind of work, and was able to employ several assistants. All our friends stood by her, none of them discarded her; new ones came; and new and old together would have helped her out of their pockets if she would have consented. She said it was worth while to know poverty, because it so enlarged and ennobled one's estimates of the world in general as well as of one's friends. Almost every paper in the land used me generously. There was but one man who was bitter against me; even the injured bankers made no trouble, and ceased from saying harsh things about me. The officers of the army believed my story, and believed it entirely. They said that a man trained at West Point might be a fool in business matters, but never a rascal and never a liar; that he was a gentleman, and would remain one. General Scott said I was a good soldier, none better; and that even the best soldier could botch a trade which he was not fitted for.

The Enchanted Sea-Wilderness

THIS STORY fragment is a discarded part of *Following the Equator*, Mark Twain's account of his round-the-world tour of 1895–1896. His travels took him through the "stupendous island wilderness of the Pacific" [1] and across the Indian Ocean. While in the South Pacific Ocean bound for Australia, he had noted, on 6 September 1895, "There are spots at sea where the compass loses its head and whirls this way and that; then you give it up and steer by the sun, wind, stars, moon or *guess*, and trust to luck to save you till you get by that insane region." [2] After he had written the first 156 pages of *Following the Equator*, he introduced a description of such a place, paraphrasing the notebook entry, and then began the tale of "The Enchanted Sea-Wilderness." Probably he reached this point in his composition of the book some time in November or December of 1896, after beginning work upon it on 24 October of that year. [3] In writing this tale of trapped derelicts, he partly followed an earlier draft, a fragment of a few hundred words which he had called "The Passenger's Story." This draft may be seen in the Appendix. The "second cabin passenger" who narrates it and the "bronzed and gray sailor" who narrates "The Enchanted Sea-Wilder-

---

[1] *Following the Equator*, I, 80.

[2] Typescript 28a (II), p. 44.

[3] Mark Twain noted that he had written the first chapter on that date. See *MTN*, p. 306. In the discarded section, paginated 157–193, the story begins on page 162; the preceding five pages contain transitional matter—mainly a discussion of "the modern compass." The last two paragraphs of this antecedent part provide a narrative frame and have been allowed to stand as an introduction to the tale. The first four lines on page 157, referring to the practice of ducking persons crossing the equator for the first time, are to be found in *Following the Equator*, I, 45; at this point Mark Twain cut out of his book the fragment that includes "The Enchanted Sea-Wilderness."

ness" are quite evidently invented characters, whose only function is to convey a story within a story.

The idea of a trap for becalmed vessels had long been in Mark Twain's thoughts. As early as 1866, when he had voyaged to the Sandwich Islands, he had recorded impressions, gained from the talk of sailors, of "baffling winds and dreadful calms" and of "month-long drifting between . . . islands." [4] In 1882 he made some notes for an intended balloon voyage story: "The frightfullest time I ever saw? It was the time I was up in my balloon and seemed to have got into that (fabled) stratum where, once in, you remain—going neither up nor down for years—forever—and I came across first one balloon and afterwards another and we three lay (apparently) motionless beside each other, the green, mummified (frozen) corpses . . . gloating mournfully from the tattered baskets." [5] Although the region of entrapment is in the upper atmosphere rather than on the seas, the situation resembles that in "The Enchanted Sea-Wilderness."

Except for "The Passenger's Story," which it substantially includes in a revised form, "The Enchanted Sea-Wilderness" is Mark Twain's earliest actual version of the voyage-of-disaster story.

---

[4] Typescript 5, p. 6qq.
[5] Typescript 16, p. 40.

The Enchanted Sea-Wilderness

S CATTERED about the world's oceans at enormous distances apart are spots and patches where no compass has any value. When the compass enters one of these bewitched domains it goes insane and whirls this way and that and settles nowhere, and is scared and distressed, and cannot be comforted. The sailor must steer by sun, moon and stars when they show, and by guess when they don't, till he gets past that enchanted region. The worst of these spots and the largest one is in the midst of the vast ocean solitudes that lie between the Cape of Good Hope and the south pole. It is five hundred miles in diameter, and is circular in shape; four-fifths of this diameter is lashed and tossed and torn by eternal storms, is smothered in clouds and fog, and swept by fierce concentric currents; but in the centre there is a circular area a hundred miles across, in whose outer part the storms and the currents die down; and in the centre of this centre there is still a final circular area about fifty [6] miles across where there are but the faintest suggestions of currents, no winds, no whisper of wandering zephyr, even, but everywhere the silence and peace and solemnity of a calm which is eternal.

There is a bronzed and gray sailor on board this ship who has had experience of that strange place, and the other night after midnight I went forward to the forecastle and got him to tell me about it. The hint came from the purser, who said it was a curious

---

[6] Mark Twain wrote that the region was "twenty or thirty miles across" and later interlined "about fifty"; the earlier reading bears no mark of cancellation but the larger figure has been accepted as the preferred form, confirmed later in the same piece.

and interesting story. I kept it in my memory as well as I could, and wrote it down next day—in my own language, for I could not remember his, of course. He said that the outer great circle where the currents are—as already described by me—is known among sailors as the Devil's Race-Track, and that they call the central calm Everlasting Sunday.[7] Here is his account.

THE ENCHANTED SEA-WILDERNESS.

We got into that place by a judgment—judgment on the captain of the ship. It was this way. We were becalmed, away down south, dead summer time, middle of December, 1853. The vessel was a brig, and a fairly good sailor; name, *Mabel Thorpe;* loaded with provisions and blasting powder for the new gold mines in Australia; Elliot Cable master, a rough man and hard-hearted, but he *was* master, and that is the truth. When he laid down the law there wasn't pluck enough in the whole ship to take objections to it.

Now to go back a little. About two months before, when we were lying at the dock the day we sailed, a lovely big beautiful dog came aboard and went racing around with his nose down hunting for somebody that had been there—his owner, I reckon—and the crew caught him and shut him up below, and we sailed in an hour. He was a darling, that dog. He was full of play, and fun, and affection and good nature, the dearest and sweetest disposition that ever was. Inside of two days he was the pet of the whole crew. We bedded him like the aristocracy, and there wasn't a man but would divide his dinner with him, and he was ever so loving and grateful. And smart, too; smart and willing. He elected of his own notion to stand watch and watch with us. He was in the larboard watch, and he would turn out at eight bells without anybody having to tell him it was "Yo-ho, the larboard watch!" And he would tug at the ropes and help make sail or take it in, and seemed to know all about it, just like any old veteran. The crew were proud of him—well, of course they would be.

And so, as I was saying, we got becalmed when we were out

---

[7] While in Pretoria, South Africa, in May 1896, he noted, "And everywhere these wide deserted streets, this deep Sunday stillness, this mysterious and impressive absence of life and movement. This is the Puritan Sabbath of two centuries ago come back to the earth again." The name for the region of eternal calm, "Everlasting Sunday," is probably his own invention.

about two months. It was warm that night, and still and drowsy and lazy; and the sails hung idle, and the deck-watch and the lookout and everybody else was sound asleep, including the dog, for it was his trick below and he had turned in at midnight. Well, along about an hour after midnight there was a tremendous scratching and barking at the captain's door, and he jumped out of his bunk, and that dog was just wild with excitement, and rushed off, and just as good as *told* the captain to come along and come *quick*. You see, the ship was afire down in the hold, and he had discovered it. Down the captain plunged, and the dog rushed off waking up the others.

Dear, dear, it was the closest fit! The fire was crowding a pile of the powder-kegs close, and in another minute or two it would have had them and we should have been blown into the sky. The captain snatched the pile of kegs out of reach in half a second, and we were safe; because the bulk of the powder was away up forward. And by this time we all came tearing down—white?—oh, white as ghosts when we saw what a close shave we had had. Well, then we started in and began to hug the dog. And wasn't he a proud dog?—and happy?—why, if he had had speech he couldn't have expressed it any better. The captain snarled at us and said:

"You may well hug him, you worthless hounds! he saved my life, not you, you lazy rips. I've never cared for dogs before, but next time I hear people talking against them I'll put in a word for this one, anyway."

Overboard went that little batch of powder kegs, and then we flew around getting food and water and compass and sextant and chart and things for the boat; and the dog helped, just like anybody else. He did a grown man's work carrying things to the boat, and then went dancing around *superintending* whilst we launched her. Bright?—oh, you can't think how bright he was, and intelligent.

When everybody was in the boat but the captain, and the flames were soaring up and lighting the whole ocean, he tied the dog to the foot of the mainmast and then got in himself and took the tiller and said—

"All ready. Give way!"

We were all struck dumb, for a second, then all shouted at once—

"Oh, *captain!*—going to leave the dog?"

He roared out in a fury—

"Didn't you hear the order? Give way!"

Well, the tears began to run down our faces; and we said, Why, he saved our *lives*—we *can't* leave him. Please, captain! please let him come.

"What, in this little tub of a boat? You don't know what you are talking about. He'd be more in the way than a family of children; and he can eat as much as a family of children, too. Now, men, you know *me*"—and he pulled an old pepper-box revolver and pointed it—"give *way!*"

Well, it was pitiful, the way that poor dog acted. At first he was dancing and capering and barking, happy and proud and gay; but when he saw us going away he stopped and stood still, gazing; it seemed as if he was trying to believe it, and couldn't. And dear, dear, how noble and handsome he was, in that red glare. He was a huge big St. Bernard, with that gentle good face and that soft loving eye that they've got.

Well, pretty soon when he saw that he *was* left, he seemed to go kind of crazy; and he rose on his hind legs in the strong light, and strained and lunged and tugged at his rope, and begged and moaned and yelped—why it was as plain as if he was *saying* Oh, *don't* leave me, *please* don't leave me, *I* haven't done any harm. And then presently the fire swept down on him and swallowed him up, and he sent up two or three awful shrieks, and it was all over. And the men sat there crying like children.

And deep down in our hearts we believed a judgment would come on the captain for this. And it did; as you will see.

II.

We were in the Indian ocean when we lost the ship—about five hundred miles south of Port Natal, and about the same distance east by south from Cape Town, South Africa. The captain set his course by the stars and struck north, because he believed we were a little south of the track of ships bound for either Natal or

Australia. A smart breeze sprung up and we went along at a good rate. In about four hours day broke, and the first thing that showed up on the westward sea-line was the hazy top-hamper of a ship! She was eastward-bound, and making straight across our course. We raised a cheer, and altered our course to go and meet her. And there wasn't as much heart in the cheer as you might expect, for the thing we were thinking about was, that our poor dog had been done to death for no use; if he had been allowed to come with us he wouldn't have cost us any inconvenience, and no food that we couldn't spare.

The captain had an idea that he was born lucky, and he said something to the mate about it now; he said running across this ship here was pure luck—nobody else could have had such luck. Well, it certainly did look so; but at the same time we said to ourselves, how about this ship's luck that's coming? Our idea was that our captain would bring bad luck to her, and trouble to himself and us, too, on account of the way he treated the dog that saved our lives. And that is what happened, as I have said before.

In about an hour we were aboard that ship; and it happened that we knew her, and knew her crew, too; for she was sister to our ship and belonged to the same house, and was loaded at the same dock with us, and with the same kind of cargo—provisions for the new mines almost altogether, and a few other odds and ends of mining supplies, like candles and powder and fuse, and such things. By name she was the *Adelaide*. She had left port a week or ten days ahead of us, but we could outsail her on a wind. Her captain had been dead about a month, now—died of a sickness of some kind— and Mrs. Moseley, his young widow, was broken-hearted, and cried pretty much all the time, and was in terror lest something should happen to her little girl, and then she would be desolate indeed. Two of the *Adelaide's* crew had died of the sickness, also; so that left mate, second mate and five men aboard. When we joined, that made it seventeen men, one woman and a child.

Our captain took command straight away, and began to give orders, without a by-your-leave to anybody—for that was his style. It wasn't the right way to go about it, and it made bad blood.

The captain allotted the watches and the ship continued on her course for Australia. The wind freshened, the sky grew dark, and inside of an hour there was a terrific gale blowing. We stripped the ship and she drove helpless before it, straight south-east. And so, night and day and day and night for eighteen days we drove, and never got a sight of the sun or the moon or the stars in all that time —hundreds and hundreds and hundreds of miles we wallowed through the wild seas, with never a notion of where we were but what we got from the dead reckoning.

For the last two or three days the captain had got to looking pretty white; and by this time he was just ghastly. Then we found out the reason, from the mates: the captain judged that we must be south of Kerguelan's Land, and maybe nearly half way between that and the Antarctic Circle. Well, that news turned the rest of us white; for if it was true, we were getting into the neighborhood of the Devil's Race-Track!

As that cold dark eighteenth day shut down, everybody was on deck, off-watch and all; and everybody silent; as a rule, nobody saying anything to his neighbor; nobody interested in any but the one thing—the compass. The captain stood over the forward one, watching it and never saying anything; the officers and crew crowded around the after one, watching it and never saying anything. The night shut down black as ink; the wind screamed through the naked rigging; gusts of hail, snow, sleet followed each other right along—a wild night, and bitter cold, and the ship reeling and pitching and tumbling in a most awful way.

You couldn't see a thing; you couldn't see your hand before your face—everything was blotted out; everything except three or four faces bending over the compass-light, and showing in the blackness like ghost-faces that hadn't any bodies.

Then all of a sudden there was a burst of groans and curses, and the faces disappeared and others took their places. You see, the thing everybody was expecting, had happened—the compass was gone crazy, and we were in the whirl and suck of the Devil's Race-Track. Most of us kept the deck all night. Some slept, but it was not much good—just naps and nightmares, and wakings-up with a jerk, in a cold sweat.

When the day came you could hardly tell it, it so little differed from the night. All the day long it was the same; you could hear the sea-birds piping but you couldn't see them, except now and then you would get a dim glimpse of a great white albatross sailing by like a ghost.

We had nine days and nights like this—always the roaring gale and the wild sea and blustering squalls of snow and hail and sleet and the piping of the gulls and the flitting of the dim albatross; and then on the tenth morning the gale began to slacken and the seas to go down and the squalls to get wider apart and less furious, and the blackness to soften up and shred away, and the sea-birds to thin out; and about noon we drifted out of the lofty wall of gloom and clouds into a calm sea and the open day and deep, deep stillness. The sweep of that black wall described an enormous circle; and it was so high that the furthest side of it still stood boldly up above the sea, though it was fifty miles away. We were in a trap; and that trap was the Everlasting Sunday.

There was no need to say it; everybody knew it. And everybody shuddered, too, and was in a cold despair. For a week we drifted little by little around the cloud-wall, and further and further away from it; and when we seemed to have gotten ten or fifteen miles from it we appeared to have stopped dead still. We threw empty bottles overboard and watched them. There was really no motion— at any rate in any one direction. Sometimes a bottle would stay where we threw it; sometimes after the end of an hour we could see that it had moved five or six yards ahead or as many aft.

The stillness was horrible; and the absence of life. There was not a bird or a creature of any kind in sight, the slick surface of the water was never broken by a fin, never a breath of wind fanned the dead air, and there was not a sound of any kind, even the faintest— the silence of death was everywhere. We showed no life ourselves, but sat apart, each by himself, and brooded and brooded, and scarcely ever moved. In that profound inertness, that universal paralysis of life and energy, as far as sentient beings went, there was one thing that was brimming with it, booming with it, crazy with it; and that was the compass. It whirled and whizzed this way and that, and never rested—never for a moment. It acted like a frightened thing, a thing in frantic fear for its life. And so we got afraid of it, and could not bear to look at its distress and its helpless struggles; for we came to believe that it had a soul and that it was in hell.

We never had any more weather—forever that bright sky overhead, with never a shred of cloud in it; not a flake of snow, nor drop of sleet or anything; just a dead still frosty cold, with a glistening white rime coating the decks and spars and rigging—a ship made of sparkling frostwork, she seemed. And as the days dragged on and on and on we grew weary as death of this changeless sky, and watched the vague lightnings playing in the distant cloud-wall with a sort of envy and longing.

Try to escape? Why, none of us wanted to try. What could be the use? Of course the captain tried; it would be just like him. He manned one of the boats and started. He disappeared in the cloud-wall for a while; got lost in it, of course—compass no use—and came near getting swamped by the heavy seas. He was not in there long; the currents soon swept him back into the Everlasting Sunday. Our ship was pretty far away, but still in sight; so he came aboard, and never said a word. *His* spirit was broken, too, you see, like ours; so after that he moped around again, like the rest—and prayed for death, I reckon. We all did.

One morning when we had been in there seven months and gradually getting further and further toward the middle, an inch at a time, there was a sudden stir and excitement—the first we had known for so long that it seemed strange and new and unnatural—like something we hadn't ever experienced before; it was like corpses getting excited—corpses that had been dead many years and had forgotten the feel of it and didn't understand it. A sailor came flying along the deck blubbering and shouting, "A ship! a ship!"

The dull people sitting moping and dreaming here and there and yonder looked up at him in a kind of a drowse, and not pleasantly; for his racket and activity pained their heads and distressed them; and their brains were so blunted and sodden that at first his words couldn't find their way into their understandings, all practice in talk having ceased so long ago. But of course we did understand, presently, and then we woke up and got wildly excited, as I was telling you.

Away off yonder we made out a ship, sure enough; and as the

daylight brightened we made out another; and then another, and still another and another and another—a whole fleet, scattered around, a mile or so apart. We were full of amazement. When did they come, and how did they get there in that sudden way, and so many of them? We were full of joy; for maybe here was rescue for us. If they came in there on purpose, they must know the trick of how to get out again.

Well, everything was bustle and hurry, now. We got out our boats, and I pulled stroke in the chief mate's. I was twenty-three and a half years old, and big and strong and an experienced sailor. We hoisted a flag, first, in the mizzen halliards—union down, of course—and left the young widow and the little girl standing under it crying for happiness when we pulled away in the frosty bright morning.

It was as much as twelve miles to the nearest ship, but we made it in three hours—without a sail, of course, there being no wind. When half of the ship's hull showed above the water we began to wave signals, but didn't get any answer; and about this time we began to make out that she looked pretty old and crazy. The nearer we got, the crazier she looked, and there was no sign of life or movement about her. We began to suspect the truth—and pretty soon we knew it, and our spirits fell. Why, she was just a naked old wreck, as you may say, a mouldy old skeleton, with her yards hanging every-whichway, and here and there a rotten rag of sailcloth drooping from the clews. As we passed under her stern, there was her name, in letters so dulled you could hardly spell them out. The *Horatio Nelson!* I gasped for breath. I knew the ship. When I was a boy of ten my uncle Robert sailed in her as chief mate; and from that day to this she had never more been heard of —thirteen years.

You will know beforehand what we found: barring the frosty litter of decaying wreckage that strewed the deck, just the counterpart of our own ship, as you might say—men lying here and there and yonder, and two or three sitting, with elbow on knee and hand under chin—just as natural! No, not men—leathery shriveled-up effigies of them. Dead these dozen years. It was what we had been seeing for seven months; we would come to be like these, by and by. It was our fate foreshadowed; that is what we thought. I found my uncle; I knew him by his watch chain. I was young, he had always been kind to me, and it made me cry a little to see him looking like that. That, and that I might be like him soon. I have the watch and chain yet, if you care to look at them. The watch had stopped at twelve minutes to four—whether in the day or in the night I don't know; but he was dead when it ran down—that was all it could tell.

The ship's log left off where we had stopped ours—three days after the entry into the Everlasting Sunday. It told the same monotonous things that ours did, and in nearly the same words; and the blank that followed was more eloquent than the words that went before, in this case as in our own, for it meant despair. By the log, the *Horatio Nelson* had entered the Everlasting Sunday on the 2ᵈ of June, 1840.

We visited ship after ship, and found these dreary scenes always repeated. And always the logs ceased the third or fourth day after the ship got into this death-trap except in a single case. Where one day is exactly like another, why record them? What is there to record? The world continues to exist, but History has come to an end. The *Horatio Nelson* was the latest ship there but one—a whaler from New England. She had been there six years. One English ship which had been there thirty-three years—the *Eurydice*—was overcrowded with men and women. She had 260 of these leathery corpses on board—convicts for Australia and their guards, no doubt, for down below were more than two hundred sets of chains. A Spanish ship had been there sixty years; but the oldest one of all, and in almost the best repair, was a British man-of-war, the *Royal Brunswick*. She perished with all on board the first voyage she ever made, the old histories say—and the old ballads, too— but here she was; and here she had been, since November 10th, 1740—a hundred and thirteen years, you see.[8]

Clean, dry, frosty weather seems to be a good preserver of some things—clothes, for instance. At a little distance you might have thought some of the men in this ship were still alive, they looked so

---

[8] After he had first written "a hundred and two years," Mark Twain changed the interval to make it consistent with the time of narration, 1853.

natural in their funny old uniforms. And the Admiral was one—
old Admiral Sir John Thurlow; he was a middy in the time of
Marlborough's wars, as I have read in the histories. He had his big
cocked hat on, and his big epaulettes, like as if he was gotten up for
Madam Tussaud's; and his coat was all over gold lace; and it was
real gold, too, for it was not tarnished. He was sitting on a gun
carriage, with his head leant back against the gun in a sick and
weary way; and there was a rusty old leather portfolio in his lap and
a pen and an empty inkstand handy. He looked fine and noble—
the very type of the old fighting British Admiral, the men that
made England the monarch of the seas. By a common impulse, and
without orders, we formed up in front of him and uncovered in
salute. Then Captain Cable stepped up to take the portfolio, but in
his awkwardness he gave a little touch to the Admiral's elbow and
he fell over on the deck. Dear me, he struck as lightly and as
noiseless as if he had been only a suit of clothes stuffed with wool;
and a faint little cloud of leathery dust rose up from him, and we
judged he had gone to pieces inside. We uncovered again and
carried him very reverently to his own cabin and laid him to rest.

And here we had an instance of the difference between navy
discipline and merchant marine. In this ship the log was kept up as
long as an officer was left alive—and that was two months and
sixteen days. That is the grip that authority and duty get upon a
trained man, you see. When the men began to starve and die they
were

An Adventure in Remote Seas

IN APRIL 1896, Mark Twain wrote in his notebook, "[A]ll world-distances have shrunk to nothing. . . . The mysterious and the fabulous can get no fine effects without the help of remoteness; and there are no remotenesses any more." [1] There was, nevertheless, the little explored Antarctic region. And in writing "An Adventure in Remote Seas," he evidently sought to exploit the romantic possibilities of that yet remaining faraway and fabulous sector of the globe. The working notes for the story are on the back sides of some discarded pages from the middle part of the manuscript of *Following the Equator;* probably they were made in the early part of 1897, when he was at work upon the travel book. However, the available evidence indicates that he probably did not write this fragmentary sea romance until late in the spring of 1898.

Fifteen years earlier, he had recorded an idea for a story situation similar to that of the marooned crew in "An Adventure in Remote Seas." In the 1883 notebook there is this entry: "Life in the interior of an iceberg. . . . All found dead and frozen after 130 years. Iceberg drifts around in a vast circle, year after year, and every two or three years they come in distant sight of the remains of the ship." [2] He might very well have attempted to write stories of a voyage of disaster, one may suppose, even if he had not met with the personal disasters of the nineties.

This fragment contains a good deal of material about the free silver question, and the working notes contain much more. Mark Twain's tale

---

[1] Typescript 29 (II), p. 37.
[2] *MTN,* p. 169.

was in danger of turning into a tract, and he must soon have found that he had not made the right beginning.

No record has been discovered of a George Parker who might have told the story to Mark Twain in New Zealand in 1895, and the narrator mentioned in the introductory note is in all probability a fictitious character.

An Adventure in Remote Seas.

(This is the tale of George Parker, an American, substantially as he told it to me in New Zealand in 1895.—MARK TWAIN.)

I WAS BORN and reared in Ohio, and I have a common-school education. My father was the village blacksmith. I was his only child. He was killed in the war when I was a baby. My mother died when I was fifteen years old—worn out and starved out by hard work and poverty. There were no relatives. I was an apprentice blacksmith, and got my keep and clothes for pay. When I was seventeen I was free, and wanted to see the world. I put my belongings in a gunny sack and made my way west to San Francisco —partly I worked it, but mainly I tramped it. There I shipped before the mast and presently arrived in Australia—Sydney. This was in 1878; and at this point my story begins. I was eighteen years old.

One day a shipmate of mine, John Boyd, an Irishman, got a berth, and he came and wanted me to go with him. It was a voyage which promised both adventure and profit, and those things attracted him. He believed they would attract me, and he was right. It was a sealing voyage to the far south, and the crew would have a "lay"—that is, a share in the take. The common seaman's lay would be one-eightieth. This in addition to his wages. So I signed the articles. Then we bought heavy winter clothing of a second-hand dealer, and laid in a proper supply of nigger-head tobacco; then we were ready.

We sailed in midsummer, toward the end of December, in blistering hot weather, and made a long course due south till we were well below Auckland island, then squared around and moved eastwardly two or three weeks through snow storms and biting cold. And now we ran into a snow-storm which lasted six days and nights without a break. Of course we lost our reckoning. We knew we were somewhere in that empty vast stretch of ocean which lies south-west of Cape Horn, but that was all. We could not come within five hundred miles of guessing our position.

The snow stopped falling, one morning, just in time to save us from shipwreck. We found ourselves in a rock-bound bay and driving straight for the shore. A cast of the lead gave twenty-five fathoms, and we let go a couple of anchors, they took a good grip and we were all right.

The skies soon cleared, and outside the bay we saw an archipelago of rocks well peopled with seals. We recognized that we were in fine luck. Although we did not know where we were, we were at least where we wanted to be. By the look of things we should all be comparatively rich when we struck homeward again.

Two days later the skies cleared and the weather quieted down, and Captain Hardy and a boat's crew of us went ashore to see if we could find a good place to make a camp. We were on an island. It was level, except in one place, and not very high; and as there were no trees, we could see the whole size of it. We judged it to be three miles long and about half as wide. There was a skin of soil, with here and there dead and frozen patches of what seemed to be some kind of a weed. This is description enough to show that it was a dreary and forbidding place. As far as the eye could reach, on all sides, the vacant ocean stretched to the horizon. The level of the island was broken in one place by a steep ridge of rocks seventy or eighty feet high and half a mile long. In this we found the opening to a cave, but we had no candles with us, and could not explore it. This was only about five hundred yards back from our landing.

Not far from the cave we came upon a surprise. This was a rude and weather-beaten house, made of rough planks and ship timbers —a building of great age, apparently. So we were not the discoverers of the island. People had been there before. Sealers? Yes, no doubt. We examined searchingly, but found not a scratch nor a sign to tell who they were. Captain Hardy said they had probably built the house as a temporary camp and had occupied it only till they had finished their sealing season, then had abandoned it and sailed for home. But it was an excellent sealing place; why had they not come again? Had they lost their reckoning, too, like us? It might be so; the house had the look of not having been occupied for half a century.

We came the next day and patched it and put it in order. It was just the thing. It had rude bunks for eight men, and abundance of room for stores. And it had a large fireplace, and in it some half-burnt driftwood—wood of a species not familiar to us. During this day and the next we stocked the house liberally with supplies, bedded the bunks, gathered a quantity of driftwood, divided the crew—half to sleep in the house, the other half aboard ship.

This is the list of the ship's company:

Philip Hardy, English, captain, good enough man, not very bright.

Abel Jones, Welsh, mate.

Jorgensen, Dane, carpenter.

"Yaller-Jacket," Maylay, cook.

John Boyd, Irish, able seaman.

George Parker, American, able seaman.

Charley Holmes, English,   "   "

"Brush," a Finn,   "   "

Jan Dam, Dutch,   "   "

"Melbourne," Maori,   "   "

Kalani, a Kanaka   "   "

Sandy McPherson, Scot,   "   "

Tom Hayes, English, ship's boy.

Thirteen. An unlucky number; the Finn had worried about it a good deal; the others laughed, but most of them not cordially. For the present, six of us were elected to be of the shore watch with the captain, the other five to stay with the mate in the ship. Then we began work on the seals—if you choose to call it work; it was only play, in fact. Plainly it was a generation that had never seen a man. They were not afraid of us. We could land on their islets and walk about among them freely, and attract no attention, unless you choose to call a lazy, friendly curiosity by that name. We could club a bull on the nose and bundle him into the boat and his wife

would lie there quiet and comfortable and think we were only
giving him a pleasure trip or something like that. It was like
murdering children, they were so gentle and trustful. We killed
hundreds that first week, and skinned them on a flat piece of
beach.

Then we had a day's holiday; next day we of the shore party
were to take our turn aboard ship, and the ship-crew would have
their chance ashore for a week. That night the captain was in great
spirits, and so was everybody, for it was a wonderful week's take.
Each of us common sailors was worth as much as a hundred dollars
more than he was worth before we anchored in the bay. I had
never cleared such a fortune in five months before—clear and
clean, I mean. By the time the voyage was done I should be worth
well on to a thousand dollars, no doubt. The captain's lay was a
tenth, and he was feeling pretty rich.

After supper we had hot grog, and lit the pipes, and built up a
rousing fire, and sat around it talking about what we would do with
our riches when we got home; and the captain unbent as the grog
warmed him up, and he let discipline go and joined in the talk
pretty much like one of us. It was blowing up the beginnings of a
storm outside and was very cold, but it was snug and comfortable
inside, and quite sociable and friendly. The captain was chatting
along, and said he wished seal skins were not of a fluctuating value,
but had an intrinsic value, like gold. Sandy McPherson was born to
argue things, and was always at it in the forecastle; and now that
his liquor was a little in his head he was ready to take a chance at
the captain. So he said—

"With all respect, what do you mean by intrinsic, sir—which is a
foolish word, and hasn't any meaning at all."

"Hasn't any meaning! I like that," said the captain.

"Please state it, then, sir."

"Intrinsic value is a value which is born in a thing, and remains
the same, and cannot change."

"It doesn't exist. There is no such thing in the earth, sir."

"I never heard such wild talk. What do you say to gold?"

"That it is like silver,—has no intrinsic value; has only an
artificial value, made by laws and customs."

"Nothing of the kind. A gold sovereign is worth its face all over the world; no more, and no less, and nothing can change it."

"Laws and circumstances can. If the governments of the earth should pass a law saying it should no longer be a legal tender for debts it would become merely merchandise at once, and its value would rise and fall according to the world's demand for watches and plate and such-like commodities."

"That is a pure absurdity. Gold has an intrinsic value, and laws cannot affect it."

"Laws can affect it, and circumstances do affect it."

"How can you prove that?"

"You have a gold piece in your pocket, sir?"

"I have."

"What is it worth here in this island?"

"The same it is worth in London."

"I will prove that circumstances can arise which would knock down its value in a commercial transaction—as compared with that slice of bread there—"

He did not get any further. A thundering gust of wind struck the house and shook down a tin pan from the wall, and the crash of it on the floor interrupted his argument. The captain said—

"We'll take a look at the vessel and see if she is all right," and we muffled ourselves up and took the lanterns and went outside. We took refuge from the bitter wind in the cave door, and from there we looked out upon the harbor, and saw the vessel's lights and dropped our apprehensions. As we stood there shivering, the captain said, "We have wasted this holiday—we could have examined the cave. Take a look, some of you, and see what it is like."

I stepped in with my lantern, and "Brush" the Finn with his. It was like a tunnel; we had to stoop a little, but it was wide enough for the two of us to walk abreast and have plenty of room. We walked about fifty steps, then there was a bend to the right, and after a few steps more we arrived in a wide place like a spacious room. I saw something glisten on the floor—a coin, I thought. Brush saw it at the same moment and plunged for it, but I set my foot upon it. He said he saw it first; that it was his, and he would have it. I said I saw

it as soon as he, and half of it was mine, at any rate. Lust for the
money made him wolfish; I don't think I ever saw such a hungry
light in a man's eye, or such a frenzied expression. He sprang upon
me, and the next moment we were rolling on the floor and fighting.
Soon I was getting the best of him; then he thought I was going to
knife him there in the dark, and he began to shout for help. The
others heard him and came running, and separated us. The captain
required an explanation, and got it. Then we found the coin, and it
was gold—Spanish; and the date of it was away back a couple of
centuries. Then straightway there was a feverish hunting and
scrambling around for more.

We found fifteen pieces. It was a very profitable hour's work.
We had examined every inch of the floor of the room, as much as
two or three times over. Were we satisfied? No—only whetted up.
The captain said the money never came there by accident; there
could be more; we must search the cave further. We struck into a
passage which was a long and crooked one, and every now and then
we found gold as we crept stooping along—altogether 39 pieces.
Another profitable hour's work. Then we entered another room,
and there—why, such a pile! Bushels and bushels and bushels of
gold coin.

No one could find breath to speak for a moment or two, but all
stood staring and gasping. Then the captain said—

"There is enough to make a thousand men wealthy—and it is all
ours. Get to work and count it—count it, do you hear!"

We went about it eagerly. At first we handled it with a sort of
awful reverence, for we were not used to that precious metal and it
seemed like something holy; but that feeling wore off before long
and we got to handling it with as little respect as if it were so much
brass. We counted and counted until we ached all over from
fatigue, and were getting drowsy, and actually growing tired of it—
a thing which looks impossible, but it is true. Some of the men
began to soldier, and the captain would break out on them just as
he had been used to do when they were shirking their work on
shipboard. At last Sandy McPherson came out frankly, though
respectfully, and said it was not fair to require men to stand such
an age-long watch as this without grog or a change; and he said,

"We've been counting for hours, sir, and you see, yourself, that we haven't made any real impression on the pile. It will take days and days to count it all, sir; there's millions of it, and we are tired to the bone."

The captain saw the reasonableness of it; and as we all looked pretty beseeching and humble and fagged out, he gave the word, and most thankfully grateful we were to knock off and stretch ourselves. Then we came out, and my, what a storm was raging! There was a driving fog of snow, and the wind was roaring and booming and screaming. We could not see the ship, of course, and that made us uncomfortable for a moment; but as there was nothing to be done, we started a big fire in the house, and had something to eat and drink, and then turned in and let the storm sing us to sleep while we planned out what we would do with the money when we got home. And after we were asleep we went on counting it the rest of the night, and so we might almost as well have staid in the cave and gone on with the business.

The captain was the last to turn in; and the last thing he said was that we must be up at dawn and ready for a busy day; for we would load the money into the ship and be homeward-bound by noon. That sounded good. Sandy McPherson said it would take longer than that to get the seal skins aboard. The captain only said, in an indifferent way—

"I reckon we can leave them, can't we? What's to hinder?"

I had never thought of that.

II.

WHEN WE were called at dawn my mind came wandering up out of a most solid and stupefying sleep, and began to settle itself and get its bearings; and then all of a sudden a thought came which made me sick and weak with disappointment: "It was all a dream, that gold." I would not like to feel that feeling again, I think I would rather suffer any other misery. Life had been a triumph and a proud possession, and now it was a shabby poor thing and a degradation. I was up, by this time; and I put my hand in my pocket, and my heart stood still!—plenty of gold there. I wish I could feel *that* feeling again. Why, it makes a person just reel! There is no joy in all your life that is like it. And you can't ever have it again—not in the same force. You can wake up next morning and pretend; but it's not the same thing. You get only the joy, you can't get back the surprise. I was not the only one that thought it was a dream, they all thought it.

While Yaller-Jacket was rationing out the breakfast we stepped outside and took a look. The sky was as dull as lead, and there was a heavy sea on, but no flash to the white-caps; they looked like a wide desert of crawly dim-white worms. The ship was gone. The captain was pleased. He said it meant that the wind had gone about in the night and threatened to blow on shore, and the mate had gone to sea to keep out of trouble.

At breakfast he said it had occurred to him to weigh the money; it would be quicker than to count it, and just as satisfactory. So we took a rice-shovel and the butcher's balances to the cave and went to work, the captain and I, the others looking on. The shovel held about ten pounds of gold. The captain weighed out 50 pounds of it and put it in a pile. He said the value of a pound of gold was $250, about £50 sterling. He said we would now separate the treasure into fifty-pound piles, and then we should know just how much of a find we had struck. It was easier said than done. The shoveling of the yellow riches was charming pastime at first, but by and by it made one's wrist ache, and you can see that by that time it had degenerated into work; and so, one by one we took a turn at it and made out to get pretty tired of it. But it had to be done, and so of course we kept at it. Changing the shovel to the left hand every now and then modified the labor; changing the shoveler with some frequency modified it further; altogether we got along well enough.

We weighed about a hundred piles an hour. When we knocked off for the day we had stocked a long strip of one side of the great cavern with piles—twelve rows, with a hundred piles in each. It represented thirty tons of gold, and was worth $15,000,000. We had made a considerable hole in the main mass.

One or another of us had been sent out about once an hour, all day, to look for the ship, but she had not returned, and the sky was still heavy with clouds. But she was but little on our minds; we were so dizzy with our good fortune that it was like being drunk; we could not think straight, we thought in a whirl.

We sat up late and the can went round, but there was no jollity. The captain walked the floor a good deal, and he did a good deal of ciphering on a log-slate, too, but he was not talkative. Once or twice Sandy or another tried to draw him out on the subject of the division and the proportion of shares, but it seemed to irritate him and interrupt his cipherings; nothing was got out of him. The Finn was touchy, too; he only snarled when he was spoken to; he mumbled to himself at times, and acted like a person who was a little off his balance. It was not a comfortable evening—very different from the splendid time we had the night before.

We weighed coin all next day, and all the two following days, and then we were done. Nights the captain ciphered and the Finn mumbled to himself and played with gold coins and kissed them and fondled them. There was no talk, no cheerfulness. The ship was still away; but everybody was absorbed in thought and indifferent about it.

We had more than a hundred and twenty tons of gold coin— more than sixty millions of dollars. And nothing to do, and the ship not in. The hours began to drag on our hands. So at last we began to take an interest in the ship. The weather was clear, now, and we took to watching and guessing and wondering. Even the captain stopped ciphering at last, and woke up and came to himself. He said he was a little troubled, but not much. Sandy McPherson said—

"With all deference, sir, I am a good deal troubled, myself."

"Why?"

"Because when we came here we hadn't had an observation for days and days, and hadn't any but a guesswork idea of where we were. Maybe twelve or fifteen hundred miles south-west-by-west from Cape Horn, but no telling—no sort of telling. A man might paddle around for two years on a guess like that and not find this little patch of rock. We got no observation here, the weather has been thick ever since. The mate hasn't any idea where this island is. He will get tired guessing around, presently, and give it up and strike for some of the old sealing-grounds and get what skins he can and go home."

That made me sick, it looked so true, but the others did not seem to realize the size of it, and the captain said it wasn't time yet to begin to worry about it. He seemed like a man infatuated; and pretty soon he was ciphering away again, just as usual.

The Great Dark

MARK TWAIN did not give this story a title, and A. B. Paine, his literary executor, designated the manuscript simply as "Statement of the Edwardses." In his dictation of 30 August 1906, the author said that he would probably have called one of his unfinished stories "The Refuge of the Derelicts." He added that his manuscript had no title, but that it began with a "pretty brusque remark by an ancient admiral, who is Captain Ned Wakefield [*sic*] under a borrowed name." [1] No draft with such an opening has been discovered; however, a notebook entry of 1897 presents what may be the remembered brusque speech: "Wakeman, Sailor-boy, 'Get to the masthead you son of a gun.' " [2] Mark Twain had planned to bring a Wakeman-like character into the voyage-of-disaster story; he mentioned Wakeman in his notes of 23 May 1897 for "Which Was the Dream?" and again in his further notes of 22 August for that work. And in the last episode of "The Great Dark" the ship captain has and exhibits the strength, the courage, and the colorful and effective language of the actual Captain Edgar "Ned" Wakeman with whom he had sailed in 1866. But the title "The Refuge of the Derelicts" can hardly have been intended for the existing draft of "The Great Dark," and the latter title, aptly supplied by Bernard DeVoto, is here retained.

Mark Twain's intention of making the first half or three-fourths of the story comic has been discussed in the General Introduction. Although in his extensive use of comic sea language he was burlesquing the writings of W. Clark Russell, he was also working in a literary

---

[1] A copy of this dictation is in MTP. This passage was not included in the dictation of 30 August 1906, as published in *MTE*, p. 200.

[2] Typescript 32a (II), p. 38.

99

mode that he had used much earlier. In 1868 he had written of a young lady who had read in a Sunday school library a tract about "a wicked sailor [who] was ordered to ascend to the main hatch and reef a gasket in the sheet anchor; from his dizzy height he saw the main-tops'l jib-boom fetch away from the clew-garnets of the booby hatch. . . ."[3] For some other comic effects, he drew upon the experiences of his global tour of 1895–1896. For example, the incident in which the Superintendent of Dreams keeps making the mate Turner's coffee disappear probably owes something to a disconcerting practice encountered in South African hotels: "And here they . . . knock on the open door, wake you up, tramp across the floor with a cup of coffee, find that you are apparently asleep, and then clear out. You find you can't get to sleep anymore, so you reach for the coffee, and discover that the idiot has carried it away."[4] The actions of the Superintendent of Dreams also have effects much like those achieved by an invisible young man in "Shackleford's Ghost," a story fragment that was probably written about the same time: "Now and then somebody sits down in his lap, or runs against him and is frightened."[5] His trip also furnished some of the more tragic incidents; a notebook entry of 28 August 1895 tells of two girls who were attacked by "an octopus with tentacles 12 feet long."[6] In the story, Edwards recalls that a boy has been badly hurt by an octopus. The description in Book II of the giant squid may owe something to Frank Bullen's representation in *The Cruise of the Cachalot*, which Clemens had read, of a huge cuttlefish, "as awful an object as one could well imagine even in a fevered dream. . . . The eyes . . . were at least a foot in diameter, and, seen under such conditions, looked decidedly eerie and hobgoblin-like."[7]

The intended conclusion for "The Great Dark" is found in two sets of notes: some working notes, probably made in August 1898 (these have been summarized by DeVoto in *Letters from the Earth*), and a notebook passage of 21–22 September 1898. The notebook entry, which appears to be the latest plan for ending the story, extends the action to a time fifteen years after the beginning of the voyage, whereas the working notes have the tragic finale occurring after the tenth year at

---

[3] Typescript 10, p. 6.

[4] Typescript 30 (II), p. 38.

[5] DV 318, p. 7.

[6] Typescript 28a (II), p. 37.

[7] Frank Thomas Bullen, *The Cruise of the Cachalot* (London: Smith, Elder & Co., 1898), pp. 143–144.

sea. However, much the same sequence of incidents is presented in both groups of notes. When in Edwards's dream of a voyage in a drop of water under the lens of a microscope the ship comes directly into the reflected light of the instrument, the sea dries up. Both Edwards and the captain take provisions and make a desperate trek overland to another ship on which children of theirs have been held as prisoners; they arrive too late and find only mummified bodies. At the last, Edwards was to awaken, finding himself still comfortably at home. His wife Alice would just then be coming in with the children to say goodnight. But these planned events were never written as a part of the story. The manuscript breaks off after a courageous declamation by the captain. The mood at the last is one not of despair but of exuberance. And it should be noted that in the fall of 1898 Mark Twain's wife Olivia observed, "I have not known Mr. Clemens for years to write with so much pleasure and energy as he has done during this last summer." [8] Perhaps it was his strength that betrayed his intention of writing a tragic and despairing conclusion.

[8] Olivia Langdon Clemens to Mrs. Frank Cheney, 7 October 1898; copy in MTP.

The Great Dark

BEFORE IT HAPPENED.

STATEMENT BY MRS. EDWARDS.

W E WERE in no way prepared for this dreadful thing. We were a happy family, we had been happy from the beginning; we did not know what trouble was, we were not thinking of it nor expecting it.

My husband was thirty-five years old, and seemed ten years younger, for he was one of those fortunate people who by nature are overcharged with breezy spirits and vigorous health, and from whom cares and troubles slide off without making any impression. He was my ideal, and indeed my idol. In my eyes he was everything that a man ought to be, and in spirit and body beautiful. We were married when I was a girl of 16, and we now had two children, comely and dear little creatures: Jessie, 8 years old, and Bessie, 6.

The house had been in a pleasant turmoil all day, this 19th of March, for it was Jessie's birthday.[9] Henry (my husband) had romped with the children till I was afraid he would tire them out and unfit them for their party in the evening, which was to be a children's fancy dress dance; and so I was glad when at last in the edge of the evening he took them to our bedroom to show them the grandest of all the presents, the microscope. I allowed them fifteen minutes for this show. I would put the children into their costumes, then, and have them ready to receive their great flock of

---

[9] Olivia Susan Clemens—Mark Twain's Susy—was born on 19 March 1872.

102

little friends and the accompanying parents. Henry would then be free to jot down in short-hand (he was a past-master in that art) an essay which he was to read at the social club the next night. I would show the children to him in their smart costumes when the party should be over and the good-night kisses due.

I left the three in a state of great excitement over the microscope, and at the end of the fifteen minutes I returned for the children. They and their papa were examining the wonders of a drop of water through a powerful lens. I delivered the children to a maid and they went away. Henry said—

"I will take forty winks and then go to work. But I will make a new experiment with the drop of water first. Won't you please strengthen the drop with the merest touch of Scotch whisky and stir up the animals?"

Then he threw himself on the sofa and before I could speak he uttered a snore. That came of romping the whole day. In reaching for the whisky decanter I knocked off the one that contained brandy and it broke. The noise stopped the snore. I stooped and gathered up the broken glass hurriedly in a towel, and when I rose to put it out of the way he was gone. I dipped a broomstraw in the Scotch whisky and let a wee drop fall upon the glass slide where the water-drop was, then I crossed to the glass door to tell him it was ready. But he had lit the gas and was at his table writing. It was the rule of the house not to disturb him when he was at work; so I went about my affairs in the picture gallery, which was our house's ballroom.

STATEMENT BY MR. EDWARDS

WE WERE experimenting with the microscope. And pretty ignorantly. Among the little glass slides in the box we found one labeled "section of a fly's eye." In its centre was faintly visible a dot. We put it under a low-power lens and it showed up like a fragment of honey-comb. We put it under a stronger lens and it became a window-sash. We put it under the most powerful lens of all, then there was room in the field, for only one pane of the several hundred. We were childishly delighted and astonished at the magnifying capacities of that lens, and said, "Now we can find out if there really are living animals in a drop of water, as the books say."

We brought some stale water from a puddle in the carriage-house where some rotten hay lay soaking, sucked up a dropperful and allowed a tear of it to fall on a glass slide. Then we worked the screws and brought the lens down until it almost touched the water; then shut an eye and peered eagerly down through the barrel. A disappointment—nothing showed. Then we worked the screws again and made the lens *touch* the water. Another disappointment—nothing visible. Once more we worked the screws and projected the lens hard *against* the glass slide itself. *Then* we saw the animals! Not frequently, but now and then. For a time there would be a great empty blank; then a monster would enter one horizon of this great white sea made so splendidly luminous by the reflector and go plowing across and disappear beyond the opposite horizon. Others would come and go at intervals and disappear. The lens was pressing *against* the glass slide; therefore how could those bulky creatures crowd through between and not get stuck? Yet they swam with perfect freedom; it was plain that they had all the room and all the water that they needed. Then how unimaginably little they must be! Moreover, that wide circular sea which they were traversing was only a small part of our drop of stale water; it was not as big as the head of a pin; whereas the entire drop, flattened out on the glass, was as big around as a child's finger-ring. If we could have gotten the whole drop under the lens we could have seen those gruesome fishes swim leagues and leagues before they dwindled out of sight at the further shore!

I threw myself on the sofa profoundly impressed by what I had seen, and oppressed with thinkings. An ocean in a drop of water— and unknown, uncharted, unexplored by man! By man, who gives all his time to the Africas and the poles, with this unsearched marvelous world right at his elbow. Then the Superintendent of

Dreams appeared at my side, and we talked it over. He was willing to provide a ship and crew, but said—

"It will be like any other voyage of the sort—not altogether a holiday excursion."

"That is all right; it is not an objection."

"You and your crew will be much diminished, as to size, but you need not trouble about that, as you will not be aware of it. Your ship itself, stuck upon the point of a needle, would not be discoverable except through a microscope of very high power."

"I do not mind these things. Get a crew of whalers. It will be well to have men who will know what to do in case we have trouble with those creatures."

"Better still if you avoid them."

"I shall avoid them if I can, for they have done me no harm, and I would not wantonly hurt any creature, but I shan't run from them. They have an ugly look, but I thank God I am not afraid of the ugliest that ever plowed a drop of water."

"You think so *now*, with your five feet eight, but it will be a different matter when the mote that floats in a sunbeam is Mont Blanc compared to you."

"It is no matter; you have seen me face dangers before—"

"Finish with your orders—the night is slipping away."

"Very well, then. Provide me a naturalist to tell me the names of the creatures we see; and let the ship be a comfortable one and perfectly appointed and provisioned, for I take my family with me." [10]

Half a minute later (as it seemed to me), a hoarse voice broke on my ear—

"Topsails all—let go the lee brace—sheet home the stuns'l boom —hearty, now, and all together!"

---

[10] After deciding that Edwards's family would accompany him on the voyage, Mark Twain deleted a part of his original paragraph and added words following the deletion:

". . . creatures we see; (send the family to the microscope to watch me on my adventures, and get the ship ready at once while I write a line to comfort my wife and allay her fears.) and let the ship be a comfortable one and perfectly appointed and provisioned, for I take my family with me."

I turned out, washed the sleep out of my eyes with a dash of cold water, and stepped out of my cabin, leaving Alice quietly sleeping in her berth. It was a blustering night and dark, and the air was thick with a driving mist out of which the tall masts and bellying clouds of sail towered spectrally, faintly flecked here and there aloft by the smothered signal lanterns. The ship was heaving and wallowing in the heavy seas, and it was hard to keep one's footing on the moist deck. Everything was dimmed to obliteration, almost; the only thing sharply defined was the foamy mane of white water, sprinkled with phosphorescent sparks, which broke away from the lee bow. Men were within twenty steps of me, but I could not make out their figures; I only knew they were there by their voices. I heard the quartermaster report to the second mate—

"Eight bells, sir."

"Very well—make it so."

Then I heard the muffled sound of the distant bell, followed by a far-off cry—

"Eight bells and a cloudy morning—anchor watch turn out!"

I saw the glow of a match photograph a pipe and part of a face against a solid bank of darkness, and groped my way thither and found the second mate.

"What of the weather, mate?"

"I don't see that it's any better, sir, than it was the first day out, ten days ago; if anything it's worse—thicker and blacker, I mean. You remember the spitting snow-flurries we had that night?"

"Yes."

"Well, we've had them again to-night. And hail and sleet besides, b'George! And here it comes again."

We stepped into the sheltering lee of the galley, and stood there listening to the lashing of the hail along the deck and the singing of the wind in the cordage. The mate said—

"I've been at sea thirty years, man and boy, but for a level ten-day stretch of unholy weather this bangs anything I ever struck, north of the Horn—if we *are* north of it. For I'm blest if I know *where* we are—do you?"

It was an embarrassing question. I had been asked it very

confidentially by my captain, long ago, and had been able to state that I didn't know; and had been discreet enough not to go into any particulars; but this was the first time that any officer of the ship had approached me with the matter. I said—

"Well, no, I'm not a sailor, but I am surprised to hear *you* say you don't know where we are."

He was caught. It was his turn to be embarrassed. First he began to hedge, and vaguely let on that perhaps he did know, after all; but he made a lame fist of it, and presently gave it up and concluded to be frank and take me into his confidence.

"I'm going to be honest with you, sir—and don't give me away." He put his mouth close to my ear and sheltered it against the howling wind with his hand to keep from having to shout, and said impressively, "Not only I don't know where we are, sir, but by God the captain himself don't know!"

I had met the captain's confession by pretending to be frightened and distressed at having engaged a man who was ignorant of his business; and then he had changed his note and told me he had only meant that he had lost his bearings in the thick weather—a thing which would rectify itself as soon as he could get a glimpse of the sun. But I was willing to let the mate tell me all he would, so long as I was not to "give it away."

"No, sir, he don't know where he is; lets on to, but he don't. I mean, he lets on to the crew, and his daughters, and young Phillips the purser, and of course to you and your family, but here lately he don't let on any more to the chief mate and me. And worried? I tell you he's worried plumb to his vitals."

"I must say I don't much like the look of this, Mr. Turner."

"Well, don't let on, sir; keep it to yourself—maybe it'll come out all right; hope it will. But you look at the facts—just look at the facts. We sail north—see? North-and-by-east-half-east, to be exact. Noon the fourth day out, heading for Sable island—ought to see it, weather rather thin for *this* voyage. *Don't* see it. Think the dead reckoning ain't right, maybe. We bang straight along, all the afternoon. No Sable island. *Damned if we didn't run straight over it!* It warn't there. What do you think of that?"

"Dear me, it is awful—awful—if true."

"*If* true. Well, it *is* true. True as anything that ever was, I take my oath on it. And then Greenland. We three banked our hopes on Greenland. Night before last we couldn't sleep for uneasiness; just anxiety, you know, to see if Greenland was going to be there. By the dead reckoning she was due to be in sight along anywhere from five to seven in the morning, if clear enough. But we staid on deck all night. Of course two of us had no business there, and had to scuttle out of the way whenever a man came along, or they would have been suspicious. But five o'clock came, seven o'clock, eight o'clock, ten o'clock, and at last twelve—and then the captain groaned and gave in! He knew well enough that if there had been any Greenland left we'd have knocked a corner off of it long before that."

"This is appalling!"

"You may hunt out a bigger word than that and it won't cover it, sir. And Lord, to see the captain, gray as ashes, sweating and worrying over his chart all day yesterday and all day to-day, and spreading his compasses here and spreading them there, and getting suspicious of his chronometer, and damning the dead-reckoning—just suffering death and taxes, you know, and me and the chief mate helping and suffering, and that purser and the captain's oldest girl spooning and cackling around, just in heaven! I'm a poor man, sir, but if I could buy out half of each of 'em's ignorance and put it together and make it a whole, blamed if I wouldn't put up my last nickel to do it, you hear *me*. Now—"

A wild gust of wind drowned the rest of his remark and smothered us in a fierce flurry of snow and sleet. He darted away and disappeared in the gloom, but first I heard his voice hoarsely shouting—

"Turn out, all hands, shorten sail!"

There was a rush of feet along the deck, and then the gale brought the dimmed sound of far-off commands—

"Mizzen foretop halyards there—all clue-garnets heave and away—now then, with a will—sheet home!"

And then the plaintive notes that told that the men were handling the kites—

"If you get there, before I do—
Hi-ho-o-o, roll a man down;
If you get there before I do,
O, give a man time to roll a man down!"

By and by all was still again. Meantime I had shifted to the other side of the galley to get out of the storm, and there Mr. Turner presently found me.

"That's a specimen," said he. "I've never struck any such weather anywheres. You are bowling along on a wind that's as steady as a sermon, and just as likely to last, and before you can say Jack Robinson the wind whips around from weather to lee, and if you don't jump for it you'll have your canvas blown out of the cat-heads and sailing for heaven in rags and tatters. I've never seen anything to begin with it. But then I've never been in the middle of Greenland before—in a *ship*—middle of where it *used* to be, I mean. Would it worry you if I was to tell you something, sir?"

"Why, no, I think not. What is it?"

"Let me take a turn up and down, first, to see if anybody's in earshot." When he came back he said, "What should you think if you was to see a whale with hairy spider-legs to it as long as the foretogallant backstay and as big around as the mainmast?"

I recognized the creature; I had seen it in the microscope. But I didn't say so. I said—

"I should think I had a little touch of the jimjams."

"The very thing *I* thought, so help me! It was the third day out, at a quarter to five in the morning. I was out astraddle of the bowsprit in the drizzle, bending on a scuttle-butt, for I don't trust that kind of a job to a common sailor, when all of a sudden that creature plunged up out of the sea the way a porpoise does, not a hundred yards away—I saw two hundred and fifty feet of him and his fringes—and then he turned in the air like a triumphal arch, shedding Niagaras of water, and plunged head first under the sea with an awful swash of sound, and by that time we were close aboard him and in another ten yards we'd have hit him. It was my belief that he tried to hit *us*, but by the mercy of God he was out of practice. The lookout on the foc'sle was the only man around, and thankful I was, or there could have been a mutiny. He was asleep

on the binnacle—they always sleep on the binnacle, it's the best
place to see from—and it woke him up and he said, "Good land,
what's that, sir?" and I said, "It's nothing, but it *might* have been,
for any good a stump like you is for a lookout." I was pretty far
gone, and said I was sick, and made him help me onto the foc'sle;
and then I went straight off and took the pledge; for I had been
going it pretty high for a week before we sailed, and I made up my
mind that I'd rather go dry the rest of my life than see the like of
that thing again."

"Well, I'm glad it was only the jimjams."

"Wait a minute, I ain't done. Of course I didn't enter it on the
log—"

"Of course not—"

"For a man in his right mind don't put nightmares in the log. He
only puts the word 'pledge' in, and takes credit for it if anybody
inquires; and knows it will please the captain, and hopes it'll get to
the owners. Well, two days later the chief mate took the pledge!"

"You don't mean it!"

"Sure as I'm standing here. I saw the word on the book. I didn't
say anything, but I felt encouraged. Now then, listen to this: day
before yesterday I'm dumm'd if the *captain* didn't take the
pledge!"

"Oh, come!"

"It's a true bill—I take my oath. There was the word. Then we
begun to put this and that together, and next we began to look at
each other kind of significant and willing, you know; and of course
giving the captain the preceedence, for it wouldn't become *us* to
begin, and we nothing but mates. And so yesterday, sure enough,
out comes the captain—and we called his hand. Said he was out
astern in a snow-flurry about dawn, and saw a creature shaped like
a wood-louse and as big as a turreted monitor, go racing by and
tearing up the foam, in chase of a fat animal the size of an elephant
and creased like a caterpillar—and saw it dive after it and
disappear; and so he begun to prepare *his* soul for the pledge and
break it to his entrails."

"It's terrible!"

"The pledge?—you bet your bottom dollar. If I—"

"No, I don't mean the pledge; I mean it is terrible to be lost at sea among such strange, uncanny brutes."

"Yes, there's something in that, too, I don't deny it. Well, the thing that the mate saw was like one of these big long lubberly canal boats, and it was ripping along like the Empire Express; and the look of it gave him the cold shivers, and so he begun to arrange *his* earthly affairs and go for the pledge."

"Turner, it is dreadful—dreadful. Still, good has been done; for these pledges—"

"Oh, they're off!"

"Off?"

"Cert'nly. Can't be jimjams; couldn't all three of us have them at once, it ain't likely. What do you want with a pledge when there ain't any occasion for it? *There* he goes!"

He was gone like a shot, and the night swallowed him up. Now all of a sudden, with the wind still blowing hard, the seas went down and the deck became as level as a billiard table! Were *all* the laws of Nature suspended? It made my flesh creep; it was like being in a haunted ship. Pretty soon the mate came back panting, and sank down on a cable-tier, and said—

"Oh, this is an awful life; I don't think we can stand it long. There's too many horribles in it. Let me pant a little, I'm in a kind of a collapse."

"What's the trouble?"

"Drop down by me, sir—I mustn't shout. There—now you're all right." Then he said sorrowfully, "I reckon we've got to take it again."

"Take what?"

"The pledge."

"Why?"

"Did you see that thing go by?"

"What thing?"

"A *man*."

"No. What of it?"

"This is four times that *I*'ve seen it; and the mate has seen it, and so has the captain. Haven't you ever seen it?"

"I suppose not. Is there anything extraordinary about it?"

"Extra-ordinary? Well, I should *say!*"

"How is it extraordinary?"

He said in an awed voice that was almost like a groan—

"Like this, for instance: you put your hand on him and *he ain't there.*"

"What do you mean, Turner?"

"It's as true as I'm sitting here, I wish I may never stir. The captain's getting morbid and religious over it, and says he wouldn't give a damn for ship and crew if that thing stays aboard."

"You curdle my blood. What is the man like? Isn't it just one of the crew, that you glimpse and lose in the dark?"

"You take note of *this*: it wears a broad slouch hat and a long cloak. Is that a whaler outfit, I'll ask you? A minute ago I was as close to him as I am to you; and I made a grab for him, and what did I get? A handful of air, that's all. There warn't a sign of him left."

"I do hope the pledge will dispose of it. It must be a work of the imagination, or the crew would have seen it."

"We're afraid they have. There was a deal of whispering going on last night in the middle watch. The captain dealt out grog, and got their minds on something else; but he is mighty uneasy, because of course he don't want you or your family to hear about that man, and would take my scalp if he knew what I'm doing now; and besides, if such a thing got a start with the crew, there'd be a mutiny, sure."

"I'll keep quiet, of course; still, I think it must be an output of imaginations overstrung by the strange fishes you think you saw; and I am hoping that the pledge—"

"I want to take it now. And I will."

"I'm witness to it. Now come to my parlor and I'll give you a cup of hot coffee and—"

"Oh, my goodness, there it is again! . . . It's gone. . . . Lord, it takes a body's breath . . . It's the jimjams I've got—I know it for sure. I want the coffee; it'll do me good. If you could help me a little, sir—I feel as weak as Sabbath grog."

We groped along the sleety deck to my door and entered, and there in the bright glare of the lamps sat (as I was half expecting) the man of the long cloak and the slouch hat, on the sofa,—my friend the Superintendent of Dreams.[11] I was annoyed, for a moment, for of course I expected Turner to make a jump at him, get nothing, and be at once in a more miserable state than he already was. I reached for my cabin door and closed it, so that Alice might not hear the scuffle and get a fright. But there wasn't any. Turner went on talking, and took no notice of the Superintendent. I gave the Superintendent a grateful look; and it was an honest one, for this thing of making himself visible and scaring people could do harm.

"Lord, it's good to be in the light, sir," said Turner, rustling comfortably in his yellow oilskins, "it lifts a person's spirits right up. I've noticed that these cussed jimjam blatherskites ain't as apt to show up in the light as they are in the dark, except when you've got the trouble in your attic pretty bad." Meantime we were dusting the snow off each other with towels. "You're mighty well fixed here, sir—chairs and carpets and rugs and tables and lamps and books and everything lovely, and so warm and comfortable and homy; and the roomiest parlor I ever struck in a ship, too. Land, hear the wind, don't she sing! And not a sign of motion!—rip goes the sleet again!—ugly, you bet!—and here? why here it's only just the more cosier on account of it. Dern that jimjam, if I had him in here once I bet you I'd sweat him. Because I don't mind saying that I don't grab at him as earnest as I want to, outside there, and ain't as disappointed as I ought to be when I don't get him; but here in the light I ain't afraid of *no* jimjam."

It made the Superintendent of Dreams smile a smile that was full of pious satisfaction to hear him. I poured a steaming cup of coffee and handed it to Turner and told him to sit where he pleased and make himself comfortable and at home; and before I could interfere he had sat down in the Superintendent of Dreams' lap!— no, sat down *through* him. It cost me a gasp, but only that, nothing more. [The] Superintendent of Dreams' head was larger than Turner's, and *surrounded* it, and was a transparent spirit-head

---

[11] Mark Twain's subsequent abbreviations S., S.D., and S. of D. have been expanded to full forms.

fronted with a transparent spirit-face; and this latter smiled at me as much as to say give myself no uneasiness, it is all right. Turner was smiling comfort and contentment at me at the same time, and the double result was very curious, but I could tell the smiles apart without trouble. The Superintendent of Dreams' body enclosed Turner's, but I could see Turner through it, just as one sees objects through thin smoke. It was interesting and pretty. Turner tasted his coffee and set the cup down in front of him with a hearty—

"Now I call that prime! 'George, it makes me feel the way old Cap'n Jimmy Starkweather did, I reckon, the first time he tasted grog after he'd been off his allowance three years. The way of it was this. It was there in Fairhaven by New Bedford, away back in the old early whaling days before I was born; but I heard about it the first day I *was* born, and it was a ripe old tale then, because they keep only the one fleet of yarns in commission down New Bedford-way, and don't ever re-stock and don't ever repair. And I came near hearing it in old Cap'n Jimmy's own presence once, when I was ten years old and he was ninety-two; but I didn't, because the man that asked Cap'n Jimmy to tell about it got crippled and the thing didn't materialize. It was Cap'n Jimmy that crippled him. Land, I thought I sh'd die! The very recollection of it—"

The very recollection of it so powerfully affected him that it shut off his speech and he put his head back and spread his jaws and laughed himself purple in the face. And while he was doing it the Superintendent of Dreams emptied the coffee into the slop bowl and set the cup back where it was before. When the explosion had spent itself Turner swabbed his face with his handkerchief and said—

"There—that laugh has scoured me out and done me good; I hain't had such another one—well, not since I struck *this* ship, now that's sure. I'll whet up and start over."

He took up his cup, glanced into it, and it was curious to observe the two faces that were framed in the front of his head. Turner's was long and distressed; the Superintendent of Dreams' was wide, and broken out of all shape with a convulsion of silent laughter. After a little, Turner said in a troubled way—

"I'm dumm'd if *I* recollect drinking that."

I didn't say anything, though I knew he must be expecting me to say something. He continued to gaze into the cup a while, then looked up wistfully and said—

"Of course I must have drunk it, but I'm blest if I can recollect whether I did or not. Lemme see. First you poured it out, then I set down and put it before me here; next I took a sup and said it was good, and set it down and begun about old Cap'n Jimmy—and then—and then—" He was silent a moment, then said, "It's as far as I can get. It beats me. I reckon that after that I was so kind of full of my story that I didn't notice whether I—." He stopped again, and there was something almost pathetic about the appealing way in which he added, "But I *did* drink it, *didn't* I? You *see* me do it—*didn't* you?"

I hadn't the heart to say no.

"Why, yes, I think I did. I wasn't noticing particularly, but it seems to me that I saw you drink it—in fact, I am about certain of it."

I was glad I told the lie, it did him so much good, and so lightened his spirits, poor old fellow.

"Of course I done it! I'm such a fool. As a general thing I wouldn't care, and I wouldn't bother anything about it; but when there's jimjams around the least little thing makes a person suspicious, you know. If you don't mind, sir—thanks, ever so much." He took a large sup of the new supply, praised it, set the cup down—leaning forward and fencing it around with his arms, with a labored pretense of not noticing that he was doing that— then said—

"Lemme see—where was I? Yes. Well, it happened like this. The Washingtonian Movement started up in those old times, you know, and it was Father Matthew here and Father Matthew there and Father Matthew yonder—nothing but Father Matthew and temperance all over everywheres. And temperance societies? There was millions of them, and everybody joined and took the pledge. We had one in New Bedford. Every last whaler joined—captain, crew and all. All, down to old Cap'n Jimmy. He was an old bach, his grog was his darling, he owned his ship and sailed her himself, he was independent, and he wouldn't give in. So at last they gave it up and quit pestering him. Time rolled along, and he got awful lonesome. There wasn't anybody to drink with, you see, and it got unbearable. So finally the day he sailed for Bering Strait he caved, and sent in his name to the society. Just as he was starting, his mate broke his leg and stopped ashore and he shipped a stranger in his place from down New York way. This fellow didn't belong to any society, and he went aboard fixed for the voyage. Cap'n Jimmy was out three solid years; and all the whole time he had the spectacle of that mate whetting up every day and leading a life that was worth the trouble; and it nearly killed him for envy to see it. Made his mouth water, you know, in a way that was pitiful. Well, he used to get out on the peak of the bowsprit where it was private, and set there and cuss. It was his only relief from his sufferings. Mainly he cussed himself; but when he had used up all his words and couldn't think of any new rotten things to call himself, he would turn his vocabulary over and start fresh and lay into Father Matthew and give *him* down the banks; and then the society; and so put in his watch as satisfactory as he could. Then he would count the days he was out, and try to reckon up about when he could hope to get home and resign from the society and start in on an all-compensating drunk that would make up for lost time. Well, when he was out three thousand years—which was *his* estimate, you know, though really it was only three years—he came rolling down the home-stretch with every rag stretched on his poles. Middle of winter, it was, and terrible cold and stormy. He made the landfall just at sundown and had to stand watch on deck all night of course, and the rigging was caked with ice three inches thick, and the yards was bearded with icicles five foot long, and the snow laid nine inches deep on the deck and hurricanes more of it being shoveled down onto him out of the skies. And so he plowed up and down all night, cussing himself and Father Matthew and the society, and doing it better than he ever done before; and his mouth was watering so, on account of the mate whetting up right in his sight all the time, that every cuss-word come out damp, and froze solid as it fell, and in his insufferable indignation he would hit it a whack with his cane and knock it a hundred yards, and one of them took the mate in the mouth and fetched away a rank of teeth and lowered *his* spirits considerable. He made the dock just at early breakfast time and never waited to tie up, but jumped ashore with his jug in his hand and rushed for the society's quarters like a deer. He met the seckatary coming out and yelled at him—

" 'I've resigned my membership!—I give you just two minutes to scrape my name off your log, d'ye hear?'

"And then the seckatary told him he'd been black-balled three years before—*hadn't ever been a member!* Land, I can't hold in, it's coming again!"

He flung up his arms, threw his head back, spread his jaws, and made the ship quake with the thunder of his laughter, while the Superintendent of Dreams emptied the cup again and set it back in its place. When Turner came out of his fit at last he was limp and exhausted, and sat mopping his tears away and breaking at times into little feebler and feebler barks and catches of expiring laughter. Finally he fetched a deep sigh of comfort and satisfaction, and said—

"Well, it *does* do a person good, no mistake—on a voyage like *this*. I reckon—"

His eye fell on the cup. His face turned a ghastly white—

"By God she's empty again!"

He jumped up and made a sprawling break for the door. I was frightened; I didn't know what he might do—jump overboard, maybe. I sprang in front of him and barred the way, saying, "Come, Turner, be a man, be a man! don't let your imagination run away with you like this"; and over his shoulder I threw a pleading look at the Superintendent of Dreams, who answered my prayer and refilled the cup from the coffee urn.

"Imagination you call it, sir! Can't I *see?*—with my own eyes? Let me go—don't stop me—I can't stand it, I can't stand it!"

"Turner, be reasonable—you know perfectly well your cup isn't empty, and *hasn't* been."

That hit him. A dim light of hope and gratitude shone in his eye, and he said in a quivery voice—

"Say it again—and say it's true. *Is* it true? Honor bright—you wouldn't deceive a poor devil that's—"

"Honor bright, man, I'm not deceiving you—look for your-self."

Gradually he turned a timid and wary glance toward the table; then the terror went out of his face, and he said humbly—

"Well, you see I reckon I hadn't quite got over thinking it happened the first time, and so maybe without me knowing it, that made me kind of suspicious that it would happen again, because the jimjams make you untrustful that way; and so, sure enough, I didn't half look at the cup, and just jumped to the conclusion it *had* happened." And talking so, he moved toward the sofa, hesi-tated a moment, and then sat down in that figure's body again. "But I'm all right, now, and I'll just shake these feelings off and be a man, as you say."

The Superintendent of Dreams separated himself and moved along the sofa a foot or two away from Turner. I was glad of that; it looked like a truce. Turner swallowed his cup of coffee; I poured another; he began to sip it, the pleasant influence worked a change, and soon he was a rational man again, and comfortable. Now a sea came aboard, hit our deck-house a stunning thump, and went hissing and seething aft.

"Oh, that's the ticket," said Turner, "the dummdest weather that ever I went pleasure-excursioning in. And how did it get aboard?—You answer me that: there ain't any motion to the ship. These mysteriousnesses—well, they just give me the cold shudders. And that reminds me. Do you mind my calling your attention to another peculiar thing or two?—on conditions as before—solid secrecy, you know."

"I'll keep it to myself. Go on."

"The Gulf Stream's gone to the devil!"

"What do you mean?"

"It's the fact, I wish I may never die. From the day we sailed till now, the water's been the same temperature right along, I'll take my oath. The Gulf Stream don't exist any more; she's gone to the devil."

"It's incredible, Turner! You make me gasp."

"Gasp away, if you want to; if things go on so, you ain't going to forget how for want of practice. It's the wooliest voyage, take it by and large—why, look here! You are a landsman, and there's no telling what a landsman can't overlook if he tries. For instance, have you noticed that the nights and days are exactly alike, and you can't tell one from tother except by keeping tally?"

"Why, yes, I have noticed it in a sort of indifferent general way, but—"

"Have you kept a tally, sir?"

"No, it didn't occur to me to do it."

"I thought so. Now you know, you couldn't keep it in your head, because you and your family are free to sleep as much as you like, and as it's always dark, you sleep a good deal, and you are pretty irregular, naturally. You've all been a little seasick from the start— tea and toast in your own parlor here—no regular time—order it as each of you pleases. You see? You don't go down to meals—*they* would keep tally for you. So you've lost your reckoning. I noticed it an hour ago."

"How?"

"Well, you spoke of *to-night*. It ain't to-night at all; it's just noon, now."

"The fact is, I don't believe I have often thought of its being day, since we left. I've got into the habit of considering it night all the time; it's the same with my wife and the children."

"There it is, you see. Mr. Edwards, it's perfectly awful; now ain't it, when you come to look at it? Always night—and such dismal nights, too. It's like being up at the pole in the winter time. And I'll ask you to notice another thing: this sky is as empty as my sou-wester there."

"Empty?"

"Yes, sir. I know it. You can't get up a day, in a Christian country, that's so solid black the sun can't make a blurry glow of *some* kind in the sky at high noon—now can you?"

"No, you can't."

"Have you ever seen a suspicion of any such a glow in this sky?"

"Now that you mention it, I haven't."

He dropped his voice and said impressively—

"Because there ain't any *sun*. She's gone where the Gulf Stream twineth."

"Turner! Don't talk like that."

"It's confidential, or I wouldn't. And the moon. She's at the full —by the almanac she is. Why don't *she* make a blur? Because there *ain't* any moon. And moreover—you might rake this on-completed sky a hundred year with a drag-net and you'd never scoop a star! Why? Because there *ain't* any. Now then, what is your opinion about all this?"

"Turner, it's so gruesome and creepy that I don't like to think about it—and I haven't any. What is yours?"

He said, dismally—

"That the world has come to an end. Look at it yourself. Just look at the facts. Put them together and add them up, and what have you got? No Sable island; no Greenland; no Gulf Stream; no day, no proper night; weather that don't jibe with any sample known to the Bureau; animals that would start a panic in any menagerie, chart no more use than a horse-blanket, and the heavenly bodies gone to hell! And on top of it all, that jimjam that I've put my hand on more than once and he warn't there—I'll swear it. The ship's bewitched. You don't believe in the jim, and I've sort of lost faith myself, here in the bright light; but if this cup of coffee was to—"

The cup began to glide slowly away, along the table. The hand that moved it was not visible to him. He rose slowly to his feet and stood trembling as if with an ague, his teeth knocking together and his glassy eyes staring at the cup. It slid on and on, noiseless; then it rose in the air, gradually reversed itself, poured its contents down the Superintendent's throat—I saw the dark stream trickling its way down through his hazy breast—then it returned to the table, and without sound of contact, rested there. The mate continued to stare at it for as much as a minute; then he drew a deep breath, took up his sou-wester, and without looking to the right or the left, walked slowly out of the room like one in a trance, muttering—

"I've *got* them—I've had the proof."

I said, reproachfully—

"Superintendent, why do you do that?"

"Do what?"

"Play these tricks."

"What harm is it?"

"Harm? It could make that poor devil jump overboard."

"No, he's not as far gone as that."

"For a while he was. He is a good fellow, and it was a pity to scare him so. However there are other matters that I am more concerned about just now."

"Can I help?"

"Why yes, you can; and I don't know any one else that can."

"Very well, go on."

"By the dead-reckoning we have come twenty-three hundred miles."

"The actual distance is twenty-three-fifty."

"Straight as a dart in the one direction—mainly."

"Apparently."

"Why do you say apparently? Haven't we come straight?"

"Go on with the rest. What were you going to say?"

"This. Doesn't it strike you that this is a pretty large drop of water?"

"No. It is about the usual size—six thousand miles across."

"Six thousand miles!"

"Yes."

"Twice as far as from New York to Liverpool?"

"Yes."

"I must say it is more of a voyage than I counted on. And we are not a great deal more than halfway across, yet. When shall we get in?"

"It will be some time yet."

"That is not very definite. Two weeks?"

"More than that."

I was getting a little uneasy.

"But how *much* more? A week?"

"All of that. More, perhaps."

"Why don't you tell me? A month more, do you think?"

"I am afraid so. Possibly two—possibly longer, even."

I was getting seriously disturbed by now.

"Why, we are sure to run out of provisions and water."

"No you'll not. I've looked out for that. It is what you are loaded with."

"Is that so? How does that come?"

"Because the ship is chartered for a voyage of discovery. Ostensibly she goes to England, takes aboard some scientists, then sails for the South pole."

"I see. You are deep."

"I understand my business."

I turned the matter over in my mind a moment, then said—

"It is more of a voyage than I was expecting, but I am not of a worrying disposition, so I do not care, so long as we are not going to suffer hunger and thirst."

"Make yourself easy, as to that. Let the trip last as long as it may, you will not run short of food and water, I go bail for that."

"All right, then. Now explain this riddle to me. Why is it always night?"

"That is easy. All of the drop of water is outside the luminous circle of the microscope except one thin and delicate rim of it. We are in the shadow; consequently in the dark."

"In the shadow of what?"

"Of the brazen end of the lens-holder."

"How can it cover such a spread with its shadow?"

"Because it is several thousand miles in diameter. For dimensions, that is nothing. The glass slide which it is pressing against, and which forms the bottom of the ocean we are sailing upon, is thirty thousand miles long, and the length of the microscope barrel is a hundred and twenty thousand. Now then, if—"

"You make me dizzy. I—"

"If you should thrust that glass slide through what you call the 'great' globe, eleven thousand miles of it would stand out on each side—it would be like impaling an orange on a table-knife. And so—"

"It gives me the head-ache. Are these the fictitious proportions which we and our surroundings and belongings have acquired by being reduced to microscopic objects?"

"They are the proportions, yes—but they are not fictitious. You do not notice that you yourself are in any way diminished in size, do you?"

"No, I am my usual size, so far as I can see."

"The same with the men, the ship and everything?"

"Yes—all natural."

"Very good; nothing but the laws and conditions have undergone a change. You came from a small and very insignificant world. The one you are in now is proportioned according to microscopic standards—that is to say, it is inconceivably stupendous and imposing."

It was food for thought. There was something overpowering in the situation, something sublime. It took me a while to shake off the spell and drag myself back to speech. Presently I said—

"I am content; I do not regret the voyage—far from it. I would not change places with any man in that cramped little world. But tell me—is it always going to be dark?"

"Not if you ever come into the luminous circle under the lens. Indeed you will not find *that* dark!"

"If we ever. What do you mean by that? We are making steady good time; we are cutting across this sea on a straight course."

"Apparently."

"There is no apparently about it."

"You might be going around in a small and not rapidly widening circle."

"Nothing of the kind. Look at the tell-tale compass over your head."

"I see it."

"We changed to this easterly course to satisfy—well, to satisfy everybody but me. It is a pretense of aiming for England—in a drop of water! Have you noticed that needle before?"

"Yes, a number of times."

"To-day, for instance?"

"Yes—often."

"Has it varied a jot?"

"Not a jot."

"Hasn't it always kept the place appointed for it—from the start?"

"Yes, always."

"Very well. First we sailed a northerly course; then tilted easterly; and now it is more so. How is *that* going around in a circle?"

He was silent. I put it at him again. He answered with lazy indifference—

"I merely threw out the suggestion."

"All right, then; cornered; let it stand at that. Whenever you happen to think of an argument in support of it, I shall be glad to hear about it."

He did not like that very well, and muttered something about my being a trifle airy. I retorted a little sharply, and followed it up by finding fault with him again for playing tricks on Turner. He said Turner called him a blatherskite. I said—

"No matter; you let him alone, from this out. And moreover, stop appearing to people—stop it entirely."

His face darkened. He said—

"I would advise you to moderate your manner. I am not used to it, and I am not pleased with it."

The rest of my temper went, then. I said, angrily—

"You may like it or not, just as you choose. And moreover, if my style doesn't suit you, you can end the dream as soon as you please —right now, if you like."

He looked me steadily in the eye for a moment, then said, with deliberation—

"The dream? *Are you quite sure it is a dream?*"

It took my breath away.

"What do you mean? *Isn't* it a dream?"

He looked at me in that same way again; and it made my blood chilly, this time. Then he said—

"You have spent your whole life in this ship. And this is *real* life. Your other life was the dream!" [12]

---

[12] This answer of the Superintendent of Dreams represents a substantive departure from the previous transcription by Bernard DeVoto, which here prints

It was as if he had hit me, it stunned me so. Still looking at me, his lip curled itself into a mocking smile, and he wasted away like a mist and disappeared.

I sat a long time thinking uncomfortable thoughts.

We are strangely made. We think we are wonderful creatures. Part of the time we think that, at any rate. And during that interval we consider with pride our mental equipment, with its penetration, its power of analysis, its ability to reason out clear conclusions from confused facts, and all the lordly rest of it; and then comes a rational interval and disenchants us. Disenchants us and lays us bare to ourselves, and we see that intellectually we are really no great things; that we seldom really know the thing we think we know; that our best-built certainties are but sand-houses and subject to damage from any wind of doubt that blows.

So little a time before, I *knew* that this voyage was a dream, and nothing more; a wee little puff or two of doubt had blown against that certainty, unhelped by fact or argument, and already it was dissolving away. It seemed an incredible thing, and it hurt my pride of intellect, but it had to be confessed.

When I came to consider it, these ten days had been such intense realities!—so intense that by comparison the life I had lived before them seemed distant, indistinct, slipping away and fading out in a far perspective—exactly as a dream does when you sit at breakfast trying to call back its details. I grew steadily more and more nervous and uncomfortable—and a little frightened, though I would not quite acknowledge this to myself.[13]

"I give you ten years to get over that superstition in!" In the holograph, just before this statement, Mark Twain wrote "OVER" and then, on an inserted page 59½, at first wrote the following statements: "You have spent two-thirds of your life in this ship. And this is *real* life. Your other life was the dream!" Thereafter he struck out "two-thirds of" and added "whole" in the first sentence. Following the revised reply, he recopied on page 59½ the rest of what he had already written on page 59 below the direction "OVER." He recopied smoothly, picking up two minor alterations that he had previously made. Although he did not actually strike lines through the superseded passage, there seems to be little reason to doubt that what he rewrote and recopied on the inserted page represents his later intention.

[13] On the reverse side of page 61 of the holograph (which includes the preceding paragraph), he noted, "And now another past began to rise dim and spiritual before me and stretch down and down and down into dreaming remotenesses of bygone years—a past spent in a ship!"

Then came this disturbing thought: if this transformation goes on, how am I going to conceal it from my wife? Suppose she should say to me, "Henry, there is something the matter with you, you are acting strangely; something is on your mind that you are concealing from me; tell me about it, let me help you"—what answer could I make?

I was *bound* to act strangely if this went on—bound to bury myself in deeps of troubled thought; I should not be able to help it. She had a swift eye to notice, where her heart was concerned, and a sharp intuition, and I was an impotent poor thing in her hands when I had things to hide and she had struck the trail.

I have no large amount of fortitude, staying power. When there is a fate before me I cannot rest easy until I know what it is. I am not able to wait. I want to know, right away. So, I would call Alice, now, and take the consequences. If she drove me into a corner and I found I could not escape, I would act according to my custom—come out and tell her the truth. She had a better head than mine, and a surer instinct in grouping facts and getting their meaning out of them. If I was drifting into dangerous waters, now, she would be sure to detect it and as sure to set me right and save me. I would call her, and keep out of the corner if I could; if I couldn't, why—I couldn't, that is all.

She came, refreshed with sleep, and looking her best self: that is to say, looking like a girl of nineteen, not a matron of twenty-five; she wore a becoming wrapper, or tea gown, or whatever it is called, and it was trimmed with ribbons and limp stuff—lace, I suppose; and she had her hair balled up and nailed to its place with a four-pronged tortoise-shell comb. She brought a basket of pink and gray crewels with her, for she was crocheting a jacket—for the cat, probably, judging by the size of it. She sat down on the sofa and set the basket on the table, expecting to have a chance to get to work by and by; not right away, because a kitten was curled up in it asleep, fitting its circle snugly, and the repose of the children's kittens was a sacred thing and not to be disturbed. She said—

"I noticed that there was no motion—it was what waked me, I think—and I got up to enjoy it, it is such a rare thing."

"Yes, rare enough, dear: we do have the most unaccountably strange weather."

"Do you think so, Henry? Does it seem strange weather to you?"

She looked so earnest and innocent that I was rather startled, and a little in doubt as to what to say. Any sane person could see that it was perfectly devilish weather and crazy beyond imagination, and so how could she feel uncertain about it?

"Well, Alice, I may be putting it too strong, but I don't think so; I think a person may call our weather by any hard name he pleases and be justified."

"Perhaps you are right, Henry. I have heard the sailors talk the same way about it, but I did not think that that meant much, they speak so extravagantly about everything. You are not always extravagant in your speech—often you are, but not always—and so it surprised me a little to hear you." Then she added tranquilly and musingly, "I don't remember any different weather."

It was not quite definite.

"You mean on *this* voyage, Alice."

"Yes, of course. Naturally. I haven't made any other."

She was softly stroking the kitten—and apparently in her right mind. I said cautiously, and with seeming indifference—

"You mean you haven't made any other this year. But the time we went to Europe—well, that was very different weather."

"The time we went to Europe, Henry?"

"Certainly, certainly—when Jessie was a year old."

She stopped stroking the kitty, and looked at me inquiringly.

"I don't understand you, Henry."

She was not a joker, and she was always truthful. Her remark blew another wind of doubt upon my wasting sand-edifice of certainty. Had I only *dreamed* that we went to Europe? It seemed a good idea to put this thought into words.

"Come, Alice, the first thing you know you will be imagining that we went to Europe in a dream."

She smiled, and said—

"Don't let me spoil it, Henry, if it is pleasant to you to think we went. I will consider that we did go, and that I have forgotten it."

"But Alice dear we *did* go!"

"But Henry dear we *didn't* go!"

She had a good head and a good memory, and she was always truthful. My head had been injured by a fall when I was a boy, and the physicians had said at the time that there could be ill effects from it some day. A cold wave struck me, now; perhaps the effects had come. I was losing confidence in the European trip. However, I thought I would make another try.

"Alice, I will give you a detail or two; then maybe you will remember."

"A detail or two from the dream?"

"I am not at all sure that it was a dream; and five minutes ago I was sure that it wasn't. It was seven years ago. We went over in the *Batavia*. Do you remember the *Batavia*?"

"I don't, Henry."

"Captain Moreland.[14] Don't you remember him?"

"To me he is a myth, Henry."

"Well, it beats anything. We lived two or three months in London, then six weeks in a private hotel in George Street, Edinburgh—Veitch's. Come!"

"It sounds pleasant, but I have never heard of these things before, Henry."

"And Doctor John Brown, of *Rab and His Friends*—you were ill, and he came every day; and when you were well again he still came every day and took us all around while he paid his visits, and we waited in his carriage while he prescribed for his patients. And he was so dear and lovely. You *must* remember all that, Alice."

"None of it, dear; it is only a dream."

"Why, Alice, have you ever had a dream that remained as distinct as that, and which you could remember so long?"

"So long? It is more than likely that you dreamed it last night."

"No indeed! It has been in my memory seven years."

"Seven years in a dream, yes—it is the way of dreams. They put seven years into two minutes, without any trouble—isn't it so?"

---

[14] Captain Morland [*sic*] was in fact the captain of the *Batavia,* on which the Clemens family had sailed; see *MTB,* II, 482–483.

I had to acknowledge that it was.

"It seems almost as if it couldn't have been a dream, Alice; it seems as if you ought to remember it." [15]

"Wait! It begins to come back to me." She sat thinking a while, nodding her head with satisfaction from time to time. At last she said, joyfully, "I remember almost the whole of it, now."

"Good!"

"I am glad I got it back. Ordinarily I remember my dreams very well; but for some reason this one—"

"*This* one, Alice? Do you really consider it a dream, yet?"

"I don't consider anything about it, Henry, I know it; I know it positively."

The conviction stole through me that she must be right, since she felt so sure. Indeed I almost knew she was. I was privately becoming ashamed of myself now, for mistaking a clever illusion for a fact. So I gave it up, then, and said I would let it stand as a dream. Then I added—

"It puzzles me; even now it seems almost as distinct as the microscope."

"Which microscope?"

"Well, Alice, there's only the one."

"Very well, which one is *that?*"

"Bother it all, the one we examined this ocean in, the other day."

"Where?"

"Why, at home—of course."

"What home?"

"Alice, it's provoking—why, *our* home. In Springport."

---

[15] As the manuscript was first written, Alice was not to recall any part of what Henry remembered. After his assertion, on page 70 of the holograph, that she "ought to remember it," her answer was, "Why, Henry, if it had really happened, the nurse and Delia and George would have been with us." Deleting this reply, Mark Twain wrote on an inserted page 70A the passage beginning with "Wait! It begins to come back to me," and continuing through "So I gave it up. . . ." In the latter part of Book I he made other revisions, representing Henry as remembering former events of the voyage and Alice as remembering the events of an earthly existence she had lived in her dreams.

The pages inserted in revision are written in gray ink on wove paper, light buff, size 5⅝″ x 8¾″; the rest of the holograph is in the same ink on paper of the same kind and color but of a slightly larger size, 5¾″ x 8⅞″.

"Dreaming again. I've never heard of it."

That was stupefying. There was no need of further beating about the bush; I threw caution aside, and came out frankly.

"Alice, what do you call the life we are leading in this ship? Isn't it a dream?"

She looked at me in a puzzled way and said—

"A dream, Henry? Why should I think that?"

"Oh, dear me, *I* don't know! I thought I did, but I don't. Alice, haven't we ever had a home? Don't you remember one?"

"Why, yes—three. That is, dream-homes, not real ones. I have never regarded them as realities."

"Describe them."

She did it, and in detail; also our life in them. Pleasant enough homes, and easily recognizable by me. I could also recognize an average of 2 out of 7 of the episodes and incidents which she threw in. Then I described the home and the life which (as it appeared to me) we had so recently left. She recognized it—but only as a dream-home. She remembered nothing about the microscope and the children's party. I was in a corner; but it was not the one which I had arranged for.

"Alice, if those were dream-homes, how long have you been in this ship?—you say this is the only voyage you have ever made."

"I don't know. I don't remember. It *is* the only voyage we have made—unless breaking it to pick up this crew of strangers in place of the friendly dear men and officers we had sailed with so many years makes two voyages of it. How I do miss them—Captain Hall, and Williams the sail-maker, and Storrs the chief mate, and—"

She choked up, and the tears began to trickle down her cheeks. Soon she had her handkerchief out and was sobbing.

I realized that I remembered those people perfectly well. Damnation! I said to myself, are we real creatures in a real world, all of a sudden, and have we been feeding on dreams in an imaginary one since nobody knows when—or how *is* it? My head was swimming.

"Alice! Answer me this. Do you know the Superintendent of Dreams?"

"Certainly."

"Have you seen him often?"

"Not often, but several times."

"When did you see him first?"

"The time that Robert the captain's boy was eaten." [16]

"*Eaten?*"

"Yes. Surely you haven't forgotten that?"

"But I have, though. I never heard of it before." (I spoke the truth. For the moment I could not recal the incident.)

Her face was full of reproach.

"I am sorry, if that is so. He was always good to you. If you are jesting, I do not think it is in good taste."

"Now don't treat me like that, Alice, I don't deserve it. I am not jesting, I am in earnest. I mean the boy's memory no offence, but although I remember him I do not remember the circumstance—I swear it. Who ate him?"

"Do not be irreverent, Henry, it is out of place. It was not a *who*, at all."

"What then—a *which?*"

"Yes."

"What kind of a which?"

"A spider-squid. *Now* you remember it I hope."

"Indeed and deed and double-deed I don't, Alice, and it is the real truth. Tell me about it, please."

"I suppose you see, now, Henry, what your memory is worth. You can remember dream-trips to Europe well enough, but things in real life—even the most memorable and horrible things—pass out of your memory in twelve years. There is something the matter with your mind."

It was very curious. How *could* I have forgotten that tragedy? It must have happened; she was never mistaken in her facts, and she

---

[16] This statement is at the bottom of page 74 of the holograph, which has *verso* some notes by which Mark Twain worked out the inversion of dream and reality that was to occur in the story. The Superintendent of Dreams "says his proper title is S[uperintendent] of R[ealities], and he is so-called in the other planets, but here we reverse the meanings of many words, and we wouldn't understand him." He noted, regarding Alice, "Where does she get her notions of mountain, valley, etc. if she has never been ashore? The S. of D. has taken her many a time —in dreams. But none of those things—permanent as they are—are substantial; they and the people are made of dream stuff. . . ."

never spoke with positiveness of a thing which she was in any
degree uncertain about. And this tragedy—*twelve years* ago—

"Alice, how long *have* we been in this ship?"

"Now how can I know, Henry? It goes too far back. Always, for
all I know. The earliest thing I can call to mind was papa's death
by the sun-heat and mamma's suicide the same day. I was four
years old, then. Surely you must remember that, Henry."

"Yes. . . . Yes. But it is so dim. Tell me about it—refresh my
memory."

"Why, you must remember that we were in the edge of a great
white glare once for a little while—a day, or maybe two days,—only
a little while, I think, but I remember it, because it was the only
time I was ever out of the dark, and there was a great deal of talk of
it for long afterwards—why, Henry, you *must* remember a wonderful thing like that."

"Wait. Let me think." Gradually, detail by detail the whole
thing came back to me; and with it the boy's adventure with the
spider-squid; and then I recalled a dozen other incidents, which
Alice verified as incidents of our ship-life, and said I had set them
forth correctly.

It was a puzzling thing—my freaks of memory; Alice's, too. By
testing, it was presently manifest that the vacancies in my ship-life
memories were only apparent, not real; a few words by way of
reminder enabled me to fill them up, in almost all cases, and give
them clarity and vividness. What had caused these temporary
lapses? Didn't these very lapses indicate that the ship-life was a
dream, and not real?

It made Alice laugh.

I did not see anything foolish in it, or anything to laugh at, and I
told her so. And I reminded her that her own memory was as bad as
mine, since many and many a conspicuous episode of our land-life
was gone from her, even so striking an incident as the water-drop
exploration with the microscope—

It made her shout.

I was wounded; and said that if I could not be treated with
respect I would spare her the burden of my presence and
conversation. She stopped laughing, at once, and threw her arms

about my neck. She said she would not have hurt me for the world, but she supposed I was joking; it was quite natural to think I was not in earnest in talking gravely about this and that and the other dream-phantom as if it were a reality.

"But Alice I *was* in earnest, and I *am* in earnest. Look at it—examine it. If the land-life was a dream-life, how is it that you remember so much of it exactly as *I* remember it?"

She was amused again, inside—I could feel the quiver; but there was no exterior expression of it, for she did not want to hurt me again.

"Dear heart, throw the whole matter aside! Stop puzzling over it; it isn't worth it. It is perfectly simple. It is true that I remember a little of that dream-life just as you remember it—but that is an accident; the rest of it—and by far the largest part—does not correspond with your recollections. And how *could* it? People can't be expected to remember each other's dreams, but only their own. You have put me into your land-dreams a thousand times, but I didn't always know I was there; so how could I remember it? Also I have put you into my land-dreams a thousand times when you didn't know it—and the natural result is that when I name the circumstances you don't always recal them. But how different it is with this real life, this genuine life in the ship! Our recollections of it are just alike. You have been forgetting episodes of it to-day—I don't know why; it has surprised me and puzzled me—but the lapse was only temporary; your memory soon rallied again. Now it hasn't rallied in the case of land-dreams of mine—in most cases it hasn't. And it's not going to, Henry. You can be sure of that."

She stopped, and tilted her head up in a thinking attitude and began to unconsciously tap her teeth with the ivory knob of a crochet needle. Presently she said, "I think I know what is the matter. I have been neglecting you for ten days while I have been grieving for our old shipmates and pretending to be seasick so that I might indulge myself with solitude; and here is the result—you haven't been taking exercise enough."

I was glad to have a reason—any reason that would excuse my memory—and I accepted this one, and made confession. There was no truth in the confession, but I was already getting handy with these evasions. I was a little sorry for this, for she had always trusted my word, and I had honored this trust by telling her the truth many a time when it was a sharp sacrifice to me to do it. She looked me over with gentle reproach in her eye, and said—

"Henry, how can you be so naughty? I watch you so faithfully and make you take such good care of your health that you owe me the grace to do my office for me when for any fair reason I am for a while not on guard. When have you boxed with George last?"

What an idea it was! It was a good place to make a mistake, and I came near to doing it. It was on my tongue's end to say that I had never boxed with anyone; and as for boxing with a colored man-servant—and so on; but I kept back my remark, and in place of it tried to look like a person who didn't know what to say. It was easy to do, and I probably did it very well.

"You do not say anything, Henry. I think it is because you have a good reason. When have you fenced with him? Henry, you are avoiding my eye. Look up. Tell me the truth: have you fenced with him a single time in the last ten days?"

So far as I was aware I knew nothing about foils, and had never handled them; so I was able to answer—

"I will be frank with you, Alice—I haven't."

"I suspected it. Now, Henry, what can you say?"

I was getting some of my wits back, now, and was not altogether unprepared, this time.

"Well, Alice, there hasn't been much fencing weather, and when there was any, I—well, I was lazy, and that is the shameful truth."

"There's a chance now, anyway, and you mustn't waste it. Take off your coat and things."

She rang for George, then she got up and raised the sofa-seat and began to fish out boxing-gloves, and foils and masks from the locker under it, softly scolding me all the while. George put his head in, noted the preparations, then entered and put himself in boxing trim. It was his turn to take the witness stand, now.

"George, didn't I tell you to keep up Mr. Henry's exercises just the same as if I were about?"

"Yes, madam, you did."

"Why haven't you done it?"

George chuckled, and showed his white teeth and said—

"Bless yo' soul, honey, I dasn't."

"Why?"

"Because the first time I went to him—it was that Tuesday, you know, when it was ca'm—he wouldn't hear to it, and said he didn't want no exercise and warn't going to take any, and tole me to go 'long. Well, I didn't stop there, of course, but went to him agin, every now and then, trying to persuade him, tell at last he let into me" (he stopped and comforted himself with an unhurried laugh over the recollection of it,) "and give me a most solid good cussing, and tole me if I come agin he'd take and thow me overboard—there, ain't that so, Mr. Henry?"

My wife was looking at me pretty severely.

"Henry, what have you to say to that?"

It was my belief that it hadn't happened, but I was steadily losing confidence in my memory; and moreover my new policy of recollecting whatever anybody required me to recollect seemed the safest course to pursue in my strange and trying circumstances; so I said—

"Nothing, Alice—I did refuse."

"Oh, I'm not talking about that; of course you refused—George had already said so."

"Oh, I see."

"Well, why do you stop?"

"Why do I stop?"

"Yes. Why don't you answer my question?"

"Why, Alice, I've answered it. You asked me—you asked me— What *is* it I haven't answered?"

"Henry, you know very well. You broke a promise; and you are trying to talk around it and get me away from it; but I am not going to let you. You know quite well you promised me you wouldn't swear any more in calm weather. And it is such a little thing to do. It is hardly ever calm, and—"

"Alice, dear, I beg ever so many pardons! I had clear forgotten it; but I won't offend again, I give you my word. Be good to me, and forgive."

She was always ready to forgive, and glad to do it, whatever my crime might be; so things were pleasant again, now, and smooth and happy. George was gloved and skipping about in an imaginary fight, by this time, and Alice told me to get to work with him. She took pencil and paper and got ready to keep game. I stepped forward to position—then a curious thing happened: I seemed to remember a thousand boxing-bouts with George, the whole boxing art came flooding in upon me, and I knew just what to do! I was a prey to no indecisions, I had no trouble. We fought six rounds, I held my own all through, and I finally knocked George out. I was not astonished; it seemed a familiar experience. Alice showed no surprise, George showed none; apparently it was an old story to them.

The same thing happened with the fencing. I suddenly knew that I was an experienced old fencer; I expected to get the victory, and when I got it, it seemed but a repetition of something which had happened numberless times before.

We decided to go down to the main saloon and take a regular meal in the regular way—the evening meal. Alice went away to dress. Just as I had finished dressing, the children came romping in, warmly and prettily clad, and nestled up to me, one on each side, on the sofa, and began to chatter. Not about a former home; no, not a word of that, but only about this ship-home and its concerns and its people. After a little I threw out some questions—feelers. They did not understand. Finally I asked them if they had known no home but this one. Jessie said, with some little enthusiasm—

"Oh, yes, dream-homes. They are pretty—some of them." Then, with a shrug of her shoulders, "But they *are* so queer!"

"How, Jessie?"

"Well, you know, they have such curious things in them; and they fade, and don't stay. Bessie doesn't like them at all."

"Why don't you, Bessie?"

"Because they scare me so."

"What is it that scares you?"

"Oh, everything, papa. Sometimes it is so light. That hurts my eyes. And it's too many lamps—little sparkles all over, up high, and large ones that are dreadful. They could fall on me, you know."

"But I am not much afraid," said Jessie, "because mamma says they are not real, and if they did fall they wouldn't hurt."

"What else do you see there besides the lights, Bessie?"

"Ugly things that go on four legs like our cat, but bigger."

"Horses?"

"I forget names."

"Describe them, dear."

"I can't, papa. They are not alike; they are different kinds; and when I wake up I can't just remember the shape of them, they are so dim."

"And I wouldn't wish to remember them," said Jessie, "they make me feel creepy. Don't let's talk about them, papa, let's talk about something else."

"That's what I say, too," said Bessie.

So then we talked about our ship. That interested them. They cared for no other home, real or unreal, and wanted no better one. They were innocent witnesses and free from prejudice.

When we went below we found the roomy saloon well lighted and brightly and prettily furnished, and a very comfortable and inviting place altogether. Everything seemed substantial and genuine, there was nothing to suggest that it might be a work of the imagination.

At table the captain (Davis) sat at the head, my wife at his right with the children, I at his left, a stranger at my left. The rest of the company consisted of Rush Phillips, purser, aged 27; his sweetheart the Captain's daughter Lucy, aged 22; her sister Connie (short for Connecticut), aged 10; Arnold Blake, surgeon, 25; Harvey Pratt, naturalist, 36; at the foot sat Sturgis the chief mate, aged 35, and completed the snug assemblage. Stewards waited upon the general company, and George and our nurse Germania had charge of our family. Germania was not the nurse's name, but that was our name for her because it was shorter than her own. She was 28 years old, and had always been with us; and so had George. George was 30, and had once been a slave, according to my record, but I was losing my grip upon that, now, and was indeed getting shadowy and uncertain about all my traditions.

The talk and the feeding went along in a natural way, I could find nothing unusual about it anywhere. The captain was pale, and had a jaded and harassed look, and was subject to little fits of absence of mind; and these things could be said of the mate, also, but this was all natural enough considering the grisly time they had been having, and certainly there was nothing about it to suggest that they were dream-creatures or that their troubles were unreal.

The stranger at my side was about 45 years old, and he had the half-subdued, half-resigned look of a man who had been under a burden of trouble a long time. He was tall and thin; he had a bushy black head, and black eyes which burned when he was interested, but were dull and expressionless when his thoughts were far away—and that happened every time he dropped out of the conversation. He forgot to eat, then, his hands became idle, his dull eye fixed itself upon his plate or upon vacancy, and now and then he would draw a heavy sigh out of the depths of his breast.

These three were exceptions; the others were chatty and cheerful, and they were like a pleasant little family party together. Phillips and Lucy were full of life, and quite happy, as became engaged people; and their furtive love-passages had everybody's sympathy and approval. Lucy was a pretty creature, and simple in her ways and kindly, and Phillips was a blithesome and attractive young fellow. I seemed to be familiarly acquainted with everybody, I didn't quite know why. That is, with everybody except the stranger at my side; and as he seemed to know me well, I had to let on to know him, lest I cause remark by exposing the fact that I didn't know him. I was already tired of being caught up for ignorance at every turn.

The captain and the mate managed to seem comfortable enough until Phillips raised the subject of the day's run, the position of the ship, distance out, and so on; then they became irritable, and sharp of speech, and were unkinder to the young fellow than the case seemed to call for. His sweetheart was distressed to see him so treated before all the company, and she spoke up bravely in his defence and reproached her father for making an offence out of so harmless a thing. This only brought her into trouble, and procured for her so rude a retort that she was consumed with shame, and left the table crying.

The pleasure was all gone, now; everybody felt personally affronted and wantonly abused. Conversation ceased and an uncomfortable silence fell upon the company; through it one could hear the wailing of the wind and the dull tramp of the sailors and the muffled words of command overhead, and this made the silence all the more dismal. The dinner was a failure. While it was still unfinished the company began to break up and slip out, one after another; and presently none was left but me.[17]

I sat long, sipping black coffee and smoking. And thinking; groping about in my dimming land-past. An incident of my American life would rise upon me, vague at first, then grow more distinct and articulate, then sharp and clear; then in a moment it was gone, and in its place was a dull and distant image of some long-past episode whose theatre was this ship—and then *it* would develop, and clarify, and become strong and real. It was fascinating, enchanting, this spying among the elusive mysteries of my bewitched memory, and I went up to my parlor and continued it, with the help of punch and pipe, hour after hour, as long as I could keep awake. With this curious result: that the main incidents of both my lives were now recovered, but only those of one of them persistently gathered strength and vividness—our life in the ship! Those of our land-life were good enough, plain enough, but in minuteness of detail they fell perceptibly short of those others; and in matters of feeling—joy, grief, physical pain, physical pleasure— immeasurably short!

Some mellow notes floated to my ear, muffled by the moaning wind—six bells in the morning watch. So late! I went to bed. When I woke in the middle of the so-called day the first thing I thought of was my night's experience. Already my land-life had faded a little—but not the other.

---

[17] The "Mad Passenger" variant (which may be seen in the Appendix), was cut out of the story at this point. After deleting it, Mark Twain continued with what now follows.

BOOK II

CHAPTER I

I HAVE long ago lost Book I, but it is no matter. It served its purpose—writing it was an entertainment to me. We found out that our little boy set it adrift on the wind, sheet by sheet, to see if it would fly. It did. And so two of us got entertainment out of it. I have often been minded to begin Book II, but natural indolence and the pleasant life of the ship interfered.

There have been little happenings, from time to time. The principal one, for us of the family, was the birth of our Harry, which stands recorded in the log under the date of June 8, and happened about three months after we shipped the present crew, poor devils! They still think we are bound for the South Pole, and that we are a long time on the way. It is pathetic, after a fashion. They regard their former life in the World as their real life and this present one as—well, they hardly know what; but sometimes they get pretty tired of it, even at this late day. We hear of it now and then through the officers—mainly Turner, who is a puzzled man.

During the first four years we had several mutinies, but things have been reasonably quiet during the past two. One of them had really a serious look. It occurred when Harry was a month old, and at an anxious time, for both he and his mother were weak and ill. The master spirit of it was Stephen Bradshaw the carpenter, of course—a hard lot I know, and a born mutineer I think.

In those days I was greatly troubled, for a time, because my wife's memories still refused to correspond with mine. It had been an ideal life, and naturally it was a distress not to be able to live it over again in its entirety with her in our talks. At first she did not feel about it as I did, and said she could not understand my interest in those dreams, but when she found how much I took the matter to heart, and that to me the dreams had come to have a seeming of reality and were freighted with tender and affectionate impressions besides, she began to change her mind and wish she could go back in spirit with me to that mysterious land. And so she tried to get back that forgotten life. By my help, and by patient probing and searching of her memory she succeeded. Gradually it all came back, and her reward was sufficient. We now had the recollections of two lives to draw upon, and the result was a double measure of happiness for us. We even got the children's former lives back for them—with a good deal of difficulty—next the servants'. It made a new world for us all, and an entertaining one to explore. In the beginning George the colored man was an unwilling subject, because by heredity he was superstitious, and believed that no good could come of meddling with dreams; but when he presently found that no harm came of it his disfavor dissolved away.

Talking over our double-past—particularly our dream-past—became our most pleasant and satisfying amusement, and the search for missing details of it our most profitable labor. One day when the baby was about a month old, we were at this pastime in our parlor. Alice was lying on the sofa, propped with pillows—she was by no means well. It was a still and solemn black day, and cold; but the lamps made the place cheerful, and as for comfort, Turner had taken care of that; for he had found a kerosene stove with an ising-glass front among the freight, and had brought it up and lashed it fast and fired it up, and the warmth it gave and the red glow it made took away all chill and cheerlessness from the parlor and made it homelike. The little girls were out somewhere with George and Delia (the maid).[18]

Alice and I were talking about the time, twelve years before, when Captain Hall's boy had his tragic adventure with the spider-squid, and I was reminding her that she had misstated the case when she mentioned it to me, once. She had said the squid *ate* the boy. Out of my memory I could call back all the details, now, and I remembered that the boy was only badly hurt, not eaten.

---

[18] Here and in a later passage, Bernard DeVoto in his edition changed the name of the maid to "Germania" (*LE*, pp. 275, 289), probably because that name had already been used in the story and the maid's name, Delia, had not. The names are here given as they appear in the holograph. Germania is the family's nickname for the nurse.

For a month or two the ship's company had been glimpsing vast animals at intervals of a few days, and at first the general terror was so great that the men openly threatened, on two occasions, to seize the ship unless the captain turned back; but by a resolute bearing he tided over the difficulty; and by pointing out to the men that the animals had shown no disposition to attack the ship and might therefore be considered harmless, he quieted them down and restored order. It was good grit in the captain, for privately he was very much afraid of the animals himself and had but a shady opinion of their innocence. He kept his gatlings in order, and had gun-watches, which he changed with the other watches.

I had just finished correcting Alice's history of the boy's adventure with the squid when the ship, plowing through a perfectly smooth sea, went heeling away down to starboard and stayed there! The floor slanted like a roof, and every loose thing in the room slid to the floor and glided down against the bulkhead. We were greatly alarmed, of course. Next we heard a rush of feet along the deck and an uproar of cries and shoutings, then the rush of feet coming back, with a wilder riot of cries. Alice exclaimed—

"Go find the children—quick!"

I sprang out and started to run aft through the gloom, and then I saw the fearful sight which I had seen twelve years before when that boy had had his shocking misadventure. For the moment I turned the corner of the deck-house and had an unobstructed view astern, there it was—apparently two full moons rising close over the stern of the ship and lighting the decks and rigging with a sickly yellow glow—the eyes of the colossal squid. His vast beak and head were plain to be seen, swelling up like a hill above our stern; he had flung one tentacle forward and gripped it around the peak of the main-mast and was pulling the ship over; he had gripped the mizzen-mast with another, and a couple more were writhing about dimly away above our heads searching for something to take hold of. The stench of his breath was suffocating everybody.

I was like the most of the crew, helpless with fright; but the captain and the officers kept their wits and courage. The gatlings on the starboard side could not be used, but the four on the port

side were brought to bear, and inside of a minute they had poured
more than two thousand bullets into those moons. That blinded the
creature, and he let go; and by squirting a violent Niagara of water
out of his mouth which tore the sea into a tempest of foam he shot
himself backward three hundred yards and the ship forward as far,
drowning the deck with a racing flood which swept many of the
men off their feet and crippled some, and washed all loose deck-
plunder overboard. For five minutes we could hear him thrashing
about, there in the dark, and lashing the sea with his giant tentacles
in his pain; and now and then his moons showed, then vanished
again; and all the while we were rocking and plunging in the
booming seas he made. Then he quieted down. We took a thankful
full breath, believing him dead.

Now I thought of the children, and ran all about inquiring for
them, but no one had seen them. I thought they must have been
washed overboard, and for a moment my heart stopped beating.
Then the hope came that they had taken refuge with their mother;
so I ran there; and almost swooned when I entered the place, for it
was vacant. I ran out shouting the alarm, and after a dozen steps
almost ran over her. She was lying against the bulwarks drenched
and insensible. The surgeon and young Phillips helped me carry
her in; then the surgeon and I began to work over her and Phillips
rushed away to start the hunt for the children. It was all of half an
hour before she showed any sign of life; then her eyes opened with
a dazed and wondering look in them, then they recognized me and
into them shot a ghastly terror.

"The children! the children!" she gasped; and I, with the heart
all gone out of me, answered with such air of truth as I could
assume—

"They are safe."

I could never deceive her. I was transparent to her.

"It is not true! The truth speaks out all over you—they are lost,
oh they are lost, they are lost!"

We were strong, but we could not hold her. She tore loose from
us and was gone in a moment, flying along the dark decks and
shrieking the children's names with a despairing pathos that broke
one's heart to hear it. We fled after her, and urged that the flitting

lanterns meant that all were searching, and begged her for the children's sake and mine if not for her own to go to bed and save her life. But it went for nothing, she would not listen. For she was a mother, and her children were lost. That says it all. She would hunt for them as long as she had strength to move. And that is what she did, hour after hour, wailing and mourning, and touching the hardest hearts with her grief, until she was exhausted and fell in a swoon. Then the stewardess and I put her to bed, and as soon as she came to and was going to creep out of her bed and take up her search again the doctor encouraged her in it and gave her a draught to restore her strength; and it put her into a deep sleep, which was what he expected.

We left the stewardess on watch and went away to join the searchers. Not a lantern was twinkling anywhere, and every figure that emerged from the gloom moved upon tip-toe. I collared one of them and said angrily—

"What does this mean? Is the search stopped?"

Turner's voice answered—very low: "—'sh! Captain's orders. The beast ain't dead—it's hunting for us."

It made me sick with fear.

"Do you mean it, Turner? How do you know?"

"Listen."

There was a muffled swashing sound out there somewhere, and then the two moons appeared for a moment, then turned slowly away and were invisible again.

"He's been within a hundred yards of us, feeling around for us with his arms. He could reach us, but he couldn't locate us because he's blind. Once he mighty near had us; one of his arms that was squirming around up there in the dark just missed the foremast, and he hauled in the slack of it without suspecting anything. It made my lungs come up into my throat. He has edged away, you see, but he ain't done laying for us." Pause. Then in a whisper, "He's wallowing around closer to us again, by gracious. Look—look at that. See it? Away up in the air—writhing around like a crooked mainmast. Dim, but—there, *now* don't you see it?"

We stood dead still, hardly breathing. Here and there at little distances the men were gathering silently together and watching and pointing. The deep hush lay like a weight upon one's spirit. Even the faintest quiver of air that went idling by gave out a ghost of sound. A couple of mellow notes floated lingering and fading down from forward:

Booooom——booooom. (Two bells in the middle watch.)

A hoarse low voice—the captain's:

"Silence that damned bell!"

Instantly there was a thrashing commotion out there, with a thundering rush of discharged water, and the monster came charging for us. I caught my breath, and had to seize Turner or I should have fallen, so suddenly my strength collapsed. Then vaguely we saw the creature, waving its arms aloft, tear past the ship stern first, pushing a vast swell ahead and trailing a tumultuous wake behind, and the next moment it was far away and we were plunging and tossing in the sea it made.

"Thank God, *he's* out of practice!" said Turner, with emotion.

The majestic blind devil stopped out there with its moons toward us, and we were miserable again. We had so hoped it would go home.

I resumed my search. Below I found Phillips and Lucy Davis and a number of others searching, but with no hope. They said they had been everywhere, and were merely going over the ground again and again because they could not bear to have it reported to the mother that the search had ceased. She must be told that they were her friends and that she could depend upon them.

Four hours later I gave it up, wearied to exhaustion, and went and sat down by Alice's bed, to be at hand and support her when she should wake and have to hear my desolate story. After a while she stirred, then opened her eyes and smiled brightly and said—

"Oh, what bliss it is! I dreamed that the children—" She flung her arms about me in a transport of grief. "I remember—oh, my God it is true!"

And so, with sobs and lamentations and frantic self-reproaches she poured out her bitter sorrow, and I clasped her close to me, and could not find one comforting word to say.

"Oh, Henry, Henry, your silence means—oh, we cannot live, we cannot bear it!"

There was a flurry of feet along the deck, the door was burst in, and Turner's voice shouted—

"They're found, by God they're found!"

A joy like that brings the shock of a thunderbolt, and for a little while we thought Alice was gone; but then she rallied, and by that time the children were come, and were clasped to her breast, and she was steeped in a happiness for which there were no words. And she said she never dreamed that profanity could sound so dear and sweet, and she asked the mate to say it again; and he did, but left out the profanity and spoiled it.

The children and George and Delia had seen the squid come and lift its moons above our stern and reach its vast tentacles aloft; and they had not waited, but had fled below, and had not stopped till they were deep down in the hold and hidden in a tunnel among the freight. When found, they had had several hours' sleep and were much refreshed.

Between seeing the squid, and getting washed off her feet, and losing the children, the day was a costly one for Alice. It marks the date of her first gray hairs. They were few, but they were to have company.

We lay in a dead calm, and helpless. We could not get away from the squid's neighborhood. But I was obliged to have some sleep, and I took it. I took all I could get, which was six hours.[19] Then young Phillips came and turned me out and said there were signs that the spirit of mutiny was abroad again and that the captain was going to call the men aft and talk to them. Phillips thought I would not want to miss it.

He was right. We had private theatricals, we had concerts, and the other usual time-passers customary on long voyages; but a speech from the captain was the best entertainment the ship's talent could furnish. There was character back of his oratory. He was all sailor. He was sixty years old, and had known no life but sea life. He had no gray hairs, his beard was full and black and shiny; he wore no mustache, therefore his lips were exposed to view; they

---

[19] Following this sentence Mark Twain first wrote and then deleted a passage in which Phillips reveals to Edwards, before the confrontation on the after-deck, that the captain suspects a mutiny and has removed the firing pins from the ship's guns.

fitted together like box and lid, and expressed the pluck and
resolution that were in him. He had bright black eyes in his old
bronze face and they eloquently interpreted all his moods, and his
moods were many: for at times he was the youngest man in the
ship, and the most cheerful and vivacious and skittish; at times he
was the best-natured man in the ship, and he was always the most
lovable; sometimes he was sarcastic, sometimes he was serious even
to solemnity, sometimes he was stern, sometimes he was as
sentimental as a school-girl; sometimes he was silent, quiet, with-
drawn within himself, sometimes he was talkative and argumentative; he was remarkably and sincerely and persistently pious, and
marvelously and scientifically profane; he was much the strongest
man in the ship, and he was also the largest, excepting that
plotting, malicious and fearless devil, Stephen Bradshaw the
carpenter; he could smile as sweetly as a girl, and it was a pleasure
to see him do it. He was entirely self-educated, and had made a vast
and picturesque job of it. He was an affectionate creature, and in
his family relations he was beautiful; in the eyes of his daughters
he was omniscient, omnipotent, a mixed sun-god and storm-god,
and they feared him and adored him accordingly. He was fond of
oratory, and thought he had the gift of it; and so he practiced it
now and then, upon occasion, and did it with easy confidence. He
was a charming man and a manly man, with a right heart and a
fine and daring spirit.

Phillips and I slipped out and moved aft. Things had an unusual
and startling aspect. There were flushes of light here and there and
yonder; the captain stood in one of them, the officers stood a little
way back of him.

"How do matters stand, Phillips?"

"You notice that the battle-lanterns are lit, all the way forward?"

"Yes. The gun-watches are at their posts; I see that. The captain
means business, I reckon."

"The gun-watches are mutineers!"

I steadied my voice as well as I could, but there was still a quaver
in it when I said—

"Then they've sprung a trap on us, and we are at their mercy, of
course."

"It has the look of it. They've caught the old man napping, and we are in a close place this time."

We joined the officers, and just then we heard the measured tramp of the men in the distance. They were coming down from forward. Soon they came into view and moved toward us until they were within three or four paces of the captain.

"Halt!"

They had a leader this time, and it was he that gave the command—Stephen Bradshaw, the carpenter. He had a revolver in his hand. There was a pause, then the captain drew himself up, put on his dignity, and prepared to transact business in a properly impressive and theatrical way. He cleared his voice and said, in a fatherly tone—

"Men, this is your spokesman, duly appointed by you?"

Several responded timidly—

"Yes, sir."

"You have a grievance, and you desire to have it redressed?"

"Yes, sir."

"He is not here to represent himself, lads, but only you?"

"Yes, sir."

"Very well. Your complaint shall be heard, and treated with justice." (Murmur of approbation from the men.) Then the captain's soft manner hardened a little, and he said to the carpenter, "Go on."

Bradshaw was eager to begin, and he flung out his words with aggressive confidence—

"Captain Davis, in the first place this crew wants to know where they *are*. Next, they want this ship put about and pointed for home —straight off, and no fooling. They are tired of this blind voyage, and they ain't going to have any more of it—and that's the word with the bark on it." He paused a moment, for his temper was rising and obstructing his breath; then he continued in a raised and insolent voice and with a showy flourish of his revolver. "Before, they've had no leader, and you talked them down and cowed them; but that ain't going to happen this time. And they hadn't any plans, and warn't fixed for business; but it's different, now." He grew exultant. "Do you see this?"—his revolver. "And do you see that?"

He pointed to the gatlings. "We've got the guns; we are boss of the ship. Put her about! That's the order, and it's going to be obeyed."

There was an admiring murmur from the men. After a pause the captain said, with dignity—

"Apparently you are through. Stand aside."

"Stand aside, is it? Not till I have heard what answer you—"

The captain's face darkened and an evil light began to flicker in his eyes, and his hands to twitch. The carpenter glanced at him, then stepped a pace aside, shaking his head and grumbling. "Say your say, then, and cut it short, for I've got something more to say when you're done, if it ain't satisfactory."

The captain's manner at once grew sweet, and even tender, and he turned toward the men with his most genial and winning smile on his face, and proceeded to take them into his confidence.

"You want to know where you are, boys. It is reasonable; it is natural. If we don't know where we are—if we are lost—who is worst off, you or me? You have no children in this ship—I have. If we are in danger have I put us there intentionally? Would I have done it purposely—with my children aboard? Come, what do you think?"

There was a stir among the men, and an approving nodding of heads which conceded that the point was well taken.

"Don't I know my trade, or am I only an apprentice to it? Have I sailed the seas for sixty years and commanded ships for thirty to be taught what to do in a difficulty by—by a damned carpenter?"

He was talking in such a pleading way, such an earnest, and moving and appealing way that the men were not prepared for the close of his remark, and it caught them out and made some of them laugh. He had scored one—and he knew it. The carpenter's back was turned—he was playing indifference. He whirled around and covered the captain with his revolver. Everybody shrank together and caught his breath, except the captain, who said gently—

"Don't be afraid—pull the trigger; it isn't loaded."

The carpenter pulled—twice, thrice, and threw the pistol away. Then he shouted—

"Fall back, men—out of the way!" They surged apart, and he fell back himself. The captain and the officers stood alone in the

circle of light. "Gun 4, fire!" The officers threw themselves on
their faces on the deck, but the captain remained in his place. The
gunner spun the windlass around—there was no result. "Gun 3,
fire!" The same thing happened again. The captain said—

"Come back to your places, men." They obeyed, looking puzzled,
surprised, and a good deal demoralized. The officers got up, looking
astonished and rather ashamed. "Carpenter, come back to your
place." He did it, but reluctantly, and swearing to himself. It was
easy to see that the captain was contented with his dramatic effects.
He resumed his speech, in his pleasantest manner—

"You have mutinied two or three times, boys. It is all right—up
to now. I would have done it myself in my common-seaman days, I
reckon, if my ship was bewitched and I didn't know where I was.
Now then, can you be trusted with the facts? Are we rational men,
manly men, men who can stand up and face hard luck and a big
difficulty that has been brought about by nobody's fault, and say
live or die, survive or perish, we are in for it, for good or bad, and
we'll stand by the ship if she goes to hell!" (The men let go a
tol[erably] hearty cheer.) "Are we men—grown men—salt-sea men
—men nursed upon dangers and cradled in storms—men made in
the image of God and ready to do when He commands and die
when He calls—or are we just sneaks and curs and carpenters!"
(This brought both cheers and laughter, and the captain was
happy.) "There—that's the kind. And so I'll tell you how the thing
stands. *I* don't know where this ship is, but she's in the hands of
God, and that's enough for me, it's enough for you, and it's enough
for anybody but a carpenter. If it is God's will that we pull
through, we pull through—otherwise not. We haven't had an
observation for four months, but we are going ahead, and do our
best to fetch up somewhere."

Indiantown

"INDIANTOWN" presents a gallery of characters for "Which Was It?" and was probably written in 1899 at about the time Mark Twain began work upon the latter story. George Harrison is identified in the working notes as a character drawn from the author's brother Orion Clemens. His friend the Rev. Joseph H. Twichell is mentioned as the original of the Rev. Mr. Bailey. David and Susan Gridley are quite evidently drawn from Samuel and Olivia Langdon Clemens (Mark Twain first used "Sam" as Gridley's first name). Squire Fairfax resembles the Lord Fairfax who was a friend of the Virginian branch of the Clemens family (see the General Introduction). Even the spectral Orrin Lloyd Godkin may have had a real-life counterpart in a patient with a case of "galloping consumption" who was taking the Kellgren cure at Sanna, Sweden, where the Clemenses were staying in the summer of 1899 (for treatment of Jean Clemens); he had, it seems, the appearance of a walking corpse and was called by others "The Shadow." [1] Another fragment, "A Human Bloodhound," the materials of which closely match those of "Indiantown," presents a character called Godkin whose acute sense of smell affords him an uncanny knowledge of the doings of his fellow villagers. In this sketch Godkin has a friend, called "The Corpse," who relishes philosophical discussion and has written an "Account of the Creation." [2]

Mark Twain's notes reveal that he was at this time planning to use

[1] DV 13, p. C-9. This fragment contains miscellaneous information concerning the Kellgren cure, which was chiefly a system of osteopathic therapy.

[2] DV 96, pp. 1–7. This holograph and that of "Indiantown" are written on laid paper, buff, size $4^{15}\!/_{16}'' \times 7^{15}\!/_{16}''$, with vertical watermark lines spaced $1\frac{1}{16}''$. This paper was also used in the holograph of "Which Was It?" (DV 302), pp. 138–158, 182–215.

again the device of an apparent time lapse in the action of the story, as in "Which Was the Dream?" The squire was to be "35 before crash, 45 after." George Harrison was to be 36 and then 46; his father Andrew, 65 and then 75. And the intended biographical parallel is shown by a listing of the children of Gridley—parenthetically identified as Susy, Clara, and Jean. When Mark Twain began to write of the Gridleys in the latter part of this fragment, he let the focus of his interest stray away from his planned story. But in doing so, he provided an interesting account, partly in the fictional and partly in the autobiographical mode, of his relationship with Olivia.

Indiantown

CHAPTER I.

I T WAS about seventy years ago; the region, the cotton belt on the west bank of the Mississippi river; the scene, the town of Indiantown and its immediate country surroundings. Indiantown was a very important place, and was well satisfied with itself, for it could prove a population of fifteen hundred. Whites, of course; slaves did not count. You would travel far, up and down the river, before you would find another town as large as that.

It stood upon a perfectly flat and narrow strip of rich black soil; its front was upon the river, whose banks—at low water—were as perpendicular as a wall and forty feet high; immediately at its northern limit, Indian river, curving down from the north, then bending east, emptied into the Mississippi. A single bridge spanned it, at the northwest corner of the village. The natives called it a river, but it was hardly that; properly, it was a rivulet, being not more than half as wide as the Thames at London bridge. For miles, westward and northward, along the sweeping bends of the rivulet, on both sides, stretched the great cotton plantations—owned, not by the many, but by the two or three wealthy men of the region. Their great mansions stood a mile apart upon the west bank of the stream and a little back from the road, each with its hamlet of whitewashed slave-huts grouped in the fields half a mile to the rear of the master's mansion.

It was a wide and pretty valley through which the Indian river

flowed, and was walled-in and protected on both sides by woodsy
and rocky hills which in summer were lovely with all the wild
woodland graces proper to the generous climate of those latitudes.
The valley's surface steadily rose, from its foot to its head, hence it
was never afflicted with overflows.

But down where the town lay, the case was different. In June,
when the snows melted in the mountains at the head waters of the
mighty Missouri river some thousands of miles to the north and
west and delivered the result into the Mississippi, it was always an
anxious time for Indiantown. The people gathered daily on the
bank and gazed out over the mile-wide yellow surface of the raging
and swearing flood, with its black freightage of enormous logs and
minor driftwood, and watched and considered and noted a couple
of details with special and wistful solicitude—the swiftness or
slowness of the rise, and the trend of the current. If they found that
the current was making up its mind to strike into their bend above
their town or abreast it, they were deeply concerned; if they found
that the river was rising fast—say six feet in twenty-four hours, the
concern was doubled, and they sent to the plantations for ox teams
at once. For a six-foot rise meant that the river would be over its
banks in a week, and then *it would be too late to move the town.*

The people would not mind the mere overflow—they were used
to that; it happened once a year, and sometimes twice; but if they
found that the current, in slanting down from the upper bend on
the other side of the river, was striking into their own bend above
the town or abreast it, that was a very grave matter: it would bite
their bank away and swallow up a street or two of houses at a
single meal, and perhaps the rest of the village next day.

This was not a frequent disaster; still, it had happened more
than once. Each time the town had been hauled back, house by
house, and saved; and each time the river had swallowed up every
foot of ground that had been previously occupied by the settlement.
After Indiantown's latest retreat there was half a mile of river
between its new position and its earliest one.

At the time of which we write it was June, and the rise had
begun, and briskly, but there was no scare: the current was striking

below the town. There was a dense forest of great trees there, and there was entertainment for loafers, and for workers who could allow themselves a holiday. It was a stirring thing to see the boiling river snatch away a couple of acres of ground and note how the mass of mighty trees leaned slowly and majestically forward, paused a moment as if in grief and dread, then plunged with a thunder-crash beneath the yellow flood, sending a vast explosion of foam high in the air and leaving a fierce maelstrom tossing where they disappeared.

It was a wooden town, with wide straight streets, unpaved, but with red-brick sidewalks—not in repair—along the main thoroughfare, and plenty of mud or dust in the channel, according to the weather. The dwellings in the town's midst were "frame," painted white, with green shutters, surrounded by grassy yards within whitewashed palings; the court house, the jail, and several churches were of red brick; at its edges the town fringed off into unadorned log houses.

The people were Presbyterians, Methodists and Baptists, and both sinners and saints were communicants and diligent attendants upon the religious services. For one thing, it was custom; for another, the lake which burneth with fire and brimstone was still the main feature of all sermons and the people were canny and cautious and did not wish to navigate it. This was a prejudice, but not a bigoted one: they could have nominated others for that kind of travel, if invited.

There was no local newspaper. Two or three copies of the National Intelligencer (weekly) came tired from Washington bringing political tidings three weeks old, and were passed from hand to hand and discussed until their contents were become ancient history; several journals of a fresher sort came down from the distant little city of St. Louis and up from the equally distant city of New Orleans.

Dr. Stevens, and other gray gentlemen of the old school, still wore queues tied with a bow of black ribbon, broad hats, formidable "stocks," broadcloth coats with square and ample tails, wrist-ruffles, bosom-ruffles, black gaiters to the knee, low shoes with silver buckles; and they carried gold-headed canes and took snuff, and when surprised said "God bless my soul, sir!" In London to-day, viewed from the rear, they would be mistaken for English Bishops.

The town reached to the bridge over Indian river—no further. On the bank of the river not far north of the other end of the bridge stood the mill; close to it on the south side stood a fair-sized log house occupied by the family of the foreman of the mill; close to the mill on the north side stood a much larger log dwelling, the property of the mill's owner.

On the river road, a quarter of a mile north of these buildings stood the country blacksmith shop of Burt Higgins, under a spreading great live-oak, the meeting-place and gossip-exchange of the small farmers who lived here and there and yonder for miles around.

A mile north of the blacksmith shop stood the large mansion of Andrew Harrison, cotton planter; a mile north of that, the great mansion—called *"the"* mansion—of Squire Fairfax, planter; a mile still further north, the large mansion of Orrin Lloyd Godkin, planter. The plantations of these rich gentlemen extended far away to the hill-ridges on both sides of the river.

CHAPTER 2.

O F COURSE the most of the people were of the commonplace sort; of course, also, a few of them had trade-mark characteristics and social positions which perceptibly differentiated them from the general herd. All the whites were free—born so. The Declaration had said it, and it was true. Also, all the whites were equal. The Declaration had said it, and it was true. That is, *equal before the law,* and not otherwise. It was comical in that day, and it is comical in our day, to see fine European intelligencies struggle gaily and confidently with that innocent phrase, "all men are born equal," and finally march proud and happy from the field—defeated, but not aware of it. Like Professor Mahaffey; who threw away an hour or two of time in proving to an American audience at Chautauqua that all men are *not* born equal in wealth, brains, stature, strength, social position, and so on, and that any Declaration of Independence that tried to create and establish these equalities was attempting the impossible. Inasmuch as the Declaration had made no attempt of the sort, the professor's time was wasted. Courtesy requires that one shall read his well-intended sermon with gravity, but not every one can do it.

Wherever the human race exists, it groups itself more or less definitely into social ranks and grades. Indiantown had its ranks and grades. They were merely the creation of an unwritten common consent—there was no law about it; and a man could go up a grade or down a grade, without (sometimes) quite knowing how it had happened. On the street, and elsewhere in public, the grades disappeared, substantially—at least no very marked prominence was given them ordinarily—but in private there were "sets," and each set knew its own frontiers and was self-respectingly content to abide within them. However, it may be said that the frontiers were only set up against intimate and familiar daily intercourse between the sets; large private balls and parties broke them down and mingled the ranks together.

At the social summit stood the "quality." This word was used by the commoner folk of the South and the Southwest, and was the equivalent of "aristocracy." There were two "quality" grades. In the top one were the Fairfaxes—all alone; in the other one were the Harrisons, the Wilkinsons, and Mr. Orrin Lloyd Godkin. Next after the second grade, and separated from it by a rather faint frontier, came the Gridleys; Judge Bates of the county court; Rev. Mr. Bailey the Presbyterian minister and the other reverends; Mr. Gilbert the principal lawyer; Randall, (by and by District Attorney); Dr. Stevens; Dr. Bradshaw; and several considerable merchants. Next below came Marsh the miser and the rest of the white population. After these, the slaves.[3]

---

[3] In the foregoing paragraph Mark Twain probably intended to insert, but failed to mark for insertion, this sentence which he wrote on the back of page 17 of the holograph: "If there had been a newspaper in the town—but there wasn't—its editor would have mustered in grade No. 3."

Charles Fairfax was called "the Squire." It was not an official title, but a title of courtesy conferred by the general voice, and was a recognition of his supremacy, his occupation of the summit of the social pyramid. He was the richest planter in that part of the cotton belt; he owned 1200 slaves, and his "nigger quarter" made a considerable village—a neat, orderly whitewashed one, it was, and its tenants were well cared for and comfortable. The Squire was about 35; robustly built and athletic, with a shaven square face and a resolute jaw, but with kindly blue eyes which engagingly modified and mollified the jaw's advertisement. His bearing and manner were rather stately and reserved toward all except his small circle of intimates. His intimates held him in high honor and had a warm regard for him; the rest stood in awe of him, but he was not popular with them. They knew his clothes came from Europe, and they did not like that excess of "style." They had believed the same of his father's clothes, and that old man had died under that cloud. With his intimates the Squire was like the average man—easy, companionable, interested in what was going on and not reserved in the matter of exhibiting the natural play of his feelings; but he was always likely to chill down and close his shell when an outsider came about. He did not enjoy being unpopular, and would have preferred to have it the other way, but his nature and his heredities had made him what he was, and secretly and at bottom he was a shy man; therefore, to learn popular ways was a thing outside of his possibilities, and he knew it, accepted it, and reconciled himself to it.

He had completed his education in a Virginian college, and later had gone back to Virginia and brought thence a charming young wife. At the time of which we are writing he had been married something more than ten years, and his only child, Helen, was now nine years old.

He was of the Maryland Fairfaxes—a house which could claim the curious distinction of being the only one in America entitled to display the symbols and assume the state and dignity of nobility. His elder brother was the reigning lord, and occupant of the Maryland homestead.

Before his marriage the Squire had been rather wild, and also rather fond of drink. The drink was bad for his temper, which was a sudden one. When he had had a glass or two it was not well to offend him; his resentment rose in a flash and he went at his work promptly and without counting the odds against him. When perfectly sober he governed his temper well, and got into no difficulties which were fairly avoidable. But in all cases he was a fair fighter; all conceded that. It was also granted, to his credit, that his fights were about as often on other people's account as on his own. It was his natural disposition to accept an invitation where none had been extended, to help a fight out, if there was an underdog in it that needed support. It was this disposition which got him into trouble with Jim Tyler, a visiting desperado from a neighboring town. Tyler was kicking and cuffing a boy, while a crowd looked on, afraid to interfere; Fairfax was passing by; he stopped, and said to the crowd—

"What are you made of? Why do you let him do that?"

Tyler squared himself before Fairfax and said, insolently—while the grateful boy departed—

"Maybe *you* want to interfere?"

"I do," said Fairfax, and broke his jaw with his fist. He turned and was walking away, leaving the man in the dust, when some one shouted "Look out, he's coming for you!" At the same moment a bullet whizzed past Fairfax's ear; but he had Tyler in his grip before he could fire the other barrel. He snatched the pistol away and cocked it, and Tyler went down on his knees and began to beg for his life. Fairfax was white with passion, but he restrained himself and said—

"I ought to kill you; and I would, but I know you have a wife and children, and *they* have done me no harm; for their sakes—" He fired the pistol in the air, then threw it down and said, "Leave the town—at once, and don't ever enter it again." He said to the crowd, "He shall have half an hour; after that, and for thirty years to come, whoever reports to me that he is in the town can have a hundred dollars and my thanks."

It proved a permanent riddance of a frequent and dreaded visitor, and for years whenever a group of citizens was sharply criticising Fairfax some one was presently sure to recal that good service and drop it in, and not without effect, as an extenuating circumstance.

The Fairfax home was called "the mansion,"—as before remarked—and was of great dimensions and pillared and porticoed at the front in the old-fashioned colonial style. Mrs. Fairfax was become a confirmed invalid and did not go out of the house. But her influence over her husband was salutary, constant, and effective. After his marriage he ceased wholly from drinking and fighting.

The Harrisons and Wilkinsons were related families. Andrew Harrison, the head of the house, was a widower of sixty-five, a practical man, scarcely even tinged with sentiment. He was uncompromisingly honest and honorable and truthful, his character was quite above reproach, and he was respected, and one might even say revered, by all. He was not uneducated, but he was not college-bred. He was half as rich as the Squire, and richer than any other man in the region. His plantation was the first one south of the Squire's, and his house was like "the Mansion," and nearly as large.

At the time of which we write, it had no occupants—barring the servants—except Andrew, his son George, and George's son Tom, aged about 11.

Andrew kept his business in his own hands and name,—for good business reasons—and George only helped. Under limitations.

George was about thirty-five. He was tall and thin, with bristly black hair which stood up unparted; intellectual sharp features; eager, restless, unstable black eyes; quick of movement, carriage not without a certain grace and dignity when with his familiars; abashed and too anxious to please when (as happened at very rare intervals) he found himself in the company of reserved people or strangers. He was over-amiable; his anxiety to please was a great blemish and made some despise him and blinded them to his worth —for in one way, at least, he had worth: he was profoundly and conspicuously honest and honorable. He was much too humble-minded, for a grown person; and his instability and his anxiety to please often betrayed him into dropping his own convictions for the adversary's after the briefest poor fight. The humble-minded are vain of their humility without suspecting it—the vainest of the vain. George read everything and digested nothing; he was a mine of misinformation and mental confusions. Among other faults, he was as good as the day was long; also, privately vain of his moral invulnerability. Everybody revered his perfect moral character and privately resented the necessity of doing it. He was a result of his mother's careful and watchful training, not his father's. She had been a moral sentimentalist all her life, and her son was the monumental result.

George had fine and lofty ideals, and was always ready to change them for higher ones. He was a temperance advocate. However, what he was today was no indication of what he would be tomorrow, in religion and politics; yet he was adamant in his honesty and honor; for when he changed an opinion it was from honest conviction. He usually deserted his party the day before election and processioned with the other party, furnished its mottoes, made a speech at night—then they stood guard over him and took him to the polls next day to keep him from voting the third ticket if there was one.

He had been a Presbyterian, a Baptist, a Methodist, an Episcopalian, an infidel, a Mohammedan; had been three times forward and back over the course and was now a Presbyterian again and due to rebecome a Baptist in thirteen months.

He was the easiest man to flatter in the world; he swallowed it without chewing, was shamefully grateful for it and ready to worship the flatterer's shoes to get more.

He had been engaged 7 times before his marriage at 23.

The first woman who flattered him wholly without stint turned his head utterly; and yet even she would have failed to bag him if she had taken any foolish chances. But she didn't; she proposed to him on the spot and took him to Mr. Bailey straight off and married him with violence. She was a man. She led him a strict life and a most irksome one, and died six months before the time of which we are writing.

George was a spasmodic man. Twice or thrice in his life he had actually struck out in his own defence valiantly—as people thought, and as he himself thought—but it was not valor, it was

the insane and blind influence of fright. After it was done he didn't
know how it had happened, but he was as proud of it as if the
impulse had been bravery.

Like most of us his real self was not known to any one—
particularly to *himself*.

The widow Wilkinson was George's sister and exactly like him.
Her husband left her fairly well off and was willing to go. Both
funerals took place in the same week. There were two children, a
boy and a girl.

George and the widow Wilkinson were ready for any new kind
of doctrine, or doctoring, or patent medicine, or any other good and
lofty diversion that came along.

But in spite of their detestable faults they were dear good
generous people, always ready for good works, and people were
obliged to like and respect them—and did.

They joined every devilish moral society that was started. George
was Knight of Temperance at intervals—in the other intervals he
withdrew and drank—a few tablespoonfuls, seldom or never many.

At the time of which we are writing he was not a Knight, but
due to rebecome one in 9½ months.

In her anxiety to please, the Widow was never still a moment:
"Won't you have some of this? won't you take some of that?—oh,
do take this chair, that one is so uncomfortable—come nearer the
fire." No quiet person could endure her. She was small and thin,
always and inveterately ungracefully dressed, and had drugged
herself with deadly medicines till there was not enough blood in
her to blush with. She had doctored herself for every disease under
the sun and had never had one of them. She was periodically in an
eager enthusiasm over some new fatal nostrum and trying to betray
her friends into taking chances in it.

She was honorable and incorruptible; still, she could have been
spared and should have been shot.

Her special friend was the widow Pilgrim. Mrs. Pilgrim was a
kind-hearted creature who didn't know anything, but didn't know
she didn't know anything, and this protected her from embarrassment. As to rank, she was unclassified. She had good instincts and
was an ass, and this made her welcome everywhere.

Mr. Orrin Lloyd Godkin completes the list of the second grade of the "quality." He was an educated bachelor of forty, and the next richest planter after Andrew Harrison, and had a house in the town and another one on his plantation, which adjoined the Fairfax plantation on the north. No stranger could guess his age by his appearance; on a cloudy day he looked several years older than he was, and in sunny weather five, seven, even ten years younger than he was, according to the grade of intensity of the light. But in any weather the stranger's eye would find him a fascinating object, because he was so unusual a spectacle and so uncanny. It was on account of his complexion, which was ghostly, spectral, ghastly. It was wholly colorless. And that was not all; that was not the marvel —far from it. It was the *kind* of pallor—that was the miracle; for this was a pallor which had never bleached-out a human face before, either in life or subsequently: it would have added a new terror to death. It was the cold, hard, smooth, polished, opaque, tintless and horrible white of a wax-figure's hands. There was no beard, and there were no eye-brows. Out of this dreadful mask looked a pair of sloe-black eyes; alert, intelligent, searching, wistful, and very human eyes; eyes capable of expressing all the various moods of men, and accustomed to doing it; eyes that could do irony and such things quite well; eyes which could even smile,—of course without the face helping, or betraying consciousness of the act— but the smile was not popular; it seemed startlingly out of place in that death's head, and got on the spectator's nerves, and moved him to say "please don't do that." We are speaking of the eyes as they appeared at a near view, when one could note their smouldering fires or detect their sparkle and flash; but at the distance of a large room's width they dismally suggested round holes burnt in a shroud.

Instead of trying to ameliorate the influences of his face by the arts of dress, Godkin chose to use those very arts to magnify and aggravate them. Winter and summer he dressed in black. From his chin to his toes he was just a thin black pillar, with no other tint appearing; for he covered his shirt-front with his vest and his wristbands with his sleeves, and he wore turn-down collars of so low a pattern that they were submerged, and hardly showed

even a white line. And he would not wear anything that had a
gloss; it must be lustreless and sombre, or he wouldn't have it. He
had long thin hands, waxy and dead, and his black sleeves horribly
emphasized their corpsy whiteness. He apparently liked to have
them naked; perhaps because when he worked the fingers it made
people's flesh creep. When he needed to wear gloves he used
undressed kid dyed a dismal and rayless black. His hair was thick
and black and lustreless, and he wore it clipped so close that at a
little distance his skull seemed painted. When he stood at rest in a
dim uncertain light he could have been mistaken for a black post
with a clown's chalky face on the top of it.

He was a gentleman. His manners were courteous, his ways
pleasant, his bearing easy and graceful, and if he had had a human
complexion he would have been comely, even handsome. He had
never had a love-match and was not expecting to have one and
knew he was not likely to have one. He pretended to be sorry about
this; not because he minded being lonely, he said, but because he
was afraid his complexion would die with him. He could talk any
kind of nonsense and get it taken at par, if he so chose, for if he
veiled his eyes the rest of his face would not give him away.

All his movements were soft and smooth and gliding; and if you
were his friend he would enter your room as noiselessly as a cat,
and then wait patiently for you to look up; for he enjoyed the start
you gave when your eye wandered around and encountered his
ghost-face. In shops and such places he liked to glide up alongside
of a stranger—particularly a woman—and wait there for results.
Before experience had ripened him he was used to stand ready to
grab her and save her from jumping over the counter and breaking
her neck when she looked up; but he found that this kindness was
a mistake, for the women fought and struggled like maniacs to get
free, and one or two of them came near dying in his arms.

One might suppose, by this, that he was not a serious man; but
that would be an error; he was a deeply serious man and sincerely
so, but he had a frivolous side to his nature, like the rest of us.

He was richer in pet names than any other person in the
community. Because of certain theories of his, some called him the

Libeler of the Human Race, or the Enemy of the Human Race; others called him the Ass-Philosopher, others the Ghost, Death's Head, Corpse, and so on; but perhaps the name that had the widest currency was that last one—the Corpse.

He enjoyed his life, for he had plenty of books and was fond of reading; he disliked work and did none, but left it all to his overseer and his factor; and he was a friendly and sociable corpse, ready to entertain and be entertained, and he was always around and interested when anything was going on.

He always spoke in light and airy disparagement of the human race; and also as if it were a species in which he had no personal concern; in fact he isolated himself from the human race by a pregnant phrase, and complacently spoke of its members collectively as "those foreigners." Invited to explain this attitude, he said he had a superhuman strain in him, and that his line was of loftier origin than any monarch could claim. He pointed out the passage in the Bible which told how the sons of the Gods, attracted by the comeliness of the daughters of men, descended to the earth and chose brides from among them. His line, the Godkins—a word meaning little god, he said, as catkin means little cat and lambkin little lamb—was a result of one of these alliances, and was the oldest in the earth and incomparably the highest and noblest. Asked how he could condescend to associate with the human race, he said it was very simple: to him, men were the same as the other animals—there was no very noticeable difference between them discoverable from the remote summit where he stood—and if men could make friends and comrades of good dogs and horses, within certain limitations, without compromising themselves, he thought he could properly go a step lower and associate with men, and preserve his dignity. Many of the ignorant and unthinking disliked him on account of his attitude toward the human race, and because he made so much of his divine streak and put on so many airs about it, but the judicious and the thoughtful argued that if he was right, as concerned his lineage, his position was justified.

He signed himself "O. Lloyd Godkin," and in this form the name was a valued convenience to people who wanted to be profane but did not dare: they turned it into an exclamation and uttered it with fiendish energy when they fell over things in the dark.

In the third rank with the Gridleys came the Bateses. Judge Bates was handsome and statuesque, with a thin, intellectual face, fine black eyes, black hair, and a silky and lustrous full black beard. A full beard was a distinction; very few men wore any beard at all. He was amiable, insinuating, and a flatterer; he was innocently vain of his elegant manners and his elegant language; he was artificial all through, and rather overcharged with mincing and dainty affectations; he was not a reality, even to himself, he was a fine and elaborate artificiality. And his wife was just like him. With this difference, that in the judge there was no harm and no unkindness; he only flattered to please; but his wife's sweetest flatteries usually had a little poison in them, and they left a bad taste in the mouth of the person who swallowed them.

Rev. Mr. Bailey, the Presbyterian minister, was a man whose face was both introduction and passport. The stranger took him into his friendship without asking questions. He was transparently good and fine and trustworthy and genuine, and his wife was like him.

CHAPTER 3.

IT IS NOT EASY to describe David Gridley, there being two of him—the one that God made, and another one. The one that God made was a sufficiently indifferent piece of work, but it was at least not a sham—all its parts were genuine; but the other one was all sham; there was not a genuine fibre in it. It was the work of Mrs. Gridley. It is not to be understood that she made the original Gridley over again, for any one who is not stupid knows that as God makes a man, so he remains; teaching and training can alter the outside of him, but not the inside. The inside is there to stay. It is nature; and nature doesn't change; it can be suppressed, smothered, hidden, but not abolished. Figuratively speaking, it is a glass of limpid salt water: teaching and training can color it red, blue, green, black, according to the trainer's desire; but none of these disguises, nor all of them mixed together, can abolish the salt; it is indestructible, it is a permanency. Mrs. Gridley did her best to make David Gridley over again, and always believed she was making progress and would in the end succeed—a pathetic error. There are millions of Mrs. Gridleys, sincere and excellent people, and entitled to all charity, and perhaps even praise, since they mean so well. Mrs. Gridley put an entirely new outside on David— a shiny new outside, and fine to consider; and this exterior Gridley was the only one the world knew. And by diligent hard work and watchful pains she kept that exterior one in such good repair that the general world did not even suspect that there was another Gridley and a solider one—a real one. But there it was: he was just a piece of honest kitchen furniture transferred to the drawing-room and glorified and masked from view in gorgeous cloth of gold.

He was himself thoroughly well aware of the bogus Gridley, and detested his holy society; but he was an easy-going, lazy, soft character, and his wife wasn't. Hence the result.

In Susan Gridley's make and character there were no flaws. She was educated, utterly refined, scrupulously high-principled, genuine to the marrow, deeply religious; she had none but high ideals, it was not within the possibilities of her nature to entertain a low one. She was firm and strong, she was as steadfast, as faithful, as trustworthy as the sun and the atmosphere and the fixed stars; she was fastidiously truthful; she was cautious and deliberate about making promises, but a promise once made, she would go to the stake rather than break even the outside edge of it; she was delicate in her feelings, and modestly shrinking, but when courage was required to back a principle, she had it. She had a sound, practical, business head, and in the next compartment of her skull a large group of brain-cells that had a vivid appreciation of the beautiful in nature, art and literature, and an abiding love of it. She was just and fair in her judgments, leaning—if at all—to the generous side always; she was loving and loveable, and although she did not open her heart to every one, or indeed to very many, whosoever entered it

was its guest forever, and content to stay. She never made a friend
and lost him; nor one who failed her when she needed him. She
was easily the most superior woman in that region, and was so
regarded by all.

Granted that David Gridley was an easy-going, lazy, soft
character, and that his pride in his wife and his love for her
were without limit, it stands to reason that he was but clay in
this earnest and able potter's hands. Innocently unaware of what
she was really proposing to do, this most genuine of all genuine
creatures set herself the task of transforming her husband into a
comprehensive, complete and symmetrical humbug; and as far as
his outside was concerned she made a master-work of it that would
have deceived the elect.

The contrasts between the two Davids were curious, and
interesting—to David (the real David); every day and all day long
he had the two on private view, and was always examining them
and wondering over them. But not in joy; in impotent protest and
discontent; for he had no pleasure in being a sham. The real David,
the inside David, the hidden David, was of an incurably low tone,
and wedded to low ideals; the outside David, Susan Gridley's
David, the sham David, was of a lofty tone, with ideals which the
angels in heaven might envy. The real David had a native affection
for all vulgarities, and his natural speech was at home and happy
only when it was mephitic with them; the sham David traded in
fine and delicate things only, and delivered them from his tongue
aromatic with chaste fragrances. The real David clothed the truth
in so many gauds and ruffles and embroideries that its mother
couldn't recognise it; the sham David turned it loose on the world
naked. The real David couldn't keep his word, the sham one
couldn't break it. The real David cared but little whether an
inconvenient debt was paid or not; the sham one would settle it
with his last shirt. The real David was seldom serious; the sham
one was a tombstone. The real David was a Vesuvius boiling to the
brim with imprisoned profanity; the sham one was apparently a
bland and peaceful extinct crater. The real David was an enthusiastic Sabbath-breaker; the sham one kept a pew in church and was
always there to look holy and help do the hymns and pass the plate.

The real David had a cow's appreciation of fine art and high literature; the sham one bowed down to the Old Masters and talked Shakspeare and the others with a devotee's devotion. The real David was born to the gait and manners of a hostler; the sham one was Chesterfield come back. The real David was slovenly, and preferred it; hated clothes of all kinds and the man that invented them; the sham David went gloved and clothed like a gentleman, and had never a speck of dust on him. The real David carried a devil's spasmodic temper inside; the sham one was as serene as moonlight. The real David loathed society and its irksome polish and restraints; the sham one was the society model whom the observing and judicious delighted to pattern after.

Only a strong and steady hand could have kept this chafing rebel straight—and Susan Gridley had that. And by what art? What was the secret of her success? It was simple: by providing the rebel's boiler with a safety-valve. She allowed David to blow off steam at home. Otherwise there would have been explosions in public. There was no way to keep the steam from generating, for its accumulation was a process of nature, and in the course of time Mrs. Gridley was obliged to recognise that fact—to her disappointment and deep regret—and after that she did the next best thing, the one available thing: she allowed the steam to blow off at home, trying to let on, when circumstances permitted, that she didn't know it was happening, and sending the children out of the way as soon as the signs indicated that presently the safety-valve was going to lift and begin to sing.

Did the elaborate sham which she had manufactured with so much labor and pains deceive herself? Possibly; we can fool ourselves with nearly any inviting superstition if we dearly want to.

There is no accounting for a woman's illusions. Every woman has one or more that flatly contradict her whole character, her whole mental and moral make-up. Susan Gridley loved her humbug with all her heart. She even worshiped him, and said so; using that very word, and repeating it daily. Not a day went by that she did not bless the hour that placed her weal and life in the guard and keep of her adored moral half-breed. He did not know why she adored him; he knew why he adored her, and how to state his reasons and prove them sane and sound; but that she should adore him seemed to him a failure of judgment—that judgment which in all other things was so lucid and so healthy. He wondered if she had reasons. He found that she had. Would he like to hear them? With eyes glowing with feeling, and with all her heart in her words, she set free her eager tongue and it painted his portrait. It was then that he found out that he was an archangel. He had not suspected it before.

She had come from the east or the south or somewhere; he had fallen in love with her at first sight and had begun his love-making instantly. Courtship lifts a young fellow far and away above his common earthly self, and by an impulse natural to those lofty regions he puts on his halo and his heavenly war-paint and plays archangel as if he was born to it. He is working a deception, but is not aware of it. His girl marries the archangel. In the course of time he recognises that his wings and his halo have disappeared, and that he is now no longer in the business; but it is a hundred to one that the wife, be she wise or be she otherwise, will keep her beautiful delusion all her life and always believe that the radiant outfit is still there. From time to time she will notice that it is getting a little out of repair, but that is nothing, it does not trouble her: she keeps a constant and admiring eye on it, and dusts it off, and tinkers it up, and re-paints it, re-gilds it, and so long as she lives is ever more and more pleased and satisfied with the stunning effects which she gets out of her restorations.

David Gridley knew that there were things in his make-up which could distress this dear unworldly young creature whom he had married if they should fall under her notice, therefore he walked cautiously and watched himself. And so, during three years none but unimportant impairments came to light—perhaps seventy-five, but not more than ninety, in any case—but at last there was an accident, and a very serious dilapidation was disclosed. Susan Gridley overheard her archangel swearing—swearing like a demon. The shock of it took her breath away. When she got it back, she listened, to make sure, for she was doubting the loyalty of her ears. The thing seemed too terrible, too ghastly, to be true. She did not faint, and she did not fall—couldn't, indeed, for she was in bed. She had wakened out of a peaceful sleep, then she noticed that the archangel was gone from her side, next she heard fervent words which she recognised as pulpit specialties, and she said admiringly, "dear good heart, he is praying;" and next she changed her mind.

The archangel had left her sleeping and gone into his dressing-room to make his toilet, and had left the door a little ajar through heedlessness and thinking about other things—a mistake which he had never made before, for toilet-making was always a perilous time with him, and required the strictest privacy.

All through his bathing and shaving he said the usual and necessary things in a low and cautious mumble; then he put on a shirt, and found a button gone; took it off and threw it out of the window—with language; put on another and found a button gone, and threw that one out, with increased language; put on a third shirt, found a button gone; threw it out, then began to throw out boots, hats, soap, toothbrushes—anything and everything he could get his frantic hands on, with always abler and abler language, delivered in an ever mounting key—and at last happened to notice that the door was a-crack. The strength went from him, and he sat down pale and sick with the sense of the magnitude of his disaster.

What should he do? What should he say? He did not know. Would it answer to explain that he was only quoting—memorising a piece which had interested him in a book? That seemed a plausible way out. . . . But no—that wouldn't do: she was bright, and there was a flavor of originality about this piece which she. . . . No, it wouldn't work. . . . Maybe she didn't hear—maybe she wasn't awake. . . . No—oh, no, she was a light sleeper, and he hadn't been whispering. There was but one poor little comfort—such as it was: he said to himself, "Some of that language couldn't get through a crack like that." He was greatly depressed; he realized that as an archangel he was compromised. Then he had a promising idea: there were two doors to the bedroom—he would pass out at the furthest one and so would not have to meet her eye; and he would go quickly—as if on business—

urgent business—business which had been forgotten and must be
attended to at once.

He dressed softly, passed softly into the bedroom, then had the
idea that the best way would be to go along deliberately and
absorbed in thought, and looking like a person who has not been
doing anything. This worked very well, until he was half way
through; then he was gratefully cheered by the deep silence of the
place; was she asleep? A mysterious magnetism forced him to turn
and steal a glance. Then his heart sank, and he knew the misery a
convict feels. There she lay, gazing at him with snapping eyes. His
own sank, under that accusing gaze, and he bent his head and
waited for the deserved reproach. It would be dear and sweet and
gentle, but charged with heart-break, and how was he going to bear
it? There was a pause, a desolating stillness, then from those pure
lips came this word, impressively delivered—

"D-a-m—*nation!*"

Gridley was shocked, and beyond expression astonished. Then
came the natural reaction: he saw the ludicrous side of the thing—
a side which was heightened and enriched by the gravity of the
intention—and was not able to keep his countenance. He turned
his back, hoping his throes would pass for sobs, for he did not wish
to make matters worse for himself than they already were; but his
wife said indignantly—

"David, you are not deceiving me; you are laughing, and there is
nothing to laugh about."

But laughter which cannot be suppressed is catching. Sooner or
later it washes away our defences, and undermines our dignity, and
we join in it—ashamed of our weakness, and embittered against
the cause of its exposure, but no matter, we have to join in, there is
no help for it. It was what happened to the young wife. A blessed
thing, and a gracious and benignant reconciler, is an unrestrained
discharge of innocent and foolish and whole-hearted laughter. It
eases the pain of many a hurt that is beyond the surgery of
argument and reproach. When Gridley stole a wistful glance and
saw that his wife was silently shaking, he knew that he was saved;
and when he kissed her and told her how beautiful she looked

when she laughed, he was aware that he was ahead of the game now. He sat down on the bedside and began to chat, and ask questions, and enjoy his escape from what had promised to be a disastrous business.

"What did you do it for, Susy—what was your idea?"

Her face assumed a gentle and reproachful gravity, and she said—

"It was for your good, David. I wanted you to see just how it sounded."

"I judged so. When I say it, does it sound like that?"

She glanced at his face, but got no information from it.

"Doesn't it?" she said.

"I hope not, Susy."

She inspected his face again—with definite suspicion, this time.

"David, I believe you are teasing me. Why do you hope not?"

He took her hand in his, and began to explain—with a gentle deference and a yearning solicitude in his voice and manner which were well calculated to deepen the impressiveness of his words—

"Because it would pain me to think that when I swear it sounds like that. And—"

"Would it, David?" she interrupted, anxiously. "Why?"

"Well, you see, dear, swearing is like any other music, and—"

"Music?"

"Yes. If it is not done well, if it is not done with a fine and discriminating art, and vitalized with gracious and heartborn feeling, it lacks beauty, it lacks charm, it lacks expression, it lacks nobleness, it lacks majesty, it lacks—"

"I think it is odious! David, you are making fun of me."

"Peace—and listen. What must I feel? Have you no humanity? After the patient years, the study, the practice, the tireless industry which I have devoted to this great art. . . . Susy, you are ignorant, and not to blame. I am not blaming you, dear; but think —to take that volcanic word, that stormy great word, and pipe it hesitatingly out in a scared insipid squeak—flat, poor, expression-less, ashy, thin, flabby, sick, ashamed, the fire all gone, the inflections misplaced. . . . Susy, you didn't *want* to hurt me, dear, but oh, you can't think how it made me feel to hear you intimate that when I said it it sounded like *that*; and I—"

"Now David, you can go along—I don't want to hear anymore about it."

"I am not blaming you, dear, you did the best you could, with your loose education and want of practice; but you see how it is, yourself—you only know the words, you don't know the tune. Now in any fine and delicate or lofty and noble music, of course the mere words—"

He passed out of the room talking, and the rest of it was lost.

The taming of her archangel kept Susan Gridley busy and happy and interested and proud, all the time, as the years drifted along; and when her little girls got big enough to notice things they were interested in her work, too—more interested in it than she approved of, sometimes, for she wanted them to think he was perfect, and she often found this a delicate and difficult business to put through, satisfactorily. For the most of his perfections were of such a peculiar and unusual sort that they required a world of explaining before the children could see them; and then, often, after all her explaining, she had the pain of perceiving that the children had doubts; or if they hadn't, that they liked the perfections better before they were explained than afterwards. They had a great admiration for their father, and she rejoiced at that; but upon examination it turned out, as often as not, that they were admiring something in him which she was doing her level best to edit *out* of him. It was very discouraging. And it was having a curious and devilish effect; for admiration begets imitation; and so in the course of time they developed double personalities: half the time they were the flawless nice children of her training, the other half—well the other half they were different.

When Mrs. Gridley wrote a letter, it was fair and blemishless to the eye: no blots, no erasures, no interlineations; if she discovered a mistake in it, she wrote the whole letter over again. And she edited David's letters for him, but not by request. Usually they had fire and brimstone and thunder and lightning in them when they reached her hands, but they were reserved and courteous and as tranquil as moonlight when she got done taming them. Sometimes he wrote literature for the eastern press—fierce and bloody Indian tales—and again she edited. He complained that he sent his Indians out on the war-path and she ambushed them and sent them to Sunday school. She wouldn't let him make an impromptu speech. He had to write his speeches out, then she tamed them and made him memorise them; and she made it a point to be present at the delivery, and within reach of his coat-tail, so that she could twitch it when he forgot himself and tried to introduce new matter. He fretted and fumed over these harassments, as he called them, but her hand was steady and firm, and he submitted, and found profit in it in the long run.

If unwatched he would try to escape from the house unbrushed and with his pockets bulging with unnecessary things; but she generally caught him on the wing, and brushed him, and picked stray bits of thread and such things from his clothes, and unloaded his pockets and sent him forth exasperatingly trim and elegant.

At dinner parties he was for a long time a difficult and troublesome feature. Sometimes he would be in great spirits, and would crowd everybody down and do all the talking himself; sometimes he would talk only to the lady on his left; sometimes only to the lady on his right—always neglecting the stupid one, the commonplace one, the one he couldn't abide; sometimes, when out of spirits, he moped and didn't talk at all. His wife was helpless; he saw none of her signs; she had to sit still and suffer. When the company was gone he would catch an informing light in her eye, and wake up to his condition, and say with a sigh—

"I know it. Go on—dust me off."

Then she detailed his delinquencies. The children took a deep interest in the dusting off, and never missed it if they could help it. They were greatly disappointed when he had committed no crimes and the dusting took the form of praises. Once, after one of his worst failures, he said—

"But Susy, it doesn't do any good to dust me after it is all over, because I forget it all before next time. If you would dust me off beforehand—"

That was reasonable, and the idea was adopted. When it was

applied, it worked; when the wife forgot it in the press of business, David relapsed. But a scheme was finally contrived by which the dusting could be done at the dinner table without the guests suspecting, and this succeeded to admiration. After that, David was a model. In the midst of the meal the wife would say—

"David, I found that date for you to-day—it was the tenth."

That meant, *"Do* talk to the lady on your left a little."

By and by—

"No, I was wrong, David, it was the eleventh."

Then David would talk to the lady on his right. Later there might be another correction—the date was the twelfth. This meant, "Don't do *all* the talking!" David would quiet down; and perhaps so entirely as presently to fetch out the final date—the thirteenth; then he would stop moping and become conversational again. If the company betrayed curiosity concerning these elusive dates, David explained without conveying information, and the secret of the matter remained undamaged.

Which Was It?

MARK TWAIN at first called this novel "Which Was Which?" but by 1902, when he wrote much of it, he was referring to it as "Which Was It?" And he used the latter name again when he spoke of it as one of his unfinished books in his autobiographical dictation of 30 August 1906. During the summer and fall of 1899 he wrote approximately the first one-third of the manuscript, working sometimes in London and more often in Sanna, Sweden, where Jean was receiving osteopathic treatment. (Some of his preoccupation with diseases and cures found its way into the story.) The greater part of "Which Was It?" was written between 1900 and 1902. By the end of May 1903 two typescripts were in existence—one of the first 215 pages of manuscript and a later one of the entire manuscript. The first typescript bears Mark Twain's carefully made inkscript corrections and revisions, which have largely been followed as his latest intention. The first nine chapters of the other typescript contain a few corrections and revisions, but many irregularities in the same chapters were left uncorrected; he may have merely glanced through this copy, or a part of it. Accordingly, the holograph has been ordinarily credited with primary authority after the first 215 pages. Revisions in the later typescript have been used when evidence substantiates their authority.

The basic plot of "Which Was It?" resembles that of "Which Was the Dream?" George Harrison, like General "X," is at first seen living in a beautiful mansion, much respected, favored of fortune, blessed with a wife and children who share his happiness. Like "X," he has a momentary dream of disaster which seems to him to last for many years. In attempting to save the family from debt and disgrace, he commits murder. This action produces a sequence of further disasters, which he numbers as the bitter fruits of his crime. As the story was planned, he was to suffer every possible degradation and then at last awaken to find his wife Alice coming in with the children to say goodnight. Although

177

Mark Twain did not carry "Which Was It?" quite far enough to reach that ending, this story is by far the longest of those in which he used the dream framework and the nightmare of disaster. The book is a compendium of his later thoughts and moods and literary enthusiasms, and the reader will find sections which parallel passages in some of his other works of the same period, including "The Man That Corrupted Hadleyburg," "The Lowest Animal," and *What Is Man?*

Although the story is loosely structured, the unusually extensive working notes show that Mark Twain did much planning for it and introduced changes as he proceeded with the writing. He used several names for the squire of the village—Baldwin, Brewster, and Fairfax; the latter name became the final choice. The daughter of the squire is first called Sadie and later Helen. The wronged Negro, who has been both sired and swindled by George Harrison's uncle and who contrives to revenge himself upon George, is called Pomp at first and later Jasper. In all such cases, the names that appear to represent Mark Twain's latest intention have been used.

A dominant theme of "Which Was It?" is that of human selfishness, with its corollary that any man will act meanly or even criminally when sufficiently tempted. This same theme, treated perhaps in a lighter way, had been a favorite one that Mark Twain used as a platform topic in lecturing his way around the world. As one newspaper reported, "To every story he applied a moral, always pert and often humorous. 'Always be brave to the limit of your personal courage, but when you reach the limit, stop, don't strain.' That was the opening sentiment of the lecture." [1] Repeatedly, in giving what he represented as his "lecture on morals," he made his anecdotes illustrate the point that every young man should learn "how far he can rely on his courage before he is compelled to begin to use his discretion." [2] As it was reported when he was nearing the end of his tour, "In a drawling tone, its very lowness adding piquancy, the lecturer was soon giving the house those quaintly characteristic touches seen in his writings. There was no particular form in the 'moral sermon,' which might have run on for weeks and been complete in its incompleteness." [3] In the same sense, "Which Was It?" has also a kind of completeness.

Two related fragments, "Trial of the Squire" and the "Dying Deposition" of Andrew Harrison, will be found in the Appendix.

---

[1] St. Paul Daily *Globe* 25 July 1895; copy in file of newspaper clippings in MTP.

[2] Seattle *Post-Intelligencer,* 14 August 1895; copy in MTP.

[3] The Natal *Witness,* 16 May 1896; copy in MTP.

Which Was It?

BOOK I

THE WIFE'S NARRATIVE.

I.

I MUST BEGIN, in order to make him do the like, according to his promise. His name is George Louisiana Purchase Harrison;* I am Alison, his wife. I was married at 18, and am 26 now; he is 33. We are to write our small history, so that the children may have it when they grow up; a thing which has long been my dearest desire, and now it is really going to be fulfilled at last. I want it written for the children's sake, but I have one other reason for wishing it: I think he is literary in his make, indeed I feel sure of it. Why, the letters which he wrote to me while we were engaged— oh, there were never such letters! But he has never had to work for his living, and so he is easy-going and indolent, and has never had any troubles or sorrows or calamities to rouse up the literary fires that are slumbering in him and make them burst their bonds and find expression; therefore they can't seem to get started, lacking that impulse, do what I may to push him and pester him and persuade him to a trial of his gift. He only laughs, and says "fetch on your calamities, and I'm your man;" which piques me and I promise them, and he pinches my ear or kisses me and says I am a little fool and says a woman's exaggerating idolatries are always

---

* It is a curious name, but in its way is patriotic. He was born on the date of the signing of the Purchase-treaty, and at first was named George only, but by and by when the slow news arrived the other names were added. His father, who is still with us, and hale and hearty at 60, has a patriotic name, too— Andrew Independence Harrison. He was born during the Revolutionary War. A. H.

finding talents in her husband where none exist. And there it all
ends for the time, in chaff and nonsense.

But he has *promised,* now—promised that he will begin this
night, if I will excuse him from the birthday party—so I am
satisfied and happy; oh, happier than I can find words to put it in!
By the terms, I am to begin on my share to-day, and do something
at it every day until it is finished. And it is real work for me, for I
only know long-hand; whereas he knows short-hand, and can dash
off 8,000 words an hour, like nothing.

This beginning of mine is more a pretence than anything else; I
am doing it to keep my contract, and partly to get my bearings—get
my hand in, get into the current and limber-up my fins for my
excursion, he calls it. I have been driven hard all day with the
birthday preparations, and my head and hands are full of what is
still to be done and suffered between now and midnight; but
to-morrow will see me take up my end of the history seriously.

It is a children's party—Alison's birthday. That is the blonde—6
years old, the dearest little fairy! all sweetness and sunshine and
affection, and the deepest and wisest and cunningest little mind,
that's always thinking and thinking, and putting this and that
together, and dropping her small dredge into the awful depths of
the mystery of life and bringing up the most astonishing results!
Margery is the brunette—5 years old, dear and sweet and loving,
like her sister, but oh, dear, what a steam-engine, what a tireless
volcanic eruption of fun and frolic and gladness! and what an
unutterable blessing they both are to this house! And how useful
they are to me! When I can't persuade George, I send him those
little rascals—he is their slave. After begging him a year to write, it
occurred to me to send them—this morning. That settled it. And
now while our children are the subject I will go on to the next—

II.

THE PARTY is nearly over, and all has gone well. I *must* make
a note, while I rest a moment, privately. This sumptuous great

house was never so beautiful before, never so glorious with light and color and spendthrift richness and charm! It is the fine colonial Old Virginia of my girlhood transplanted to this remote and primitive Indiantown. There are thirty children, rich and poor together; all good, respectable and well-mannered, and happy beyond description. Such games, such romps, such racket and laughter! there was never anything so lovely to see. What a boon and a blessing is life! what a joy it is! There are old people here, living their happy youth over again; and there are young grown-ups, also: Sidney Phillips, among others—a handsome creature, good-hearted, and a most winning and courteous gentleman; he is attracted by that sweet Agnes Burley, and she by him—I see it quite plainly. And am glad, too; it would be—*will* be—a lovely match. And Frances Osgood and her husband are here, the handsomest pair in the town—very dear friends of ours. Their bewitching twins are with them—charming lads! Our slaves—and nearly everybody's, I think—are helping; mainly of their own accord, so as to have a chance in the fun and the refreshments; of course they are having a good time, it's their nature.

At eight o'clock I carried my small first chapter to George and gave it him in his study and required him to take up his pen and keep his word! Poor boy, he was lazy and drowsy and didn't want to, but he pulled himself together, like an honorable man, and arranged his paper and sat down to his task. I bound a damp towel around his head, because he says writing makes his brain feverish, then I left him nodding over my manuscript. I waited outside a minute or two, with the door a-crack, to see if he would really begin; but down went his nose on the desk, and he was sound asleep! I thought I would go and wake him, but I hadn't the heart. However, after the least little while he raised his head briskly up like one finely refreshed, put my poor screed reverently to his lips and kissed it—it made the tears spring to my eyes, I was so proud and happy!—then he fell briskly to work with his pen.

Half past eleven. The party is breaking up, joyous and noisy; I must go and do the good-bying. In half an hour they'll all be gone, then we'll romp along up to the study and break into papa's work and tell him all about it.

THE HUSBAND'S NARRATIVE.

AFTER AN INTERVAL OF FIFTEEN YEARS.

I AM LOOKING again upon her closing words—the last she ever wrote in this life:

"After begging him a year to write, it occurred to me to send them—this morning. That settled it. And now while our children are the subject I will go on to the next—"

That is our Tom. She was going to speak of him; but it was not to be. More than fifteen black years have dragged over my head since then. I can see her yet, just as she was, her young grace and loveliness all radiant with the excitements and anticipations of the occasion. She gave me what she had written, and bound the towel about my head—the last touch of her dear hand I was ever to know —and went to her death!

I do not know at what hour the disaster happened. I was intending to begin to write, according to my promise, and I think I did begin; but I was very drowsy and I fell asleep. I woke suddenly in the midst of fire and smoke, and heard a babel of frightful sounds: crashings, the roaring of flames, despairing cries, the tumultuous rush of feet. I seized her precious manuscript and floundered down the murky stairs, shouting the names that were so dear to me; then the smoke strangled me and I lost consciousness. I was found and dragged out into the open; and when I came to, the great house was a billowy mass of flame and I was a bereft and broken-hearted man. My little Tom was all that was left to me; my wife and my little girls I was never to see again in this life. Others had perished, so it was told me, but not more than two, God be thanked. One of them was little Harry Osgood; poor Frances, the years have softened that blow but little; she mourns still, and cannot be comforted. And I have mourned with her all these years, and know what she feels. Hers is a peculiarly hard case, for while the death of one of her twins was a sufficiently heavy calamity, the survival of the other was perhaps a heavier one.

My life, before my disaster, was wholly happy. It was tranquil and eventless, and there was not much in it to exercise a pen upon; still, I would have written it if my wife had lived, since that was her wish; but I have had no heart for it since, and I shall never do it, now. Yet I am moved to write my very recent life, my life of the past months, skipping and ignoring the past fifteen years. And that I will do, for the easement it may give me to look myself in the face and confess whither I have lately drifted, and what I am become!

But I cannot do it in the first person; I must spare myself that shame; *must* is the right word; I could not say in the first person the things I ought to say, even if I tried. I could not say "*I* did such and such things;" it would revolt me, and the pen would refuse. No, I will write as if it were a literary tale, a history, a romance—a tale I am telling about another man, a man who is nothing to me, and whose weak and capricious character I may freely turn inside out and expose, without the sense of being personally under the knife. I will make of myself a stranger, and say "George Harrison did so and so."

In the hope and belief that by the protection of this device I shall be enabled to frankly tell everything just as it happened, I will now begin.

GEORGE LOUISIANA PURCHASE HARRISON.

BOOK II.

I.

Indiantown was a village of twelve or fifteen hundred inhabitants. It was away out of the world, and sleepy and peaceful, and had no newspaper, and was comfortable and content. Its climate was a pleasant one; sometimes there was a winter, but this did not happen every year. It was a corn-growing country, and from the village-edges the great fields stretched mile upon mile to the north and to the south up the valley and down it, each with its family house in a big yard; the cluster of slave cabins a hundred yards behind it; around and beyond the cabins, the orchards and gardens and melon patches. Indiantown's Christianity was of the usual Southern breeds—Methodist, Presbyterian, Baptist—and each sect had a church which was commodious but not architectural. There was a court house; also a jail; for this was the county seat. There were two foreigners, a German and an Irishwoman, and they were man and wife. The people put the precedence the other way—wife and man; and they said that in the distribution of the sexes between them a mistake had been made.

Indian river ran by the town. It was not a great stream, but it was clear and clean and bright, and its banks were beautiful in summer with overhanging willows and with curving meadow-vacancies cushioned with grass and sprinkled as with fire-coals when the prairie-pink was in bloom. The stage road ran along the river, and one of these meadow-stretches occurred at the northern edge of the village. In the middle of it was the mill, on the bank; close to it, on the south side, was the dwelling of the salaried mill-hand—that German, Jake Bleeker; close to the mill on its northern side was the house of its owner, the venerable Andrew Independence Harrison, with garden and orchard behind it. Harrison was a widower; so also was his son George Louisiana Purchase Harrison, (now 48 years old), who lived with him. George's son Thomas had his home there, too, but he was away just now. He was a budding lawyer of promise, twenty-two years old, and had been in training a good while—without salary—with Gilbert, head of the profession in the village. Gilbert had sent him down to New Orleans on a piece of slow but important business, and he had now been absent more than three months.

In an earlier day the Harrisons had stood next to the Fairfaxes [4]

---

[4] The holograph here at first read "Baldwins"; in revising, Mark Twain changed the name of the squire's family to the "Brewsters." On MS page 183 he began to write "Fairfax" as the name of the squire and continued to use that name—which has been used throughout the present edition as the form representing his latest intention.

by the public rating, because of their wealth and high character. They would have ranked as the equals of the Fairfaxes but for the fact that they were not blue-blooded, (not "quality," as the phrase went,) while the Fairfaxes were. But the Harrison property was gone, now. Andrew Independence Harrison had nothing left but the mill, and had been a poor man for ten years. Poor, struggling, worried, in debt, and the bitterness of wounded pride poisoning his peace in the day and his sleep in the night all these years.

Just at the time that he lost his property, (which was five years after the burning of the stately Harrison mansion), he lost his best friend, also—the "Squire" Fairfax of that generation, his comrade and crony from boyhood up. The son, the inheriting Squire, he and his son George hardly knew. He had always kept to himself, as boy and youth—"proud and stuck-up because he was quality," was his reputation; and when he came back from a four-years' course in a Virginian college he had developed a drinking-habit and a fighting temper which easily enabled him to keep to himself as much as he liked—and more, possibly. He returned to Virginia and soon brought back a bride. From that moment he dropped drink and set an iron grip upon his temper. One child was born—a girl— and thenceforth the wife was an invalid, and never left the house. Her young husband devoted himself to her, served her like a slave, lived in the light of her eyes. Both were fond of books; of that company they had plenty; of any other they had little, and seemed quite satisfied to have it so. As the child Helen grew along they educated her themselves. She did not find the house a solitude; there were a dozen black domestics, the dearest and loveliest company in the world for a white child; there was an idolizing grandfather, (till death took him,) and as the years came and went Helen gathered friends in the village and further enriched her life.

At the time that this story opens the Fairfax home had been for a year and more a house of mourning once more. She who had for twenty years made its life beautiful by the graces of her mind and the ministry of her love had passed to her rest. For the daughter the puissant magician Youth was working his enchantments, and the clouds were beginning to break, now, but for the father this help was wanting; the pain of his loss did not diminish with time, but grew.

The Fairfax house, which was a spacious old-fashioned mansion, stood fifty or sixty yards back from the river road, and was nearly hidden from sight among shade-trees. Behind it its fields stretched a mile to the hills, and in their midst was the hamlet of white-washed log cabins called the "nigger-quarter." The mansion was a short mile northward from the mill; between was the country blacksmith shop, on the river bank. It stood under the vast spread of an ancient live-oak, and was the intelligence-centre of the northward-lying farming region. It did the horse-shoeing and wagon-mending for fifteen or twenty farms, and under the tree in summer and in the shop in winter was usually to be found a company of waiting gossips.

To return to the Fairfax house. On entering, one passed a couple of rooms on the right-hand side of the hall; then came a third, on the same side,—the Squire's work-room—and it is with this one that we have to do, now that we are ready to begin. There is a grand wood fire flaming there in a spacious fireplace, for it is cold weather and a blustering day. The date is Saturday, November the third.

II.

Two men sat in that room. One of them was Andrew Independence Harrison. He was seventy-five, and looked even older. He was lean and sallow and shrunken and tall, and his bony long fingers looked like talons, and he had a sickly aspect, and coughed a good deal. He wore a coarse linen shirt, sagging open at the neck and exposing the stringy throat and something of the breast; cowhide boots which had not been recently greased; a battered slouch hat; and his body was clothed in an old blue-jeans suit whose seams showed whitish, from wear. The other man was perhaps forty-five years old. His dress was plain and simple, but of fine material and perfect in fit, and he had a grave, intelligent face and the port and bearing of a gentleman. This was the Squire. Just at this moment he was saying—

"Mr. Harrison, I suppose you know why I sent for you?"

The old man winced, but did not look up. He said morosely—

"Say your say—I reckon I can stand it. I've got to."

"I gave you back your note for the four thousand dollars and interest—the only evidence of the indebtedness."

"Yes"—impatiently.

"I suppose you knew the money you paid me was counterfeit?"

Harrison fidgeted in his chair; took off his hat and twirled it nervously in his hands; his face worked, but he found nothing to say, and gave it up.

"You knew it was counterfeit?"

After another struggle—doggedly—

"I was in a tight place—you know that."

"Not in a tight enough place for you to return a kindness with a swindle. In what way were you in a tight place?"

Harrison evidently found an explanation difficult, for the moment. Then he began an effort—

"You could have come down on me and taken the mill. And then —well, it's everything; I haven't got anything else."

"The excuse is not well conceived. I lent you the money to *save* the mill. From your creditors. The debt was two years and a half old—had I ever asked you to pay?"

"Well—er—you *could* have done it. It was always hanging over me. It was a tight place."

"Harrison, I'm ashamed of you."

"Oh, go on—pile it on. I'm down; walk over me. I reckon you never lent it to me for love, anyway."

"For love of you—no, I didn't. Nor out of love for George your son, who was my schoolmate, who mistook my natural shyness for 'quality' airs—they all did—and has never liked me, though as I knew him to be in error as to the cause, I have not held it against him. No, I did it because my father and you were close friends all his life till he died, ten years ago. It was for my father's sake—that was all. He respected you and believed in you. You have deteriorated since—in several ways; and at last, your honesty is gone. George is a reproduction of your old former and excellent self—there is not much left of you but a caricature of it. To look at you now, and remember what you were in those days!"

"Oh, go it!" snorted the old man; then, rather irrelevantly, "*Those* days! If you only go back far enough *you* warn't just a model, yourself. You used to drink and fight, and had a devil's temper—it's not for *you* to talk, Squire Fairfax."

"Maybe so, maybe so," said the Squire, his eye lighting angrily for a moment. "I *was* that person; it is twenty years ago. It is ancient history and does not interest me; come back to the other subject."

"All right," said Harrison, with an insolent air, "you've sent for me—I'm here—now what do you want?"

"Your note again, for four thousand and interest, payable one day after date, and secured by a mortgage on the mill."

"Oh, you *do*? And supposing you don't get it?"

"I'll send you up for twenty years!"

The old man crumpled together in a sudden collapse, and sat ghastly white and trembling, during more than a minute, a pathetic object; then humbly, and in a voice shaky with fright and distress, he said—

"Lord, I never thought of that. Oh, I'll do it—I'll do anything you say. Twen-ty years! It's for life, at my time! I'll do it; I will, on honor. But *don't* tell on me, don't! I'm a poor old fool, and down in the world; you *won't* tell on me, *will* you?"

An expression, partly of pity, partly of disgust, passed over the Squire's features, and he said—

"Drop that; I am not that sort. Now, then, *you* will never pay this money, nor any of it—I know that quite well, and I shan't ask you; but George is made of better stuff, and some day, if he is ever able, he will pay. Until he is able he will not be asked; I am not a squeezer of the helpless. Whatever is mine is my daughter's. If I die with the debt unpaid, the mortgage is an asset; she will do with it as she pleases—that is her affair."

And so the interview ended, and Harrison went his way.

Squire Fairfax sat a while, thinking. "I wonder if he is quite straight in his brain," he mused; "he was always honest and honorable, and now all of a sudden . . . hm . . . very strange —can't be natural . . . and that harassed look in his eyes . . . his cares and troubles . . . on top of these, some visits from Deathshead Phillips, if rumor is right, a thing well calculated to dangerously disturb a distressed and superstitious mind. . . ." He took from his pocket the counterfeit money, a fat roll of bills, and reached out to put it on the fire, but paused. . . . "No—to merely *tell* him these witnesses are burnt—he would always be in doubt—the terror of the uncertainty would be an awful thing for that broken old creature to bear. . . . I'll give them to him when he brings the note." He put them on the table and went on with his thinkings. Presently he was aware that he was not alone. He glanced up and said—

"Oh, it's you, Bridget." He tossed the notes into the drawer of the table, and closed it. "Well, what is it?"

"If you please, sir, I've finished the sewing, and Miss Helen don't need me now, and my husband's not willing for me to work here anny more, so I've come to go."

"Not willing? What's the trouble?"

"Well, your 'anner will remember you called him a hard name, sir, and he can't get over it. It's got around, and they keep nagging him and pestering him and joking him about it and saying it's true —and that's the *worrst* of it."

"*I* called him a hard name? Impossible. What was it?"

"Your 'anner said he was an ill-mannered, muddle-headed, over-sentimental German jackass."

"Oh, *that*. I had forgotten it."

"Well, he don't forget it; and they don't let him, annyway. It just makes him boil, so it does."

Her eyes snapped, and she was evidently about to warm up, but the Squire interrupted her. He said gravely—meditatively—

"It is a pity. Many would consider it a compliment."

The young woman's jaw dropped, in surprise, and she stood gazing at the Squire as if trying to make out just how the remark ought to be taken. But she got no information there—the face remained grave. She was nonplussed; the stream of talk that was about to flow was apparently dammed at its source. She made a futile attempt to start it, then gave it up and said—

"It's four dollars, sir."

The Squire paid her, answered her curtsy with a bow, and she went her way muttering, "A compliment, is it? I wonder would he give thanks to God if *he* was flatthered so?"

She was not in a pleasant humor. She had expected the Squire to make a sort of constructive apology for the hard name and ask her to go on sewing for his daughter; and she had been badly disappointed. She hadn't at bottom cared for that "compliment," for it was rather weak and incompetent compared with some she had paid her husband herself from time to time, and she wished now that she hadn't said anything, but had told her husband to mind his own business and leave her to take care of her own commercial affairs; but it was too late, now; the mischief was done, she had lost an easy and well-paid three days' sewing per week and a gossipy and comfortable time with the Squire's "niggers" thrown in, and nobody's fault but her own. And so, naturally, she put the blame on the Squire, and began to hate him and to approve her husband's hatred of him, and said she would pay him off, one of these days. But at the same time she would put the blame on her husband, too—there could be no sense in wasting opportunities and throwing away God's good gifts. She began on him as soon as he came to supper, that evening.

"He let me go—without a worrd—just the same as dischairged me! And who's to blame? *You*, you Dutch pirate!"

"Ah, now den, Pridget, don't talk like dot. It spoil de supper again; always it spoil de supper when you talk like dot; *I* didn't know you would lose de place."

"You didn't! Didn't you tell me to quit work there? Didn't you?"

"Well, you see, I didn't expect you would do it, and so—"

"Well, I did, and I was a fool, too. And I told him what he called you—*you'd* never have spirit enough—and he said it was a compliment; and it *was*, too."

"Gompliment? *Du lieber Gott!*"

"*Don't* squirt that Dutch loblolly on me, Jake Bleeker, I hate the very sound of it. He said it was a compliment; and if you had even the rags of a man in you, you'd—but law, *you'll* never do anything. You're always talking about the big things you're going to do, but I never see you *do* anny of them, and talking's cheap. A man can call *you* annything he wants to."

"Now you'll see, Pridget, you'll see; you yoost wait till I get a chance—you'll *see!*" and he brought his fist down on the table and made the dishes jump.

"Oh, *shut* up, you make me sick. Look here, have you spoke to old Harrison about raising your wages, which he said he would when he got the Squire's debt paid off?"

"Well, you see, it's like dis. He—"

"So he *hasn't* raised them. What's the raison? *Why* hasn't he?"

"You see, *Vorgestern*—"

"Say it in a Christian tongue, you thingumbob!"

"Well, it was before yesterday he has said he will begin tomorrow; but to-day—well, to-day he has said I can hunt another blace if I want to, he don't raise no wages."

"Another place? there *ain't* anny other place. Jake Bleeker! you don't mean to tell me you took him up? It's just like you, I never saw such a mudhead. *Now* what are we going to do?"

"But Pridget, you go so quick. You don't let me tell you. *I* didn't take him up."

"Oh! All right, then. But it's an accident: it's only because you didn't think of it."

"But Pridget, even if I had thought of it—"

"Oh, don't worry, you weren't in anny danger. *You* think! Oh, dear me, what would you *do* it with?"

"Do it with, Pridget? Why, I—"

"*Don't*. Don't explain; I can't stand your explanations, they fuddle me so. And so we've got to go on hobbling along on sixteen dollars a month again, just the same as ever. And I've lost my sewing! Oh, you're done at last, are you? Then clear out—I want to wash up the dishes."

That talk was in the cabin, by the mill. About the same time, or somewhat later, perhaps, another one was going on in the neighboring house, on the other side of the mill, occupied by the mill's owner. It was between old Mr. Harrison and his son George. The two sat before a hickory fire in the sitting room, a tidy and homelike place, with a rag carpet on the floor, splint chairs, books on a shelf, on the mantelpiece and on the table, tallow candles in polished brass candlesticks; on the table a jug of cider and glasses, a plate of apples and a plate of cracked hickory nuts; on the walls some sufficiently primitive pictures and a humble engraving of Washington.

George was forty-eight years old, as has been already remarked. He was tall, and strongly and symmetrically built; his dress was the common blue jeans, but it was neat and shapely and becoming, and a good fit. The face was refined and intellectual; it had some decision and much kindliness in it, and anyone would concede that it was a face to be trusted.

"Father, is it true that you told Jake to-day that you had changed your mind and—"

"Warn't going to raise his wages? Yes."

The son waited for him to go on, but he didn't.

"But why? He had the promise."

"So he had. On a condition."

"A condition? I didn't know of any."

"I reckon you *did.*"

"I don't call any to mind. I thought it was understood that as soon as the Squire was paid—"

"*That* was the condition."

The son looked puzzled. Then—

"Well, that condition being fulfilled—"

"Which it *isn't!*"

George was startled.

"Why, father, you said you had paid the debt, and got back your note."

"The money turned out to be counterfeit!" and the old man rose and began to stride up and down excitedly.

The son's eyes followed him with an amazed fascination. The

money spurious! How was this? What could be the explanation of it? After a little—

"But father, how—"

"Don't ask me any questions!"

"But—"

"I tell you don't ask me any questions—then you'll be a mighty sight better off."

It was a confession! The son was silent. Here was matter merely for shame, not talk. He bowed his head. The father noticed this attitude, and came near and stood looking down upon him.

"Oh, yes, whine about it—do! *I* don't care, I'd do it again! Wait till *you're* ground down into the earth with trouble and debt and bad luck and everything, and temptation comes along! You wait till then—that's all. Some people can be almighty high-toned and pure and goody-goody and all that, when there's nothing to hinder; you wait—that's all; see how many gilt-edged airs you'll put on *then!*"

"Ah, but father—"

"Don't talk to *me*—I won't hear it. Curse him, he could have passed the counterfeits along; twouldn't have hurt him, and it would have saved me, and he wouldn't do it, and I so old and poor. Oh, I'll get even with him some day, you mark my words. He made me give him a new note payable one day after date and back it up with a mortgage on the mill—"

"This is aw—"

"Shut up and let me talk! Swore he'd jail me for life if I didn't do it. So I've sent it to him. I reckon he thought I'd fetch it myself, the hound—yes, take another dose of his medicine, eat some *more* dirt! Promised he wouldn't tell on me, and said he would burn the bogus money as soon as he got the note and mortgage, but sho!—"

"It was splendidly generous, father! I'm unspeakably thankful. A harder man would have kept that money by him, so that some day in case—"

"*Believe* him, don't you?"

"Certainly I do; his word's gold."

"All right; I wish I had *him* in the same place; if I wouldn't make it sultry for him—"

"I'm glad you haven't; and I'm glad he's got the new note and the mortgage. If I live I'll see to it that—"

"He's paid? Oh, of course—oh, certainly; and you can take it *out* in paying him—hang the copper he'll ever get out of me, and I *told* him so. Said he wouldn't ever crowd me, and I told him to go to hell—"

"Oh—"

"Said he wouldn't ever crowd *you,* and I told him to go to hell again—"

"O, I do think—"

"Think away—think what you like!"

"I'll go and thank him tomorrow, and say—"

"You will, will you? He *hates* you, and said so; and said if you ever spoke to him, even to say God bless you, he'd smash down with the mortgage on the spot. Oh, yes, I *would* go and thank him, by *all* means—I wouldn't lose any time about it—oh, yes, it would be such a noble good thing to see your old father bundled out of house and home before dark. Look here!"

"Well?"

"Promise you'll never speak to him till the day that debt's paid."

"Why, I can't see why I—"

"Promise!"

"But what good—"

"He'll never speak to *you* in the world—he *told* me so; and if you speak to him he'll insult you—he told me *that.* Promise, I tell you!"

"Very well, if nothing else can satisfy you."

"All right. Glad you can be reasonable for once in a while—it's not your habit."

The old man mashed his hat down on his head and went frothing and foaming out of the place. The son got up and walked the floor in miserable distress, thinking bitter thoughts and putting them into muttered and mumbled words.

"He has gone steadily down hill ever since he lost his property; within the week he has made a sudden drop to profanity, but that he would or *could* ever sink to swindling—it was unthinkable!

. . . I could as easily have imagined him telling a lie. There must be something fearfully disintegrating to character in the loss of money. Men suffer other bereavements and keep up; but when they lose their money, straightway the structure which we call character, and are so proud of, and have such placid confidence in, and think is granite, begins to crumble and waste away, and then . . . the granite that had been sand once is sand again! He— why, God bless me, he warned *me!* . . . *Could* debt, and trouble, and loss of people's deference—and the humiliation of it—and impending poverty and want—and the humiliation of *that*—*could* they make me do a dishonorable thing under temptation? It seems impossible—it *is* impossible! No, no, it is preposterous—even grotesquely preposterous. . . . and yet, see what *he* was."

His walk came to a sudden stop. Something had risen in his mind—a memory.

"It must have been as much as fourteen years ago," he muttered; "yet I remember it clearly, although I am not sure that I have thought of it since. He argued with Rev. Mr. Bailey about temptations, and said a character that hadn't been exposed to them and solidified by fighting them and *losing* the fight was a flabby poor thing and couldn't be depended on in an emergency. He said a temptation successfully resisted was good, but a fall was better. He said he wouldn't go so far as to put temptations in the way of a child of his, but had always been willing to see them come; and said a person wouldn't ever be safe until he had been tried and had *fallen.* Mr. Bailey was amazed; and grieved, too; and said the wisest men of all lands and ages had taught that the only safe way was to flee temptation, shun it, avoid it, keep out of its way; and that they were right. Ah, I would God my father had laid that lesson to heart! Then this miserable business would not have happened."

His thoughts drifted to another detail, and his face flushed. "And so Walter Fairfax hates me, and said so. I wonder at his *saying* so. It is not like his dignity. Still, he was hot-tempered in bygone times, and father could have provoked it out of him—he would be competent for that in these strange latter times. . . . Well, there is not much love lost; although I always wanted to like him I never could and never did; even at school he couldn't seem to forget that his family was 'quality.' And now—ah, well, *now* he wouldn't wipe his aristocratic boots on a Harrison! . . . *Come in!* In this time of trouble I suppose a thoughtful Providence has sent me that intolerable Paul Pry. *Come in!* Of course I've got to open the door, or he'll knock there till he *hears* himself do it."

Dug Hapgood entered. He was twenty-five years old, but had no beard—at least not the letter but only the spirit of it: a silky faint yellowish fuzz which was not visible in all lights. His complexion was fresh and rosy; he was five feet ten and sturdily and compactly built; he had smart bright eyes that were full of friendliness and interest and good-humored zeal; on his head and down over his ears was crowded a partly bald dog-skin cap; around his neck was wound a red yarn comforter whose tasseled ends hung down his back; on his hands were red yarn mittens; his overcoat hung down to the middle of his boot-leg, had bone buttons of great size, and was made of coarse white blanketing and had a very broad and conspicuous green stripe running round its skirts low down.

He had had scarlet fever when he was a boy, and it had injured his ear-machinery; the defect had increased with the years until at last he couldn't hear himself talk, and didn't believe anybody else could. His people were all dead; he lived by odd jobs, which were infrequent and he did not regret it; he was a sociable animal, and knew everybody, including the "niggers," and everybody knew him.

He came in stamping and flapping, pulling off his mitts, unwinding his comforter, tugging off his cap—which released his spiky hair and gave it a chance to stand up and stretch its legs, and it looked grateful for that—and lifted up a stupendous voice and shouted—

"Snowing like Sam Hill!" Stepped a stride nearer his host, put up his big hands trumpet-fashion, and thundered, "I said it's snowing like Sam *Hill!*"

"Yes, *I* heard you. Don't yell so."

"*Hey?*"

"I *heard* you."

"Oh, you did!" He sat down and spread his legs and hands before the fire. "It's awful comfortable here." Then louder—"I said it's awful *comfortable* here—*hey?*"

"I didn't say anything."

"Louder, George, I'm a little hard of hearing, lately."

"I said—I—didn't—*say*—anything."

Dug began to help himself to the eatables. Sipping cider and munching an apple, he went cheerfully on with his whoopings and shoutings.

"Say! Where's the gov'ner?"

"Just gone out. Gone to bed I reckon; he is not very well, these days."

This was repeated, and Dug got it.

"Say! What's up, George? I've just come from Jake Bleeker's. Stopped in, a minute, to see how things are going, there."

"Very kind of you. And customary."

"*Hey?*"

"Very *kind* of you!"

"*Oh*—that's all right. I don't mind it, I *like* it. I got plenty time. Say! the gov'ner didn't raise his wages. Had the promise, you know, when the Squire's paid off. Well, he *got* paid. What's the hitch?"

George yelled coldly—

"That's my father's affair." (Repeated.)

"Oh—just so. And the Squire's got a *new* note—to-day; and a mortgage. How does that come?"

"What is that to you? And what the devil do *you* know about it?" shrieked George, angrily.

Dug yelled in his most friendly and placating and soothing tone—

"Oh, that's all right, George. The gov'ner and the lawyer sent the things to the Squire by the old auction-bell nigger and gave him a quarter, and I run across him; and it happened that the Squire's was on my road, so I offered to do the delivery for nothing; but the nigger couldn't tell me what was done up in the red tape; so as I went along I reckoned there wasn't any hurry, and set down to rest at the blacksmith shop and undone the tape—"

"You meddling scoundrel!"

"Who? Me? Why, George, where's the harm?—you know it's perfectly safe with me."

"Safe with *you*—the idea! You've told a hundred people, and you know it."

"Why George, I haven't done any such thing; and *you* oughtn't to talk to an orphan like that, that hasn't got any relations left in the world, even distant ones, except himself; and as for—"

"Oh, stuff! every time you do a piece of calamitous stupidity you think it's sufficient palliation that you are an *orphan*. Great guns! you're enough to drive a man—look here, how many people *did* you tell?"

"George, I can lay my hand on my heart and give you my word of honor that I never told a soul but Rube Haskins, and Ben Thurlow, and the Bleekers, and Burt Higgins, and—"

"The *blacksmith!* Burt Higgins! Oh, my goodness, why didn't you tell him *first,* and save yourself the trouble of telling the rest of the human race?"

"It wasn't any trouble, George, I only done it because—"

"Oh, never mind, let it go—it's a curs̀ed world we live in, and a person's got to stand it. Look here, I thought the Squire told you a while ago that if you came yelling gossip around his house any more he'd break your back; how did you dare to venture there again?"

Dug roared out, with dignity—

"It was my duty, George. I *had* to take him the papers, hadn't I? Of course. A person that hasn't got any principles won't take any risks; but a person that has, has *got* to. *He* can't shirk, he knows the All-seeing Eye is upon him. And then—" He looked cautiously around the room, as if to note if there were any possible listeners, then leaned far over and thundered into George's ear, "Say! he's *drinking* again!"

"No!"

"Yes!"

"Ah, that is pitiful—that is too pitiful. I hope it isn't so."

"*Hey?*"

"I—hope—it isn't—*so!*"

"Oh! Well, but it is. Not much, but a little—and *regular.*" He took another cautious look around the room, then bent over and screamed, "Don't let it go any further, but it's true. I *know* it. I smelt his breath. And you know, he was irritable—I noticed that. He said something, and I said *hey?* and he said something again, and I said *hey,* and he said something again, and I said *hey* again, and then he appeared to lose his tranquillity, as you may say, and put his mouth close and raised on his tip-toes and said 'If you say *hey* again I'll *strangle* you.' His very words. Yes, sir, he's been drinking; and it affects his serenity. You can *see* it. I offered to sit down, and he gave me that kind of a glance, you know, and that little wag of the head that you give a nigger when you're ready for him to go, so I thought I wouldn't sit down then, but wait till he might change his mind; and then I started to ask him how it come that he got paid the other day and now here was this new note— but you know that big cane he carries?—*cane* he calls it, *club* I call it—you could knock a bull down with it—well, it was laying on a chair—this was in the back room, ground floor, where he has his desk, you know—and he begun to edge towards it and his fingers begun to work, and so I didn't wait but promised to call again. Oh, yes, he's been drinking, George, I've got other evidence. He's been —at it—three—*weeks*—do you *hear?*"

"Oh, impossible!"

"You listen. As I was coming away, as luck would have it I saw one of the niggers striking up back towards the fields, and I struck out after him. I let him get about a quarter of a mile from anywheres, then I closed up on him. It was young Ben—not a very smart Aleck, for a house servant—not one of the kind that sets the river afire, you know—and I got at the particulars. He didn't want to tell, but I hung on, and at last I milked him. George!"

"Well?"

"He was mournful and melancholy all the year, but he kept the cheerfulest outside he could for Helen's sake, and stayed by her like a mother, and put in the bulk of his time diverting her mind and shoring up her spirits—oh, he's a *man*, George, these people don't know him, but *I* do, because I know his niggers—but here lately he has got his reward all of a sudden and she's as happy as a bird; and now it's all the other way, and she's putting in all her time, nearly, trying to keep *him* up; but you see, the minute she was happy and his job off his hands, he begun to get melancholy again, and then melancholier, and at last I reckon he thought he would take just one little drop—dangerous, after going dry twenty years, George—and he was a *goner!* He's been at it three weeks, George. Not heavy, but regular—and *increasing;* that's the worst of it. And do you know how he kept it dark from everybody? Did it all after ten at night—up stairs in his room, Helen [5] and the niggers all in bed, away back in the other end of the house. Next day, cloves and coffee-grains, and the other breath-extinguishers."

"It is pitiful; it's too pitiful for anything."

"If he hadn't lost his wife—"

"Yes, I know. He worshiped her, and she deserved it. Anything she wanted him to do, it was no trouble for him to do it, but a pleasure. I've been told it by Gilbert and the doctor. They said she only had to ask him, on the marriage day, to stop drinking and learn to master his temper, and she never had to mention it to him again. They said she was his moral stay and support."

"Just revolutionized him, George! *My,* but he was a fighter, they say! Give him a toddy, and start his temper, and furnish him a subject, and *land,* but he would make the fur fly! That's what they say. It *is* a pity, George."

"Oh, yes, it's an unspeakable pity. Poor Helen!"

"She don't know it, George, good luck! Nobody knows it but the niggers, and they'd lie about it—the same as Ben did with me. Swore it wasn't so; and stuck to it as long as he could. Say, George, I hear it's four days since you've been out of the house; but you're looking all right. Not sick?"

"No," and George colored slightly. "I haven't seemed to feel like it. I haven't had a holiday for a good while, and this is good weather for one. I think I shall stay in a few days longer, and smoke and read and rest up."

"You couldn't do a better thing, George. Hearing the talk that's around wouldn't do you any good; I don't listen, myself, half the

---

[5] He at first wrote "Sadie" as the name of the squire's daughter, then changed the name to "Helen." On page 54 of the holograph he began writing the latter name as the original form and continued to use it.

time. You lay low, and be comfortable, and let this thing blow over
—that's my advice, and I reckon you know me for a friend. Well, I
must be going, but I'll look in from time to time." He was getting
into his things, now, and there was peace for a pair of minutes, for
he had sunk his teeth into the last apple, and couldn't yell. He
started toward the door but turned back and shouted, "Say—Tom's
back!" Harrison started. "You warn't expecting him, I know; but
he's back. Got back safternoon late and is making his report to old
Gilbert; one of Gilbert's niggers told me. Good-bye—so-long—any
time you want me, send for me, George."

He passed out into the wheezing storm, and left a sore-hearted
man behind him.

Harrison chunked the fire and sat down before it with a tired
and dejected air.

"Poor Dug, he never means any harm, and so he goes on doing it
all day long. He doesn't know what trouble is, and yet goes
distributing it around, all his waking hours. *Send* for him when I
want him! If anything could make me smile, that would. There
was a time when I loved to hear his mill go, but every remark he
makes seems to bite like a fang, now, and squirt poison. Dear me,
why didn't the Squire quiet him with the club when he had the
idea? . . . Drinking again! what a pity that poor woman died.
Everybody will know, now. It's Dug's secret—consequently the
world's."

After a pause: "And so my Tom's back. I'd rather see his face
than anything in this world, but it will be a pain, too; for he knows,
by this time, that the splendid news I sent him about the debt was
false—Dug's diligence has made that certain. He thought he was
coming back to a house of joy, a house that was holding its head up
again, a proud house—and that is all spoiled, spoiled, spoiled! Lord,
it's bitter hard! Of course he came with *his* head in the clouds, too,
poor boy, and now he knows we are down in the dirt again, and the
whole town talking! I don't know how I am to look him in the face;
I don't know how to say any comforting thing, any hopeful thing—
we are down on our backs! he will want to know what it all means,
he is entitled to know, and what am I going to say? I can't explain
—we have to leave him in the dark,—he were better dead than to

know that crime! . . . I ought to be impatient to see him, and I am; and yet if he didn't get through with Gilbert till midnight, God knows I could endure to wait! Ah, what *am* I going to say to him!"

He did not need to be so troubled about Tom, but he did not know that. If he had a secret, Tom also had one, and it was one of a pleasant sort. It is a matter of small interest to us; we need not enlarge upon it; an outline of it will answer our purpose. In the previous year Helen Fairfax had engaged herself to Tom, but a misunderstanding had broken off the match; Tom was the party in fault, but he could not bring himself to acknowledge it—nor, in fact, believe it. At his time of life one gets a kind of melancholy pleasure out of pouting over an imaginary wrong, and for long he indulged himself with this romatic pain; but that was while the wronger was in sight. His three months' absence in New Orleans on Mr. Gilbert's business took the pride out of him and he wrote and made confession and asked forgiveness. Helen answered promptly, and to his full content, and her letter reached him just as he was starting home.

CHAPTER II.

I T W A S on the third of November that old Mr. Harrison had been charged with fraud in the Squire's study and been required to furnish a new note; that the Squire's interview with Bridget Bleeker had taken place in the same room, and afterward Dug's delivery to the Squire of Harrison's new note. It was still on the same date that Bridget and her Jake had discussed the Squire's compliment; that old Mr. Harrison had indirectly confessed his criminal conduct to George; that Dug had revealed to George the fact that the Squire was drinking again; also that Tom was back. A pretty full bill for a day, yet the record is not finished yet.

Toward eight in the evening Helen's mulatto maid, Emly, appeared in the kitchen greatly impressed, and reported that she hadn't had such a job of combing and brushing and dressing-up and decorating her young mistress since she could remember. What could the meaning of it be?

"Liza, if she's tried on one gown, I'm blamed if she hain't tried on fourteen; en dey don't none of 'em suit her. Dey's sum'n de matter; dey's sum'n de matter, shore; she hain't ever acted like dat befo'. Allays I say, 'What you gwyne to put on to-day, Miss Helen?' en allays she 'spon, 'Any'll do, don't make no diffence.' Allays I say, 'Which julery, Miss Helen?' en mostly she say, 'don't want none.' Allays I start to 'vestigate some mo' 'bout de 'rangements, en gen'ally she say, 'Oh, jist dress me de way you want to'; but to-night, my lan'! Why, dey ain't *noth'n* good enough. Dis one's too red, dat one's too blue, 'tother one's too yaller, en none of 'em don't suit her complexion no mo'; en look at all dem silks en satins en velvets en one thing er another jist fitten for de queen to wah, en blame my cats dey ain't none of 'em *fine* enough. En it's all so owdacious *sudden*—dat's what bangs *me*, Liza."

"Why, it's awful, Emly; her pa ought to know 'bout dis, so he kin sen' for de doctor befo' it's too late. What *do* you reckon's de matter, chile?"

"Goodness knows—*I* don't. If I've got her 'ranged once, I've got her 'ranged nine times, I do b'lieve; en every time she can't hold still no how till I jam in de las' hairpin, but 'way she goes a hoppin' en a skippin' to de lookin' glass, en tucks her head down so —en den roun' so—en den roun' tother way—en her cheeks a burnin' en her eyes a sparklin' all de time, en my, she *do* look pooty! en den she pulls all de roses out en sticks 'em in again en takes another look, en next she jerks 'm all out en thows 'm down en s'lecks some mo'—"

"Yes," interrupted Jasper, the gardener, "en she's done robbed de greenhouse till it look like one er dese-yer cyclones—"

—"en every little while she reach 'roun' en haul her gown aroun' den kick it outen de way en march off fum de glass a lookin' back over her shoulder for to notice de effecks; en right away she ain't no mo' satisfied dan she was in de fust place, en sho' 'nough I got to pull her all down again en buil' her up a diffunt way; en trouble enough it is, too, for she can't no more hold still dan if she was on sum'n hot; but 'course *I* ain't a mindin', becase somehow she *do* suttenly come out mo' lovelier every time, I got to 'nowledge *dat*, anyway. En den—"

"Emly," interjected old Liza, with apprehension in her tones and a quiver in her voice, "I has nuss'd dat chile fum de day she was bawn, en dey put her in my arms en her mother say to me, 'Liza, if anything ever happens to me—'" She broke down and sobbed, and all the black company joined in and sobbed, too, with the ready sympathy of that lovable race. Liza rose, now, wiping her eyes with her check apron, and said, moving toward the door, "I's gwyne to her; I's gwyne to comfort her. Her mother's a lookin' down on me dis minute outen de skies, en she know' ole Liza ain't gwyne desert de chile. Dey's sum'n de matter wid her *mind*, dey sholy is, I know it by de way she act. I's gwyne to ast her to lemme sen' for de doctor, dey ain't noth'n *he* can't k'yore—"

Chorus of "Dat's it! dat's de very thing!"

"Yes, I's gwyne to ast her to lemme. He'll take 'n give her some er his truck dat'll soothe her down, en take it outen her—whatever 'tis—en in de mawnin' it's gone, en she won't ever know dey's anything de matter wid her."

When she reached Helen's dressing room it was vacant. A glance at the wreckage strewn about this place which before had always been so trim and orderly, gave her a turn which made her old legs tremble under her, and confirmed all her fears: certainly something was the matter with the girl. She moved, troubled and anxious, through the bedchamber, and stopped suddenly in its open door, with her eyes fixed and her heart standing still. For before her sat her young mistress with her face bowed in her hands, sobbing. The black woman tottered forward and gathered her to her breast and began to pour forth her distress.

"O, my Gawd, honey, what *is* de matter, what is happen' to my darlin'? Tell yo' ole Lize, honey, her heart's a breakin' for you. Lemme sen' for de doctor, den you git well, chile, you git well right away."

The girl lay contentedly in her arms, smiling up through moist eyes, and said—

"The matter with me? Oh, I'm so happy I can't *endure* it!"

Liza was frightened.

"What—en *cryin'* 'bout it?"

"Yes—it's that kind, you know. I've been on such a strain for two days and nights, mammy; and I had worn out all the other ways of expressing joy, and there was nothing left but to cry."

"Goodness knows it's a funny way, but if dey ain't no mistake en you's dead certain you's happy—"

"Happy? Look at my face!"

It was a convincing witness; none could doubt its testimony.

"You mos' sholy is, honey—I kin see it. Thank Gawd for it; I's satisfied; I don't want no better news 'n dat. En I was a huggin' you for to comfort you!"

"But now—"

"Oh I's huggin' you now 'caze I's so glad. You ain't been happy sence sich a long time; en when Emly come down a minute ago a talkin' de way she done, we was dat scairt! So I says I's gwyne straight up en find out what's de trouble, en sen' for de doctor."

"But you don't *ask* what is the trouble, you dear old aggravating thing! Why don't you ask? Haven't I as good as *asked* you to ask, a dozen times? Can't you see that I'm dying to tell?"

"Why, bless yo' soul, honey, *I* didn't know. How was *I* to know? You see—"

"*Ask!*"

"Well, what *is* de trouble, if—"

The girl pulled the old head down and whispered.

"My goodness gracious sakes alive, Miss Helen!"

"It's true, mammy. I shan't need the doctor, think?"

"Doctor!" and she broke into the free-hearted African laugh; "thanks to goodness, dey ain't no doctor kin k'yore *dat* complaint!"

"Remember, it's a secret for the present, but you can tell the servants by and by when—well, I'll tell you when."

"Miss Helen, I's gwyne to hold in if I bust."

"I know it isn't going to be easy."

" 'Deed it ain't, honey; it's de bigges' secret was ever stuffed into me sence I was bawn. Fust-hands, too—even befo' ole marster. But you kin pen' 'pon me, honey; I's gwyne to hold in if I bust."

"They suspect something down stairs, don't they?"

"Oh, bless yo' soul, yes! Dey 'magines. . . . dey 'magines. . . ."
A laugh was trying to get a chance. She stopped and waited until it
had emptied itself, then got out the fact that the servants supposed
her mind was affected, and that they were much alarmed in consequence.

"You must go down and tell them it's all a mistake, nothing's the
matter; invent something that'll satisfy them, and . . . 'sh! it's a
footstep—fly!"

Tom, trim and fine in New Orleans clothes, entered, closed the
door behind him and stood, drunk with the vision before him; but
only for a moment, then Helen was in his arms and his kisses on
her lips.

This is getting private; let us skip half an hour. The couple are
seated on a short sofa in front of the fire, now, the head of one of
the pair on the breast of the other, and the talk is proceeding. The
hysterical stage is already safely passed, the planning stage is
arriving.

"Helen, what do you think! We shan't have to wait till I get
started in business."

"Why, Tom?"

"Because I'm already started."

"Oh, tell me all about it!"

"I'm Mr. Gilbert's partner—it happened to-day. Mainly, it's my
reward for my New Orleans success. I was hoping, but not
expecting—it was a splendid surprise. I can help my people, now;
their troubles are ended."

"It's perfectly lovely, Tom. Go on—I'm listening."

"It's a secret, yet. Nobody knows it but you and Mr. Gilbert, and
I asked him to keep it quiet. Day after tomorrow I appear in court
in all my new grandeur, to represent the firm of Gilbert and
Harrison, Attorneys and Counselors at Law, for the first time. How
does that sound, dear?"

"Why, it's poetry, Tom! Say it again."

"Gilbert and Harrison, Attorneys and Counselors at Law. And
Mr. Gilbert is going to manage so that my father and grandfather

shall be there, on some pretext or other, and it will be a paralyzing surprise for them when the clerk calls the firm and I rise up."

"O, I wish I could be there!"

"I wish so too, dear-heart. I think they'll want to shout for joy and pride. It will strain me to keep the secret when I go home, presently, but I mean to do it or die. What are you laughing at?"

"Because it's almost what Liza said. But you mustn't die, you must do as she is going to do."

"What is that?"

"Bust. That is, if she can't hold in she's going to bust. That's what she says."

Then the incident was related, and the pair had a cackling and silly and care-free and charming time over it. They were so young, and youth is so beautiful, and they couldn't know that there was any trouble hanging over them. They wouldn't have known how to believe it. Not at *their* time of life.

Then Tom thought of another surprise. Instead of telling his father to-night of the renewal of his engagement, he would save that also for day after tomorrow; he would spring it on the heels of the first surprise and get large effects out of it. It was agreed that this was a good idea.

"You know, Helen," said Tom, "it is just the lucky time for these surprises. There's a mystery somewhere; something has been going wrong, I don't know the explanation of it; but there was an old debt due your father from my grandfather, and it was paid the other day, and for some reason or other the consummation wasn't perfect, and by the town gossip I learned that a new note was made to-day and secured by a mortgage on the mill. Of course my people are in trouble, now—oh, yes, it's cloudy weather at home, I know it —but if I can hold in till day after tomorrow! Helen, it's a romance! it's good to be alive and in it. I'll sit and listen to them worry, and they'll wonder how I can be so calm—"

"Tom, you'll never be able."

"O, yes I shall. I'll keep day after tomorrow steadily in mind. The more worry the finer the effects when the sunburst comes. Your father won't tell about the re-engagement, will he?"

"No, it isn't his way. He will rejoice with us, as he did before; but not with the public—he left that to us before."

Meantime Stevens, the doctor, had dropped in, down stairs, to warm himself, and had found the Squire looking troubled. He didn't ask the Squire what was troubling him—it was not the custom—and the Squire did not volunteer an explanation: that was not *his* custom. Two things were disquieting him: Andrew Harrison had *sent* the new note instead of bringing it himself—therefore he had not been able to give him back the false money; also, he was disturbed by the strange light which he had noticed in Harrison's eyes. Presently he brought the talk around to the Harrisons, in a general way, and the doctor said—

"Speaking of the Harrisons, Squire, I will tell you, confidentially, that the old man's mind is affected by his troubles." He was reaching for a fire-coal for his pipe, and did not notice the start the Squire gave. "Nobody knows it, not even George, but it's so, I know it. In my opinion he hasn't been responsible for his actions here lately. And to-day—well, to-day he has developed an entirely new thing, for a Harrison—*lying*."

"Lying?"

"Yes. Of course I wouldn't state this publicly, but I know it to be so. It's his troubles, poor old fellow; and if they are not relieved before long he will be worse."

The Squire moved uneasily in his chair, and changed the subject. The doctor soon perceived that he was absent-minded and not giving heed to the talk; so he took himself away. The Squire sat troubled and brooding. The counterfeit-money swindle, then, was the act of an irresponsible man, and was not criminal. If he could have known this earlier! "It is his troubles that are wrecking him—well, and I have *my* share in them. He must have his new note back at once, and the false money. I will carry them myself—and *now*." After some further musing: "No—I must have a private and undisturbed talk with him, and get all his confidence, and wholly undo my part of this work—promise to stand by him and see him through; and *convince* him. He must come here. I will send him the note and mortgage, canceled, and say I have something *for* him —he will understand it is the false money, and he will come."

He canceled the note and mortgage, then went musing up and down the room with the papers in his hand. He was interrupted by a knock, and Liza entered, her face beaming with the pleasantness of her secret and with the happy surprise in store for the master, and said young missis was waiting to kiss him good-night.

"Why, is it so late as that?"

" 'Deed it is, Marse Walter. Ten o'clock."

"So it is. Send up my hot water."

When he arrived in Helen's parlor he found the pair standing in the middle of the floor, and holding hands. There was something expectant in the attitude.

"Dear me!" said the Squire, astonished. "Is it you, Tom? What's all this?"

"Guess," said Helen, joyously.

"I don't need to, dear; it guesses itself."

"Are you satisfied, papa?"

"Take my blessing—both! And a kiss for you, and a hand-shake for Tom." Then to himself, "This helps me undo my share of that work—in fact obliterates it! it comes at a lucky time."

He lingered a while, finding the talk and the society very agreeable; then he noticed the papers in his hand and said to his daughter—

"Here is some property of yours; what shall be done with it?"

Helen took the papers, noticed that they were canceled, and said—

"That is very nice of you, papa. What is mine is Tom's, now," and she passed the papers along.

"Another jolly surprise for Wednesday," said Tom; "it's going to be a grand day, and nobly theatrical!"

The Squire inquired, and got the program of surprises. He was disappointed; he had wanted his share of the undoing of "that work" to begin to-night. But he said nothing, not wishing to spoil the young people's scheme of dramatics. However, here was his opportunity to send for Andrew Harrison, at any rate, and return to him the false money; so, in taking his leave he said to Tom—

"Ask your grandfather to come and see me—and tell him I've got something for him."

But Tom was in too excited a condition, and too anxious to be obliging to this house, to wait and hear the whole remark, but broke into the middle of it to say with fervor that he should "be so glad," and so he didn't hear the important and suggestive and significant half of it at all. That was unfortunate.

It was difficult for Tom to get away, but Helen got him started at last—about eleven or a little later.

CHAPTER III.

H E REACHED home frozen without but glowing within, and found his father waiting up for him. There was a surprise for Tom, who was doing so large a trade in that commerce just now; but it was a surprise with a sharp pang in it. Could this haggard man be his father! How could a strong man, a cheery man, be pulled down and saddened to this degree in so short a while? And could mere financial worry do this? It seemed impossible; but then he didn't know his father's bottom secret; he didn't know that disgrace was hanging over the house.

Tom's letters had shown that he was proud of the success he was achieving in New Orleans, and that he was coming home feeling the exultation which conquerors feel, therefore it grieved his father to have to blight all this, and he did his best to make a cheerful face and not spoil the lad's home-coming in its first moments. He made a pathetic effort to be gay, and hearty, and cordially praiseful of Tom's little triumphs abroad—and overdid it; and broke down in the midst, and leaned his head in his arms on the table and sobbed.

It wrung Tom's heart to see it; and he laid his hand caressingly on his father's shoulder, and begged him not to grieve so, (and could hardly keep his struggling secrets in his breast), and added—

"You are trying to save me sorrow, father, and you mustn't, and you needn't—I know all."

Harrison's face came up white with consternation.

"*All?*" he gasped. "*What* do you know?"

Tom was astonished, and said wonderingly—

"Why, that there was a hitch somewhere and the old debt is on, again."

"Oh," ejaculated his father, in a tone that was eloquent of relief. Tom noticed that tone, and was puzzled by it—not much, still, enough to move him to ask casually—

"Why, father, is there something more?"

The result astonished him again—

"*More?*" exclaimed his father with a heat and energy which seemed to Tom quite out of proportion to the occasion, "*More? No!* Of course not! *Why* should there be more? What put that into your head? More? *Why* should there be more?

Tom was bewildered; he hardly knew what to say; it hardly seemed safe to say anything at all. Since a couple of quite innocent remarks had touched off a pair of such explosions as these, his father must surely be honeycombed with mines, and dangerous from all points of approach. He presently ventured to say, sooth-ingly—

"Father, you are not well; you are not your natural self. These money troubles have harassed you to this, and you mustn't worry about them so—everything is going to come right, I'm sure of it," and he took his father's hand and began to pet it and fondle it. "*I'm* not worrying, and you mustn't. I am at your side again, I am young, I am getting a start, I am going to be a help—you'll see."

Harrison raised a grateful look to his son's face, and said—

"It lifts me up to hear you say that—keep that spirit and stand by me, Tom. For these are black days—awful days—"

"Cheer up, the clouds may pass at any moment, father." Then to himself, "if he only knew what I know!"

"No, Tom, the clouds will not pass soon; there is no hope of that. You know, we don't stand to-day where we stood yesterday, and long before. This new note is collectable at *a day's notice*—and why is it made like that? Because the Squire has turned against us, and means us harm, Tom. That blow can fall at any moment; and it means ruin. He hates me—I did not suspect that; I didn't, really."

"Hates you? Oh, come!"

"It's true. He told your grandfather so to-day."

"*Told* him so? Are you sure? It isn't like him to *say* his feelings, it's only his habit to *have* them."

"Yes, I know; but this time he said them."

A light seemed to break, in Tom's head. His re-engagement to Helen had modified the Squire's feelings, and he wanted to see Andrew Harrison and take that hard word back.

"Father," he said, "that reminds me of something. When I was done work to-day—" He colored, and altered the remark a little: "When I was through with all I had to do, I mean, I happened to meet the Squire, and he told me to tell grandfather he would like to see him, and would he please call around."

"What!"

"Yes. I shall be gone to work before he gets up. Will you tell him for me?"

"What does he want to *see* him for?"

"He didn't say."

"Hm." Harrison's fears began to rise. He worded them to himself, thus: "What can he want to see him for? It has a bad look. He means to give him notice that the note must be met at once!" The thought made him shudder. He said, with a sigh—

"I will tell your grandfather."

"Why do you sigh, father?"

"Oh, well, we're in the ditch. I know what he wants to see him for. He wants to tell him he must settle that note in twenty-four hours, or he will foreclose and sell the mill. Nothing can save us, Tom. It's a little thing, that scrap of paper, that note; but it weighs a ton on my heart."

The note burnt Tom's pocket. His fingers itched to take it out, and show the cancellation, and—

"Tom?"

The interruption brought him to himself, and he left the note where it was. And that was a pity.

"Sir?"

"Whatever happens, my boy, let us keep our honor whole. We *will*, Tom—*won't* we?" He said it pleadingly, anxiously.

"Indeed, yes."

"We'll let *no* temptation beguile us from that, Tom. That is understood between us?"

"Why, certainly, father. What temptation *could* do it? What has turned you into this strange mood?"

The father was silent in thought for a while, then he said—

"Ah, well, I don't know—I don't know. I have been thinking over the things which strong, fine men have done, under the blight of money-difficulties, and I have wondered—" He stopped, and turned a glassy gaze upon his son. "Tom, what should you say if you found that the most honorable man you ever knew, and the firmest and sternest in his principles, had been caught cheating? What should you say to that?"

Tom was bewildered again. What *could* be carrying his father off into such strange by-paths?

"Why, I don't know. It does not seem to me that it could happen."

"Tom, it *has* happened! I know of an in—I mean, I know of a dozen instances. It makes a man feel as if the foundations of things were falling out. But Tom, they were not educated men! It palliates it, Tom; it palliates it, *doesn't* it? it even excuses it—*doesn't* it? Don't you think it does?"

His burning eyes were fixed upon Tom's face, eager, wistful, almost as if life and death depended upon the answer. Tom replied, confusedly—

"I—well, yes—I suppose that it—"

"But *we* have no such excuse, Tom—remember it—*remember* it! My father educated me; I have educated you. We have the support of training, teaching, admonition—puissant safeguards that some have lacked, poor souls. *Nothing* could excuse us, Tom. Oh, no, nothing—*nothing*. For myself I am not afraid, Tom, let come what may; and you—Tom, you will never disgrace your training?—*say* it, Tom."

"Why, father, I don't believe I ever could—I cannot imagine such a thing."

"Thank God—it's all I want. I am satisfied. Keep to it. These are awful times. Watch yourself—*watch* yourself. I have seen things—

when men were in money-troubles—things which—which—" He rose and went fumbling his way toward the door like one in a daze; then turned and put out his hand in good-night salutation. "Ah, let *nothing* tempt us, Tom; let us watch ourselves—oh, every hour, every minute!"

He passed out, with his candle in his hand, and Tom dropped into a chair, with his brain spinning.

"It's all dark," he said to himself, "I can't understand it. Somebody has committed a crime under strong temptation—somebody whom ruin was threatening—somebody of whom such an act was not to be expected—and it has frightened him, and he doesn't know who will fall next. He generalizes it, and makes a dozen out of it, but I reckon it's an individual, and recent. Does he know the man personally? No—or he would have named him. He has read about it or heard about it, and in his distressed condition it has taken hold of his nerves. And what an irrational fright it is—he thinks *I'm* going to fall! Why next, if this goes on, he'll be getting afraid on his *own* account, if he doesn't look out!"

He went off to bed, still cogitating, but he could not get to sleep, for the muffled sound of a footstep kept coming to his ear, and he knew who was walking the floor. Thoughts of his father's misery haunted him, accused him, and would not down; would not even allow him to think of Helen. The burden of these thoughts was a persistent and pleading reproach: how can you be so cruel? how can you be so selfish? he is enduring a year's suffering in a day, and you could stop it in a moment; you could stop it in a moment, and yet to satisfy a foolish and theatrical vanity, you meanly leave him in his misery! even *one* of your so treasured vanities could heal his heart and make it sing, and you miserly withhold it; give him the canceled papers!

Human nature cannot stand everything, and Tom surrendered at last. It was now three in the morning. He listened—the floor-walking had ceased. A pity! why hadn't his conversion come a little sooner! Remorsefully he took the papers and went and listened at his father's door—hoping. But there was no sound; sleep, the compassionate, was come. Tom went back eased in mind, for he had a plan for the tranquilizing of his conscience. When he went down to his breakfast in the morning, he was prepared to carry it out. He laid the papers by his father's plate, when his meal was finished, and left them there. But they did not stay. When Martha, the old colored cook, came in by and by to arrange for the two other breakfasts she took them up and inspected them, and said—

"I wonder what dem is?"

She carried them to the window to get a better light, but she was interrupted; a log rolled down from the fire, scattering coals, and she ran to set the matter right, laying the papers on the mantel-piece, which was the first place that came handy. They were out of her mind, now, and remained out.

Toward ten o'clock old Martha gave up waiting for George Harrison to come down to breakfast—something must be the matter, she thought—and went up and called him. He said he wanted no breakfast, and should not get up; he was tired, and not well.

" 'Deed you look it, Marse George; I hain't ever seen you lookin' so dreadful. Does you want de doctor?"

"No, Martha, I only want rest—rest—rest. You've felt like that, Martha?"

"O, yes indeedy, Marse George—many's de time. But niggers is more used to it 'n what white folks is. Better lemme fetch you up sump'n, Marse George; might do you good."

"No, I don't care for it, Martha. Ask my father to come up; I've got a message for him."

"O, he done gone to town, long 'go, Marse George."

"Why—is it so late?"

"Ten o'clock, Marse George; you's overslep' considerable, dis mornin'."

"Well, If I had seen him—But it's no matter; tell him when he comes in."

"Yes, seh."

When she was gone, he said to himself: "Maybe it gives us another day. But what is another day? Better to have it over and done with, maybe. I half wish I had gotten the word to him."

At two in the afternoon a gossiping pair of groups was present at the blacksmith shop. They were gathered in circles around a couple of wagon tyres that lay on the ground undergoing the process of being made red-hot under blazing heaps of chips and shavings; and while these men held out their hands over the grateful warmth they entertained themselves with chaffing and teasing Jake Bleeker over Squire Fairfax's characterization of him as an over-sentimental German jackass. His wife's reproaches and sarcasms of the night before over the same matter were still scorching him; and now, in an access of indiscretion brought on by these new torments, he forgot himself and swore roundly that he was going to settle with the Squire the first time he caught sight of him. This was received with vast hilarity; and just at that unlucky moment the Squire hove in sight, riding out from town. Poor Bleeker paled, but he had said the word—there was no way out of the difficulty. Taunts broke out, all around:

"There he comes, now, Bleeker!"

"*Now* let's see you do it!"

"You *talk* big, Jakey, what're you going to *do!*"

"I'm going to insult him—*that's* what I'm going to do!"

This brought a burst of laughter.—

The Squire was slowly approaching.

"Oh, you are, are you? Then why don't you start along—who's a-hendering you?"

"I *told* you what I will do, didn't I?"

Jake started toward the road. The crowd were astonished, and stopped laughing. Jake moved steadily forward.

"Boys, do you believe he will?"

"Blamed if it don't look like it."

"Well, then," said Burt Higgins, the blacksmith, "all I've got to say, is, we've carried this thing too far."

"Right you are," said Park Robinson; "but *I* didn't believe he—"

"Why, nobody *could* believe he would," said a chorus of voices.

The men were sorry; they hadn't wanted their joke to go this length—at least they thought, now, that they hadn't.

"Look—he's put up his hand."

"Yes, and the Squire has stopped."

They saw the German range up and apparently begin to speak. Apparently there was a reply. Then they saw the German step close and look up in the Squire's face and apparently speak again. Straightway they saw the Squire reach down and collar him and begin to fiercely lay his cowhide over his head and shoulders. Six sounding blows were struck, then the German broke away and came flying back to the witnesses, and the Squire rode slowly off, homeward.

The men crowded around poor Bleeker, who was sobbing, and wiping his eyes on his sleeve, and pouring out threats against the Squire in fervid English mixed with German words and phrases.

"What did you do, Jake? what did you say?"

"You never mind, *he* knows what I said, and *I'll* fix him for this, and I *told* him so—you'll see."

"But what made him hit you? What was it you said? can't you tell a body what you said?"

"Never you mind, I tell you—*he* knows, and he ain't going to forget. Oh, *I'll* fix him! I *told* him so. Yoost you wait—you'll see."

"What are you going to do, Jake?"

"I'm going to play a *trick* on him, *that's* what!"

A trick! This sad descent from such a heroic height brought a burst of laughter, and the crowd's budding respect for Jake withered to disgust. Soon the news of the cowhiding was all over the village, and it made a great sensation. Half an hour later, old Andrew Harrison arrived at home with it, and went up to his son's room and told it. Then his distempered imagination began to work. His excitement passed away, and his air became grave. He drew a chair to the bedside, sat down in it, and made one or two unsuccessful attempts to get a start upon something which he evidently wanted to talk about, then he said, very gently—

"George, can you bear some bad news?"

The manner and the words together gave George a sickening sinking of the heart, and he answered almost inaudibly—

"I can divine it. You have seen—*him*."

"I have."

"I feared it. I had a message for you, but you were gone. He wanted to see you."

This was news to the old man, but he didn't know it. He added it calmly to his imaginary tale, and went on—slowly and impressively:

"Yes, he told me so. He overtook me just a few rods out of the village, and said he expected me to call this morning, because he had something to say to me, and he would say it now. And then, George—you can bear it?"

"Go on, father—God help me!"

"He gave me one day's notice."

George covered his face with his hands and groaned. He said—

"Oh, I knew it! The note—payable one day after date—I knew, too well, what that meant. But I can't seem to realize how a man can be so cruel!"

The old man drew a deep sigh, and said—

"I'm to blame for it, George. He's bitter about the counterfeits."

George could say nothing to that.

"Yes, he's bitter, George. He can't get over it, he can't forgive it. And George, his mind was on Jake Bleeker, and it made him worse. He said he was hunting for him and was going to cowhide him."

"What for?"

"He didn't say, but he was terribly stirred up—I never saw him so,—at least not inside of these twenty years." He dropped his voice a tone lower and added, "George, I haven't told you the worst. Can you bear it?"

George raised himself to a sitting posture, gasping.

"Go on, for God's sake—don't torture me so!"

"George, if the money's not in his hands by three o'clock tomorrow afternoon, he'll not only foreclose, but—"

"But what!"

"Tell about the counterfeit money!"

George fell back as if he had been struck down by a blow.

"Oh, infamous! Father, he told you he wouldn't do it."

"Yes," said the old man scornfully, "and who said his word was *gold?* Hey? Who said that? *I* didn't!"

"O, disgrace, disgrace! The rest was hard enough—but it was nothing to this. Father, do you understand? we shall be the talk of the countryside—of the State! Oh, I can't have it! I can't endure it!

There *must* be some way out. Leave me, please; leave me, and let me think. And let no one come here till I send."

At the end of three hours of wasting and wearing thought—grisly plannings that early got upon a descending grade and continued to drift lower and lower—he said to himself, despairingly: "No, there is no way out—but one: another crime! Oh, I am amazed to see how far I have come in this little time! Yesterday I despised my father in my private heart, because his honor had a limit; and so soon as this I am finding that mine has one also. He would commit a crime to save the house from poverty; I am on the imminent verge of committing one to hide a disgrace. How trifling the difference is—if there *is* a difference! And last night I implored the boy to watch himself—watch himself!" He broke into a ghastly laugh. "Oh, I yield; I drag my self-righteousness in the mud and spit upon it. I was proud of my invincible uprightness—*mine!* and all the time was rotten to the soul, and needed only the test of my limit to find it out! I am an exposed sham; I have found myself out." After a long pause: "I will do it; no man will ever suspect *me,* with my reputation." He laughed again—in scorn of himself; and took the candle and went to the glass. "How many times I have looked in it before—and thought I knew the man." He sat down feeling better—refreshed, almost contented. He said it was a satisfaction to be in the society of an honest rascal, after having been deceived so long into keeping company with a dishonest one. Then he began to hunt for palliatives of his proposed crime. He found one: his father had paid insurance on the mill for more than a generation; if the mill got burned now, the companies would still be ahead, and the insurance-money would pay his father's debt and save his good name. And besides, they should have the money back in time—he would see to that. Tom was coming along; Tom was going to prosper; Tom would let him have money from time to time and wouldn't ask questions nor care what he did with it; and he would save it up, every cent, and the companies would get it all—with interest. Why, looked at rationally, instead of sentimentally, what becomes of the crime? Why, it's nothing but a loan!

It cheered him up considerably; in fact made him almost happy. It was very pleasant, and he thought he would examine the matter further. But *that* was a mistake; the ice began to get thin; for the thought intruded itself that to borrow money without the owner's knowledge is—

No, it was best not to pursue the inquiry too far; to let well enough alone was wisest. He changed the subject.

Now, what course should he adopt, by way of a plan? He must wait until after nine before going on his nefarious errand. Nine was Bleeker's hour for looking the mill over to see that everything was right before going to bed. That was also old Andrew's usual hour for going to rest. Tom would still be out at his work, Martha would be out of the way in the kitchen; the night would be dark; he could get out unperceived, fire the mill, and be back in his room and in bed, all inside of twenty minutes, and no one would ever know or suspect that he had been out of the house.

CHAPTER IV.

A
T A QUARTER past nine he put on his heavy winter wraps, blew out his light, took his boots in his hand, closed his door softly behind him and crept to the head of the stairs in the dark and listened. Within there was no sound; outside only the wailing of the winter wind. He crept down the stairs, trying not to breathe hard, and halting often, for the dry old wooden steps creaked horribly in the stillness. At the bottom he put on his boots, and stood a moment, breathing fast and swallowing repeatedly to moisten his dry throat; then he groped his way to the back door, fumbled for the latch, raised it cautiously, and as cautiously opened the door. The cold wind blew into his feverish face, refreshing it, and he stepped out, closed the door, and found himself in the pitchy darkness he was hoping for and expecting.

Arrived at the mill, he unlocked it with his pass-key, stepped inside, shut the door, and stooped with a match in his quaking hand, to rake it on the floor. Hark! A noise outside—feet on the steps which he had just ascended! He scrambled behind some meal barrels, threw himself on the floor, and lay trembling. A key rasped in the lock, footsteps passed grating in, and gleaming flecks of light from the piercings of an old-fashioned tin lantern went dancing over the beams and stanchions. George was aware, now, that he had come too early, and had preceded the mill-inspection. Bridget Bleeker's voice said—

"Now then, sit down and finish; and then I'll have something to say, myself."

Then Bleeker's voice—

"I'll yoost do the inspection first, and then—"

"Let it wait. I'm in a wicked mood, I'm telling you, with these gangs coming and gawking and asking questions ever since the middle of the afternoon, and I a burning to get at this thing and settle it—looked as if they weren't ever going to let us inspect at all. Sit down—there's a box, and here's another. Mind, now, I'm not hard of hearing. Go on."

Jake began, in a low voice—

"He lashed me like I was a dog. *Donnerwetter!* I'd hardly got the words out of my mouth till—"

"Never mind that! Haven't I heard it the whole afternoon, till I'm that boiling—oh, if I had my hands on him! What are you going to *do?*"

"I'm going to burn his house down over his head this night! He lashed me like I was—"

"Lave it! Go on."

"That is all, Pridget. I'll be at his back door yoost at midnight— ah-h! no, maybe that won't do."

"Why?"

"It could be locked."

"You're a fool. You're not in Germany. They don't lock dwelling houses here."

"It's all right, then, Pridget. I'll be there when it strikes twelve and I'll burn him out, I don't care what happen."

"Now then, are you done?"

"Yes, that is all."

"Very well—listen to me, and I'll give you an errand worth a dozen of it. Revenge is what I want, and revenge is what I'm going to have. But I'll have profit, too, along with it. Jake, you'll not burn the house, you'll *rob* it."

"Rob it?"

"Yes. Anny objections to that?"

"Me? Why, Pridget, I'd *love* to do it."

"Very well—let me think a minute."

A ghastly stillness followed, whose impressiveness deepened to solemnity as the moments passed; and presently when George Harrison heard his watch ticking in his pocket he wished the hush might end; these people might hear that ticking, otherwise. The wind rose and moaned outside; then a rat scuttled across the floor, giving all present a start. Bridget resumed at last:

"Yes, it's the thing to do. It's a heap better than the other. Do you know that room where the Squire works?"

"Back on the ground floor?"

"Yes."

"There's a table in it."

"There's two, Pridget."

"I'm meaning the one he writes at. It's a considerable bit to the left of the door as you go in."

"I know."

"Jake, he keeps his money in the drawer of it!"

"No—does he?"

"That he does. And it's not locked."

"But Pridget, he wouldn't keep enough there to—"

"He wouldn't, wouldn't he? He keeps it there by the handfuls! I've seen it—seen it with my own eyes. He's the carelessest man that ever was!"

Silence, and the moaning wind and the ticking watch again. Was the slow and not bright—but not extinct—German mind finding a defect in the situation? After a little the man's thinkings reached his tongue and found expression—

"Pridget, it don't look reasonable dot a man would treat *much* money like dot. He might do it with a little, sometimes, when—"

"Don't I tell you it's handfuls? *Handfuls,* don't you understand? enough to make poor scum like us rich!"

The strenuous eagerness in her voice showed that all her heart was in this matter, and that hunger for the money was getting precedence over thirst for revenge—if, possibly, it hadn't been the real motive from the beginning, with revenge doing duty as a pretext-salve for her conscience's protesting dignity.

"Is dot so? . . . *Handfuls.* . . . But you see, Pridget, he might do it *once,* when he is thinking about something else—"

Bridget broke in with passionate earnestness—

"Jake, I give you my word I have seen him do it dozens of times —dozens, I tell you." Her voice was husky with excitement. "And he has left it there days and days together. I have handled it many a time—thousands of dollars in a wad!"

This was not true; Bridget's anxiety to persuade her husband was carrying her away. But her effort told.

"Why, of course, if *dot* is so—"

"It *is* so, Jake, I give you my word. Now if you'll only—"

"I tell you what I will do, Pridget. I'll go for the money. If I get it, all right; if I don't get it I will burn the house down."

For once in his life Bleeker laid his wife's admiration under contribution—

"Why, Jake, that is well thought; you have a better head than anyone would think. Many that look down on you wouldn't have had the wit to double-string the bow that way." She rose. "Let's move along, now, I'm frosted through. If we think of annything more to arrange about the business, we can talk it as we prowl around the mill."

"It's a rotten world!" said George to himself; "we are all rotten together, and the most of us don't suspect it. The worst that anybody has said of that woman is that she has a temper, and is spiteful, and sunk to the eyebrows in her popish superstitions; no one has ever impeached her honesty. Of course she has never impeached it herself, nor thought of such a thing. Poor as she is, she has fondled that careless man's hoards time and again without ever a thought that her probity could be in any danger—and now, see! The moment a good plausible pretext creeps in the back way among her principles, they go to ruin. *She* thinks she's after revenge; and I—well, I'm after a loan. We are a pair. The others haven't discovered themselves yet—the rest of the world. Their pretext hasn't arrived—the one out of a million that each of them, in his turn, can't stand out against: when it comes—well, when it comes they will join *us;* they will look in the glass and bow to a new acquaintance."

Meantime the pair had started on their inspecting tour, talking low and earnestly, the spots of light dancing on the beams and rafters as they receded. At the other end of the place the sparks vanished in darkness; the inspectors had started aloft. The next moment Harrison was out of the mill; five minutes later he was in his room, and had seen nothing, heard nothing, on the way. The house was dark and still.

CHAPTER V.

H E M A D E no light; he was merely going to think, and the kind of thoughts he would be exercising his mind upon would not be specially helped by light; plenty for all needs was being cast by the little tongues of flame that flickered about the fire-logs, rising, falling, winking fitfully to the flurries of wind that came with hollow rumblings down the chimney from time to time, puffing the ashes out on the hearth and causing weird lights and shadows to play over near objects, but leaving the rearward depths of the room permanently shrouded in gloom. His thoughts would be in harmony with these uncanny conditions.

He sat with his feet on the low fender and munched with relish a "cold snack" which he had cribbed below and brought up with him, and thought his thoughts—somewhat to this effect:

"I *must* do it, there is no other way. . . . And it is better than the other, and more excusable; far more, indeed. The insurance companies have done me no harm, they are not enemies, they have nothing against me, but this man hates me, and has said so; hates me without any cause; I have not harmed him in any way. If the circumstances have so placed me—by no fault of my own—let me keep that in mind, no fault of my own—that I am forced to save myself at another's expense, surely I ought to choose an enemy for a victim rather than one in whom I have no cause of offence. It is plain; I see it more and more clearly. . . . And then the money shall be paid back in time; every penny of it; and with interest—yes, interest—I pledge myself to it. Not even an enemy shall permanently suffer by me." The thought made him feel virtuous—almost fine. "Yes, interest shall be paid—interest to the last farthing; if anything, *more* than is due, rather than less. And at twelve per cent—for I will pay twelve—the investment is by two per cent better than any he could possibly put the money into in these times." He was feeling better still, at this stage; he was beginning to have a sense of putting the man under obligations to him. "It is plain that this is much better than the other. The other could result in *real* crime; because the fire could extend to Bleeker's house and cause loss of life. That would be horrible! By luck I have had a narrow escape; the present scheme endangers no one's person; it was most fortunate that the mill-inspection got delayed. . . . Bleeker is going at midnight. . . . Eleven? . . . Eleven should be safe. . . . Yes,—yes; if I go at eleven. . . ."

He made a mask; by cutting eye-holes in a handkerchief. Then he saw that it bore his initials, and made another—this time out of an unmarked one. Presently a noise startled him, and he thrust one of them in his pocket and the other under his mattrass.

Meantime Tom was at the Squire's, having a pleasant time. He reached there at eight; and when he described to Helen the tortures he had seen his father suffering, and the torture it had cost himself to keep back the tidings that would transmute his father's miseries into joy and thanksgiving in a moment, her pleasure in the anticipation of Wednesday's arranged surprises fell dead. Her lips quivered, and the tears came.

"Oh, Tom," she said, "you *didn't* let him go from you without telling him? oh, you *couldn't*. You are only pretending; no one could be so cruel as that. Tell me you didn't, Tom."

He could not resist the temptation to work up her distress a little higher and a little higher, as an effective preparation for the happy climax he would finish with, and so he went on confessing one cruel detail after another until she knew that he had left his father uninformed the whole night through; then, through her tears she looked up aghast and said—

"Oh, Tom! And so you went to your work and he doesn't know yet!"

It was time for the climax.

"Why, what am I thinking of?—I forgot one detail, Helen; a perfectly awful one, too; it turns me cold, now, to think of it."

"Oh, Tom, don't say it! What was it?"

"I left the canceled papers by his plate; and if he didn't jump for joy when he saw them, then—"

But her arms were about him and his mouth was obstructed before he could finish.

About half past nine the Squire came up to say good-night, and when he was going away after a quarter-hour visit, he said to Tom—

"I expected your grandfather to-day; did you give him the message?"

"Yes, sir. That is, I gave it to father."

"That was sufficient; what your father undertakes to do he can be depended on to do—even when it's a small thing; and we all know that that is an uncommon virtue."

Tom flushed with pleasure, and meant to report this speech to his father and ask him if he thought he could find anything in it that suggested hate.

"Your grandfather didn't come," the Squire added. "I'd like him reminded that I've got something for him."

There was nothing about the words to strike Tom, but there was something about the way in which the Squire said them that attracted his attention. Was this perhaps an important message?

"I didn't know you told me to say that, sir. I said you wanted to *see* him."

"It was doing very well, Tom—you gathered-in half of the message; you can carry the other half now."

Tom colored and said—

"I will, sir. I—well, I suppose I am not as good as my father is, in the little things."

The Squire indicated his daughter with a gesture and said—

"There was a disturbing element; it wasn't a fair test, lad. Goodnight again," and he went his way.

"Isn't he lovely!" said Helen. "Don't you think he is?"

"Lovely? I never knew what he was before! And this community doesn't know him; nor my father and grandfather; but I mean they *shall*, before I go to bed."

A few minutes later the Squire was saying to himself while he stirred the sugar in a steaming toddy, "It is a pity Harrison didn't get the important end of the message; he would have understood, then, and would have come, and his mind would be at peace, now." He sighed. "And my spirit would be healed of the hurt it gave itself in wounding that irresponsible old man. But he will come to-morrow."

At eleven o'clock Tom came proudly out at the front door while his father was sneaking in at the back one; sneaking in, noiseless, his feet muffled in rubbers, the white curtain of his mask hanging from under his hat and hiding his face. He groped his way cautiously in the dark, feeling his route along the walls with his hands. He found the Squire's work-room door, tried it, it yielded, and he entered and closed it softly behind him. He struck a match and held it up: yonder was the table, down the wall to the left; he moved toward it, and just as he reached it his match went out. In reaching for the wall, to strike another, he knocked something from the Squire's chair, and the object struck the floor with a heavy dull noise which made his heart stand still with fright. He stood a while, quaking on his limp legs, listening, straining his ear for any sound; then, nothing happening, he drew a deep and thankful breath, and reached for the wall again. His brimstone locofoco burned blue and dim, and sputtered and stunk, then brightened to a steady flame. The thing that had fallen was the Squire's heavy oaken cane which Dug Hapgood had called a "club" for accuracy's sake; he noticed it, but was not interested in it, his mind was on the drawer. It was not fastened, and came open easily.

"The woman said the truth!" he muttered; for there indeed lay a roll of bills. He thrust them into his pocket, and just then his match went out.

Hark!—was that a noise? His heart stood still again; someone was fumbling at the door.

"It's Jake—come an hour before his time. Ah, my God, what shall I do! I am no match for him; if he catches me, there's no escape; he will alarm the house and say he tracked me here, taking me for a common burglar." He stooped down, fumbled about for the club, and closed his trembling fingers upon it. "I shall get but one blow; if it should miss, or fail to stun—" He listened—listened; the stillness was perfect. "Can he be in the room? I didn't hear the door open. . . . There—I heard a sigh! . . . Another—and nearer! . . . there's *something* creeping about here!" At this moment a match was raked on the wall! and not down by the door, but near by, not six feet away—for Jake was shod with rubber, too. The match came up, and the two men stood revealed to each other. Jake saw the white mask and the lifted club, and with a loud and anguished *"Um Gottes willen!"* he plunged at the apparition. But Harrison struck him a staggering welt; as the blow descended, Bleeker uttered a piercing shriek, then went reeling toward the door and fell, an inert bulk, in front of it. Harrison threw the club from him and felt his way swiftly along the wall to the door, which he found open, and a few seconds later he was out of the house and flying southward over the frozen fields in its rear. "I had to do it," he said remorsefully to himself, "but Bleeker shan't lose anything by it—I will see to that."

Meantime Tom was swinging gaily down the road unaware that for a minute or two he had his father for company—with some space and a good deal of darkness between. But the father was making the better time, and would beat him home.

Behind them now, there was bustle and excitement in the Fairfax house. Three men of Indiantown, passing by the place, heard Jake's piercing shriek and ran through the grounds and into the house, and plunged into two rooms without finding anybody, and then into a third—where by the light of their lantern they found Squire Fairfax, crimsoned with blood, standing over a prostrate man who mumbled something not comprehensible, then gasped out his life and was still. The body lay in a lake of blood, and near it lay an oaken staff which the men recognised.

CHAPTER VI.

GEORGE HARRISON entered his house by the back way, chunked up the fire in the dining room, lit the candles, threw off his wraps and sat down, panting from his long flight but many degrees nearer to being happy than had been his case for many a month. He said to himself—

"It will not be wholesome to allow myself to look upon any but the pleasant side of this matter; it would be folly, and worse than folly; I will purge my mind of the perilous stuff, and keep it sane and healthy. I will think of only the pleasant side of it, the sane side, the right and best side: the good name of the house was in awful danger, and I have saved it—saved it!—let me be grateful for that; we can hold up our heads again—how good the words sound! Something had to be done, and it's done. Nobody shall lose by it, least of all Jake Bleeker. He shall have his raise. Raise? We will not stop at that; his wage shall be doubled—trebled!"

He had taken out his roll of bank notes, and was caressingly smoothing them on his knee, face-side down, and lifting their corners and counting them.

"Five thousand dollars—they are life for us, salvation, honor!"

He turned the pile over. An expression of terror flared up in his eyes, and he sat staring and motionless, like one who had been turned to stone. Written in a bold hand across the face of the note that was uppermost were the words: *"Counterfeit. W. Fairfax."*

After a little he took that note up in his trembling fingers, loosed it and it fluttered to the floor. The words appeared upon the next one. That note followed the first one. One by one the others followed these, exposing always the fatal words. Then in his anguish he moaned like one who is in physical pain, and said—

"O, my God, why cannot I die!"

He got up and walked the floor, wringing his hands and uttering despairing ejaculations. Presently he noticed those papers on the mantelpiece, where Martha had left them. He took them absently up, not conscious of what he was doing, and went upon his weary tramp again, now and then emphasizing a bitter thought with a gesture. One of these gestures finally brought the papers into collision with something, and he stopped and said, "What are these? where did I get them?" He glanced at them and sank, like one smitten mortally, into his chair. "*Canceled*—God pity me! O! O! O! how can a man bear this! . . . I am a thief—stealer of my father's false money—thief to no purpose—thief to save the house's honor, and it was *already* saved—through what mystery and by whose heaven-sent compassion there is no divining! Oh, if—"

There was a sound of approaching steps. He gathered up the bank bills and threw them on the fire; then, by a strenuous effort of will, he assumed, as nearly as he could, the look and bearing of a man whose affairs have taken a new and favorable turn, and whose business it is to look comfortable, and even smile upon occasion; for the house's honor *was* saved, the fact would soon be known, and all comers must be made to see that the house was proud of it and happy in it. Tom entered. The father stepped briskly to meet him, with both hands out. Tom wrung them cordially, and the response was as cordial.

"Oho!" Tom said, "the clouds are gone, are they? Well, I was expecting it;" and throwing off his wraps he placed chairs in snug juxtaposition before the fire, and said, "Sit down, now, and I'll make my confession and tell you all about it, and get my forgiveness. You see, I happened to run across the Squire, and he gave me the canceled papers—"

"*He* did?"

"Yes, and told me to give them to you—"

"*When?*"

"Yesterday—er—late—"

The father gasped—

"Water—give me water!"

Tom sprang to obey, and when his father was revived he was

about to ask what the matter was, but was saved the trouble—

"There, Tom—I'm all right, now. This generosity from a man who hates me rather upset me. I was not looking for it from *that* quarter."

"Father, it's all a mistake!" said Tom, joyfully. "It's a misunderstanding, entirely, and I know it. When he gave me the papers" (Tom was antedating a little,) "he said a very handsome thing about you, and said it in a most friendly way, too. He said that when you engaged to do a thing you could be depended on to do it; and not merely the large things but the little ones; and that *there* was the merit—for, to be faithful in the little things was a most rare quality. Oh, he is a noble man! these people don't know him; and to hear *him* say that—oh, it made me proud to have such a father!"

He accompanied this speech with some of his customary caressings and pettings. They burnt, but he didn't know it; and the father groaned inwardly, and said to himself, "I *was* that kind of a man; and now my own boy's praises sting me."

"Well, when I got through, last night, I brought the papers home, but I had a little scheme for a pleasant surprise for you, so I thought I would keep them back a day—"

"Oh, the pity of it, the pity of it!" moaned the father to himself.

"—but away in the night I heard you walking the floor and I couldn't bear it. So by and by I gave up trying, and got up and took the papers and went to your room—"

"And what did you do—what did you do!" the father broke in, excitedly.

"But you were asleep and I hadn't the heart to disturb you."

The father turned away his head to hide the grief that was in his heart and must show in his face.

"But I left the papers by your plate this morning and went away walking on air, for I had got in my little surprise at last, and all day I've been so happy, picturing to myself how you looked when you came down to breakfast and recognised that the clouds were gone! And there's one surprise more—I'm a partner in the firm! And another yet, and the noblest of all—Helen and I are engaged again!"

George Harrison rose unsteadily, and groping with his hands like who is in a vertigo—and just then came a thundering at the door that shook the house, and Dug Hapgood thrust in his face and shouted—

"Say! Somebody's killed Jake Bleeker in Squire Fairfax's house!"

George Harrison staggered to the door and said—

"Not *dead? Don't* say he's dead!"

"Dead as a smelt! Why, the way you look, you'll do for his ghost! Just fish-belly white, slack-lime white—why, a body'd say Deathshead Phillips has been here and—" He was out and away on his errand without finishing.

Harrison tottered to the fire and steadied himself with a hand on the mantelpiece, keeping his back to Tom to hide the agony in his face from him. But Tom was not heeding him, his thoughts were with Helen, he must fly to her. Article by article he flung on his winter wear without stopping to bother with buttons or buckles, and just as he was springing for the door it burst open and Helen flung herself on his breast.

"Oh, my darling, all our happy to-morrow's surprises are fallen to ruins; our betrothal, your new-made membership in the firm, our plans for—oh, come with me, my father is arrested for murder!"

A moment later Harrison was alone, bowed and haggard and white, torturing himself with vain upbraidings, breaking his heart with vain remorse.

"And to think—I could have been spared it! If I had only waited —only waited a day!—*one* day! Ah, if my father hadn't told me notice had been served upon him. . . . Why, there was nothing *in* that! How did he come to tell it me? . . . Yes, that is a mystery—I cannot make it out. . . . This whole day we have been swimming in prosperity, and I didn't know it! The note canceled; Tom a partner in the firm; and they betrothed—our good name saved, our fortunes made—oh, Tom, one little word could have saved me, and now I am a thief and an assassin. And oh, my God, an innocent man is seized for my crime—and he the man that could have destroyed us, name and all, but put forth his good kind hand and saved us whole! . . . If I were a *man* I would go and take his place. And I will *do* it, by God I will!" He got up and strode with energetic step across the room and threw on his overcoat and began to button it. With the third button his zeal began to waver a little; he buttoned the fourth with hesitation; with the fifth in his fingers he stopped and began to reflect. He stood so, during several moments; then he sighed and began to slowly unbutton. The process finished, he stood thinking once more. Presently he resumed the buttoning; but not with alacrity, this time; it was an effort, and had but little life in it; he got no further than the third button; then he undid his work. After a little he pulled himself together and made one struggle more. But it ended with the first button. He took off the coat and went wearily back to his place at the fire and sat down to grind the grist of his bitter thoughts again. "I am not a man," he said.

The door opened and the gaunt figure of his father entered, in night-clothes.

"Why, lad, aren't you up a little late?" said the old man, sociably.

For answer the son pushed toward him the canceled papers, with a look which was a reproach, and which said, "How do you reconcile this with what you told me?"

The old man examined the papers indifferently, and said in a matter-of-course way—

"Canceled. Yes, that is all right. I went to him after supper this evening, and told him to cancel them on the spot or I'd kill him. And I would have done it, too. And I made him give me back the counterfeits; and I've got them hid away safe." Noticing an expression of horror and astonishment in his son's face, he added, appealingly, "Don't look at me like that, George; it had to be done; he would have ruined us tomorrow, and blighted our good name besides. But we are safe, now, George, and I take all the blame—if there is any."

The son said to himself, "I see it all, now. It only needed this to make the disasters complete—he is mad!" Then, gently, "It is late and cold, father; you need rest; you will be better in bed."

He led the old man away, both of them walking feebly and neither of them saying anything more. George returned, after a little, and sat down to wait for Tom; he had no desire to go to bed, sleep was out of the question.

He began to think over the happenings of the previous fortnight, and now his father's madness threw light upon certain of them which had been dark before. For instance, his father had reported that the Squire had required him to pay up his indebtedness; manifestly this had not happened, his father had only imagined it. His father had proposed to appeal to his rich bachelor brother in Memphis for help—a strange idea, it had seemed to George, for that had been tried several times before, with no result; not a penny would his uncle lend or give. But no matter, let it be tried again. This time, to George's surprise, it succeeded: his father reported that his brother had sent the money—grumblingly and ungraciously—and that he had paid it to Squire Fairfax on the 27th of October and had extinguished the debt. It was plain, now, that that was another output of an insane imagination. Without question his father had bought the counterfeit money somewhere and paid the debt with it.

Nobody to talk to! In all his life he had not known a time before when he could not pour his troubles into some friendly ear and get something of solace and assuagement for them, but now when he needed this help as he had never needed it before, he must seal up his tongue though his heart burst: there was no one with whom he could share *his* kind of secrets.

What an avalanche of calamities had swept down upon him!—and how had it all happened? what was the source? He took from the fire a charred stick and went to the whitewashed wall and began to make a rude drawing there; meanwhile muttering to himself:

"The genealogy of a lapse. The fruit of a temptation. What was the seed—the source—the root whence the tree of disaster sprang? *False pride.*" He drew the root and the trunk, and labeled them. He hung the fruits upon the branches, and gave each one a number, soliloquising as he went along. "A false shame, springing from a false pride, makes me dread poverty and loss of the common herd's consideration, and under this stress my principles turn out to be showy shams, I yield to the first specious temptation that offers, and burn the mill. I did not commit the crime in fact, but in spirit and intention I did, which is the same thing.

"That crime is *Fruit No. 1.*

"Next, I commit the crime of robbery: *Fruit No. 2.*

"Then the crime of murder: *Fruit No. 3.*

"Upon a innocent man's head this crime falls: *Fruit No. 4.*

"By this same crime I have made a widow, and taken away her support: *Fruit No. 5.*

"By this same crime I have smitten to the heart the innocent man's daughter: *Fruit No. 6.*

"By this same crime I have made my own son a sharer in the daughter's shame and grief: *Fruit No. 7.*"

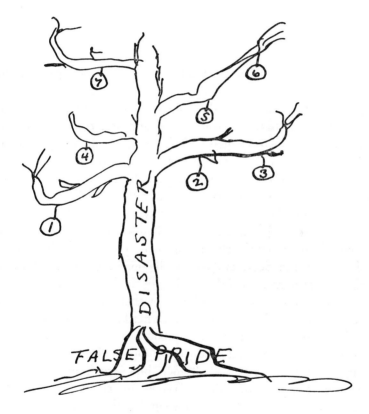

He surveyed his work dismally.

"After a reproachless life, a single lapse and all this array of horrors is bred of it—a calamity per hour almost! It seems incredible—and so unfair, so out of proportion to the size of the transgression. Ah, Moral Law, you are a hard trader; Shylock of the Shylocks, you exact your pound of flesh a hundred fold!"

The night wind bore to him out of the distance a sound which he recognized, and he hastily rubbed out the words *"False Pride"* and *"Disaster"* from the roots and trunk of his tree, and waited upon that approaching sound with a quickened pulse. Soon Dug Hapgood burst in, eager and excited.

"Say, George, there's been a riot. I say there's been a riot—you hear?—a *riot!*"

"Yes, yes, I hear—don't shout so. What was it about?"

"By gracious, they tried to lynch him!"

"Lynch who?"

"Squire."

It made George reel in his tracks. The human newspaper went briskly on, while he warmed his red hands at the fire.

"Yes, sir, they got him to the calaboose all right and got him in, but by that time the news was around and here comes the whole village flocking, men, women and children, putting on the rest of their clothes as they come, and just buzzing, they were so mad. Then comes the sher'ff a-tearing, and had his double-barrelled gun, and only just in time, too, for here comes Bridget Bleeker, and she had a Fourth of July torch, and begun to shout 'Lynch him, lynch the bloody assassin!' and the crowd raised a yell and made a surge for the calaboose, but the sher'ff was *there,* you see, and he put his back against the door, and whilst he made a speech to them constable Catlin smuggled the Squire out the back way and around the alley and into the county jail, and by that time Tom and Helen were on hand, and Helen went in with her father, and Tom stayed outside to help the sher'ff; and in about a minute here come the mob just a booming, and Bridget she mounted onto a dray and waved her torch and yelled, 'Lynch him, lynch him!' and the sher'ff called on all good citizens to come and stand by him, and a lot done it; and then the crowd went for that pile of brickbats that's there by the jail, and begun to rain them, and Tom was by the sher'ff's side, and a brick fetched him—"

"Oh, my God!"

"Sit down, sit down! Where you going?"

"To Tom, of course!"

"The more fool, you—sit down, I tell you. You can't do any good. *He's* all right. He's got a bad knock, but that's nothing. I'll tell you why, in a minute. Lemme light a pipe." While he was doing it George wrung his hands in silent distress, and muttered to himself, *"Fruit No. 8, to be added."* Then Dug went on. "They crowded the sher'ff and his people pretty lively, but he clubbed his gun and laid out several, and you bet you they won't 'tend any more riots *this* week—"

"Fruit No. 9," muttered George.

"—and Doc Stevens, he was by the sher'ff with his stick and laying into the mob like a little man, and then the thing happened that stopped the riot."

"Ah, thank God—what was it?"

"Somebody fired a shot and it took Doc Stevens in the heart and killed him dead."

George plowed his hands through his hair, and moaned *"Fruit No. 10*—a good man gone, and the fault all mine—how am I to endure all this?"

That man's death was a heavier calamity for George Harrison than he suspected at the time.

"Well, as soon as that happened the mob stopped carrying on, and it was as still as a graveyard; and they took their hats off and gathered around the corpse and you could a heard a pin drop; and while they were standing so, there were some wild shrieks, and here come the widow Stevens—"

"Oh, God pity me!—"

"—and her two daughters, and flung themselves on the body—"

"I shall go mad—I know it!"

"—and hugged it and kissed it and cried over it—"

"Fruit No. 11—oh, it is awful!"

"—and it was so pitiful to see, that the people couldn't stand it, and turned away. Then they begun to break apart and go off talking low, two and two. And Tom was laying there insensible—"

"Lord, Lord, if I could only die!—"

"—and when they were gathering him up, out of the jail comes

Helen Fairfax with her hair flying, and flung herself at Tom and put her arms around him and she was crying, and said, 'Oh, is he dead? don't say he is dead—he is mine, mine, mine!' That's what she said, and everybody wondered, and said, 'Why, it's been made up between them—that's good.' That's what they said. And Tom come to, and she was that glad, poor thing, you never see anything like it; and she said help her get him to the widow Wilkinson's, she was going to 'tend him herself till he got well. And they helped her, and there they are, and don't need *you,* I can tell you. And she wants her old Liza and Emly, and I'm on the way to send them, and distribute the news. Hel-lo, is that clock right?—three in the morning!—I must be moving along. How's the gov'ner?"

"Not well. He came down here a while ago, very imprudently dressed, and got chilled."

"*That's* bad. I said that's *bad*—for a man as old as he is. Say—I'll go for Doc Ste—oh, I forgot."

"Oh, dear, dear, these are awful times!"

"Inquest at half past eight in the morning—only about five hours from now. It'll be mighty interesting. I'll come by for you, George—we'll go together."

George shook as if he had been smitten with an ague. For the moment he couldn't speak, but he indicated with a gesture that he did not wish to go.

"What! You don't mean to say you're not going? Why, what in the world's the matter with you? George, you ain't right in your mind; I never heard of such a thing."

"I'm not well, Dug; I'm far from well these days, you know—I'm staying in the house."

"Yes, I forgot. Yes, that's so. But my! that was all trouble, it wasn't sickness. Tom and Helen's make-up—why, man, he's rich! You're out of all your troubles now—ain't that so?"

"Ye-s."

"B'gracious you ought to be the gayest of the gay. Don't you feel so?"

George tried to say yes, but the word stuck in his throat.

"Blame it, George, you don't look it—hang it, I don't understand it at all. You haven't anything on your mind *yet,* have you?"

"Oh, he is torturing the guilty soul out of me—*why* doesn't he go!" wailed George, to himself.

"Say, George, chirk up. We'll go to the inquest. That'll brighten you up; it'll make another man of you. All you want's a change. It's going to be mighty interesting. Everybody'll be there, and you'll see poor old harmless Jake laying there in his blood—"

"Oh, for God's sake—don't!"

"Why, what *is* the matter with you, George? I never *saw* a man act so. I tell you, man, I'm troubled about you. *This* ain't any common sickness. I'm going straight for Doc Ste—I forgot again, poor old Doc—ah, dear, we shan't ever see *him* any more, and a great loss he is to this town, I can say that for him. I hope to goodness the man that was the cause of his death'll swing for it; don't you, George?"

"Oh, I know he ought to—oh, yes, he ought to."

"And will, *I* hope. Put it there—shake!"

George lent his hand, but Dug did the shaking.

"You're kind of weak, George; you get to bed and get some sleep and brisken up; I'll be here for you at eight sharp, and—"

"Damnation, I'm not *going* to the inquest!"

Dug was so startled that his mouth dropped open and his pipe fell out.

"Goodness, George, what a start you did give me! Well, all right, stay away if you like, but when I come to tell you about it you'll wish you'd been there, and then it'll be too late. Hel-lo! what's this? Family tree?"

"Ye-s."

"Hm. On account of Tom going to marry into the quality—hey? Got to skirmish around and rake up some ancestors? Bully good idea, too. Who's No. 1?—Adam?"

"Yes—name it to suit yourself."

"And then comes Moses and Deuteronomy. No, Abel and Cain. Cain's No. 3, ain't it? Knocked his brother out with a club—same as the Squire done with poor Jakey to-night; blamed good coincidence, *ain't* it, George? Say, ain't it striking, don't you think?"

"Oh, yes, yes, yes, *yes!*—are you done?"

"But you let the Squire have this one, George, and you build another. Just fits his case to a dot; but you—oh, you build another, and leave out the clubs and murders. Say, I must be going, and start them servants along; Helen'll be getting impatient—said she wanted them right away." He got as far as the door, George anxiously following; then he paused, and surveyed George with a compassionate eye. "But you're lonesome, and ain't got anybody to cheer you up, George, and so, if you'd druther I'd stay—"

"No—no—no!" shouted George, aghast, "send the servants—hurry them along—she needs them—and I *must* get some sleep;" and before Dug could protest he was gently pushed outside and the door closed against him.

"He was here only half an hour," mourned George, "and yet in that little time he added four disasters of my manufacture to this tree's dismal burden"—and he took his charred stick and drew the four fruits and numbered them.

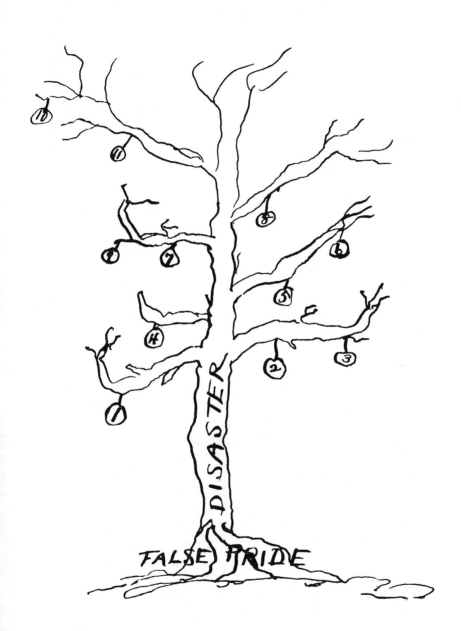

CHAPTER VII.

Gᴇᴏʀɢᴇ ᴅʀᴀɢɢᴇᴅ himself to bed, and during several hours he slept the sleep of the troubled in spirit. When the process of waking began, his developing consciousness found him a grateful and happy man—a man with a vague sense of having passed through a desolating dream, which has melted away and gone from him like a cloud—

Then followed that ghastly sinking at the heart which comes when we realize that the horror which seemed a dream was not a dream but reality. It is an overwhelming moment, the last perfection of human misery, it is death in life; we do not know how to take up our burden again, the world is empty, the zest of existence is gone. The time dragged drearily along, and it seemed to Harrison that his spirit would nevermore rise up out of this darkness and gloom; then a thought drifted into his mind which brought the relief of a passing interest in the practical concerns of life and the world: *what had he done with the mask which he had worn?* He must have put it in his pocket, of course, but he could not remember when he did it, nor where. He got up and examined his pockets; the mask was missing. Very well, in the excitements of the tragedy and his flight, he must have dropped it without noticing it. No matter—it could not be identified as his, it could furnish no consequential evidence; it could not betray him. There was comfort in that, and he needed any crumbs of comfort he could find in these harassing days. He took the other mask out of its concealment, now, purposing to destroy it, which was a natural impulse. He held it up and glanced at it, then made a wild catch at the bedpost, missed it and sunk limp to the floor. It was the wrong mask—it had no marks on it!

An awful fear came upon him, a wave of despair swept over him; he realized that a vast disaster had befallen him. Hardly conscious of what he was about, he sat thinking, thinking, and tearing the mask to shreds, his body trembling and the cold sweat gathering on his forehead.

What should he do? Oh, there was but one thing to do: he must go to the inquest; he must learn his fate and quickly, an hour's suspense would kill him. He gathered himself up and began to throw on his clothes. There was a knock, and Martha bustled in, bursting with news.

"Marse George, Dug Hapgood, dat dey calls de Yeller Press 'caze he yell so and carry de news aroun' when anything happen, he's been here, en Squire Fairfax has killed our Jake, en somebody killed doctor Stevens, en oh, my lordy, Marse Tom he's—"

"Never mind it! I know all about it. Rush—get my breakfast!"

"She's all ready, seh. En do please hurry en go en see Marse Tom—"

"Tom's all right—never mind Tom; I'm going to the inquest. How is father?"

"I been watchin' de do', but he ain't awake yet, seh."

"Get along, then; pour the coffee. Fly!"

Seven minutes later, George was swallowing his coffee, and a few minutes afterward was striding up the river road in the frosty morning air. A belated citizen—Bowles, the tavern keeper—came lashing along in an open wagon, and took him in, glad to do a favor to so important and influential a man, and worried him all the way with talk about the murder, the riot, the killing of Stevens, the wounding of Tom and the others, and with congratulations; for all the village knew of Tom's re-engagement, now, and had a proper appreciation of the great financial uplift it meant for the Harrisons. But George hardly heard what the man said—his mind was elsewhere and busy with terrors.

When he entered the fatal room and began to work his way through the pack and jam, the people divided and let him pass as soon as they saw who it was, and coroner Evans most courteously insisted upon his coming forward and sitting by his side; and had a chair brought, and wiped it off with his coat tails, and put George in it, whispering "now you can see him good, and hear everything."

George was obliged to accept these undesired courtesies; obliged also to look at the dreadful object on the floor—stretched there by his hand; the thought and the spectacle together made him sick and he could feel the blood leave his face.

"I don't wonder it makes you turn pale," mumbled the coroner, "it *is* an awful sight, *ain't* it? one of the dirtiest deeds that was ever done—though of course you understand *I* ain't saying who done it. Of course I don't know; I only know I don't want the man's conscience inside of *my* hide that done it."

Then came a roof-shaking bellow. Dug Hapgood was whispering in a friend's ear and pointing:

"Say! it's begun to bleed fresh—the murderer's in the house, according to the old saying!" and he laughed.

It gave George a grisly shock; also, it set the people to wondering and whispering.

One after the other the witnesses testified, and George, hardly breathing, hung upon their words, listening for mention of the mask, waiting for its production, and wildly trying to invent a plausible and hopeful tale to tell when that terrible exposure should be made. At the end of an hour, in the midst of an impressive stillness, the coroner announced the result of the inquest:

"It is found that deceased fell by the hand of Walter Fairfax— under what circumstances the jury have not been able to determine. The inquest is finished—let the place be closed."

And no mention of the mask! George was cold to the heart. It seemed to him that he could not bear this: it would have been better to see the mask produced, and know the worst and be done with it. The mask was in existence, sure. Some person had it; why had he kept it back? Why had he not testified? The mystery of it! *Why* hadn't he testified? With this persecuting question beating upon his brain he left the place like one lost in a dream.

Bowles was watching for him, and captured him before some others who would have liked the honor of driving him got a chance to apply. The journey townward began, and again the fat, good-natured tavern-keeper's tongue was loosed.

"It's great times, sir, great! I don't know when we've had the like.

A cold-blooded murder, a riot, our best doctor killed, young Mr. Tom and others wounded, two inquests in one forenoon, two big funerals getting ready, and one of our most principal citizens, head of a grand old blue-blood family, locked up in the common jail! Why, sir, my house is going to do four weeks' business in the next three days. I've ordered—now how many barrels of whisky should you say I've ordered?—and only for three days. How many should you say?" and the sandy man beamed a look of glorified expectancy out of his watery blue eyes.

The pallid figure at his side twitched impatiently, and the reply came with a weary accent—

"I don't know. I have not thought of the matter."

"But give a guess, sir, only just a guess," said the landlord, supplicatingly, "How many barrels should you say?"

Out of a mind that was far away and which now performed its function automatically, unconsciously, without interest, and with no purpose but to discharge a duty of courtesy, came the dreamy answer—

"I—well—perhaps—fifteen hundred thousand?"

Bowles's beefy face flushed purple and he flung an indignant glance at his guest; but the guest was not aware of it; the guest had already forgotten the answer and had taken no note of its dimensions when it was furnished; his half-closed eyes, with the lines of pain above them, showed that his mind was absorbed in matters of grave and earnest import, and was not accessible to a village tavern's sordid trivialities. Bowles sensed the situation, and realized that no jest had been intended; his resentment melted away, and gave place to a creditable feeling of regret that he had intruded his small matters upon the great citizen at this ill-chosen time. He hauled his wind and went off on a proper tack.

"Well, it's a time for us all to grieve, I'm free to say that, sir. When such things happen, it hits us all—can't any of us escape; it lowers the whole community a peg. Now a way-up man like the Squire—think of it!" and he touched up his horse with the tip of his whip, as if he were setting an exclamation point to his remark. "I reckon there ain't any doubt but the Squire done it?" He turned, expecting the perfunctory reply, but he did not get it; George had hardly heard him—he was thinking of the lost mask. "There *ain't* any doubt, is there, sir?"

"I—I haven't heard any expressed." Then to himself, *"Why* must my life be made bitterer than it already is, by these infernal unconsciously-accusing questions! This creature looks at me as if he half suspects—something. I wonder—oh, no, he can't; it is impossible. *Why* doesn't he look the other way? why must he look at *me* all the time?—and in that prying, searching way!"

His guilty soul was doing the landlord a wrong; the landlord was not prying, he was merely doing a natural thing: when he addressed his guest he turned toward him.

"Gum! but character's a grand thing—ruputation! You see, the Squire has always turned a kind of a cold shoulder to folks, and that ain't a wise thing for the quality to do—it makes them unpopular; and it makes people sort of privately satisfied when anything happens to them, and ready to look on the worst side of it instead of the favorable one. But it ain't so with the Harrisons—their ruputation's different. Lord, just change it around, and see! Suppose *you'd* been found standing over that murdered man and you all bloody, that way—"

"Oh, curse the pitiless idiot!" muttered the sufferer.

"Just suppose it. What would everybody have said? Why, they'd a said 'Sho! *he* never killed him; some low-down blackguard done it, and turned tail and run when the dead man let go that yell.' Now sir, I put it to you: if you had been found like that—"

Here with the idea of blowing his nose, which was one of his ways of punctuating preparatorily a coming climax, he drew out his handkerchief and flourished it, exposing by a glimpse a couple of holes in it. George fell up against him an inert and half lifeless mass.

"Good land, sir! What's the trouble?" exclaimed the landlord, thrusting the handkerchief into his pocket and putting his arm around George to steady him in his place.

"Ah, I am far from well—far from well—"

"I can see it, sir; you gasp like a fish—"

"I have been obliged to keep my room for days—"

"I heard of it, sir—"

"—and the exertion of this outing has been too much for me, and—"

"Good luck, here's your house—"

"No, drive on, I shall be all right in a minute. Drop me at the widow Wilkinson's—"

"In three shakes of a sheep's tail, sir, as the saying is. G'lang—spread yourself, Meg! Your Tom's there—in just the charmingest hands, too! He'll be wanting to see you, sir—*they* will!"

They soon reached the Wilkinson gate, and Bowles tenderly helped George out, then drove away with a cheery

"Don't forget the other inquest, sir!" During the day he told of his adventure to many a friend, and always wound up with "Now *there's* a *man*. Chock full of noble emotion—most fainted, as I told you, over this awful thing. Yes, sir, he's a *man*, every inch of him; *he* ain't any Squire; if he had killed Jake, he would come right out and *say* so, he wouldn't give a damn for the consequences. Because why? He's a Harrison—that's why. They don't know *how* to shirk."

If Harrison had heard him, his private comment would have been, "He is describing a man that *did* exist." As he passed up through the yard he said to himself, "I am weak from the fright it gave me; but it was not my mask. If it had been, he would have produced it in court, of course. What *has* become of that mask! Am I to go on like this—frightened stiff every time I see a white handkerchief with holes in it?" He entered the parlor and sat down to wait while the announcement of his visit was made. His mind went back, and back, step by step over the ground; at last he sprang from his chair as if he had been fired out of it, and began to walk the floor in a consuming excitement, clinching his hair in his hands and muttering in anguish, "Oh, oh, oh, *now* I remember, God help me! as I was slipping out at the back door, insane with terror, I came near sneezing, and seized my nose in an iron grip to prevent it —and there was no mask in the way! It is horrible—horrible! It means that the mask was dropped inside the building—along the hall somewhere?—in that room itself? Was there some one else hiding there to steal that money? Did that some one find the mask?

Then why didn't he produce it at the inquest and ward suspicion from himself? . . . No—that wouldn't do. They would ask, 'How did *you* come to be there? and are you sure *you* didn't kill the man?' "

He was a natural conclusion-jumper, and his spirits came up at a bound. Everything was perfectly plain to him, now: there *was* another person there, on an evil errand; in the very room itself, maybe; hidden behind the furniture; witnessed the tragedy, no doubt. "And yet there's nothing to fear from him; even if he saw my face there's nothing to fear from him. Ah, yes, let him keep the mask—it is in safe hands." He was feeling very much relieved, now. Then came a thought which spoiled the whole scheme: why should the man carry the accusing mask away? "Oh, dear, dear, of course he wouldn't; he would naturally leave it there, and let it tell its fatal tale." He was down in the abyss again. "But someone *did* take it away—that is absolutely certain; and didn't produce it at the inquest. Why? what is the mystery of it? . . . That mask is in no friend's hands, or he would not have left me in misery all these hours. Handkerchiefs with holes in them!—I shall see them at every turn, they will flap along in endless procession through my nightmare dreams." It made him groan to think of it.

The door flew open, and Helen tripped in and welcomed him with an affectionate embrace.

"He is doing very well; come and see him—*papa;* my new papa, my dear papa," and she kissed him on both cheeks. It almost shamed him into going and taking her abused father's place; but not quite. He smiled down upon the upturned face that lay against his breast, and said—

"You dear and beautiful creature! I am so glad that all of the sunshine has not gone out of your young life, and so sorry that your poor father—"

"O, tell me the verdict! It isn't bad? say it isn't bad; for—"

From a block or two away the clarion voice of the Yeller Press rose upon the air—

"Verdict unanimous—Squire found guilty!"

George hastened to support Helen, but she disdained it. "Oh, the lie!" she said, and straightened herself up, the indignant blood mounting to her face. "It is like those unreasoning clods; they might as well accuse *you* of such a thing." Which made George wince. "But I am not troubled: I should be ashamed to be troubled —bearing the name I bear. The Grand Jury is to be heard from, yet; and before that, the miscreant who did that cowardly murder upon a poor unarmed wretch will be found; I know it—I feel it!" and there was a confidence, a certainty, a conviction in her tone and manner which made the goose-pimples rise on Harrison's skin. "You will hunt him down! it is a sacred commission—I put it in your hands, with full trust; my second father's hands, my good and noble second father! and all my days I shall be so grateful to you, and so proud of you. You will not let that base thing escape, of that I am sure. But remember! you must not denounce him—that must be *my* prerogative, my pleasure, for the shame he has brought upon us. I will stand before him, so—and I will look him in the face, so —and I will say, 'I am looking into a murderer's eyes; I'—but *look* at me, don't turn away—"

"But you—you—do it so terribly!"

"Do I? Oh, that pleases me. And I ought to do it well, because I *feel* it so. But it is nothing to the way I shall do it when I am looking into the real assassin's eyes. You shall be there to see; I will not do it till you are there to see. Does that make you happy, dear?"

"Oh—yes—immeasurably."

"I am so glad. I'm going to practice. Wouldn't you practice?"

"Well—yes—yes, I think so."

"*Dear* papa; I will practice on you—every day."

"I shall be—be—I shall be delighted."

"It cheers me up and makes me happy and hopeful and confident, just the thought of it. Come, now, let us go and tell Tom all about it; it will do him good."

She put an arm around his waist, he put an arm across her back and under her arm, and they moved away upon their errand.

About this time Martha was passing the house upon a momentous quest. She found the District Attorney, and gave him a note. It read—

"Come. Lose no time. Bring a notary. ANDREW HARRISON."

He turned, with the question on his lips, "What—is your old master ill?" but thought better of it, and said instead, "Tell him it's all right," and Martha went her way. Then he called his clerk, and went with him to Harrison's house—a twelve or fifteen minutes' walk.

They found the old gentleman tranquil, composed, but bearing the look of a very sick man.

"Draw up a chair here, Randall," he said, in a weak voice, "and don't ask me questions and don't interrupt me; for I am a dying man, my time is short, and I wish to say what I have to say before my mind shall lose anything of its clearness. I have a solemn duty to perform; I cannot die, I *must* not die until it is discharged and justice done. Martha has just told me about the inquest. I had no intention to give evidence in that case, it was my purpose to hide in my heart what I knew. For this wickedness my offended God has meted out just and swift punishment to me. Write!"

When Randall and his clerk left the room, half an hour later, they were very pale; and the one was saying to the other, "It is a dismal secret to have to carry around until the Grand Jury meets." They found Martha below, and advised her to call in a neighboring woman or two to help nurse the patient, and they said they would send a doctor, and also George Harrison.

CHAPTER VIII.

G EORGE FOUND Tom with his head turbaned with bandages, but pleasantly situated, for besides Helen's society he had that of the widow Wilkinson and several of her neighbors. However, it was not a comfortable place for George; he was soon in distress and anxious to get away; in fact obliged to get away, for these people not only said the unkindest things about the murderer, but they also required of him the details of the inquest, which was the equivalent of asking him to walk through fire for their accommodation. He had a pair of good excuses for cutting his visit short, and he used them and was grateful that he had them in stock. He said he could not even bear to think of the inquest, let alone talk about it—Helen and Tom would understand this, and he believed the others would, also. This delicacy and sensitiveness scored a point for him, and the point was strengthened rather than weakened by the fact that its genuineness could not be questioned, since it was a recognised trait of his character. His other excuse was that the true friends of Squire Fairfax should not be tardy, at this sad time, in going to him and by their presence make known to the world where their sympathies lay. This sentiment scored another point for him, and was applauded. Helen was touched, as indeed they all were, and she hurried him away on his good mission, and gave him many loving messages for her father, whom she had not seen for two hours and would not see again for a couple more.

The Squire had the warder's room in the jail and was as comfortable as a prisoner might well be, for the chamber was well furnished and there was a good fire. He and Harrison were left together by the warder, and they shook hands and sat down, the Squire courteously thanking Harrison for coming, and taking blame that they had not met oftener since their school days and become better acquainted with each other. George said he had always supposed that the Squire did not like him, and this had made him shy about making advances. The Squire said it was a misconception; and a pity, too, for no doubt much had been lost by it, for both; for his part he was sincerely sorry, and hoped that thenceforth they might be good friends—adding, with a wan smile, "that is, if you care for the friendship of a man in my position."

George assured him that he did care for it. The ice was broken, now; the men understood each other; and after that their talk proceeded without restraint. But George was soon in distress once more, for now he *had* to tell about the inquest—there was no escape; each phrase of the evidence fell upon the innocent listener with something of the effect of a blow; and when the tale was finished Fairfax said gloomily—

"It is as I supposed it would be—in fact, as I knew it would be.

There is no way out; the evidence leaves no door, no loophole. It means a manslaughter term in the State Prison for me—ten years, at least. It will break my pride—and my child's heart."

George said to himself, "It cuts me to the quick to see him so, and I the cause. If I were a *man*, I . . . . But I am not a man—I am not equal to it." Then he said aloud, with a show of confidence which he felt was a poor counterfeit, "You must not allow yourself to feel that way; we must clear you; we must find a way."

"*Clear* me?" said Fairfax, looking up reproachfully. "Talk that to Helen; talk it to her constantly; I shall be grateful for all the words of the sort that you can say to her. But we are men, you and I, and can do without that; and must—for we know better. *I* know I didn't touch the man, but that is of no value—that is no evidence; but there is strong and abundant evidence that I *did*. We need not fatigue ourselves with discussing a clearance; we know what is going to happen." Then he turned suddenly upon his new friend and said with energy, "It does credit to your heart, and I honor you for it; but I am a *man*, Harrison, and I know quite well how this matter stands, and so do you. *You* don't believe me innocent, you haven't any right to believe me innocent in face of this evidence; and I don't blame you in the least—I am far from blaming you. I should blame you if you knew me, but you have had no opportunity to know me. In the circumstances I should have a small opinion of your intelligence if you were able to say with all your heart, or half of it, that you believed me guiltless." He looked Harrison steadily in the eyes, as if to keep him from shirking or paltering, and continued, "I know you to be intelligent, and as we are to be friends, I want you to do a friend's part by me: be frank and square with me; let us be masculine, not feminine; and don't, I pray, have any mistaken tenderness for my feelings at the expense of candor and truth. You are necessarily obliged to believe me guilty; now then, *say* it, then I shall put full confidence in you and thenceforth have what I particularly need and strongly desire in these days—a manly and rational friend to talk with who won't insult my dignity with soft words and silver-gilt phrases, but will speak the blunt truth all the time, and so make conversation a refreshment and worth the trouble."

Harrison hesitated, and a faint color rose slowly into his face. It was a difficult place; there seemed a sort of incongruity about setting out to establish a reputation for blunt truth by beginning with a lie.

"Say it!"

It was plain that there was no escape; so, with as good an appearance of blunt truth as he could give to the words, Harrison said—

"It hurts me—it *hurts* me to say it; but in view of the evidence I am obliged to believe you guilty."

Fairfax reached for his hand and shook it, and said—

"That is sane and right; I hate a weakling and I love a man. Now we shall go on well together. And we can discuss *my* side of this tragedy. Not that discussing it can affect the case in any way, for it can't; yet it will be of value to me to discuss it, for I should like to have one good man believe me innocent; I should prize that—prize it supremely—it is a natural feeling; we are all made in that way; if we know that one good man believes in us we can rest serene in that solace and support, and let the common herd believe as it likes. I shall not be able straightway to convince you that I never touched the man, but in time you will believe; in time you will come to know me and then you will not doubt."

Then, detail by detail, he furnished his version of the tragedy, beginning with the shout which had startled him, followed by an agonised cry and a heavy fall, and ending with his discovery and arrest by the three villagers; Harrison listening, all the way through, with a suffering interest and a sore conscience.

"Now, then," said Fairfax, "I come to a queer mystery—a thing which I have puzzled over to weariness, to no purpose: I can't understand it."

"What is it?" asked Harrison, with a vague apprehension.

"That shout that startled me. The form of the phrase."

The phrase flashed through Harrison's memory: *"Um Gottes willen!"* His mind was a diligent factory of fanciful and irrational fears in these days, and for a moment he was alarmed; but only for a moment. He had picked up a good deal of German from Jake Bleeker, and had supposed he was the only man in the region, except Jake, who understood the language; but apparently here was another one. However, a relieving thought quieted his mind at once: it was a natural exclamation for Jake to make, in the circumstances,—the court would perceive that. Then he asked,—

"What was the phrase?"

"It was this: *You godless villain!*"

Harrison said to himself, "He doesn't know German, after all," and the thought gave him comfort, though he would not have been able to explain why, even to himself.

"I thought it was Jake's voice, but I had been drinking a little, and my wits were not as clear as they should have been. I see now, that it was the other man's."

"Well then, where is the mystery?"

"Where is it? Why, in the *form* of the phrase."

"Its form?" said Harrison, dubiously; "I don't quite get your idea."

"Why man, see how literary it is, how formal, how stately, how dramatic, how bookish! It could have come out of a novel or a play."

"It's true; I hadn't noticed it, but I see it now. It certainly is a very uncommon form."

"Here in this region? Indeed I should say so! Can you name the man in this community that can put his language together in that large style?"

After seeming to run over his list of acquaintances, Harrison conceded the point.

"No," he said, "upon reflection I do not call to mind anyone who—"

Fairfax cut in with a gesture, accompanied by a genial smile, and said innocently—

"Why, Harrison, *you* are the only man in the community that talks like that! What makes you start so!"

"Did I?" said Harrison, mopping his forehead with his handkerchief to hide the pallor which he felt was overspreading his face; "I am a bundle of nerves, these days, and—"

"Take some whisky. There—that will set you right. Don't you feel better, now? It's the best remedy there is. Allow me—I'll take some myself; for you gave *me* a start: I thought you thought I was hinting that *you* were the assassin—I honestly did; but you won't hold that against me," and he stroked Harrison's hand, which rested upon the chair-arm; "I was trying to compliment you; it's a good compliment, too, and deserved; many a felicitous phrase of yours has traveled the town and reached my ear. Now, then, do you know what I get out of that stately remark? In the first place, when you come to know me you will believe I didn't invent it or imagine it, but *heard* it, and that will convince you that there was another man there, since Jake could not frame that phrase; and as soon as you arrive at that you will be on your way to believe that it was that other man and not I who used that club. That is one of the things which I get out of that remark."

"And the other?"

"That the man who employed it was a stranger here."

"Well argued!—and correct," said Harrison, much comforted to see matters taking this new direction.

"The man was a stranger, sure; an educated stranger, a reader of books; a man who has been up in the world, and is down in it, now; a man whose needs are great, who probably grew up serenely confident that his training would always be an iron protection for him against temptation—"

Harrison darted a suspicious look at Fairfax—was Fairfax reading *him?* But Fairfax went tranquilly on, unconscious of the glance—

"—and as likely as not this burglarious entry of my house was his first attempt at crime, poor devil—who knows? A man to be pitied, if that was the case. Wouldn't you pity him?"

"Oh, with all my heart," said Harrison, and a blind man would have known that he was sincere this time, by the mere testimony of his tones.

There was a pause, and both men sat thinking. Presently Fairfax said with animation—

"Harrison, that man might be found! He would be detectible in a moment by his stylish language. There was never a better clue in the world. There were not *two* strangers like that in this village last night. Isn't that so?"

"Necessarily. There couldn't be two."

The futile hopefulness in the Squire's face sent a pang to

Harrison's heart, and he wished he could have been spared the sight of it. The Squire got up and walked the floor, cogitating, and the spring in his step showed that the clouds in his sky were lifting. He stopped presently and put his hand on Harrison's shoulder and said almost affectionately—

"Thank the good fate that sent me you! and to think I might have had you for a friend all these years! I see a hope, Harrison, I really do—don't you?"

"I—yes, I—believe I do."

"I know it, Harrison! It may not save me—that is not to be expected; but there's a chance to cast into the world's mind a large doubt that I was alone with Jake—a doubt worth a gold mine, for it would carry with it the powerful suggestion that that third person *might* have struck the blow, and not I. Harrison! if that stranger can be found, it is possible that people saw him near my house or pointed in its direction. Think of the force that that would have with a jury!" He was excited, and his eyes glowed. "It might not save me, but it would remove half of my disgrace; everybody would say I went to the State Prison upon an uncertainty. Think how that would lighten the burden for Helen and me!"

A ray of gladness burst into Harrison's clouded soul, and he forgot that there was no such stranger, and cried out fervently—

"Splendid—the Governor would pardon you out in twenty-four hours!"

The Squire straightened in his tracks, and the pride of seven generations of Fairfaxes rose crimson in his face.

"*Pardon* me—when I am innocent? I wouldn't accept it!"

Harrison was ashamed of his mistake, and stammered out—

"I only meant—meant—why, no, of course you couldn't."

Fairfax's eyes were snapping.

"I would rot in prison a century first!" Then observing Harrison's humble distress and shame, his brow cleared and his manner changed at once and he said, "Oh, you must forgive me, Harrison, I've been brutal; it was your good heart speaking, not your head— and for *me*; and I have thanked you with an arrogance. Don't hold it against me."

"Don't say a word, Fairfax, I can't stand it!" said Harrison, with honest emotion; "I can bear your rebukes, but your generosities kill me. Hold it? I can't hold *anything* against you."

The Squire was touched, and said this was the right friendship and must be consecrated—it was entitled to that honor. They consecrated it.

"Now then," said the Squire, putting away his glass, "find that stranger, Harrison, find the Shaksperean stranger, and come and we'll consecrate again."

Once more the stranger was real to Harrison for a moment, and he said fervently—

"I will!" Then he sighed, remembering that there was no such person.

"You will have no difficulty; there isn't two of him, and whoever has heard him talk will remember him. He stopped with Bowles, no doubt, and he can tell you about him. Meantime I have not asked after your father. He—well, I saw him a day or two ago, and I thought he did not seem quite well."

Fairfax remembered with a pang that in that interview he had been severe with the old man, not suspecting that his mind was disordered and that he was not responsible for the strange fraud which he had committed. The remark reminded George, too, of that sorrowful episode, and his heart sank, for he feared that the Squire was now going to speak of the counterfeit money—and what could he say in return? That *he* was not implicated? But how explain his father's act—tell him his father was mad? How could he do that? He resolved that he wouldn't. There would be no need; the secret would get out before many days, then the Squire would understand, and forgive.

"My father has not been very well, lately," said Harrison, and waited for Fairfax to go on. Fairfax did not find it easy to go on. He said hesitatingly, and watching George's face—

"I sent and asked him to come and see me, and—but—he did not come."

He paused. George said, with the manner of one who is not attaching importance to the matter—

"He ought to have gone. I will remind him, and he will come here."

Still watching George's face, the Squire said, tentatively—

"I—well, what I meant to convey to him was, that I had something for him."

"Oh," said George, with gratitude in his voice, "the canceled note! We got it, and I haven't said a word of how thankful we were, and how—"

The Squire put up his hand, and George stopped. Fairfax said to himself, with a sense of relief, "He knows nothing about it; it is easy sailing, now." Then aloud—

"No, that's a trifle—never mind about that. It was something else."

George shrunk in his clothes. "It is coming, now," he said to himself.

"It is another matter, Harrison, and"—seeing that Harrison was about to speak, he put up his hand again, and added with an appearance of indifference—"one which is of no consequence, and which you are not acquainted with." The words were a gracious surprise, and they came as a reviving breath to Harrison's troubled spirit; he hoped he had heard aright; the tidings seemed too good to be true. "The matter is private between your father and me, and I sent for him because there was no need that you or others should know about it; and so, if he can come to me here—"

The warder put his head in at the door and said—

"Mr. Harrison, there's a message to say your father is sick and Doctor Bradshaw can't be found."

The door closed, and Harrison began to put on his overcoat. Fairfax hesitated a moment, then said—

"This makes a change of plan necessary. He can't come, and I shall feel better to have the thing arranged to-day; therefore I must put it into your hands. As soon as you have found the doctor, go to my house and look in a certain drawer"—he described it—"and there you will find a roll of bank bills; they belong to your father, and he ought to have had them before this. But you can tell him the delay was not intentional, and he will be satisfied."

"I will attend to it—" and while he struggled into his overcoat he tried to think of something more to say, but nothing occurred to him, for he was in a new trouble: those counterfeits were marked

—they revealed the secret—was Fairfax forgetting that? He paused, to give Fairfax a chance to take him out of this dilemma. His suspicions were fired at once, and a thought came that made him sick: "Maybe he doesn't intend to take me out of it—maybe he means me to know!" He was in a condition where any remark or act which was not crystal clear to him was as scary as a white handkerchief with holes in it. The silence was awkward. Fairfax seemed to want to say something, but apparently he found the framing of it difficult. Presently he got it out. He laid his hand on Harrison's arm and said—

"You mustn't mind—but this matter—well, it is a little bit delicate, and I am going to ask you to put that money in your pocket without looking at it, and hand it to your father. I give you my word that there is nothing improper about this—your father will tell you so himself." He laughed an embarrassed laugh and said, "You are tongue-tied with surprise to see a grown-up man so secretive about a trivial matter, but never mind, we can't help the way we are made, you know, and I am made in that way."

Harrison said to himself, "I am tongue-tied with self-reproach for suspecting a man like you of being as obnoxious to mean suspicions as I am myself, and tongue-tied furthermore with gratitude for the generosity which would save a son from knowing of his father's disgrace." Then he said aloud, with heartiness, "I will carry out your instructions exactly to the letter, and—"

"Good. Go on. What is it?"

"Why, come to think, the money is not there."

"Not there? Why?" and the Squire's manner showed anxiety.

"Because an inventory of the room's contents was made and the place locked up and put under guard, and that inventory was produced at the inquest. There was no mention of money in it."

"The damned assassin got it!" and the Squire seemed aghast at the idea. "Harrison, I swear to you that the money was there. Nobody could have gotten it but the man that killed Jake Bleeker. Don't you believe that?" Without waiting for an answer he went on, excitedly, "You *must* find that stranger; it is of the utmost consequence that that money shall reach your father."

"I will do my very best, Squire; but you must not be troubled about this. I know by what you said a while ago that the amount is so small as to be inconsequential, and I am sure that when my father learns—"

"Oh, it isn't the *amount*—he must have *that* money, and no other."

"But I assure you he will not care. You can pay him in any kind of money you—"

"Harrison, don't—don't—*don't!* You don't understand the case, you don't know anything about it. Why 'didn't' I get it to him in time! perhaps he wouldn't be ill, now. He must have *that* money, I tell you, and no other. Find the stranger; hunt him down! I can never cease to reproach myself if—"

The door opened a crack and the confidential roar of the Yeller Press abolished the rest of the speech—

"Say, George, get home! They think the gov'ner's dying. He's been laying speechless ever since ten o'clock, and they can't find that cuss of a doctor. They think it's congestive chill. Hear? I said they think it's CONGESTIVE CHILL!" And he was gone, to spread the news.

"It is too late, now," said the Squire, miserably. "Too late—and I could have saved him. Go, Harrison. I was a brute; but before God I didn't know it and never meant it."

Harrison went away sick at heart, and saying to himself: "Oh, I foresee it, and there is no help; just for that one departure from rectitude I am to swim chin-deep in shames and sorrows the rest of my days. If I could only change places with my father, and die—or had the commonplace courage to change with that clean man yonder!" [6]

---

[6] The first typescript (DV 302x) ends at this point, p. 215 of the holograph. Of the foregoing part, p. 1–11 of the holograph, which include the story frame and were written later, are on a cheap pearl-gray tablet paper, size 5¾" x 8¹⁵⁄₁₆". Thereafter, three sequences numbered 1–7, 1–137, and 156–181 are on wove paper, light buff, size 5⁹⁄₁₆" x 8¹¹⁄₁₆". Pp. 138–158 and 182–215 are on a paper which has been described in note 2 for "Indiantown." Following p. 215 a new sequence begins, paginated 62–474; all of this part is on the same tablet stock that was used for the initial 11 page frame. The first typescript does not include this frame, which constitutes Book I, but begins thereafter, with Book II.

CHAPTER IX.

W<small>HEN</small> <small>HARRISON</small> reached home he found a sentry at the door, in the person of old Martha—she was waiting there to prepare him for the worst. His father had had the third chill "on'y a little while ago," she said, and of course there was no hope now.

"He's in a doze, Marse George; he don't speak; he ain't gwyne to speak no mo' in dis life; jist breaks a body's heart to see him layin' dah so still, en don't reconnize nobody. Doctor's come, a minute ago."

In the sick room the doctor sat holding the dying man's wrist; neighbor-women sat in couples about the room, softly whispering; one elderly lady was already removing the medicines and spoons and putting them out of sight, another was doing the same with hot-water bottles and mustard plasters. All the women came on tiptoe to meet George and say words of tenderness and sympathy; and they went with him and stood by the bed, and wept silently while he gazed upon the old father's white face; and when his own tears began to flow down his cheeks, and his lips to quiver, pictures of bygone bereavements of their own rose before them and they said to themselves they knew what he was feeling; then they were strongly moved by this communion of sorrow and suffering, and they murmured pitying things and sobbed aloud.

They really thought they knew what he felt, and all he felt, but it was not so. He was busy with miseries and pangs and self-reproaches which were outside the pale of their guesses. While they were praising him for a good son who had never cost his father a grief or a regret, he was mentally adding another bitter "fruit" to his tree of crimes and labeling it "patricide." They could not know this, poor souls; so they went innocently on with their deadly compliments—each in its turn a knife in his heart—and when at last one said "He couldn't do a dishonorable thing, and has left behind him a son that can't even *think* one," he felt the knife turn in the wound.

Two days later. They had all the funerals booked for this day, and Bowles said it was going to be the greatest day Indiantown had ever seen. "Three at a whack," he said with satisfaction, "and all aces; there ain't any community in these regions that can call that hand. Say, Allen, Deathshead Phillips has lost his grip, don't you reckon?—quit a-prophecying, hey?"

"How?"

"Well, here's three deaths in a lump, and he didn't appear to any of these folks to warn them. At least not to Doc Stevens and Jake Bleeker."

The dissipated-looking young fellow to whom these remarks were addressed—Allen Osgood—considered a moment while he gnawed a corner off a black slab of tobacco, then said—

"Niggers know more than whites about these things, you'll allow, I reckon?"

"Yes, it's so. Well, then?"

"Well, then, Fairfax's Jasper [7] says it don't always mean death when Crazy Phillips appears to a person; often it means worse luck."

"Worse luck than *death?*"

"It's what he says."

"Gosh, what an idea! Why, there ain't any worse. It's foolishness. Come—didn't he appear to Mahaly Robinson?—she died in a week. And Ben Chapman? died in ten days. And Sally Furniss?—died in a month; and Billy Fletcher; and there's others, if I could think of them; why, you know there's a lot of them. How does Jasper get around that?"

"I don't know; but it's what he says. He says if you could get at the secret facts you'd know it was a warning of worse luck, in

---

[7] The holograph here has "Pomp" as the name of the wronged Negro who is later called "Jasper"; to avoid confusion, the second name, representing Mark Twain's latest intention, has been used throughout the story.

some of the cases; particularly if he appears to a person several times."

"Land, that's easy to *say,* but how's he going to *prove* it? It's foolishness, I tell you. Why, lookyhere, he appeared to old Mr. Harrison three times in the last two or three weeks; you know it; everybody knows it. Why, it nearly scared him crazy. So there, now. I reckon you won't say *he* was in for any bad luck, considering what's come to the family. No, sir, it was just *death*—that was the warning. That's what *he* took it for; and so did George Harrison; he said so, himself, and Buck Thompson was by, and heard him."

"Well, then, all I've got to say is, he's changed his superstitions, for it's only two years ago that he was talking the other way, the time that Hank Frisbee got four warnings in four months and then it got found out that he'd been falsifying his books and robbing the county treasury for ten years. George said if Deathshead Phillips ever appeared to *him* he hoped it would be only *once,* and let him get ready for the funeral—didn't want him to come four times and intimate he could get himself ready for worse luck. Just his words. My mother heard him. He was laughing when he said it, but she said it was the kind of a laugh a person laughs when he's superstitious and is a little ashamed of it and wants to let on he's only funning. And she *knows* George; they were children together, and great friends; greater friends than ever, since that fire a long time ago that hit both of them so hard."

Bowles had dropped into a brown study, and was not listening. He was excitedly chewing a straw and mentally heaping up the profits this great day would bring to his tavern. There was a moment or two of silence. This woke him up, and he said briskly—

"Procession'll be moving pretty soon, now. So-long, lad—I've got to hustle; talk about Sidney Phillips's doings another time."

Everybody turned out, the secret societies in full regalia: the Masons following the mourners; then the Odd Fellows; then the Sons of Temperance; then the Cadets of Temperance; then the three Sabbath schools; then the militia company in uniform—all these organizations bearing banners muffled in crêpe—and last of all came the general public. It was the longest procession that had marched to the village graveyard in fifteen years—a thought which occurred to many, and awoke in their minds recollections of that long-vanished day which had brought such grief to the Harrison home and to two or three other households.

When the procession took up its homeward march it was noted that George Harrison had forsaken it; he had remained by the grave of his father. He stood there motionless, with bowed head and bare, a lonely figure among the tombs, and the receding column passed from sight and left him so. The day was bleak, and this reverent piety was remarked upon to his credit. Many said there were few such sons.

But Harrison was only waiting to be alone. His thoughts were not with his lost father, but with his long lost wife and children. He turned to their graves, now, and knelt there, and read their dimming names upon their grave-stones through a mist of tears, and felt again the heart-break which he had felt so many times before in this place. An elderly woman in black appeared, and greeted him, and he her, and she was crying; and he rose and they talked of their sorrows together, using the language of old friends and calling each other by their first names, as they had done from the cradle. The woman said—

"It is fifteen years, George, since the fire robbed you and me. I am not reconciled, I cannot *be* reconciled. What has time done for you?"

"Nothing. If it has not helped you, Frances Osgood, how could it help me? You lost one, I three."

"God pity you—as I do! But my loss . . . George, it was heavier than yours."

"Heavier than mine?"

"Ah, a hundred times, a hundred *times*," said the woman, bitterly. "To others my twin boys had no advantages, no attractions or merits one above the other—but what did *they* know! Nine years old, beautiful to look upon, and to the ignorant eye just alike; but they were no more alike than . . . think! death took my Harry, with his fine mind and his sound good heart—my Harry, that would have been a blessing to me and the pride of my life— and left me my poor Allen, my poor soft temptation-ridden irreclaimable lost sheep, to make his life and mine a burden and a shame! My God, what is your loss to mine, George? You know only grief; ah, wait till you know shame!—*then* you will know that there is a bitterness beyond the bitterness of death."

George glanced uncomfortably at her—always watchful, always suspicious, these days—but perceived that her shot had been a random one; then he worried out a remark, since he must say something:

"But Allen is not so bad, Frances. The fact that he drinks more than is good for him, and is idle, and is by many held to be a—that is to say—a—a not good example for—"

"And isn't that enough! What is left, but crime? Do you want me to go the whole pulpit-spread of pious servility and thank heaven that he isn't down to *that,* yet? Why, of course he's not an actual reptile—I'm not claiming that. He wouldn't burn a house, he wouldn't cheat, he wouldn't steal, he wouldn't murder—even a poor thing like Jake Bleeker; but what does all that amount to? Nothing, except that he isn't a dog. Well I never *said* he was a dog."

Harrison could hardly keep back a groan; her words tore him like a saw. He was in such a panic, for a moment, that he believed she had all his fearful secrets shut up in her heart and was trying to trap him into an exposure. Burn, cheat, steal—could she happen upon these initial steps of his criminal progress by accident? How could she? they were known to none but himself. Was she a clairvoyant? Or—the thought made him shudder—had he been talking in his sleep? He could feel himself turn white!

He shot a searching glance at the woman. But already her thoughts were far away—he could see it, and he felt a vast relief. Presently she said gently—

"Do you know how often we've met here since that day we buried them, George?"

"No, but it is many times."

"Yes, three or four times every year. And always we talked about how old they would be *now,* if they had lived—oh, my God, the sweetness of it, and the bitterness! George, we have watched them grow up, like that, so to speak, just as if they had been with us and not in the grave. Those little, little creatures—and now they would be men and women! . . . It makes you groan, poor man, and well it may. Those dear little girls; Alison, the blonde—"

"She was the picture of her mother, Frances, you remember it; beautiful as the morning. She would be twenty-one, now, if she had lived. And the little noisy one, a year younger, that was all fire and energy, after the way of brunettes—how still, all these long years! How dear they were—and their mother!"

"And my lost boy! Oh, my God, if they could only come back!"

The words, in earlier times so pleasant and so welcome, struck a horror to the man's heart, now: they had the seeming of a profane prayer; a dreadful prayer that might be answered.

"God forbid!" he said, in a quaking low voice.

The woman gazed at him, shocked and wondering.

"Do you *mean* that?"

"I do—God knows I do."

"I—I—George, I cannot understand this. Always before, you have said that if our dear lost ones could only come back to us—"

"I was younger, then."

"Why, only last year—"

"I was younger *then*. And a fool."

The woman seemed dazed, and for a time she could not find words for her thoughts; then she said, with strong feeling:

"It is wicked. I mean it—wicked. I have never heard such language before—and to think that it should come from you, of all men! you, the honored, the envied, the pet of fortune, a man esteemed, beloved, a man without a care, if these graves could but give up their dead. The wife and the children—have you no sorrow for what *they* are losing?"

Harrison answered dreamily, and almost as if he were talking to himself:

"She was beautiful and good, she was precious beyond words; and they—they were the light of our life, the joy of it. They were all young, they saw all of life that was worth the living. In their innocence they took it for a boon and a reality, and never suspected it for what it is, a treachery and a sham. They died at a happy time, they were worthy of that grace; and though my heart should break with longing for them, I would still pray for strength to say God send they may come no more out of the blessed refuge of the grave!"

The pair moved away, thinking but not speaking, and said good-bye and separated. For long the woman continued to muse, then she said—

"By what I have suffered I know that he is right. But how can they who have not suffered have this insight?"

CHAPTER [X]

As he sat thinking in his lonely home that night and listening to the dirges of the wintry wind, George Harrison reviewed his troubles and checked them off and put them behind him one by one, hoping to "close the account" if he might, and take up life again from a new base, if a new base were discoverable.

The result was not good. His troubles would not stay put back; they flocked to the front as fast as they were banished, and with every return they seemed to come refreshed and reinforced for their bitter work upon his conscience, and more sharply competent than they had been before.

His ghastly secrets were safe—that was all, that was the whole! Safe—in what way? Safe from the world! It made him sick. He couldn't rid *himself* of them, and that was the main misery. They gangreened the very heart and soul of him. And that man Fairfax's innocent trust and friendship and gratitude—the thought of it burnt like fire! How could he go on enduring it? He rose and walked the floor, moaning in his misery.

Presently, still walking, still muttering and ejaculating, he took up his situation and examined it on all sides, to see if he could invent any plan to improve it. But at the end of an hour he slumped into his chair exhausted and defeated. There was no way out—matters must remain as they were.

What attitude to take, then? There was but one sane one: keep his deadly secrets, drive the thought of them out of his mind, brace up and be a man!—for once. In time they would lose their devilish force, their sting would cease from persecuting, the tragedy would pass from men's memories, and remain but as a vague and doubtful dream in his own, perhaps; then his soul would have peace, and he could hold up his head again. . . . Why, these were wholesome thoughts, reviving thoughts!—why couldn't he have thought them sooner? He felt better already; life was not so black, after all. Now, a cheery little drop of whisky—

A rap at the front door startled him. He put down bottle and glass.

"Come in," he said.

The door swung open, and a ghastly figure appeared in it. Harrison shrunk together paralysed, and a name rose to his lips but died there for lack of strength in his tongue to utter it—

"Deathshead Phillips!"

The figure was tall and slender, and clothed from skull-cap to stockings in dead and lustreless black, the hands included. It stood motionless—a statue made of charcoal, as it were. The cut of the raiment was not modern, but ancient and mephistophelian. Save for a short cape that hung from the shoulders, it fitted the contours of the long body as tightly as a skin. It absorbed light and quenched it, reflecting none; not a glint showed upon its gloomy surface anywhere.

Without speaking, and without sound of footfall, the sombre apparition glided slowly past the master of the house and seated itself in a chair; not in a negligent attitude, but upright and rigid, like a piece of sculpture. And now the light fell full upon its face; Harrison shuddered, and turned away. It was the face of a ghost; a strenuous white, a ghastly white, dead and lustreless; a white artificially produced, with powdered chalk or some such thing, thickly laid on. A faint crease marked the place of the mouth; the eyes were like burnt holes in a sheet; they were fixed steadily upon Harrison; at intervals they closed for a moment, then the mask was wholly white and horrible; even more so than when they were open, if such a thing might be possible.

The slow minutes dragged on and on, the dismal guest sat

motionless and mute; the mournful baying of a dog floated down out of the distance, the wind rose and rumbled in the chimney, the mice came out and played on the floor, thinking there was no life present, the place was so still. This for a century, a hideous and heart-straining century—though marked by the clock as only half an hour.

Then Dug Hapgood burst in, immensely excited, evidently loaded with great news—took one glance, said

"Jesus!" and was gone again.

The apparition gave no sign, uttered no word, relaxed no muscle of its rigid frame, but sat as before, ominously gazing. Harrison groaned inwardly, and his weary head drooped and sank upon his breast. When he lifted it again, he was alone.

"Thank God, if it means death!" he said. "There is nothing for me to live for. . . . They are at peace yonder. Lord, how fortunate are they that die in their youth! . . . Surely I have suffered enough, it *must* mean death."

Mechanically he rose and opened the door; evidently a weight had been pressing against it, for it yielded with unusual suddenness —and Dug Hapgood fell into his arms with a shriek. Then he plunged free, and stood trembling and gasping and staring, for a moment.

"Land!" he said, recovering himself, "I thought it was *him!*"

He flung off his wraps, tossed off a taste of whisky, smacked his lips with satisfaction, sat down and stretched his feet to the fire, and yelled—

"Say, George, set down and let's be cosy—I've got news for you. You *get* it? Said I've got NEWS for you."

"Yes, I heard—don't yell so."

"Who, me?"—in a hurt tone. "I reckon I don't smell any worse than *others*, when you come down to that."

George shouted—

"I never said anything about smelling; I said don't *yell* so."

"Oh, all right, then; I didn't understand. Gee-whiz—nearly nine! Say, that old clock's got the jim-jams. What's that you say? She's right, you think? Well, it don't matter, anyway—no occasion to hurry, I got plenty of time. Say, George, I got just one look at his mug, and it gimme the blind staggers. Why, I was fifty yards up the road before I could pull up, I was that scared. And it took me *one* while to work up strength enough to come back and listen. And then, by gracious, he was gone. What did he tell you, George?"

"Nothing."

"Nothing at all?"

"No."

"What? Didn't even speak?"

"No."

"The idea! Well, then, how do you know who's going to die?"

"I *don't.*"

"Goodness gracious, why it's a perfectly hell of an idea! It might be you, it might be Martha, it might be Tom. Why, *he's* no good—scaring a whole tribe to death thataway, when he's only after one of them. Which do you think it is, George?"

"Hang it, how should *I* know!"

"Well, anyway you needn't get huffy about it, I ain't asking for any selfish reason—*you* know that, George—but only out of sympathy."

"Oh, well, I'm not denying it, but the subject's offensive to me."

"All right, then, let her slide, but blamed if I can see what's offensive about it. Say, George, I reckon you know what drove him crazy? He put on a sheet and a dough-face, so as to represent a ghost or a corpse, one night late, and slipped up behind his sweetheart where she was reading by a candle all alone, and poked his face around in hern; and she screamed, scream after scream, and fell down, clear out of her senses; and next week, 'stead of they two getting married she was in the madhouse and been there ever since—over fourteen years—moaning and crooning and crying, and going into spasms at every sudden noise she hears; and he went mad, too, before she'd been there a month—and lucky for him, I say, for it's better to be mad and forget such a thing than have it on your mind a-scorching your heart all the time; and poor devil, he such good stock, and so rich and gay and breezy, and in for everything that's going—just the life of the wake, as the saying is

—and fairly worshiped the ground she walked on, and they all say
she did have the sweetest, gentlest face that ever was, and they'd
have been awful happy, George, if that mistake hadn't been made
—just that poor little two-minute mistake! and here's fourteen
years squandered into that hole trying to pay for it and settle up
and satisfy Nature, who's just a hog when she's got an account
against you; yes, sir, the hog of hogs, that's what Nature is, you
can't owe *her* two cents and square up for less than fourteen
thousand dollars; I wish I had her where the hair's short, just once
—if I didn't take it out of her I wish I—say, George, I never seen
him in his war-paint before; my, but ain't he just hark from the
tomb to look at! Not many's seen him in it, they say; and *they*
didn't live long to brag about it. Do you begin to feel anything,
George?—anything different from common, I mean?—'s if you
warn't feeling as hearty as—"

"Oh, cram a pillow down that crater of yours! give a suffering
man some peace. Have you *no* reserves, no refinement? I do not see
how you can have the heart to ask such atrocious questions."

Dug was deeply wounded, and said in thunder-blasts mellowed
by emotion—

"I never expected this from *you*, George. If a poor forsaken
humble friend's friendly interest and sympathy for a friend who's
in trouble and needing a true friend's sympathy and consolement,
though an orphan and consumptive, and considered not long for
this world, is a crime—"

His eyes filled, his lips quivered, his voice broke; and George
hastened to say—

"There, there—don't, old chap, I didn't mean it. Here, take
another drink, and let bygones be bygones. Go on with your
ancient histories, but don't be pathetic, I can't stand it."

"Now that's *like* you, George," shouted the soft-hearted and
easily appeased orphan, wiping his eyes with one sleeve and his lips
with the other; "I said, that's LIKE you. Your heart's in the right
place—*I* know that—but your nerves is raw on account of that
corpse-face, and no wonder. If he was to appear to me, derned if I
wouldn't jump out of my skin and leave it a-quivering on the floor,
same as if it was jelly. . . . By Jackson! lucky I wasn't here

beforehand—he'd have appeared to both of us, then, and we'd be
booked for the cemet'ry in the same hearse; but he didn't appear to
me, I appeared to *him,* so there's only one of us. No occasion for *me*
to worry, don't you think, George?" he added, a little anxiously.

George said he thought there was none, and Dug's face brightened and he was at once his cheery self again.

"It's as I think, myself, so I ain't a-going to worry. There's plenty
to worry about in this world without hunting around, that's what I
always say. Now I reckon—say, George, he don't ever put on his
war-gear except when there's business in his line and he has to turn
out and notify somebody to settle up with this world and get
measured for his last suit; and he don't stay shut up in his tall walls
all the time in the intervals; no, he comes out now and then,
dressed like anybody, and looking gentle and sad, and not really old
—why, he ain't quite forty yet; he don't talk much, just moons
around, kind of dreamy, motioning soft with his hands, and
muttering to himself; my, it's the pitifulest sight—I've seen him,
George. *You* have, too? Yes, of course you have. But I've seen
her!"

"Why, Dug!—come, you are dreaming. Are you sure? When
was it? where was it? Tell me about it. Poor child—why, I knew
her when she was a dear little creature with plaited tails down her
back."

"Yes, sir, I saw her. It was last summer. She'd escaped; and away
up yonder on the river bank where they used to play in old school-
times they came together all of a sudden and unexpected, and there
they stopped, and stood stock still, looking at each other thisaway—
with their heads forward and bent, and looking out intense from
under their eye-brows, sort of scared, and wondering, and thankful,
you know, and just as if each one thought the other was dead and a
spirit—stood so, for a minute, maybe as much as two, and never a
word, and the tears running down their faces; then she turned and
went away crying, with her head drooping, and he stood watching
her till she was out of sight; and his face was as if he'd seen the
glory of God and the heaven everlasting."

A deep silence followed. Both men sat absorbed in thought, busy
with memories and dreams, unconscious of the drift of time. When

at last the master of the house raised his head he perceived that he had two guests; his gaze met the gaze of that black statue with the snow-white face. It was standing behind the other guest's chair. While Harrison muttered miserably to himself, "Oh, it was not death—that charity is not for me," it moved without sound to the rear door and passed out.

The latch of the closing door rattled slightly, disturbing Dug's revery, and he glanced up.

"What was that, George?"

"The wind." The words sounded like a moan.

"Lord, you needn't be so *sad* about it! And you needn't *look* so sad, either. And I can tell you why, George. Didn't I say I've got news for you? Well, I just *have*. You listen; and if I don't make you jump for joy I wish I—are you ready?"

"Go on." It sounded like a sigh.

"I was right from Gilbert's when I first struck in here a little bit ago to tell you about it. He'd got a letter that minute, with the biggest news in it!—from Memphis. George, that old uncle of yourn has dropped off the hooks at last, and b'gosh you're rich enough to buy this county and everybody in it! Shake!"

Harrison sprang to his feet with the fury of a maniac flaming in his eyes, and plunged at Hapgood, shouting—

"Take it back! Take it back, I tell you! Say it's a lie!"

"Oh, George, keep away, keep away!—don't look at me like that! What have *I* done? It's the God's truth, as sure as I'm a-standing here—you ask Gilbert if it ain't."

Harrison, frightened to think how his words and his conduct might seem to the public if reported without modifying explanations, promptly changed his manner and said, sadly—

"Oh, don't mind me, old friend; the thought maddened me: it seemed such a cruel fate, that my poor old father couldn't have lived to have his share of this great joy, and he so poor and so downcast and hard pressed so long. Laid in his grave this very day! and these happy tidings speeding to him—to arrive too late, too late! I cannot have pleasure in them, now—oh, not yet; it would be brutal. Forgive me, Dug; anger carried me away; I was not myself."

Tears stood in the impressionable orphan's eyes; he wrung Harrison's hand fervently and said—

"George Harrison, I think you're the noblest white man that ever walked—and the unselfishest, by God! There ain't another man in this township but would be thinking of himself; but you—you only think of others when luck jumps your way. Shake again, and God bless you. Now I'm happy, and I'm a-going."

He went his way, and Harrison took up that dreary march, up and down the floor, which is the only relief which captive bears and persecuted and despairing men can find for their miseries. He kept turning a single thought over and over in his mind—over and over, over and over, plowing a furrow through his tired brain with it:

"If I could have known!—if he could have known!—such a little while ago! Ah, dear, we should have been saved, we should have been saved."

CHAPTER [XI]

Next morning there was a stream of visitors. The principal citizens came—all of them. First, to condole about the departed father; next, to congratulate about the inherited great fortune. These were fairly easy tasks, and were achieved creditably, but when the visitors tried to lead up to the subject of next importance and interest—Deathshead Phillips's warning—few were able to do it. Most of the people had been trained from the cradle in superstitions by their negro nurses; to them, ghosts, dream-warnings and such things were matters of course; Phillips's reputation was well established, and when, officially costumed for his dread office, he appeared to a man, hardly any—if any at all—doubted that that act was as authentic as the death-rattle. A visitor got along very well as long as he was condoling and congratulating, but when he came up against the third subject his talk became disjointed and scrappy; in spite of him his gaze fixed itself with an awed and absorbed fascination upon the doomed man, and a single thought set its clutch upon his imagination and would not let go: "Just to think! there he sits alive, and so soon he will be in his shroud, poor fellow." These people could not know that the object of this shuddery thought was at this moment envying Charley Axtell the consumptive, who sat apart, silent and sorrowfully brooding, with sunken cheeks and protruding eyes, and coat and trousers dinted and caved in, everywhere, and seeming to contain nothing—a really doomed man but not believing it, as is the way of consumptives.

Among the chief citizens present were General Landry, Mr. Gilbert, Rev. Mr. Bailey, and Sol Bailey [8] his brother—privately called Ham-fat Bailey the Idiot Philosopher, by the public. General Landry was a grand figure and majestic, seventy-three years old, suave, erect, perfect in health, clothed in the fashion of a forgotten past, with ruffled wristbands, ruffled bosom, long vest, black velvet coat with broad tails, black velvet knee breeches, low-quarter shoes with silver buckles—the very image of Benjamin Franklin, broad benignant face and all—including gold-headed cane: the only man in the region so dressed since old Squire Fairfax passed away ten years before. As first lieutenant this military relic had been in the fight at Lundy's Lane; and in the succeeding forty years had gradually climbed up through all the grades to General—a notable proof of his popularity, for these promotions had been conferred, each in its turn as it was seen to be deserved; and not by the War Department but by the citizens of Indiantown, by spontaneous inspiration and common consent, and without consultation or collusion. He was orthodox.

Mr. Gilbert, fifty, clean shaven, with short iron gray hair which was upright and stiff, like Andrew Jackson's; severely trim and correct in dress, no fleck of dust upon him anywhere; dignified in bearing; austere, unsmiling, untalkative, the acknowledged head of the bar—he was the citizen of next importance. He never went to church. If he had a religion, it was private. Persons who had

---

[8] The holograph here had "David" as the first name of the Rev. Mr. Bailey's brother. Later in the story his name appears regularly as "Sol." The latter name, representing the author's latest intention, has been used throughout the story.

inquired about it once had not felt like inquiring again. He had come to report the news from Memphis, but said he would come again—at a more private time.

"Any time will do," said Harrison, drearily; "it would interest me if my father were still here; it comes like a mockery, now. Tell me one detail—let the rest go: how much ready cash is there?"

The lawyer hesitated a moment, not much liking to talk business privacies in public, a most irregular procedure, then answered—

"Forty-five thousand dollars."

It was an incredible sum, an unheard-of sum, and made every heart bound, except Harrison's. It struck a pang to his, and he grieved to himself, "The misery of it, the irony of it! it was there, and ours—in our very pockets, so to speak—when he and I were swindling, burning, stealing, murdering, for the poor sake of a ninth of it. Everlasting curses on the malicious fate that devised that brutal trap! curse Nature and all her cruel ways!"

Hamfat's mouth watered over those enchanting figures, his eye wandered over his shabby clothes, and he sighed. For Hamfat was a failure from the cradle; one of those pathetic creatures who get into this world by accident, let us hope, not design; unstable as water; who try everything—at other people's expense—are fitted for nothing, and never succeed in a single instance. If they could only be born hopeless! then they would sit down and keep still and eat the bread of charity in peace, and be a sort of endurable burden. But no, their devilish mission would be unachievable, then; therefore they are born loaded to the eyes with hopefulness, and with nothing else; nothing else but caprice, and fickleness, and confidence in themselves, and grand ideals, and inflated enthusiasms, and destitution of the sense of shame, and—to say it in a word,—they are loaded to the eyes with every worthless quality (worthless when misplaced,) that can be named; that is to say, they are loaded with emptiness, and they don't know it.

Hamfat was fifty-three, and could have carried in his vest pocket all the money he had ever really earned. He had partly learned the carpenter's trade, but wouldn't work at it, because it was not high-toned enough for him. All his life he had been living on his brother the soft and persuadable Presbyterian clergyman, who had married a woman dowered with some property; had lived on him by "borrowing," as he called it, though why he should name it so when the borrowings had been persistently permanent, was his own secret. However, to be fair to him, there was really a sort of tin-plated justification of the term; for when he borrowed a sum he always instantly took from it enough to pay three months' interest on it, and sent it back, with a receipt to be signed; and it was always his intention to continue to pay interest and to eventually return the principal, but he always found that God had willed otherwise, and he submitted with such resignation as he could command. He had tuckered out a wife or two as he went along, and distributed children around wherever they would be handy to his brother's pocket; and meantime he had drifted from place to place in three States, and been lawyer without clients, preacher without congregation, lecturer without audience, political candidate without nomination or following, village newspaper owner and editor without subscribers, promoter of speculations that went promptly to the devil, fervent disciple and advocate of every frantic "ism" that had ever come his way, everlasting purchaser of humble homes triple-shingled with mortgages for his brother to nurse—and meantime, also, he had skirmished under the banner of every religion known to history, including Mormonism, infidelity and the Voodoo, and was now "due to be an Atheist, next revolution of his spiritual bowels," as Dug Hapgood said.

He regarded these insanities as bricks in what he called his "edifice of experience," and really believed that as he had traveled more than any other man in Indiantown and had personally tested more different kinds of life than any other Indiantowner, he was for these reasons the best qualified man there to debate high questions of morals, religion, politics, business and philosophy, and settle them. This serene and immense conceit of himself was impervious to ridicule, contempt, sarcasm, and even frank abuse and insult. He rose tranquilly superior to these things, and looked pityingly down upon their utterers as being poor innocent irresponsibles who hadn't been anywhere and didn't know anything, and so were not to blame. He was above hating them; indeed he loved them, "in a large, Supreme-Being kind of a way," as Dug Hapgood phrased it; and the orphan was right, bar himself. "Hamfat" and "Idiot Philosopher" were inventions of his, and these courtesies had not won for him the favor of the man thus labeled. In fact Hamfat could not bear the sight of him, and often said so. Hamfat was here to condole and congratulate, like the rest; and also to caress and beguile and persuade the new capitalist to a good deed, in case opportunity should offer, for he had an appetising scheme or two in mind which lacked nothing but capital to be perfect and fruitful; and if these did not "take," no matter: he always had an emergency-card up his sleeve which was sure to win in those regions. This was the Oriental Missions of the Presbyterian Church. With him, religions came and religions went, but to that charity he was always steadfast, always loyal, whatever spiritual flag he might be flying. It always brought money, regardless of the condition of the financial weather. For thirteen years, now, he had been working it in the interest of Turkey, and in that time had saved one Turk and part of another. With the American Board he was a pet, and he kept its lurid praises framed. He sometimes did questionable things; things which in the case of other men would have been sins, but in his case were not, for his Moral Sense was feeble, dubious, erratic and cross-eyed, and could seldom tell right from wrong with any kind of certainty. He had a smart intellect, but it was of small use to him, for it was under no mastership, and it capered around everywhere and generally landed him nowhere in particular. He had a conscience that could bite him, and it did it; but he could soothe it and satisfy it with impromptu remedies of his own invention which would have made another man's sea-sick.

Meantime the condolements were proceeding. General Landry spoke feelingly of the departed veteran, and said, in his courtly large way—in his Johnsonian way, for he was an admirer of that great man and his imposing diction—

"It was my privilege, sir, to enjoy the confidence and esteem of your lamented father during a period of forty years, and I mourn him, sir, I mourn him with sincerity. His was a character without spot, a character of noble integrity. He was, sir, in a word, a Moral Gibraltar. It is matter to be grateful for, that in you, sir, we have his perfect duplicate. In you, sir, resides the same nobility of character, the same purity, the same unshakable integrity, the same devotion to high principles; in a word, in you, sir, it is this community's privilege to possess another Moral Gibraltar. Remain a beacon and a guide to the weak! what you are, may all who come in contact with you become!"

"God grant it!" said several, with unction. What George said, he said to himself, with a nipping pang; and with a blush which was taken for an output of modesty, and got him credit.

"Like his son," said the aged clergyman, Mr. Bailey, with an affectionate tone in his voice, "he did not know what a baseness was, nor a selfish impulse. He had a lucid mind and a healthy judgment; and if I may say it without seeming to compliment myself, his opinions and mine were the same on all great subjects. No, there was one exception. There we disagreed. He believed that a character could not become firm and safe upon mere mouth-teaching and the shunning of temptation; he said it was best and securest when tried by fire: it must confront temptation—and *fall!* Then it would be safe after that; it would be grounded on a rock, and the winds and waves of temptation would beat upon it in vain. I disputed his position many times with him, but he always stuck to it."

"He was right," said the Idiot Philosopher, with easy confidence. "I have had a large experience of the world and of life, and I know he was right. I have been tempted, in my time, I have also fallen. I do not regret it. It established my character, it made me what I am. To it I owe everything."

There was opportunity for compliment, but there was an awkward silence instead. No one seemed to know how to get the talk started again, and the awkwardness increased. But the Philosopher was not disturbed, he was only lost in weighty reflections. He came to, now, and furnished the start himself.

"For instance, consider this fact—these related facts. Almost every man in the world has temper. It follows that almost every man in the world is a murderer. Am I right?" (He indicated this, that and the other guest with a nod). "Are you a murderer? Are you? And you, and you?" Each in his turn stared, amused. "Aren't *you* a murderer, George Harrison, and don't you know it?"

Harrison gasped and turned white. It was supposed that his sensitive nature rose against the insult; and so his sensitive make got unworded compliments from the guests. The Philosopher went placidly on.

"Sometime or other, when in a rage, all men of masculine temper and force have been murderers—in their hearts, I mean. But there was no weapon at hand, and the man did not get murdered —*just for that reason*, and no other. Or, the weapon was there, but the offending man wasn't—and *that* is why he escaped. If weapon, offender, and the moment of supremest rage had all happened to come together at once, there had been murder, *sure*. To be a murderer in your heart, and only saved from committing it by an accident of circumstance, what is that? It is murder just the same, isn't it? Of course. It is no merit of *yours* that you didn't do the deed. You are all murderers here, every one. And not one of you is safe from committing an actual homicide between here and the grave. If ever the three circumstances shall fall together, you will commit murder, to an absolute certainty. But if either of you here shall ever have that experience and kill a man, *that* lesson will stick and stay; you can never be caught out again by the passion of hate; grief and remorse will protect you, never again will you shed blood."

Harrison sighed to himself, in an agony of misery, "God knows he is saying the truth."

The Philosopher placidly continued:

"Take it in the littlest little things. In times when I have been a preacher of some denomination or other, and had to wear collars, they would not button because they had shrunk in the wash; and in struggling with them, and frothing and raging against the man that invented collars, I have wished, deep down in my heart, that he was present and I had an axe. See how little a thing that is—but the hate and the rage were not little; they were sufficient, and I should have killed him. Killed him, and been full of remorse the next moment. Don't you people believe that? Don't you believe it, George Harrison? Don't you believe there have been times when you could have killed a man? when not even the thought of the heart-break and the sorrow and the mourning—and perhaps the hunger and privation—you would bring upon his unoffending wife and children would stay your hand—perhaps not even enter your mind?"

Harrison murmured an indistinct "yes," and said to himself, "Oh, *why* does he torture me so? is there no other subject to talk about?"

Several granted that if you look at it *that* way, there is a rich abundance of murderers—and stopped with that; and all the company dropped into musings, with noddings of the head, and wrinkling of brows, and seemed to be recalling incidents in their lives which had suddenly taken on a new aspect and a new and grave meaning. Then the old clergyman spoke up and said:

"Why, really this is curious, and reminds me of something which our lamented late friend said to me several times when we were disputing. He had a most strange delusion; just a plain, straight, manifest delusion, you understand, and I used to tell him it was that, and laugh at him; but he had entertained it so long that he had come at last to believe in it, and to soberly regard it as a reality. According to him, he lived in its protection. He said that as long as he should keep in his right mind he would be safe from committing a crime, because—because why? What do you think was his reason?"

Nobody was able to guess.

"Because he had already committed one!" Mr. Bailey laughed, and the others joined in.

"Think of it!" said the amused minister. "That dear soul, that beautiful nature, that gracious spirit—try to conceive of it! But there it is; he believed in it. And so it is as I have always said and believed, since then: if delusions can enslave a strong and healthy mind like that, how can we justly criticise weaker people for having them?"

He began to branch off, now, on another topic, this one being exhausted, as he judged, but Hamfat interrupted, and asked him to state what the delusion was. The faces of the other guests showed interest, too, for curiosity is a human trait, and is not confined to any particular sex. Mr. Bailey was disappointed; his heart was in his new topic; however—

"Well," he said, "if dream-stuff can interest you, you can have it; but it will lose by my telling, for I can't put into it the deep air of truth and conviction and sincerity that made it so moving and impressive when he told it; and all that, of course, was just the *life* of it. I remember the first time he spoke of it. It was in my study, and we were alone. We had been having one of those debates. Of course I had been maintaining that the candidate should be carefully kept out of the way of temptation until his principles should be in a condition to defy it, and he had been trying to convince me that my position was unsound and perilous. I said again, as I had said more than once before, that it was a new and most strange and shocking doctrine; but he insisted that there was argument on his side, and asked how old I was. I said I was forty-six. Then he asked—

" 'Have you ever been under very strong temptation?' [9]

" 'No, sir,' I said, 'my parents protected me from it in their time, and since then I have always kept out of the way of it myself.'

" 'Then you are not safe. If you live to be a hundred you will always be unsafe. You see, one may successfully resist a thousand temptations—everybody does it—and still not be *sure* his principles are absolutely and unassailably established.'

" 'Why?'

" 'Because—well, overcoming temptations is good, is excellent; but ten thousand of them are not as valuable as one *fall.*'

" 'A fall! You call *that* valuable, sir?'

" 'More than valuable—*in*valuable. There is nothing teaches like a fall. The man that gets a fall *realizes* things.' " (Harrison's eyes were glassy, and he was breathing short and nervously wetting his dry lips with his tongue.) " 'He recognizes that he was moral in theory before; he is likely to be moral in *fact* after that rude experience. He was walking on precept and sentiment before—he is likely to walk on the ground afterward. You are not safe, sir. I am not jesting. Until a man falls, once or twice, he isn't safe, I tell you! His virtues have not been tested in the fire; until they have been

---

[9] At this point in the holograph there is a gap of three pages (111–113). The missing part is, however, in the second typescript (DV 302a), and has been used, in the form in which it there appears, as the remaining part of this chapter.

hardened in the fire they are not to be depended on.' He paused, a moment; then continued, in a voice and manner that were deeply earnest and impressive. 'Mr. Bailey, is there a stain of any kind on my name?'

" 'No, sir.'

" 'Am I considered a man wholly beyond the reach of temptation?'

" 'Yes, sir.'

" 'Mr. Bailey, I think I *am* beyond the reach of it. I may say I know it. For *I've been through the fire.*'

" '*You*, sir?'

" 'Before I was twenty-five I committed a crime—a grave one.'

" 'Impossible!'

" 'If I had had my deserts I should have spent as many as ten years in prison.'

" 'Why, it seems abso—'

" 'I was not found out. I was not even suspected. And yet I lived in hell for three years.'

" 'For fear that you would be suspected?'

" 'No; secret worry and distress because another man was suspected. Four times he came near being arrested; and each time, by desperate effort and the influence of our family name and standing I prevented it. For two years I sweated blood! If that man had ever come before a court the circumstantial evidence would have convicted him.' " (George Harrison was straining at his collar and gasping for breath.) " 'I saved him from prison, but that was all; he was a ruined man in character and estate. I could not endure the sight of his piteous face, and I left that region and never returned.' The tears were in his eyes; and his voice broke when he added, 'I had him on my conscience till he died—died of his misery. I have been through the fire, Mr. Bailey. The man who has had my experience does not commit a second crime. *Not while he keeps his reason.*' For the moment it sounded absolutely true—so true and so real that I said in all seriousness,

" 'Mr. Harrison, you had a plain duty: when he was suspected you should have come forward and confessed.' He bent a steady gaze upon me for a few moments, then he asked—

" 'Would you have done it?'

"Without hesitancy I answered—

" 'Yes, sir, I would.' Dear, dear, it was so strange and funny! and many a time since, when I think of it—"

"Good God! What is the matter with him?" This from the General. He was gazing at Harrison, who, limp and ghastly, was sinking out of his chair to the floor. Half a dozen cried out, "Help! bring water—he has fainted!" There was bustle and tumult for a few minutes; then Harrison lay in his bed, weak and pallid, with pitying women about him, ministering to him—among them Bridget Bleeker, in her poor and coarse widow's weeds. The guests were gone, talking among themselves as they walked, and saying it was like George Harrison, with his sensitive and fine-strung nature and his wasting grief for his father's loss, to be overcome by a weird and fantastic story so dramatically and impressively told as that one had been.

CHAPTER [XII]

For some little time Harrison lay with closed eyes, and probably unconscious of the faint swishing of gowns, the women's whispered consultations, and the other vague and seemingly distant sounds that customarily wander spectrally through the dreamy stillness of a sick-room and deepen it rather than disturb it; then his lids parted and he saw Bridget's compassionate Irish face hovering over him. It lighted friendly, his eyes responded gratefully; and she, seeing that he wanted to speak, put her head down close, and he said, in a feeble voice—

"Good girl—and kind. I am a sick man. Stay by me, Bridget."

"God knows I will, sir. You always stood by us, sir, and it's not the likes of me that'll forget it."

"Thank you, Bridget. Go and thank these good neighbors for me, and send them away; say I am better, and will sleep, now."

"Yes, sir."

"Thank Mrs. Frances Osgood particularly."

"Yes, sir."

She did her errand and returned for orders. But he had a weight upon his mind, and was feverishly eager to free it of its burden.

"Let the orders wait, Bridget, I want to talk about a matter. My father was in deep trouble, in his last days—"

"God rest his soul, he was! there's not anny, now, but knows it, by token that Dug Hapgood—"

"—and being in trouble and worried, he—well, he did one or two things which were not natural to him—that is, I mean—I mean—Bridget, *you* know how it is when a person is distressed and worried, that way?"

"Ah, and don't we all, sir! it's the truth you are saying, sir; and if—"

"And so he. . . . Bridget, if he were here now, you *know* he would make his word good about the wages."

"He would, sir, he would indeed; I've thought hard thoughts of him, sir, being in trouble meself, but all the same I know, and none knows better—"

"Bridget, he would make his word good, if he were back. He would raise the wages, as he said he would. And *more.* Because of the wrong he did, he would double them. More still: he would treble them. And so they are *now* trebled—to you—for life. It is himself, speaking from the grave, by my mouth. Forgive him, Bridget."

She could not find the words; but her flowing eyes and her eloquent face said it all. From poverty to independence—in a breath! She sank to her knees and sent her heart's gratitude streaming up to her saints for it—who had probably had nothing to do with it. Into Harrison's wan soul stole a healing peace and comfort and solace which it had not known for an age, as it seemed to him.

Dr. Bradshaw had been sent for. He arrived now, and made an elaborate examination of the patient and asked a multitude of questions, on a medical basis of a couple of generations earlier, science and the fashions being about that far behind, out West. He questioned Harrison for small-pox; for measles; for phthisis; for liver complaint; for whooping-cough; for cholera morbus; for fits; for "yaller janders," for bots, heaves, scrofula, blind staggers, gravel, hydrophobia—for every ailment mentioned in the books, in fact—and never got a responsive symptom. He was puzzled. Here was a very sick man; he could see that; yet there was nothing the matter with him. Not a thing, so far as he could see. Very well, in such cases there was but one thing to do: so he treated him for suppressed itch.

Bridget held the bowl, and he bled the patient in the foot and arm; cupped him in the back; hung a fringe of leeches on his temples; ordered a raiment of mustard-plasters for him; gave him a purge and a vomit, timed to go off together; then devised a soothing draught, which Bridget was to compound on the premises, boil down, distil, concentrate to a "compromise with hell-fire" as Dug Hapgood afterward described it, and wake him up and give him a shovelful every three-quarters of an hour until he got better or died. He wrote the tranquilizer down.

It took him fifteen minutes to do it. It contained a bushel of assorted and chaotic ingredients; among them all the forest weeds and herbs in the neighborhood, along with cloves, lunar caustic, castor oil, cinnamon, horse-dung, aqua fortis, sugar, dried lizards, turpentine, blue vitriol, molasses, and so on; and he was about to add another—a paper of tacks, probably—when he became conscious that some one was looking over his shoulder. It was Dug Hapgood. He yelled, cheerfully—

"Good-bye, George! I said good-*bye*,—understand? Better to have him than Deathshead—hey? *Quicker*, you know—and certainer; I said *certainer*—get it?"

"How did *you* get in here?" shouted the doctor, with asperity. "I told Martha to let no one in. This man needs quiet. *Quiet*—you hear?"

"Well, I like *that*," responded Dug, deeply injured; "do you reckon *I'm* going to disturb him?"

"You—indeed! You would disturb the dead."

"Sho! you wait till you're done with him, and see."

The doctor gathered up his assassination-tools, and bustled out, muttering that he would not stay to be insulted. Bridget tried to persuade Dug to go, but he took a chair and said, in reassuring thunder-tones—

"Don't you worry about me, Bridget; and don't you worry about him, either; you go 'long and prepare him for the grave—I'll tend him like he was your own baby till you get his pison mixed, I ain't in any hurry, got plenty time."

So Bridget gave it up, and left for the kitchen with the prescription. Dug resumed:

"Of course you ain't going to mind me, George, I'm your friend, you know that. Do you reckon I would leave you to die lonesome and solitary and needing the last consolements of a friend? *You* know I ain't made that way, George. The minute I heard you was in the grips according to Deathshead's arrangements, I just laid down everything and come on the jump. It's the way I'm made, George, I don't claim any merit for it. Always stand by your friend —that's my motto, and I reckon you know whether I live up to it or not. Martha didn't want to let me in, but I knew that meant others, and was only intended to keep troublesome people out that would disturb you; I said people that would *disturb* you—get it? But I ain't agoing to—I'm always careful about things like that. Born so, I reckon.

"Say, George, you didn't need them both; I said you didn't need them *both*. Get it? Deathshead and the doctor, you know. Either'll do, though of course if there was a bet on, I'd put my money on the doctor. Deathshead's good—I ain't meaning to disparage Deaths-head, George—but he's only an amature, when all's said and done, whereas old Bradshaw's been in the business since creation, I reckon; and besides he's got *science* back of him, and it makes an awful difference, George, don't you know."

Dug was doing the sick man good, without knowing it. He was starting a reaction. His screaming and shouting were splitting Harrison's head, and inducing a simmer under his temper which could rise to a boil, with proper encouragement. Dug proceeded to furnish the encouragement. It seemed to him that the best way to be helpful to a dying man should be to lighten the boding glooms which gather about his spirit as the night of life closes down and upon his failing senses falls the muffled surf-beat of the shoreless dark ocean over whose uncharted wastes his soul must soon be wandering: beguile the glooms away, yes, that was it; light-up the journey, make it sunny with hope and promise. And so, with the best intentions he went to work upon this benevolent enterprise.

"Say, George, it ain't so bad, after all, death ain't, when you come to look at it right. You see, we've all got to go, some time or other anyway, and so, what is the odds whether we go now or another time, so long's we are prepared? Prepared—that's the main thing; main, why, it's the *whole* thing. And you are *that*, George, if ever a man was, I reckon you know that; everybody knows it, everybody'll say it. I only wish I was half as well prepared, myself —and that's honest. I reckon I'm prepared what you may call *well enough*, as far as that goes, but that's really all; there ain't any margin over, to speak of. I could pull through—it's about all I can claim; but *you!* why, blame my cats—say! if I was up on your spiritual level, if I wouldn't take a chance in that prescription and pull out with you, I wish I may be—ouch! there's a pin in this chair. No, there t'is, it's a tack. Yes, sir, I'd pull out with you; I would, b'gosh. Prepared! That's the thing, George, and the whole thing. You're that. George, it'll be grand. You'll see how you'll be received. They'll all come—come a-flocking: Isaac, and Exodus, and all the boys. Torch-light p'cession, too—I can just *see* it. It's because you're prepared, George. Preparation's everything. You've led a square life, everybody respects you, everybody loves you, you've never done a mean thing, nor a wrong thing, nor a low-down thing, nor a treachery, nor—"

A tortured groan which was almost a shriek burst a passage through the comforter's din; and the sick man, his eyes blazing, flung himself to a sitting posture and shouted—

"Damnation, *will* you be quiet!"

The reaction was accomplished, the perishing man was saved.

Dug sat petrified in body, bewildered in mind. Such an explosion as this from a person with both feet in the grave—there it was; it had happened; he had witnessed it, there was no mistake about it, yet it seemed clearly impossible. He sat gazing, wondering; at last a grateful expression lighted his face, and he rose and patted Harrison on the head and said—

"Lay down, George, it's all right, p'cession's postponed for to-day, *sure,* and thanks to goodness for it."

"Postponed! confound you, it's never been appointed."

"George Harrison!"

"I tell you it's never been appointed. Can't you believe me?"

Dug said, reproachfully—

"George, you know I saw him myself."

"What *of* it, you idiot? he came twice!"

Dug's face glowed and worked with joyful excitement and surprise, and his words came like explosions from a gun—

"Oh, George, it's *too* good to be true. Say it again—honor bright!"

"Twice. Honor bright."

"Lemme hug you, George, lemme hug you. There, now, lay down, everything's all right, for sure. Another blanket? No? Too warm, as it is? All right, and a good sign, too; your machine's a-starting up again. By Jackson, I wouldn't missed this for—appeared *twice!* Ain't that good—ain't it just noble!"

"Why?"

"Because it means good luck."

"Who told you so?"

"Sho—everybody knows it; everybody says so."

"Not everybody, Dug."

"Oh, well, there's a few says different, but it's mighty few, I can tell you; all the rest says it means good luck."

Harrison wanted to believe it—longed to believe it. His superstitions were promptly at work; for the moment he was almost hopeful. He said—wistfully, hesitatingly—

"Dug, he—he appeared to my father three times."

He waited for the response with a yearning anxiety which he would have been ashamed to confess in words. Dug answered triumphantly—

"I know it—and look at what happened. No. 1: taken to his reward in his honored old age before infirmities got a-holt of him. No. 2: taken before he had to see his best friend's son jailed and the old family name disgraced by a bloody murder. No. 3: thish-yer splendid fortune, and you spared to enjoy it. Luck? Well, I should

say! And now he's been twice just on your own personal account:
luck? Cheer up, old friend, there's more a-coming! By gravy, it's
just grand—you're *born* to it, George!"

Harrison's half-reviving hope perished and his spirits went down
—these evidences were not convincing. He sighed, and said
nothing. Dug did not notice; he was busy tearing up some rude
drawings which he had painfully scrawled at home the night
before—after his chance glimpse of the apparition. Designs for
tombs.

Then he went below and ransacked for an apple. He returned
presently, munching it, and found Bridget at the bedside and the
medicine at Harrison's lips. He plunged forward with a vehement
"Say—drop that!" and snatched the dose away. He surveyed the
patient reproachfully, and said—

"George Harrison, I can't see what in the nation you—thank
goodness I was in time, you'd 'a' been in hell in two minutes."

Harrison retorted, petulantly—

"A while ago you said I would be in—"

"Say, George—there ain't any sense in provoking Providence
thisaway and Him a-doing His level best to keep you out of trouble.
You've just got shut of one appointment, yet the minute a person
turns their back—lookyhere, Bridget, there ain't any use for this
slush now, it's all been arranged different since you was in here."

Bridget thought he was referring to the reaction, and she said she
could see, herself, that there was a wonderful change, and maybe
the medicine was not needed; but what about the doctor? Who was
to take the risk? Suppose there was a relapse—what then. The
orders were positive; the doctor said the medicine must be taken.
Dug thought the situation over a while, then said—

"No names named. Only somebody's got to take it. All right,
then."

He took it himself.

"George, you've seen me do it. I reckon you'll know me for a
friend, yet. There ain't many that'll risk their life for a friend. But
you've seen me do it—and Bridget, too. I'm young, I'm strong, and
there's hope—I ain't giving up, not by a long shot; but if anything
does happen, all I ask is, that you won't forget poor old Dug,

but think of him sometimes. . . . There—it's a-working. . . . George, it's tying things up in sailor-knots and pulling them taut— my! Don't you mind me a-squirming around and twisting up this- away—gimme room, gimme room! . . . George, old Savvanarola —gee! they only just *burnt* him; why, it's pie to being chawed."

By help of imagination the orphan's fancied pains became quickly real; and not only real but sharply so, excruciatingly so, intolerably so, and his groans and shrieks and retchings momen- tarily augmented in violence and grew steadily more and more dreadful to witness. Soon he was wallowing and floundering all about the floor in his anguish and fright, and now he began to beg and implore and beseech that a preacher be sent for. Bridget and Harrison were seriously alarmed; Harrison forgot his own illness and left his bed, and he and Bridget plunged in amongst the thrashing limbs of the young Hercules and bore them down with their weight, and were flung off sprawling; and charged bravely again and still again, and at last won the victory and tumbled the creature into the bed, and climbed up and sat on him and held him down, they two panting and perspiring, and Dug struggling and scrambling under them, and sobbing, crying, groaning, retching, and still wailing for the preacher.

Then the doctor entered and stood looking, astonished and perplexed; behind him old Martha, ash-tinted with consternation. Dug saw the doctor, and a great fear came upon him which stilled his utterance and paralysed him where he lay. The doctor rasped out sternly—

"What is the meaning of this? Come down out of that!"

The victors shame-facedly obeyed. The doctor contemplated Harrison a moment or two, and was manifestly pleased—and perhaps privately surprised.

"Next thing to a miracle!" he said. "It's a grand medicine— grand! But you don't need any more of it, Harrison, you are all right again. What is the matter with this slab?" and he approached Dug.

"G'way from here! Don't you put your hands on me!" and Dug sat up and looked fright and battle mixed. "If you touch me dern'd if I—"

"Shut up—will you!" and the doctor halted and stood. "What's the matter with you?"

"Nothing, so help me!"

"Then what are you doing in that bed?"

"I—I had a pain; but it's gone, now."

"Put out your tongue."

Dug obeyed.

"Well—well. Healthy as a cow's."

He applied to the others for a history of the case. They described the circus; and told him every detail except one—the part the medicine had in it.

"It's remarkable, most remarkable. His tongue shows he's normal, perfectly normal—to all appearance." Then, after a reflective pause, "Hmp. Very strange, very strange indeed: suppressed itch again—right here in the same house. A discovery, too, a notable discovery: shows it's contagious. Will make a stir in the medical world when reported—as you will soon see." He took his leave, oozing pride and joy from every pore, and pausing in the door to say—

"Give him one dose now, and if the pains come on again send for me."

Dug did not hear, but Harrison tendered the medicine, and reported the speech. Dug put it from him sorrowfully, and said in thunder-tones of gentle rebuke—

"George, I risked my life to save yourn—and done it. You know I wouldn't done it for myself. Now, then, how you can be so low-down and unfeeling as to offer me, with your own hands, thish-yer hellfire and be willing—be *willing*, George—to see me suffer like I done before, when you seen, yourself, it was like I had my bowels full of cats—"

His voice broke and he turned away whimpering, and wiping his eyes with his sleeve. It took the funniness out of it for Harrison, over whose blasted and arid and desolate system the divine refreshment of a breath of humor had been blowing a moment before for the first time since he couldn't remember when; and he was touched and ashamed, and said so; and said he had been thoughtless and unkind, and was sorry; sorry, and grateful for

Dug's friendly devotion, and would rather hurt almost any other friend than him; and as these delicious words went crashing into the orphan's ear at close range the hurt look wasted away out of his face and a proud and happy one stole by visible stages into its place and beamed there like the morning. Such words! and from this source! they won the humble orphan as the master's caresses and praises win a worshiping dog, and he wrung Harrison's hand and said—

"George, I wasn't in my right mind when I refused. Gimme the slush. Say the word and I'll gullup the whole of it—I will, honest."

Martha put her head in and said—

"Here's de preacher, sir; I couldn't git him no sooner."

"Tell him to go to—"

Dug did not finish, for Bridget put her hand on his mouth and said—

"Shame on you! haven't you got anny manners?"

The minister was Hamfat. It was near sunset, now, and he had gone over to the Presbyterians during the afternoon, and had resumed the clerical coat which he had worn a year earlier when he was in business in one of the theological lines. He was disappointed to find he was not needed, but was reconciled when Harrison asked him to stay to supper. Dug was invited, also.

CHAPTER [XIII]

THE SUPPER passed off pleasantly, with oracular philosophisings from Hamfat and frank deridings of them from Dug Hapgood; and as a result Harrison had a rest from brooding over his miseries, and his spirits rose healthily under the stirring influence of this wordy war; his tired soul was refreshed, and he was almost a happy man once more. Helen Fairfax flitted in, presently, charmingly distressed over the town-talk that he was a dying man; a distress which profoundly pleased him; her grateful surprise at finding him well was another pleasure for him; and when she impulsively kissed him and put her thankfulness into petting and affectionate words, and added the tidings that Tom's hurts were doing well, his cup was about full. Bridget was a little chilly toward her at first, but Helen did not seem to be aware of it, nor conscious that there was any reason why Bridget should have any hostile feeling against her—as indeed there wasn't, as Bridget perceived after a moment's reflection—so the chilliness dissolved away under the young girl's friendly interest in her and her affairs, and ceased to be. Harrison noticed this, and it added another satisfaction to his growing store.

The young women departed for their homes, but other company soon began to arrive, in order to look, and wonder and re-congratulate; for Dr. Bradshaw was spreading the news of his medical miracle, and the friends of this strangely and persistently fortunate house wanted to come and see for themselves. Over and over again, as friend after friend arrived, Harrison had to re-tell the story, and read the formidable prescription, and by implication give the prescription the glory; and was austerely reminded, each time, by the Rev. Mr. Bailey, that the glory belonged "elsewhere"— which was a fact, and Harrison very well knew it, but he and Dug kept their secret. By and by Hamfat said, with a touch of irritation in manner and voice—

"Now then, brother, suppose you leave that detail alone. We all know the glory belongs to God, but why keep at it so? It was foreordained from the beginning of time that it should happen just the way it did. There is glory in it, true, but nothing special; at least not the particular glory you find in it: God could have cured him *without* the medicine; indeed, as any sane person can see, the real miracle was that He didn't kill him *with* it—and therein lies the glory."

"Yes, but—"

"Never mind—drop it. Predestination covers the whole ground. It was ordained from the beginning of time, that this man should commit suicide with that remedy and survive it."

"So it's all predestination, now. Only last week you said that so far from there being any such thing as pre—"

"I wasn't a Presbyterian last week."

That blocked the wheels of discussion. There was no way to turn the position, and the subject had to be changed. The talk went glibly on, and the company did not break up until nine. All said they had had a most pleasant evening; said it over the parting glass, and Harrison was able to say in sincerity that he had had the same and was grateful for this amelioration of his sorrow in the loss of his father.

Hamfat did not go with the rest, but lingered a while, chatting in a general way about what a blessing it was for a good man to have large means in a world where there was so much suffering, and so much true happiness to be got out of relieving it. After drifting about for a time without developing any definite object or appearing to have one, he finally got into his overcoat and said his good-night; but halted, on his way to the door, and said—

"By the way—did you know the Memphis uncle personally?"

"No."

"Had he a family?"

"No."

"Are you sure?"

"Well, I suppose he hadn't. I have never heard of any. Why?"

"Nothing. The thought occurred to me. I knew him a little."

"Is that so?"

"Yes, I met him; it was some years ago—about fifteen, I think. He had a plantation six miles out of Memphis, and he lived there —nights, at least. I was doctor for an adjoining plantation a few weeks, and was in his house several times. I doctored him for a few days once. A tough customer. There was a woman there—with a little child—a boy."

"Yes, that was his housekeeper. She was with him several years, I think, but has been gone a long time. You are thinking of Mrs. Milliken."

"Ah, yes—yes, I remember, now. They called her that—it comes back to me, now. A matronly and rather pleasing person—about thirty, I should say. Ah, yes, he was a tough customer. You know, he owned Jasper once."

"Colonel Fairfax's Jasper?"

"Yes."

"I didn't know it."

"Yes, Jasper was a slave in those days. A valuable nigger, too—mulatto, I mean; twenty, athletic, and a devil to work. Smart, too. When he was sixteen he bought himself, on time, from your uncle, and learned the carpenter's trade in no time, and was a free man inside of three years."

"At nineteen? And a slave again at twenty? How could that be?"

But Hamfat was musing, and did not answer.

"Mm . . . mm," dreamily nodding his head; "ye-s, he was a damned tough man. Oh, I *beg* pardon; my mind was far back in the past, for the moment—when I was a barkeeper—the remark was reminiscent, and not intentional. Good-night—good-bye, I've had a delightful evening, and thank you ever so much."

He was gone. Harrison was feeling uncomfortable, now, he did not know why. Had Hamfat's random and pointless talk produced the feeling? Why, no, it could hardly be that; there was nothing *in* his talk. His manner, then? Possibly; he could not say, for sure; and yet, on the whole—

Well, he was uncomfortable, anyway; he realized that much, and his pleasant evening was in a manner spoiled. He went to his bed saying petulantly—

"Oh, well, when a man's down and badgered and worried, his imagination hunts up something to get in a sweat about, out of every trivial thing that comes along. Lord, I get so tired of it all!"

Presently he did what all troubled souls have done, from the beginning of time: by a supreme effort he drove the disquieting matter out of his mind, and set a watch to keep it out. The customary result of this scheme followed: by pleasant degrees his protected brain sank deeper and deeper toward a soft and sweet and blissful unconsciousness, and soon he was dozing. But of course, the watch was now dozing, too, and this brought still another customary result: the gates parted, and a new enemy sprang in. Harrison groaned and came wide awake in a moment, saying—

"Bailey called it a 'delusion,' but lord, lord, *was* it? It could have been a fact. A fact, and prophetic. If there was no peace for him, with his strong make, what is the outlook for me?"

He knew there was no more sleep for him that night.

Hamfat struck down toward the village, pondering deeply. An idea had been born to him some hours before, out of a chance memory of the past, and the more he turned it over the more he was impressed by it and pleased with it. At first it had meant nothing to him, and he had given it but little attention; but it stayed by him and insisted on being considered; with the result that he was at last getting quite full of it. At the edge of the village he met Park Robinson, and asked him if he had seen Allen Osgood.

"No. What do you want of him?"

"Nothing in particular. I thought I'd—"

"I don't know where he is, because I don't know whether he's dry or not. If he's dry, he's at Bowles's; if he ain't, he's at the ice cream parlors, because I saw Asphyxia Perry pointed for there half an hour ago with some other spring chickens and chaps."

"Thanks. Good-night."

"So-long."

The girl owed her singular name to her mother, who was ignorant and romantic, and afflicted her children with any chance name she found in a book, if it had a pretty sound, without stopping to inquire into its pedigree or relationships. She had a son named Solar Plexus, and other children with similarly over-conventional names; but this is a matter which does not concern us.

The ice cream parlors consisted of a single room, which was gay with cheap and inharmonious splendors, and was the pride of the village. Notched and perforated pink paper-lace (tissue), blue paper-lace, crimson paper-lace, yellow paper-lace decorated every-thing that would stand decorating; the mirror-frame, the shelf-edges, the sconces, the lamps in the chandelier; even the pasteboard man who was impaled on a crooked wire on the drum of the wood-stove, and miserably and maddeningly whirled and spun there day and night in the torture of the ascending heat, eternally waved a flag of it. All of these gauds were freckled with fly-specks, but that was matter-of-course in Indiantown, and not objectionable. The stenciled window-shades displayed Swiss pictures, with snowy Alps in the background, and chalets and milk-maids and remarkable cows in the front. In the wall paper a press of fast-spurring knights with lance in rest and visor down was issuing from under the frowning gateway of a medieval castle, and this same thing was happening in unreposeful repetition in every six-inch space all over the whole place. If the forces had been concentrated they could have taken the Holy Land. And done it easily. Some of the framed pictures were the old stand-bys—American classics: such as Washington bulling his way across the Delaware, Tecumseh at the battle of the Thames, the Signing of the Declaration, Warren falling at Bunker Hill, and so on; the others were recent: Kossuth, Jenny Lind, the J. M. White tearing along on her record trip up the Mississippi, and the like. The latest of all, and also the choicest, was the Western favorite of the time, a lithograph, delicately colored by hand, representing a sweet young girl pensively bowed over a large open book, presumably the Bible, with a rose in her fingers, the dainty rose and the dainty hand resting upon the sacred page. It was having a run, and could be found tilted above the bar-keeper's back and his bottles on every steamboat in the Orleans trade, let her hail from whence she might. The little ice cream tables had pictured oil-cloth covers—the American eagle with bunches of flags and cannons in his grip and a scroll in his beak bearing the E Pluribus Unum motto. He had a fiery eye. Each table had cruets on it containing vinegar and flies and such-like condiments, for the parlors furnished oyster stews—a recent thing and all the go, as the leaders of fashion said. The oysters were small and could have been mistaken for tonsils which had been removed to put a stop to throat diseases. That is, before stewing, for then they were soft and rounded and elusive; but after stewing they were wrinkled, like raisins, and had character, and in a struggle would resist to the death. They came in cans, from Baltimore, and had cloves floating in their juice, and were called pickled oysters, and were in all respects damnable. When a person had drunk up his stew, he lolled back with a look of contentment, and chewed his oyster. At such times he did not talk, but attended to business, tilting his head first to one side and then the other and bearing down on his subject earnestly, and getting new leverages by shifting it alternately from the tired jaw to the rested one. When both jaws were disabled and threw up the job, he gave it to the dog, who got an hour's practice out of it, and passed it on to his friends. Sometimes a crank planted his oyster, dreaming of India rubber and wealth, but the soil or the climate was not suitable, and nothing came of it.

The proprietor of the parlors was a spruce and natty young fellow, the dandy of the town—Templeton Gunning; handsome, brisk, easy, elegant, a lady-killer; wearing the tightest boots in the village and the tallest collars; proud of the front end of his name, which he believed had come down to him from an aristocratic source somewhere. He was much envied for the winning freedom of his manners, and for the gay and pretty and unembarrassed way in which he could—and did—accost all comers with his "Now then, ladies, gents,—don't all speak at once!—what's it goin' to be *this* time?" When on duty he wore no coat, winter or summer, but moved sociably about from table to table, in his vest and with his shirt-sleeves drawn up and restrained with pink elastics—moved about in a sparkling way, re-animating failing conversation, rallying shy people to put them at their ease, joking sweethearts and forcing them to laugh for appearance' sake when one of them would have preferred to swear and the other to cry; always busy, he was, distributing charm and superintending his negro waiters and seeing to everything with his own eye. A prosperous young man was Templeton Gunning, and very popular and much respected. A diligent flirt, too, and sang tenderly, and played the guitar, and led the serenaders.

Most of the tables were full, to-night; nearly all the smart young journeyman-mechanics and dry-goods clerks were there with their young ladies, and there was a great din of chaffing, joking, and boisterous laughter. The talk was not on cold and lofty planes, but was strictly light and personal. Snatches of it were catchable everywhere:

"Leggo me, Jim Gatewood; if you muss my hair again, I lay I'll break something over your red head!"

"Oh, you will, will you?" (A sound of strenuous scuffling ensues, accompanied by pantings and by gleeful cacklings from all the table-mates, in which the girl joins.) "There, now, it's done—why don't you break something? You said you would."

"*You* didn't do it, plague take you, I done it myself."

"Oh, but didn't I, though?"

"No, you didn't."

"I did."

"You didn't."

"Did."

"Didn't."

He plunges for her, she squirms out of reach and makes a mouth at him; whereat they all laugh, she as gaily as any.

The one sample will do. All over the place the like was going on. There was no harm in it. They were clean-minded young people; their ways and language were silly and vulgar, but in their hearts was no evil and no impurity.

Not all the groups were noisy; there was one exception. At a table apart, in a corner, sat Allen Osgood and Asphyxia Perry. These two communed quietly and earnestly. They had been engaged for a couple of years, but the parents of Asphyxia, who had favored the match in the beginning, had early changed their minds, and had opposed it since. The change had occurred when Allen had been discharged from his dry-goods clerkship for indolence and for losing his membership in the Sons of Temperance by breaking his pledge. For a while he had tried to get another place, but had soon ceased from efforts of that kind and turned his attention to idleness and dissipation—at his mother's expense, who could ill afford it. Asphyxia had reasoned with him many times, and was reasoning with him now.

"But you don't try, Allen. If you would straighten up and be a man—"

"Shaw, that's what you're always saying—you and everybody—and I'm tired of it."

The girl colored, and said, with dignity—

"We have at least said it for your good, Allen."

"There, now, you're hurt again. *I* don't want to hurt you, and I'm sorry. But lord, you can't think what it is to—to—Asphyxia, everybody avoids me—I can see it—everybody despises me. If I—"

"Allen, you are dear to me, I do not avoid you, and you know I don't want to despise you—"

"But you can't help it. Oh, say it—you might as well."

"Don't speak so loud. Allen, I would do anything in this world to help you, to lift you up, to—"

"Lord, life is so tough, so tough!"

"Try an oyster for a change," suggested the genial proprietor, passing by on his rounds.

"Listen at that," growled Allen, under his breath. "That's a specimen. I owe him money and can't pay. And can't resent."

"Oh, Allen, I pity you so. I do wish I could think of an opening for you. Listen to that clatter—everybody is happy but you and me. You *would* work, if you had an opening, wouldn't you, Allen?"

"Yes, I would, I give you my honor I would. For your sake. You are so good to me, and so forgiving, in spite of all I do and say to distress you. I give you my word I will make a try tomorrow—honor bright, I will."

The clouds in the girl's face lifted, and in warm and earnest words she expressed her content. Then she revealed a secret:

"I can go home happy, now, Allen, for you have given your promise, and father said I must bring it or the engagement must be broken off."

The young fellow burst out with "I'll keep it, on honor I will! You will tell him so—and you will plead for me—*don't* let him break it off—I've nothing left but you—you are my life—I couldn't live without you!"

She was happy, and her heart spoke through her eyes.

Five minutes later the couple rose and moved toward the door; as they passed out, Templeton Gunning whispered in Allen's ear, "I'm letting you off again. Say—you ain't even the little pasteboard man's equal: he earns his living and pays his way."

Hamfat was shivering in the dark recess of a doorway near by and communing with his uneasy mind: "I hope it's honorable; I hope it's what ought to be done . . . . Suppose I was in *her* place—wouldn't I think it ought to be done? wouldn't I know it? . . .

Anyway, it's not a crime, *that* I know. I've done foolish things, questionable things, but I've never committed a crime. I'm very poor, and this—this—well, this temptation is very strong; I've not been tempted to this degree before. Is that why I've held out? We all have our limit—we all know it. We ought to pray Lead us not into temptation *beyond our limit.* Is this mine? . . . Lord, I hope the motive is good!"

A double rank of young people filed by, plaintively singing "Sweet Ellen Bayne," and a minute later Allen and Asphyxia appeared. Hamfat gave them good-evening, and asked Allen to return presently—he would wait for him.

While Hamfat waited, he went on arranging his mind—arranging it to fit the new circumstances. He had had much practice in this, and could depend upon fetching it around. After some reflection, he retired from the ministry. After further reflection he dropped back to an earlier condition of his, and became a freethinker. The decks being now cleared for action, he began to consider that other embarrassment, the "motive." This presently landed him on good firm ground in another former position of his —that all motives are selfish. All motives being selfish, a man needs only to choose between selfish high motives and selfish low ones. What was the nature of this present motive? As it affected "her," it promised justice, and was high; selfish too, of course, because it promised to profit himself. What then? Leave poor Mrs. Milliken injured because he could not right her without advantaging himself? That would indeed be a crime! No, the motive was all right—and plenty high enough on the one side to even up the other and make the general average good. If he got a little tangled in his reasonings he was not aware of it, and he came out of them ready for business and gay. When Allen returned, Hamfat said—

"I want to have an important talk. I've got a good thing for you."

The young fellow's face brightened pleasantly.

"Do you mean it?" he asked.

"Yes, I do. Come in here and we'll talk it over and have a stew."

The newly brightened face was swiftly overclouded.

"No—you'll excuse me. I owe money there, and I'll not go in that place again till I can do it with my head up."

Hamfat was gratified, and said to himself, "Things are happening just right." Then aloud, bringing out a wad of State bills, "Very good, you can do it now. I collected this for a charity, but that's all right, take what you want; I'll make it good. Come along."

Allen put out his hand eagerly, then drew it reluctantly back.

"No," he said, "I'm turning over a new leaf. Borrowing's not a good beginning."

"Borrowing? It's not borrowing. It's on account."

"How do you mean?"

"In a few weeks you'll have a plenty. Don't you worry—you'll see."

Allen still hesitated. He sighed, and said—

"Good news don't stir me the way it used to. But maybe luck's turned; I don't know. I'll take five dollars."

They entered the parlors and sat down remote from the small company which still tarried in the place. A winter storm was brewing, and the parlors were becoming a solitude in consequence of it. Templeton came airily forward with his usual "Now, then, gents—don't all—"

"Send stews and the change. Square up the account—you understand?" and Allen handed over the banknote.

Templeton observed, indolently, "They *told* me 'twas snowing, but they didn't say what," and sauntered away with the order.

Hamfat began earnestly.

"Allen, you are as poor as I am. And as tired of it, too—isn't that so?"

"Speak of something cheerfuler, Bailey," said Allen, gloomily.

"It's just what I'm coming to. For instance. How would you like to pick up a hundred thousand dollars in the next month or two?"

It was an electric awakening for the sluggish young fellow.

"Great Scott, what do you mean, Bailey! Don't joke—I can't bear it—is there anything in it? Tell me what you are driving at."

"Now then, I will. I've good reason to believe George Harrison's old Memphis uncle left a private wife and a son behind him somewhere. Disappeared, you understand—say fifteen years ago."

"Well?"

"Suppose they could be hunted out and found?"

"Well—what then?"

"Suppose *we* find them—you and me?"

"Do you mean—"

"Don't you see? They'd own the estate, and it's worth more than four hundred thousand. We'd charge them half for discovering them. It requires us both: you go up there and search around and get on their track, I stay here and raise money for your expenses, from week to week."

For a while young Osgood was dazzled—bewildered—intoxicated with the splendid dream; then be began to have misgivings, and said, wistfully—

"But George Harrison—it would ruin him."

"Ye-s," hesitatingly, "but then, you know, we'd be working for justice—justice for that poor abused woman. That ennobles it. What right has he to be living in luxury on her property, and she no doubt suffering for bread? I just ask you that. Where's the fairness of it? And I'll ask you another thing: now that you know she's probably the rightful owner and suffering in poverty and want, what is your duty? You've got a duty, as an honorable man; and everybody will concede that you are that, Allen, at the same time that they call you frivolous and a no-account. Very well; as an honorable man are you going to meanly keep still and let her go on suffering—a poor soul like that, who has never done you any harm? When you didn't *know*, it was another matter, and you were free, and nothing required of you; but it's different, now. Now that you know, you can't sit quiet and let her be robbed, without being a plain and self-confessed *accessory* to that wrong, and guilty down to the bottom of your conscience!"

The young fellow tried to get away from this aspect of the case, but Bailey held him to it and kept it remorselessly before him. He was obliged to concede, finally, that a right-feeling person would not and could not in fairness desert a wronged woman when he could help her and save her; and certainly it was such a person's duty to at least try, and do the best he could, in the present hard case.

An important stage was won. Bailey rubbed his hands with satisfaction, and hastened to fortify the captured position. He said—

"Here's thirty dollars—enough for three or four weeks. Keep me posted on your whereabouts, and I'll raise more and send it as it's needed."

Osgood contemplated the money a little while, dreamily, then put it in his pocket, still dreaming, still thinking, with Bailey's eye on him, alert and watching. At length came this remark:

"Bailey, we mean well by the woman, and that's all right. And so we ought to feel good and clean, but somehow I can't. There's something that spoils it. Don't you see that at bottom our motive is mainly selfish?"

The second stage was reached. But Hamfat was ready. He answered indifferently—

"That's all right. There *aren't* any motives but selfish ones."

"Bailey! What a rotten statement!"

"It's true, all the same."

"Ah, but come, now, you're not serious."

"But I am serious, I tell you."

Young Osgood turned the immense proposition over several times in his mind in a groping and helpless way, then ejaculated—

"*No* motives but selfish ones!"

"Allen, I've never encountered one of another sort in my life, little or big. Did you ever take a motive apart, piece by piece, and examine it?"

"Well, no, I don't think I ever did."

"*I* know you never did."

"How do you know it?"

"Because you're like the rest of the community—you don't know how to think."

"Oh, I like that!"

"All people think they think, but there's not two in a million that ever do it. They never think out a question for themselves; they get it at second-hand, from somebody else; and that somebody else gets it at second-hand from some other somebody else—and so on. The whole world has believed from Creation down that there are motives that are not selfish ones. It shows that there have been billions and billions of people who never thought, but took their ideas—as they call their foolishnesses—at second hand without ever examining them. The very finest intellects the human race has produced have done very little thinking."

"The very finest? Oh, come! Prove it."

"It's perfectly easy. For instance. For thousands of years the entire world believed in witches—the Shakspeares, the Sir Thomas Brownes, the Sir Matthew Hales, Luther, Calvin, and all. You see, they took their opinions at second hand, and did no thinking and no examining. But the minute a few people—and not the brightest —sat down and calmly and coldly and without prejudice took the evidence apart and intelligently examined it, the witch-humbug went to the devil. Why, Allen, all of that evidence—every detail of it—had been before the world's master-minds for ages and ages. In all that time it had never occurred to one of those gifted conservatives to coldly and dispassionately examine it. Now by reason of this age-long negligent habit there's a good many Truths with a capital T running at large and dressed as gentlemen, that would lose their liberty if they were arrested and sharply cross-questioned."

He paused, and waited for this position to be attacked. But it was a short pause—nothing really more than a courtesy-pause, in fact—then he broke it and moved on toward his object:

"Why, if people really thought, instead of only thinking they think, somebody would have taken a motive to pieces ages ago and found out that there was never a one that had its origin anywhere but in selfishness."

"Why, Bailey, there are certainly *some* motives—"

"That are not selfish? Allen, it would trouble you to find an instance."

"I don't think so. I can find you one in that St. Louis paper there —a good one, too; I read it this evening when I was waiting for—

here it is. It's an incident connected with those new-fangled cars in New York—horse-cars."

He read it, while Hamfat kept sharp watch upon the details. Osgood laid the paper down and said:

"There you have it—as straight as a string, and not an attackable place in it. Summarized, it stands thus—to-wit: The man lives three miles up town. It is bitter cold, blowing hard, snowing hard, midnight. He is about to enter the car when a gray and ragged old woman, a touching picture of misery, puts out her lean hand and begs for rescue from hunger and death. The man finds that he has but a quarter in his pocket, but he does not hesitate: he gives it her and trudges home through the storm. There—it is noble, it is beautiful: its grace is marred by no fleck or blemish or suggestion of self."

"What makes you think that, Allen?"

The victory had seemed easy and complete. The question was a surprise. A surprise and an annoyance mixed.

"What else could I think, Bailey? Do you imagine that there is some other way of looking at it?"

"Why, yes. Can you put yourself in the man's place and tell me what he felt and what he thought?"

"Easily. The sight of that suffering old face pierced his generous heart with a sharp pain. He could not bear it. He could endure the three-mile walk in the storm, but he could not endure the tortures his conscience would suffer if he turned his back and left that poor old creature to perish. He would not have been able to sleep, for thinking of it."

"What was his state of mind on his way home, Allen?"

"It was a state of joy which only the unselfish know. His heart sang, he was unconscious of the storm."

"He slept well?"

"One cannot doubt it."

Allen had recovered. His spirits were up again. His case seemed to be invulnerable, and he felt pleased with his performance, and not anxious about results. He said to himself, "Let him chew on that oyster a while, and see what he can make out of it."

Hamfat considered the situation a moment or two, then said:

"Now then, let's take it apart and examine it—a thing which people never do, as I have been telling you, and so they don't get at a truth, but only at a falsity. Let us coldly add up the details and see how much this man got for his twenty-five cents. Let us try to find out the *real* why of his making the investment. In the first place he couldn't bear the pain which the suffering old face gave him. *He* couldn't bear it, you see. So he was thinking of *his* pain— this unselfish man. He must buy a salve for it. In the second place, if he did not succor the old woman his conscience would torture him all the way home. Torture *him,* you see. Thinking of *his* pain again. He must buy relief from that. In the third place, if he did not relieve the old woman he would not get any sleep. *He* wouldn't, you notice. He must buy some sleep. Still thinking of *himself,* you see. Thus, to sum up, he bought himself free of a sharp pain in his heart, he bought himself free of the tortures of a waiting conscience, he bought a whole night's sleep all for twenty-five cents. It should make the sharpest nigger-trader on the river ashamed of himself. On his way home his heart was joyful and it sang—profit on top of profit! usury! Allen, the impulse which moved the man to succor the old woman was wholly selfish, utterly selfish. But there was nothing base about it, nothing ignoble. You have the idea that *all* selfish motives are base. I think you must grant that this case is an exception to your rule."

Young Osgood made several efforts to reply, but he was not practised in the argumentative arts, and Hamfat headed him off each time. Osgood furnished instance after instance in support of his position, but Hamfat took them coldly to pieces, one by one, and finished each in turn with the remark—

"It's always just so—the seed-impulse is selfishness, every time; there aren't any exceptions. What a body needs to do, is to train himself to prefer *high* selfishnesses, not low ones. Why, Allen, look at that divine thing, a mother's love—the very selfishest of all. She will starve herself to death, that her child may have food. Why? Because *she* can't bear to see the child suffer. She could manage to bear it if it were another person's child, but—

"Damn such a philosophy!"

"It isn't a philosophy, it's a fact."

"I don't care what you call it, it's just loathsome."

"I'm not saying it isn't."

"Well, then, why do you think about it, and fuss at it, and propagate it in your mind? What good can it do? If the world believed as you do, it would lose heart, and be ashamed of itself, and never do a fine and noble thing, because the impulse back of it would be selfish—and being selfish, ignoble."

Hamfat was waiting for that.

"Well, Allen," he said, musingly, "I may be all wrong, and you may be right, but really I don't feel that I am the worse for these notions. There was that man that gave the old woman the quarter. His act was not the outcome of his *opinions*, but of his *feelings*. Feelings are inborn and permanent; opinions change. Let that man think as he might, he would rescue that helpless old woman just the same. Don't you believe it?"

"Yes, perhaps so. Yes, of course he would."

"You would, yourself. Isn't it so?"

"I think so."

"Don't you know it?"

"Yes."

"Even if you believed your impulse was selfish you would save her from her trouble—you couldn't help it."

"What's the use of nagging me so! I couldn't see her suffer, and I wouldn't try—I'd help her if I could."

Without emphasis—and in a manner casually, so to speak—Bailey remarked—

"There's another poor old woman that's suffering—and unjustly. We can help her."

He dropped that seed and left it to grow, and do its work; and straightway changed the subject. He chatted sociably along, about one thing and then another, without halting for responses, and without seeming to care for them or to desire anything better than to hear himself talk. But he kept a side-glance on Allen all the while, and was contented; for Allen was thinking, or thought he was thinking, and Bailey did not doubt that the result would be satisfactory. He wandered pleasantly on and on with his talk, and enjoying it all by himself, and finally he took a chance at the little pasteboard man as a text.

"Look at him spin," he said. "Thinks he thinks. They all do. Thinks it was *his* idea to whirl like that. Thinks *he* does the whirling. Whereas he is nothing but a puppet, worked by an exterior influence—that heat: that surrounding and enveloping and brain-stifling public opinion, which he's the slave of and doesn't know it. He'll wear out, and they'll put another in his place, and another and another—a hundred, in time; and they'll all think they think. They'll all think they are spinning out wisdoms which the parlors couldn't do without. But the spring will come and the fire will go out while the last one is whirling; then the cold air of truth will blow on him and he'll perceive that his trade is pl—"

"Bailey!"

"Well?"

"I believe it's right, and I'm ready."

"Good. I knew—"

"But there's one thing I've got to be satisfied about, first. I don't want to seethe a kid in its mother's milk."

"What do you mean?"

"Who is contributing to that charity you are borrowing from? George Harrison?"

"Not a cent."

This was a mistake. Possibly a lie.

"Very well, then. Come along; it's midnight."

They passed out into the storm, leaving the parlors empty of guests. A dog was asleep on the floor, Templeton Gunning was asleep in a chair, the knights were cavorting along the wall, the J. M. White was flying up the river, the lithographed girl was absorbed in her lesson, the pasteboard man was disseminating the truth as he understood it.

There was a guest in George Harrison's house—in his bedroom, in fact: a vague and almost invisible figure which sat remote from the night-taper and enveloped in glooms and shadows, but surmounted by a face which Harrison could have seen if he had looked in that direction—a face which seemed to emit a pale glow and to float in the murky air unsupported.

CHAPTER [XIV]

As the two benevolent conspirators stepped out into the black night and the driving snow and closed the door of the ice cream parlors behind them, a tall and stalwart man brushed by them with his slouch hat pulled down over his face. He stopped beyond the range of the show-window lights, the only ones now visible in the street, and waited until the pair had disappeared in the storm; then he returned, warily and with an eye out for passers-by, and knocked vigorously on the Templeton door—three sounding raps, and after a pause, two more—after which he slipped into the darkness again. There was no result for a minute or two, then one by one the parlor lights went out. All but one, which was behind the high screen which protected the delivery-wicket where the waiters did their traffic with the kitchen from public view. Being only a humble tallow candle its rays were effective in the sheltered corner only; they were not able to carry beyond the screen.

The skulker entered, now, and locked the door behind him. The darkness of the parlors did not trouble him; he went straight to the screen and behind it without colliding with the table. It could be guessed that he had made the trip before, in like circumstances. He found Templeton standing at ease behind the screen, but looking only indifferently glad, if even that much. The guest shook off a cloud of snow, tossed his hat on the floor, and seated himself. He proved to be a darkish mulatto.

"Whah's yo' servants?" he asked.

"Gone to bed."

"How long?"

"Half an hour."

"Well, den, set down." Templeton did it. "I've come for de straight o' de news de Fairfax niggers is talkin' so much about. About Jawge Harrison a-comin' into de property o' dat ole uncle up to Memphis." He got out a cob pipe, packed the remains of its charge home with his finger, and motioned for the candle; Templeton passed it to him, he got his light, and passed the candle back. The young white man looked humiliated, but made no comment. "Say—it's so, ain't it?"

"Yes, of course; there wasn't any other heir, Jasper."

"I hear say dey's rafts o' cash, besides de lan' en de niggers—mos' fifty thousand. Is dat so, too?"

"Yes—forty-five."

A gratified light flashed in the mulatto's eye. Templeton noticed it, and said, with a timid attempt at his usual light manner—

"That seems to interest you. How?"

The light changed—changed to an unpleasant gleam; and a surly growl followed:

"I reckon it ain't any o' yo' business." After a cogitating silence of some moments, impressively broken by the booming of the storm-blast outside and the muffled slamming and banging of distant shutters, "Gimme a dram."

Templeton provided rye whisky and a glass, and the guest tossed off four fingers neat. He smacked his lips and said—

"It's warmin' and good! Say—whah is she?"

"Up stairs—asleep."

"Healthy? Sperits good?"

"Healthy?—yes. As to the rest, middling."

Another pause. Then—

"You seen anybody dat's been to de jail?"

"Yes, several."

"How do ole marster take it?"

"Keeps his head up, they say."

"I reckon he killed Jake, didn't he?"

"I reckon so. Of course he did; everybody says so, even Harrison, they say, though Tom's as good as a member of the family; and Harrison is a man that wouldn't condemn a dog if he didn't think he knew the dog was guilty."

"Miss Helen don't believe he done it. But o' cose she'd say dat anyway."

"Have you seen her, Jasper?"

"I has. On'y jist a minute."

"How's Tom?"

"Gitt'n along right smartly, she say."

"They say Colonel Fairfax is drinking again."

"On'y jist lately. I been on de place ever sence we come, en I knows. Say—you's done pretty well in dis town."

Templeton involuntarily put his hand in his pocket. The remark was not followed up, and he left it there, and said, not with any perceptible eagerness—

"Well—perhaps well enough for a two-year go in a little place like this."

"It ain't two years yit. We hain't been here two years till Janiwary. You've done prime."

"Yes, for such a town; but if I could go down to Orleans, with my experience—"

"Looky here," interrupted the mulatto, roughly, "dat's de second time you've said it. Don't I always move dis fambly when I's ready? Well, den, you wait. Hit suit me fur you to stay whah you is. Dat settle' it. You unerstan'?"

The young white face flushed deeply, but no words came.

" 'D you heah me?"

"I wasn't suggesting anything, I only just made the remark."

Jasper was silent for some little time, now, and his knitted brow suggested that he was probably arranging something in his mind with special care. A scheme, Templeton thought, and was not happy; Jasper's schemes usually included him as a detail, and seldom in a desirable way. Finally Jasper asked—

"Whah was you, 'long 'bout de time Jake was killed, dat night?"

Templeton was relieved.

"Midnight? I was coming home from superintending the refreshment-end of Mrs. Batterson's party."

"Den you was passin' behine Cunnel Fairfax's 'bout de time Jake scream' out."

"No, it wasn't just at that time. And I didn't pass behind the house, but in front."

The mulatto looked him gravely in the eyes and said—

"I said *behine*. You was passin' *behine* de house—un'stan'?"

Templeton's feeling of relief lost something of its repose. What might these questions be leading up to? He answered, resignedly—

"Yes, behind. I was passing behind the house."

"Dat's all right. Keep it in yo' mine, en don't fogit it. Now, den: fust, you h'yerd de scream—"

"Why, no, Jasper, I—"

" 'Tend to what I says, will you! Fust, you h'yerd de scream—"

A waiting silence for a moment or two, then Templeton dropped his eyes and his voice, and said his lesson:

"First, I heard the scream—"

"Den a man rush' outen de back do' en whiz pas' you—"

"Then a man burst out of the back door and rushed past me—"

"I reconnize' de man en he reconnize' me—"

The victim lifted his eyes pleadingly to his torturer's face and hesitated, a sickly pallor stealing over his cheeks—

"*Say* it!"

"I—I recognized the man and he recognized me—"

"Den Jasper busted outen de back do' en reconnize' me en tole me Jake Bleeker is killed, en ast me to ketch de man, en I rush' arter him, en he beg off en say if I don't say nuth'n he'll gimme a pile o' money. Say dat over, now, en don't leave none of it out."

The lesson was recited.

"Now, den, you ain't gwyne to be no witness, onless dat man act contrary wid me. Well, dat ain't gwyne to happen. But all de same, you keep dem facks in yo' head, so's you kin be ready if it do happen."

The youth, moved by deep anxiety, innocently inquired—

"What man is it, Jasper?"

The colored man gave him a sharp look and answered—

"You mine yo' own business. I'll tell you when de time come for you to go en swah in de cote."

After a little, Templeton made another venture:

"Will one witness do, without anybody to back up what he says?"

"I's gwyne to 'ten to dat."

Templeton was puzzled, and said, a little timidly—

"But you know—well, you forget that they won't take your evidence."

Jasper snapped out an oath and retorted—

"Who said dey would? D'you reckon I's a fool?"

This left Templeton in the dark. He was afraid to ask for further light on the matter, but after a pause he shifted his ground and ventured this remark—

"You know they would ask me why I come at such a late day and never said anything before."

The frank guest responded, despairingly—

"Hit do seem to me I never see sich a chucklehead befo'. Why, it's 'case you couldn't sleep no mo', Gawd was a-pullin' en a-haulin' at you so." Then he rose to his full height, yawned cavernously, and stretched—upward and still upward, luxuriously, prodigiously; helped himself to another glass, refilled his pipe and lit it, indicated his hat with a nod, and as Templeton picked it up and handed it to him, opened out his brawny hand and stood with it projected to the front, palm up. Templeton laid in it the five dollar bill recently the property of Allen Osgood and of Hamfat and of the ravished charity, and of George Harrison. The guest pocketed it and moved away, Templeton following. The pair parted without a good-night, and the proprietor of the parlors locked the door, grinding his teeth and muttering—

"I wish he may land in hell before breakfast! He's got no pass, of course, and I hope Catlin will catch him and calaboose him and give him thirty-nine."

His first prayer miscarried, for some reason, but all three of the specifications particularized in the second one arrived and found favor. Jasper had not gone two blocks before Catlin the constable, who was the entire police department of Indiantown, had him. He spent the rest of the night in cold and forlorn captivity, and in the early morning was stripped and given his "forty-save-one," frightfully laid on. Then, in the gray dawn, with his swollen back streaming blood and caking his clothes to his body, he staggered his way homeward through the fleecy snowdrifts, brooding vengeance and cursing all the white race without reserve, out of the deepest deeps of his heart, and rejoicing that in fifteen years he had spared no member of it a pain or a shame when he could safely inflict it; and finishing with—

"I's sweated two of 'm good, dese two years, en dey dasn't open dey mouf; en I's stacked de k'yards on another one, now, en I lay I'll make *him* sup sorrow, you see if I don't. He won't das't to open *his* mouth, nuther. You wait ontel I kin git around agin—Gawd, I'll s'rivel him up!"

CHAPTER [XV]

N EXT MORNING at the late hour of eight, Templeton was still in bed, and that was a most strange thing; it was his custom to rise with the sun. His breakfast was on a table close by, but he had not touched it nor felt any interest in it. He was pale and languid, and profoundly low-spirited. The appointments of the room were bright and cheerful, and a hospitable fire was roaring in the stove and showing flamboyantly through its teeth, but the aspects outside the window were dreary and saddening. It was a windless morning, the snow lay deep upon the houses and the street, there was no traffic, no sound of wagon or footfall, a white desolation spread everywhere, the stillness was uncanny, oppressive, mournful. Templeton drew down the blind; he could not endure the picture, in the mood that possessed him.

The door opened and closed, and his mother was with him. One could recognize the relationship at a glance. She was about forty-five, and still comely, albeit pathetically careworn, and the signs were present that she had been very pretty in her younger days. She had an intelligent face, normally reposeful and contemplative, and her eyes were warrant that she possessed feeling and imagination. In her dress she was neat and trim, and she carried herself well and with a sedate dignity. By nature she was good and kindly —one could see that—but she was not a very strong character; one could see that, also. She bent over her son and caressed his forehead and his hair a while, affectionately, then sat down by him and took his hand and held it, stroking it and petting it with her other hand and saying tender and sympathetic things to him; and no doubt she would have liked to kiss him, but that was not the Southern way among mothers of the middle rank and below. Templeton responded gratefully with his eyes and by pressure for pressure with his hand; and presently his memories of the night flared up in his mind, and he said bitterly—

"Mother, he has been here again."

"Ah, poor boy, I know it. I heard his signal, and slipped down to be near you and suffer with you."

"Then you heard him."

"I heard it all, from behind the screen."

"I'm glad, for now you must see, yourself, that something's got to be done; we can't stand this any longer."

The mother showed apprehension, and said:

"Oh, don't think any rash thoughts, my son! Don't, for my sake, and for your own. There's nothing in the world we can do, but endure and wait."

"Wait! It's been wait, wait, wait, all these years. I'm so tired of it. And nothing ever comes of it, mother. Lord, to be talked to like that, by a nigger, and have to stand it!" The thought of it tortured him, and made him writhe. "And now—why, it's a hundred times worse than ever!" He suddenly sat up in bed, and his breath came and went in gasps. "Think! Every time it crosses my mind it frightens me cold: I've got to go and swear some innocent man's life away—God only knows whose. I can't do it, I'll never do it— *how can* I do it!" He fell back upon the pillow and thrashed about with his hands in wordless despair.

His mother pleaded with him, wept over him, put all her heart into her persuasions, the burden of her reasonings being that Jasper might never require it and had said as much—"Wait and see, wait and see; oh, be patient and wait!" She made an impression, she gained ground; her words did their share of the work, her tears the most of it. The son was at last tranquilized, but not persuaded. He said—

"I love you, mother, and I have proved it by living in this sort of hell ten years without knowing why. I am not a boy any longer, I have passed the blabbing age, I am twenty-one, and I've a right to know. I have begged, you have said wait a little longer; so I have waited a little longer, and a little longer, and again a little longer. But now I must know."

"Oh, my boy, don't require it—don't! I can't bear that you should be ashamed of me."

The son looked astonished.

"Ashamed?" he said. "I knew it must be something dreadful, but I did not think of that. I supposed that this devil had got you under his heel in some unfair way, and that if we only waited, in patience, everything would clear up, and then—"

The woman was sobbing out her heart in a welter of tears. The youth was moved with pity, and said—

"Look up, mother, and take heart. Do not be afraid of me. I will stand by you through everything."

"Through shame!" and she looked up surprised, through her tears.

"Yes, through everything. Who am I, to be ashamed of you?"

She gathered him to her heart and said—

"I never knew you! Why, I have burned to tell you—burned! but I was afraid. I will tell you gladly, gladly. I—" She hesitated, and looked down; then added, appealingly, "You know you have promised me—"

"To stand by you—and I will; to share the shame with you—and I will do that, too, whatever it is. Aren't you my mother, and have I ever—"

"No you never have! You have been the best son a mother ever had, and I wish now, that—that—but never mind, you shall know it all, now."

She took up her history and carried it down, step by step, and by and by arrived at marriage, then three years of wedded happiness, then sudden widowhood and poverty.

"You were two years old. There were no friends or relatives who were able to receive me and support me, so I hid myself behind a fictitious name and wandered from place to place and got such work as I could,—often menial—and supported myself. This during two years; two years of hard work, hard usage, miserable wages, often hungry—oh, often!—hungry and cold, and always friendless and forlorn; a hideous life, an odious life, and filled to the lips with bitterness and humiliation—it comes to me in my dreams, yet, and I live it again, and curse it.

"Two years of it. Templeton, in such cases one learns to *long for money*—for therein lie comfort, peace, the world's respect, one's own respect, every precious thing nameable in language. That is what I thought. The poor and the miserable *worship* money. I worshiped it. To get it—that was my dream, asleep and awake. At last I drifted to Memphis, bringing nothing in the world I valued but you; you, my comfort, my solace, my heart's stay and support. I had earned my crusts in all ways; I could do anything. I got a place as housekeeper, and I was competent. The man's name was Harrison, whom we are hearing much about, here, in these days."

"Land! You knew him?"

"Knew him, and served him. Two years. He was a bachelor and rich—and just a devil; uncle to George Harrison, and sixty when he died the other day. It was odd luck that forced us to come right into daily contact with that blood again."

"Luck—yes, we may call it that, mother, but it wasn't accident. That mulatto devil gave the order—that black-hearted scoundrel, that inf—"

"Let me go on, dear—you are breaking my thread. Harrison was a hard man in every way: hard on his subordinates, and stingy and unfair; hard and grasping with everybody he dealt with, ready and glad to take any mean advantage he could, and merciless with a creditor when he got him down; and he was the cruelest master that ever owned a nigger. He owned Jasper—"

"Out of my heart I'm thankful for that! And if he—"

"But you are interrupting again. How cruel he was! Jasper was not then what he is now; not idle and shiftless, not sour and vengeful and ungentle—no, just the opposite. He would do anything for you he could; and many's the kindness he did me when it was a brave thing to venture it, and many's the comfort he gave me in my need when no other would have risked it."

"Do you mean to tell me that this—this—"

"I am telling you just the truth. Jasper was in his second slavery, then. Several years before, he had bought himself and his time of Harrison on credit, and had worked out the debt by the most prodigious and unremitting energy and industry—talent, too, for he was full of it—and was a free man at last and was soon prospering. He worked on Harrison's principal plantation, out back of Memphis, and was the best hand Harrison had; he had learned a trade, and was as good at it as the best; and now he was learning fancy gardening, and had a passion for it. One night his cabin burned down, and with it his bill of sale. In his simplicity he went to Harrison and asked for a new bill. Harrison coolly repudiated the sale."

"Well, of all the low-down—"

"Repudiated the sale. He ordered Jasper back to his work, and said if he heard any more about this nonsense he would sell him down the river."

"Didn't Jasper sue him?"

"Sue? In a white man's court, and no writings, and no white man's testimony on his side? What good would that do?"

"Yes—I see."

"Jasper did a wiser thing. He bought himself and his time again, on credit, and went straight to work to earn the money."

"Mother, it was brave," said the youth, touched.

"He had just begun on his task when I came. A very hard task, this time; before, he had started without a trade, but he had two, now, and between them he could employ the whole of his time, winter and summer. His value had increased four-fold. He was worth two thousand dollars—and that is what Harrison charged him."

Templeton opened his mouth for an outburst. His mother closed it with her hand, and went on:

"Jasper was the cheerfulest soul, and the gayest, on the place, and the most indomitable worker. And he had need of all his energies and all his native buoyancy, for he had a bitter long job before him. I never saw a sign that he hated anyone but Harrison. But he hated him enough to make up. He concealed this from others, but not from me. He talked it freely to me, and I welcomed it.

"Harrison treated me about as he treated his other house servants. They were slaves, and could bear his brutal speeches, his injustices and his conscienceless requirements in the matter of work—I mean they could bear these things better than I could. I had to bear them with outward meekness, and I did, but it was a most bitter and degrading life that I led there, and I longed to quit it and go away; but would that improve my case? No. Without money I was as well there as anywhere.

"In the last half of the second year I saw that I must give it up and go. I was worked to the bone, my humiliations and resentments kept me in a smouldering rage all the time, they invaded my sleep and spoiled it, life was not worth living, on those terms, and I made up my mind to quit my anchorage and drift at large again.

"There were a few old books in the house, and sometimes when I foresaw that I was going to have a particularly bad night I carried one to bed with me and did what I could to divert my mind with it. One night I took one that was made up of curious little narratives which professed to be inventions, but were told with such good art that they had all the look of verities. One of these narratives took a sudden and powerful hold upon me and I read it with a devouring avidity. It told how a man in France—"

Without knock or notice the door opened a little way and a turbaned young negress thrust her head in and shouted—

"Miss Charlotte, ole Miz. Hopkins she wanter know kin she borry our wush-bo'd fo' jist a—"

"Clear out!" interrupted Templeton. "Let her have it; and don't you come here again till you're sent for."

The wench ducked her head in acceptance of the order, then dropped her voice to a confidential key and said—

"Marse Temp, dey's a farmer down stahs got a load o' prime hick'ry he wanter sell cheap 'case he kin fetch it on de sleigh ef he kin sell it right off whilst de snow las'. Kin I tell yo' mother?"

"No. Tell him she'll take it. Now clear out, will you!—and shut the door."

"You ought to have asked the price, Templeton."

Without other comment she resumed her story.

"It told how a man in France made a large fortune in a month or two on a capital of two thousand francs. He advertised to invest money for people and guarantee to return ten per cent profit every week."

"Upon my word! The writer made such a piece of nonsense as *that* look plausible, mother? I reckon your harassed condition helped out his art a good deal, don't you think?"

"Maybe; but what helped it the most was that I had had four years of close contact with worried and anguished poor people hungry for large money easily gotten. I believed I knew *one* class of the human race down to the bottom. The man's advertisement was quoted; I copied it, and changed it to fit American conditions.

"I spent the rest of the night in frenzied castle-building. I counted my gains, I saw them pile up higher and higher and higher, till in effect I was submerged in bank notes. Now and then the cold thought invaded the furnace of my brain that I was projecting a crime. I fiercely banished it. Every time it came I drove it resolutely out before its influence could get a chance at my conscience. Its attempts diminished by degrees in strength and frequency, and by and by ceased altogether and I was free for good. I had always been honest, serenely and perfectly honest, and I was astonished at myself. But I am not astonished now. I am older, now, and I understand. You see, *I had my limit;* we all have our limit; I was tempted beyond mine. That is always fatal; I am aware of that now.

"It's what the Idiot Philosopher has said about four thousand times."

"It will still be true when he has said it ten thousand," said the mother, placidly. "My mind was made up; I would try that swindle. Then came the thought, I haven't any money, where is the capital to come from? The answer came of itself: Jasper is saving money to buy his freedom with; he has several hundred dollars hidden away. So I told him I was going to leave, and that if he could let me have some money I would pay it back within three months; I said I had a good business plan, and should set up in Memphis; and I reminded him that I was held to be a good business woman. He was quite willing. I said I was going into a business not practised by ladies, but only by gentlemen, and I shouldn't want to be known in it; therefore I should disguise myself and change my name—which was Mrs. Milliken at that time—to Miss Lucy Wallace, and have an imaginary widowed sick brother with one child, and carry on my affair under shelter of his name.

"Jasper gave me all he had, which was three hundred dollars, and said he would keep my secret. When I was ready I went away without notice to Mr. Harrison, and told the house servants that if he took the trouble to ask any questions they could say I was tired of the work and was going far away. In a few days I was established in Memphis. I took a cheap little cottage overlooking the river, on the bluff, at its northern end, and I did my own work. I had no very near neighbors. Over the front door I put a very inconspicuous sign: 'Joseph B. Wallace, Teacher of Oriental Languages by Correspondence.' I wore colors, now, instead of widow's weeds, but my chief disguise was the universal green veil of the period. I hired post office drawer No. 37, explaining that it was for my brother, 'Joseph B. Wallace, Teacher of Oriental Languages by Correspondence.' The smarty young clerk smiled, and said Mr. Wallace probably wouldn't disable himself running to the office for his mail —*that* kind of a mail!—in a small place like Memphis. I said my brother had the whole Union as a field to glean customers from, and had been successful in the North, but the climate was too hard on invalids; and I added, rebukingly, that whether his mail was small or large he would not need to disable himself more than he already was, so long as he had a sister to fetch it for him. That brought a very genuine and right-hearted apology out of the thoughtless young chap; made him blush, too.

"I bought a rubber alphabet, and printed my own circulars. They were rude and inartistic, but I knew the customers I was after. I wrote (in the name of Joseph, teacher, etc.), and asked the postmasters of Cincinnati, Indianapolis and Harrisburg for lists of the newspapers of their States, and got them. Then I sent my advertisement to a dozen papers, widely scattered, in each of the three—country papers, not a single city one. It read like this:

TEN PER CENT PROFIT A WEEK.

The above is guaranteed on investments made through me. Profit returned in cash every seven days. Ten dollars brings a dollar a week, five dollars brings fifty cents. Send for Circular. Address Joseph B. Wallace, Memphis, Tenn.

"I ordered a single insertion only. I did not want to attract too much attention. Three weeks had been swallowed up, now. I had a very private office off my small sitting-room, and I pains-takingly habituated myself to lock it and pocket the key whenever I left it. I did not even allow you in it. You were an energetic busybody of four years, then.

"I had spent a hundred dollars, now. My trap was set, there was nothing to do but sit down and wait. As long as I had been at work I was excited and happy; but this empty idleness! Oh, how drearily the time dragged! Four days—five—six, and not a letter. My scheme was a failure, then! I was in a panic; I couldn't sleep; what could I say to Jasper, who knew where I was, and might look in, any night? And that is what he did, the very next night. But instead of getting scared himself, and losing his head, he only tried to comfort and encourage me. I was so grateful that I said I would help buy his freedom if I succeeded, and I told him what my scheme was."

"You did?"

"Well, I told him *a* scheme, at any rate, and said it was done by mail, and if ever the letters began to come they would bring money. It put him in great spirits, and he said the letters were sure to come, and said he could see his freedom rushing towards him right now! and Templeton, he was half beside himself for joy, on such a thin basis of hope as that, and he couldn't seem to find words enough to thank me with, poor thing.

"He wanted to come once a fortnight and see how the thing was going, but that might be risky, I thought, so we arranged that he should wait a little longer than that, in case the business remained unpromising, but that if in the meantime if it prospered, or if it failed and had to be given up, I was to send for him—by a messenger who would merely hand him a bundle of 'Cuba sixes' —and he would understand.

"Sure enough, letters came the next day,—ten—asking for circulars. I sent them. More came the following day; and after that, they came right along, and increasingly. In ten days I had mailed two hundred circulars.

"And now the tragedy began! The poor little ragged and dirty bank notes began to pour in for investment. They came from pauper widows; from despairing poor clergymen with big families; from sempstresses with bedridden mothers and hungry small brothers and sisters; from all God's forlorn and forsaken creatures; and to me they held out their supplicating hands, and in moving phrases flung hap-hazard out of thankful hearts they called me benefactor, and blessed me!"

"Ah, mother—"

"Hush! Can you put yourself in my place? Have *you* been through what I had been through? No. Then you are barred from criticising—you and all the breed of comfortable professional moralists! I broke my heart over a dozen of those letters, and came near to breaking my purpose and abandoning my scheme; then I read no more of them—for a time, but took the signature and address and stopped there.

"In a register I wrote the names and addresses, and with each name I entered the date of the reception of the money, and the amount. With my rubber alphabet I printed a bale of blanks—two sets of them—worded thus:

Received (date) of (name) the sum of ($. . . . .) for investment.
                                                    Joseph B. Wallace.
    Herewith please find (sum) being seven days' dividend on ($. . . .) received for investment on (date).
                                                    Joseph B. Wallace.

"Inasmuch as I stamped the name, there were but three blanks in each to fill with the pen, and usually fewer than that; for the investments were in the great majority of cases $5 and $10, and I used stamps for them and for the corresponding interest-blanks. Certainly my labors were light enough. At first, at any rate.

"The first time a bank note fell out of a letter. . . ." She paused, her bosom began to rise and fall, a sort of ecstasy rose and

burned in her eyes, then she burst out with "What a moment that
was! Lord, if I could live it again! Ransom!—emancipation!—the
gates of heaven flung open to the damned!—*that* is what it was to
me. That money—that worn and foul and mangy bill, blurred and
dimmed by the grime and sweat of ten thousand dirty fingers—
how beautiful it was, how divine and worshipful, how aureoled
with promise; first of the cloud of angels commissioned—I knew it,
I felt it!—to set me free of the hell of poverty, that hell in whose
presence the flames of the other one are goblin stuff and make-
believe to such as have been through the real one and weltered in it
and are seamed and splotched with its scars and blisters. The bill
represented a crime. What did I care for that? What does a life-
prisoner care for the shot or the stab that murders a warder but sets
himself free? Avarice rises to a *madness* when its opportunity
comes after long and bitter waiting. And so—"

Without notice the wench put her head in again, and shouted—

"Miss Charlotte, dey's a dog done been en gone en gobble up
most a pint uv eyesters en got away wid 'em. De dog b'long to—"

Templeton broke in upon her speech:

"Charge them to him, you fool! And—"

"To de dog, Marse Temp?"

"No, to his owner—idiot! Shut the door; and if you open it again
I'll break your back."

"Yes, marster," responded the wench tranquilly, and was gone.

"If ever a creature needed killing, that is the one!"

The mother said, gently—

"They have a hard fate, poor things. And they are ignorant. One
must make allowances."

The youth said, impatiently—

"You are always saying that, mother. It is getting pretty old. If
you would punish that girl sometimes, she could learn."

A faint flush rose in the mother's cheek in response to the
speech's sarcastic clause, but only this mute notice was taken of it.
Her mind was mainly on the concluding clause. With a soft
reproach in her tone, she said—

"How can I punish her? Sold from her home twelve hundred
miles away; not a friend here, and she so lonesome. She has a

mother, and will never see her again. I am a mother; how can I punish her?"

The young fellow, disabled for the moment by this projectile, searched for some way to counter it. He fidgeted a minute, then did the best he could in the circumstances—

"Well, anyway, if she wouldn't *sing!* Two or three times a week that racket of hers breaks out, and it's enough to drive a person distracted: 'Goin' home! goin' home! I's done wid tears and sorrow!' And you never say a word; I swear I don't know how you can stand it."

"Stand it? I could take that poor forlorn thing to my breast for pure thankfulness when her burden lifts and lets those joy-bells ring out of her heart. Stand it? That friendless child! Lord, if she can sing, God knows, I—"

The song burst out paean-like from below, at this moment, and interrupted her. The listeners heard it through to the end, then after a pause Templeton, evidently touched, said—

"I see. I hadn't looked at it in that way before. . . . Go on, mother."

CHAPTER [XVI]

"VERY WELL. Let me see. I was talking about my work. The money began to flow in fast. The average was as much as ten dollars a letter; some contained considerably less, but many contained fifteen and twenty. Before that first bill had been in my hands a week I had a thousand dollars."

"Caesar!"

"I put aside the first three hundred of that thousand for Jasper— the sum I owed him—and added two hundred to it, for a happy surprise; and I resolved to make him a half partner in all the profits that should come."

Templeton pressed her hand, and said—

"I judged you would do that, mother; a body could foresee it."

The woman put his hand gently away, and said appealingly—

"Don't—oh, don't, my son, you kill me!"

"Kill you?" said the youth, puzzled, "how?"

"I am coming to it. Spare me now, judge me later; pity me, I mean."

"Ah, mother, you can't mean that you. . . . But never mind; go on."

"I—I—it shames me so! and *you* can't understand it—only the desperately poor can. Within an hour I had repented a little. I reflected that I was giving him more than his share. A dividend had to come out of the extra two hundred—twenty dollars, you know. Why should that come out of me? Oughtn't he to pay it? Twice I removed it, twice I returned it. I tried hard to leave it, then, and put it out of my mind. But I was not strong enough. I took it the third time, and did not return it any more."

She paused—a pause which was a supplication—but there was no comment, for she had unconsciously fired a train of surprising thoughts in her boy, and he was absorbed in examining them and marveling over them; so she sighed and dolorously took up her tale again.

"I went out and got the Cuba sixes, and for a moment I was eager to find a messenger and send this sign of happy tidings. But the feeling quickly began to fade. Why send so soon? There was no hurry. Why not wait until—well, until I could better spare the money? So I did not send the cigars. I kept on reflecting and reflecting, my avarice kept on persecuting me. At last, to get peace, I postponed all payment for the present, and returned the bills to my general hoard."

Suddenly Templeton's perplexed face cleared, and he said with the astonished air of one who has discovered America—

"Why, *I've* had an experience like that! I supposed it was abnormal, and couldn't happen to another. I was ashamed of myself, and hid it. Maybe it's only just human nature; do you reckon it is, mother? By George, it's immensely curious—interesting, too! It was the time they had the public meeting in Slaterville and took up a collection for the poor Hodgsons, that lost everything in a fire and hadn't a rag nor a penny left, and the appeal of the first speaker was so moving that I pulled out fourteen dollars, which was every cent I had, and—and—but go on, mother, it makes me half sick, yet, to think about it. Go on—consider that I haven't interrupted."

"Very well," said the mother; and there was a something in her tone or her manner that seemed to indicate that a sore place in her had been salved; "I feel as you felt; and I will not dwell upon that part of my record, but will cut it very short. The plain, odious truth is, that the more money I got, the more I couldn't bear the thought of parting with any of it; and so, before long I had entirely renounced the idea of making Jasper a partner—"

"I reckon it was bound to happen! I wonder if we aren't all made like that?—if we get a chance to postpone. That Idiot Philosopher says that if your left hand wants to find out what your right hand doeth the right hand has got to hump itself or there won't be anything for the left hand to find out. It doesn't seem to sound so foolish, now, as it did before. Go on, mother."

"Pretty soon I indefinitely postponed sending for Jasper. Next, I concluded not to send for him at all, but let him come when he should get tired waiting—then I would give him his three hundred dollars; meantime it would be a consolation to me and a solace, to have it and hold it and be able to look at it. It came to be to me as a dying child, dear and beautiful, whom I must presently caress for the last time and see no more. I put it away, in a place by itself, and watched over it with a sorrowful solicitude."

"Good!" said the young man; and added with a playful pretence of immense relief, "by gracious I was afraid you were going to hog that, too!"

His mother blushed, but he did not see it. After a reflective pause her sober face began to brighten with pleasant memories, and she resumed her tale with cheery animation.

"As fast as an investment was seven days old I mailed its ten per cent dividend promptly. The weeks sparkled gaily along, and my daily mail soon required a basket. Young Simon Bunker, post-office clerk, was astonished, and asked me how much my brother got for a lesson. I was expecting this dangerous question, and was prepared for it. And that was well, for there was a meditated proposal lurking in his eye. I could see it. I told him two dollars for three months; half payable in the middle of the term and the other half at the end of it; that most of the pupils were poor youths studying for the ministry and took Hebrew, and often could not pay, and that often the other pupils got tired in a month and dropped out and forgot to send any money; but, that taking good and bad together my brother could always depend upon a large and steady cash income—*never* less than fifteen hundred dollars in a year, and once it had risen to nearly two thousand. I said it ostentatiously, and gave my head a grand toss. The proposal faded out of his eye. I saw it out of the corner of my own. He was always as courteous to me afterward as ever, but indifferent to my affairs; and he never asked after my poor brother's health any more. We dropped into the nickname stage of friendliness, and on that pleasant and harmless footing we continued."

"The nickname stage of friendliness, mother? Oh, yes, I know what you mean; but it isn't always a friendly stage, for Dug's pet name for Sol Bailey—"

"I know; but with Simon Bunker and me it was friendly."

"What were the nicknames?"

"That isn't important, and my tale is more interesting. Let me go on. In the second week I took more than two thousand dollars— and promptly paid the dividends out of it. The third week brought me five thousand, the fourth week fifteen. And then such jubilant letters began to arrive from customers who had received three dividends! Their gratitude was deep, sincere, outspoken, and was poured out in the most eloquent of all speech, the quaint and odd and unconventional centre-driving language of the poor—that marvelous phrasing which is above all art, beyond the reach of all art, and goes straight to the heart—and sometimes breaks it!

"There was one very noticeable thing; a thing which I was expecting, however, for I knew the poor. It was this: the twenty-dollar customer kept his rich 'find' to himself, but the very poor told their neighbors of their good fortune and sent me new customers. Poverty and misery soften the heart and make their victims good to each other. The widow's mite has gone yearly out in mountains of pennies in all the ages. But for the poor, what would become of the poor?

"I say, the fifth week brought me fifteen thousand dollars. What with registering new customers, acknowledging the receipt of investments and mailing dividends, I was writing as much as 3,000 words a day, possibly 4,000, and the work growing by leaps and bounds. Six hours of hard labor daily. What would it be in another week? Eighteen! I should have to employ clerks. Could I venture that? It was a time for reflection.

"I tossed about in my bed half the night—reflecting. *Must* I give up and fly? Must I? when in two or three weeks more I could go away with a hundred thousand dollars? I was wild to have it; avarice is a pitiless master when one has been through the vile miseries of poverty, humility and subjection. I couldn't bear the thought of losing that fortune, and I ended by resolving to dare the worst and stay. Maybe I could get safe clerks—oh, surely I could; surely I could get through, somehow. It was settled, and I went to sleep.

"But alas! the very next day, along with more than five thousand dollars in bank bills, came a couple of *checks* in my basket of mail matter. That would never do! To handle checks—well, that would be handling fire. Put a tale-bearing check through a bank? Oh, no, I was not mad enough for that. In fact I was quite sober by now. Very well, I must go; and not tomorrow, but to-day, if I would secure a good start. It had taken one of the checks four days to come, the other a day longer. I returned them to their envelops, put them aside, and sent no acknowledgments. The four-day man would expect an acknowledgment in four or five days; then he would get uneasy and begin to inquire. I must be far away by the time this should happen.

"I was prepared. I was ready, disguises and all; for I had foreseen from the beginning that when fleeing-time should come, delay could be disastrous. I had bought an old skiff, and I kept it chained at the foot of the bluff, and on pleasant nights I had given you outings in it, and myself exercise while I educated myself in the management of it. My last act every night at bedtime had been to put the day's receipts into a rusty old carpet-sack, under some old

Marseilles jackets, and lock it. It was always ready for removal. In a similar bag I kept changes of underwear for you and me, some soap and other toilet things of a cheap sort, and a ration or two of crackers and cheese. That was all. It, also, was always ready. For you and for myself I had a suit each, of old and coarse clothing such as only the poor wear. These I kept where they would be always handy. It was my purpose to carry nothing out of the house but these old clothes and the carpet-sacks. In a closet I kept a little pile of shavings, with several of my ordinary gowns loosely heaped upon them, my idea being a smouldering fire that would give me time to get a good way down the river before it made an exposure of itself.

"That last day was a long and cruelly exciting one, but it came to an end at last; we donned our disguises, and at nine o'clock I locked the house and soon you and I and the odds-and-ends bag were under the bluff—the bag in the boat, in the bow-locker, and you and I snug at our ease in the cool shelter of one of its caved indentations, a play-house you were used to and at home in. I had chosen your bed-time, and you presently drowsed off to sleep, as I was expecting. Then I went back. According to habit, I had left the day's receipts to be put in the cash-bag with their brethren the last thing. I was trembling like a thief, and starting at every sound; but I thrust them in, put a match to my incendiary shavings, and hurried away. I was so glad when I reached you and found you safe and still sleeping peacefully! It made a revulsion and brought me to myself, my cool and normal self. And then, of course! My first thought was—Jasper's three hundred dollars. Also, of course I began to reason about it. What a pity it should be wasted! Yes, yes, what a pity. With this start, the next stages of thought were inevitable: *Ought* it to be wasted? was it morally right to throw it away? Surely it were better that I should have it than that it should be burned up. As ashes it could do him no good, nor anyone. I had faithfully kept it for him; he could have come and gotten it; why hadn't he? Was I in any way to blame? Well—true, I could have sent him word, according to agreement, but had I time? Now, really, had I? How could I think of everything, in such an exciting day, and I not knowing what I was about, half the time? I was hurrying back to the house, steeped in these dreams, by this time. Before I had reached it I had put all the blame on Jasper, and was saying his loss would be good for him—perhaps the very making of him—because it would teach him to be more careful. By the time I had the money in my hands I was feeling that I was putting him under an obligation to me."

"By gracious! Mother, if I hadn't thought of that Hodgson business, I couldn't believe it."

"Avarice is a remorseless master! I was its servile slave. A rag-smoke stench was creeping through the house; I locked the door, and ran. My conscience was trying to trouble me, but I pacified it easily. How? The memory of a generous action did it: necessarily those checks were from trustees of poor widows and orphans, who had proposed to themselves to gamble with the fiduciary money in their charge and keep the winnings—nobody living on a bank-check level of commercial intelligence would risk his *own* money in such an insane gamble as a ten-per-cent-a-week scheme put forward by an unaccredited stranger. I knew much about widows' and orphans' trustees, I knew the ear-marks of the tribe, and I knew I had saved a little batch of their victims by not cashing those checks. The thought cheered me, uplifted me, made me feel almost noble, and I raised my depressed head and was thankful that I had had that good impulse and had obeyed it."

The son spared his mother an ungracious interruption, but the thought passed through his mind: "Why, she knows that the reason she didn't collect the checks was because she *dasn't*; has she forgotten that? I reckon this confusion of mind comes of what Sol Bailey calls 'the habit of misapplying facts: making counterfeit coin out of them to deceive other people with, and then passing it on yourself.' She didn't save the orphans, they saved *her*."

"So I ran along comforted and content. When I arrived under the bluff I found you outside our shelter and awake. The fright of it took my breath away. You could have wandered into the river, poor little tot, and been drowned. I hugged you to my breast in unspeakable thankfulness—then I heard a sound of approaching voices; in another moment I had cast off; flung the bag into the boat, scrambled in after it with you, and we were away. I pulled noiselessly out a quarter of a mile and then stopped rowing; the current would do my work for me now. We were safe! A storm was threatening; no matter, we were safe; the storm could only hide us and make us safer. It began to sprinkle, the thunder began to mutter. You were troubled, I was not. I snuggled you to my bosom and was content; safety was the great thing, the only important thing, and we were safe.

"I fixed my gaze upon the receding bluff, now looming dull and massive in the growing darkness, and waited with serenity for my fire to burst up and consume my witnesses and obliterate me and my peril-laden history. Waited so, five minutes. My serenity began to ooze out, then. Five more, and the remains of it vanished. The rain was increasing; I could hardly make out the outlines of the bluff through it. Plague take the fire, what was the matter with it? A steady downpour began, now, and pretty soon we were under an old-fashioned Southern summer deluge, and couldn't see anything at all. Was it putting out my fire and rescuing my deadly witnesses? There was no answer to that question. I was in deep anxiety for a while, then I thought, 'What does it matter? we are safe, we are free, we shall hide far away and never be caught.' Two hours later the storm ceased and the stars came out. We were drenched, but it was a hot night and we did not mind it—and neither did our shabby clothes. You slept through a good part of it. When you waked I taught you my new name—'Mrs. Sarah Lynch'—and your own—'Johnny Lynch'; and urged you to forget you had ever been 'Franky Wallace'; just as I had taught you a few weeks earlier to call me 'aunt Lucy Wallace' and forget you had been 'Tony Milliken.'

"It was peaceful and pleasant under the blinking stars, and you learned very well until you got weary and then hungry. Do you remember that night?"

"A suggestion of the storm remains—a rather dim one; nothing else."

"Think."

"Well, let me see. Mm. . . . Somehow it seems to me that you. . . . Mm. . . . No, I believe. . . . Didn't something frighten you, and didn't you scream, or fall, or—"

"Yes, both. You were hungry, and I crept forward to get the bag out of the locker. *It was gone!* It was then that I screamed—and fell in a faint, too. When I came to, you were petting my face and crying, poor thing. The carpet-sacks were alike, and were always kept hidden under the bed; in my worry and excitement and flightiness that night, I had carried down the wrong sack and stowed it in the bow-locker. It had twenty thousand dollars and more in it, and was gone. All we had now, counting in Jasper's three hundred, fell a little short of six thousand.

"That was a bitter hour, a horrible hour! Then of course all the devils that are lodged in a person to persecute him when a chance comes, rose against me and mocked me, reviled me, scorched me with reproaches. What a fool I had been to go back after that paltry three hundred when I already had what to me was immeasurable wealth! If I had only not gone back, if I had only been satisfied, the disaster would not have happened, and I should be rich, now, instead of being a half-pauper and unutterably miserable! I know I can say honestly, even at this distant day, that I would rather die five common deaths and one at the stake than live that wretched hour over again."

"How had the sack disappeared, mother?"

"I got the tale out of you, delivered in your prattling nursery-English; a guileless little tale, told with happy interest in dear little stumbling words—and every word a blade in my heart, though you couldn't know it. A dog followed our track into our shelter and sniffed you over and woke you up; a man followed the dog, and questioned you and asked if you were lost, and where was your mother. You said I was coming soon, I was not gone far. He said he would wait; he was very hungry, and maybe I would be kind and give him something, for he was very, *very* hungry. That seemed dreadful, and you said you knew where our food was; and went outside with him and told him about the locker, and then you went to playing with the dog, which was a friendly creature, and you did not think of the man any more; and after a little there was a whistle in the distance and the dog bounded away."

There was a long silence. Then Templeton said:

"Did the house burn down, mother? Did you ever hear?"

"Not for a year or more. Not until we had wandered hundreds of miles through the South and were at last established, prospering and respected, in the town of Baker's Mills. Then by chance I learned—it was an old and nearly forgotten story there—that the house had not burned; that my mail-matter accumulated so prodigiously during three or fours days after our flight as to cause amazement and then inquiry. That clerk went to the house to see what was the matter. My witnesses were all present: record-book, circulars, every accusing thing you can think of. Harrison identified my handwriting without any trouble, of course, and the machinery of the law was set in motion. Descriptions of 'Mrs. Milliken' and her little boy 'Tony,' also of 'Miss Lucy Wallace' and her little nephew 'Franky' were published and heavy rewards offered. That three or four days' mail contained a total of upwards of sixty thousand dollars in bank notes, and seven thousand in checks— trustees' checks, there's not a doubt of it."

She sighed profoundly. After a little, she said—

"I learned another thing: my sentence to ten years in the penitentiary."

"My God!"

"It is hanging over me yet. *Now* you know why I would never tell you my history. Can you forgive me? Do you forgive me?"

The answer was prompt and earnest:

"For letting me be happy and light-hearted all these years when I should not have been strong enough to bear up under the worry and the terror of the facts? You chose wisely, and I thank you for sparing me at such heavy cost to yourself. I can help you bear your burden, now, and I will. You are a criminal, but I am your son, and my place is by your side, let come what may. Mothers do not desert their sons when they transgress, they stand by them against the world; then why shouldn't a son do by his mother what she would do by him if the—"

"Oh, you are the best and dearest son that ever—"

"No, you are not to say a word, not a single word. Whatever comes, we are going to face it together. I am older now than I was when I woke this morning—years older; and you will see that I shall be a help to you—a real help, mother; you will see. Now cheer up and let's take a new start. What is done can't be helped; we are living an honest life, and will continue it. Where you fell many would have fallen—good people, too, and primarily sound at heart. Bitter poverty and misery, then stupendous temptation and opportunity—why, if Sol Bailey is right, the fall was substantially certain. He says it's Circumstances, Temptation and Opportunity —this tremendous trinity—that make criminals, not native wickedness. He says we all have our limit, and he wouldn't even trust George Harrison if circumstances, temptation and opportunity fell together and caught him beyond his limit."

"Ah, well, I don't know. Possibly it might be so, but one can't quite imagine it, Templeton."

"Yes, I know; it's one of Sol's extravagances, but take humanity by and large and the rule will hold good I reckon. Mother, I remember the first time Jasper dropped down upon us. There in Braxton. I was fourteen or fifteen, then. By the new light this talk of ours has thrown, I infer that he was hunting for us then. Is that so?"

"Yes. He had been on that hunt for three or four years. With revenge for his object. With the loss of his three hundred, ill luck began for him. For two years, when I was housekeeper, he had stood my friend when others were afraid of that office, and it did him an ill service now. He was questioned, and they got out of him the fact that he had been privy to my disappearance, and had visited me in my house. He said we had had no money-transactions together, but this was doubted, and he was jailed on suspicion, to wait for evidence which might prove him to have been a confederate of mine. He was confined a year; then he was set free, but the thirst for revenge had largely taken the place of interest in his work. He nursed his hate, and brooded. He labored himself free at last and got his papers, but it had taken him six years after he got out of jail. Then he began his hunt for me. When he found us at Braxton he had been patiently tracking us down for three or four years.

"Twice he had been notified to leave towns or be sold into slavery, in accordance with the six-months law, and this and his former troubles together had embittered him against the whole white race. That hate has grown in vindictiveness since, year by year.

"When he found us at last in Braxton, he told me he would live on me the rest of his life, and would do the best he could to make that life a curse to me. He has kept his word. He said our secrets were dangerous ones, and he warned me to keep you in ignorance of them—which I of course meant to do anyway as long as I could. From the beginning of the Braxton days you perceived that there was something between us and that he caused me suffering—which of course angered you and made you wretched—but I made you keep still and leave the matter alone. Jasper said that when you were old enough he would visit you as well as me, and thus double his persecutions and his satisfactions. So he has now begun it at last, here in this village. I could endure all he did and said, for my liberty depended upon it; but you have endured him without a reason except my prayers and supplications, and my assurances that a heavy calamity would befal me if you should rouse the fiend that is in him. I cannot tell you how grateful I am."

"You have borne this hell six years, mother, I six weeks. But I am not to be complimented on my fidelity and fortitude, for I have been anything but patient, in my heart, meantime, but just the reverse. I shall do better now—now that I know everything. If he will continue to let you alone and give all his attentions to me, I will swallow my pride and content him. I always wondered why we left prosperous businesses, now and again, in the past six years, and changed our names and moved to a distance, but I begin to understand, now."

"Yes, it was I that made the flight the first time. It was to escape from Jasper. He made me repent it. The other flights were by his order. Twice he was threatened with enslavement, and we went elsewhere on that account. On the other occasions we fled because I got uneasy, believing I was in danger of being found out and identified; but it was he who chose the new places of refuge. It was he that devised my disguises, sometimes. It was he that made me play blind woman in one place, play cripple in another, and so on. He is the reason why I am as deaf as an adder here."

"There's one compliment I can pay you, mother: you've acted your parts well."

"He practised me. He is a smart creature. And he had a good pupil. No one can trick me into hearing a sound which I don't choose to hear, I don't care how carefully the project has been devised."

"You've vain of it, little mother! but that's all right, you have said the truth, and you have a right to your compliment. It is a marvelous accomplishment, and there are very few who could acquire it. Tell me, mother—for I have a small vanity of my own: I know that Gunning is a fictitious name, also Franky and Tony and a lot more, but how about Templeton?"

"You have borne it twice, my son: when you were born, and up to the time that your father died and we had to go wandering in poverty and white servitude; and I gave it you again a couple of years ago when we had to fly to this region."

"Then it's not fictitious, but real!"

"Yes."

"Thank heaven—fervently! The Frankys and Tonys and Millikens and Lynches and Gunnings and so-on are plebeian, but Templeton isn't. Templeton is lordly; the very sound of it harks you back to castles and broad lands and noble blood and titles."

"It was your father's."

"Mother, it's splendid! What was his surname?"

She hesitated, colored, then dropped the name in a low voice: "Ashes."

"*Ashes?*"

"Ashes."

"Tem—pleton——*Ashes!* . . ." Then, under his breath, "Dam—nation!"

CHAPTER [XVII]

TEN DAYS poked along by, in the little town. A thaw came early and swept away the snow, and the village life resumed its course under the customary conditions. Young Tom Harrison had been up and about the house for a day, but was down again, with a backset, and Helen was nursing him, as before, and both were happy, there being no danger. George Harrison visited them daily for a moment, then visited Fairfax in the jail for another moment, and in both cases tried to be at ease and cheerful, but he was glad when the visits were over, for Helen lavished innocent caresses upon him and praises of his noble constancy to her father in his trouble which filled him with shame and self-contempt, and Fairfax praised him for his patient and devoted efforts to find that elusive and mysterious stranger, and kept him inventing difficult and painful lies about these devoted efforts all the time, a thing which wearied his head and polluted his heart and wounded his self-respect. And then Fairfax always welcomed him so heartily and so gratefully with his eloquent eyes and his cordial voice; and called him "the best friend and the bravest and faithfulest a forsaken and detested unfortunate ever had in this cowardly world!" and these cruel compliments did cut and carve and mutilate so unendurably! And often Fairfax said, "You've got to condemn me now—you can't help it in the circumstances, and I shouldn't respect you if you tried; but you will have your reward, for all in good time you will come to know me, and then in all sincerity you will take my hand and say 'There is no blood on it, it's as clean as my own.'" Harrison always went from the place feeling like a cur.

But in his own house his wilted spirits revived in some degree—for a little while at a time, at least; for the friends came nightly and sat with him, and smoked and drank hot whiskies, and talked politics, religion, agriculture and gossip—thus paying the homage always paid to money and persistent and indestructible good luck by the majority of our race and to high and blemishless character by the rest of it. Sometimes the talk would continue an hour or two without dripping any vitriol into his sore places; he was a grateful man, then, and in a vague dull way happy—something as one's foot is when it is asleep. Then came the chance drop of vitriol and the answering shrivel. Some random and purposeless remark was sure to administer it now and then give Harrison a turn and make him wince, but the intervals between were sweet; sweet as the heavenly numbness that follows a hypodermic injection, and he was deeply thankful for the reprieves from pain they brought him.

He had a new worry in these days, and his hard-worked and half-demented imagination made the most it could of it. That Milliken woman—what did Sol Bailey's curious references to her mean? Might she have been privately married to his uncle Harrison?—might she? And might she and her son be still alive, somewhere, and findable by meddling persons and producible before the world? He worked the idea up until it became the next thing to a certainty. Oh, yes, there was no good luck possible for him, ever again: those heirs would be found, and he would know the biting shames and miseries of poverty once more—God send death instead!

He came to regard the Idiot Philosopher as the possessor of his fate—the man whose silence could save him, and whose speech could take his bread from his mouth and his roof from over his head. He would placate him, he would move his pity, he would make him kind—then Bailey would keep the terrible secret shut up in his breast. Fired with this hope, this dream, he astonished the Philosopher by the effusiveness of the welcomes he began to get at Harrison's house and the manifold attentions Harrison showered upon him. He was astonished, but gratified; moreover, he was early emboldened by this improved condition of the atmosphere to try for another little contribution to the missionary industry. Twenty-five dollars? Harrison doubled it, without a remonstrance; and was so eager about it that one might have thought he regarded the chance as a favor done him. He wanted Bailey to be his friend, and said so; and wanted him to come often, and said that also; and wanted to know whenever the missionaries needed help—he should only be too glad, and all that. Bailey, child of poverty and privation, life-long sport of evil fortune, listened with charmed ears to this strange and sweet and miraculous music, and was grateful. The wind-tossed and weather-worn derelict had found a haven at last, and he felt all that derelicts feel—if derelicts can feel—when this blessed thing happens and their rusty anchors go down, a-stem and a-stern, and take a holding-grip on the firm bottom.

Anyone who knew Bailey could have told you what he would do with his fifty dollars. Anyone who knew the Bailey kind—which is a wide-spread breed, and often findable in commonplace families and *always* in families which number a genius as an offset, among its members—could have told you. The Sol Baileys are by nature honest—vainly so, sentimentally so, deliriously so. They are the most conscientious devils in the world. Their conscience is not anchored, and it goes floating around; but wherever they happen to find it they are loyal to it and obey it. If it is in an inconvenient place they move it to a better position—but not ruthlessly, not arbitrarily: they reason with it, they show it the right place, they convince it. But not until it is convinced will they act; not until it approve will they swerve from its desire by a hair's-breadth. Their minds are ill balanced, and they reason curiously, often fantastically, but always sincerely. Often their reasonings would seem absurd to a practical person and would stand no chance of deceiving him; but they deceive the Baileys and the Bailey conscience—and they do it well and thoroughly, too.

Yes, anyone familiar with the Bailey type could have told you what Sol Bailey would do with the fifty dollars which Harrison had given him as a contribution to the Presbyterian Oriental Missionary Fund. He paid twenty-two of it into that fund—the sum he had borrowed of it to equip Allen—added 5 cents for 5 days interest—and felt the glad uplift and the warm heart-glow which an honorable man always feels when he has discharged a just debt and can stand before his conscience with clean hands and his head up.

His credit and his trustworthiness being established by this upright and straightforward conduct, he borrowed the rest of the fifty for present use. In doing this he had that applauding heart-glow again, for he recognized that he was doing the Fund a very real favor in finding a safe investment for its money which paid 38 per cent above legal interest—a rate which he was determined to continue, burdensome as it was.

These things have a curious and impossible look on paper, and the fact that they are true, and not only true but common, does not relieve them of that look. The Sol Baileys are a quaint and interesting breed. Judged by the ordinary standards, they commit crimes, little or big, every day, yet there is seldom a conscious criminal among them, seldom a consciously and purposely bad man. They have beliefs, principles, convictions; and while they have them they are ready and willing to suffer for them. But there is nothing permanent about them, they change with every chance thought of their owners and with every vagrant wind of opinion that blows upon them from the outside. It seems a strange and wonderful thing to claim and insist upon, yet one may claim with confidence and insist upon it as a certainty: that these people have one great big special and commanding virtue—sincerity. They may hold a principle only a week or a month—maybe only a day—but while they hold it their belief in it is sincere and their championship of it enthusiastic. Often they are lovable creatures, but there was never one yet who was not a sorrow and a vexation to his kin and friends. One never knows where to find them, one never knows what they will do next. When they have a new conviction in stock they are a peril; to themselves and to all who hold them in affection; for while they may be physical cowards, and generally are, perhaps, in moral intrepidity they know no fear and no discretion: they will thunder that conviction out, let the consequences be what they may.

Once, during one of those times when Sol Bailey was temporarily serving in the ministry, his life was for a while an actual success. During four Sundays the anxieties of his friends had a rest. He was preaching a series of sermons upon the Fatherhood of God, his whole heart was in his theme, and he poured out his wonder and worship in reverent and beautiful words. But by next Sunday his spiritual perceptions had got a new focus and new light, and he said so; and then went blandly on and knocked the brains out of everything he had said in the four preceding discourses. His brief triumph lay in ruins about him and he was a wanderer again.

One morning, in the heat of a political campaign and while he was for the moment a vindictive and uncompromising democrat, a committee applied to him for mottoes and sentiments to paint upon the transparencies which were to be used in the torchlight procession that night. He promptly furnished them, and made them red-hot. Before mid-afternoon he had talked with half a dozen able and instructed whigs; and in the evening, when the democratic boys marched huzzaing by the whig mass-meeting with his abusive mottoes gaily flaring, he was up there on the platform compelling thunders of applause with a scathing and libelous and enthusiastic whig speech.

After squaring up with the Missionary Fund and lending the rest of its fifty dollars to himself at 38 per cent above legal interest, Sol Bailey sat down with a disburdened conscience and a contented spirit to consider the mystery of Harrison's new attitude toward him and what might be the reason of it, the source of it. This did not occupy him many minutes. It was hardly doubtful that the source of it was the conversation about the Milliken woman.

If that was it, Harrison was alarmed! that was certain. Bailey's imagination-machinery was in motion, now, just with that handful of fuel, and it could be trusted to do some gallant work. If Harrison was alarmed, *why* was he alarmed? Because the Milliken woman *was* the old uncle's wife and Harrison knew it! Wasn't that plain? Nothing could be plainer.

So that was settled: that woman was actually the old uncle's wife. Bailey was entirely convinced of it, now. Within fifteen minutes he had deceived himself into the belief that he had harbored this conviction for fifteen years; quite forgetting that when he had had that talk with Harrison the notion had just been born to him, and was a mere random thought picked up by chance in his mind and inflated into a half-suspicion on the spot by his nimble imagination; then expanded to a probability within the next hour; and to a large charitable duty toward the wronged woman half an hour later. We know the result: the dispatching of Allen to hunt up the maltreated heirs.

Bailey now went around and had a private conversation with Harrison. It began with constraints, shynesses and small alarms on Harrison's part, but ended in a frank and open heart-to-heart talk, stripped of subterfuge and concealment on both sides. Toward the last, poor Harrison broke down several times, in view of the privations and miseries that would come upon him in his growing age if the heirs should be found and should be pitiless and turn him out destitute and forlorn to beg his bread, and the result was what anyone who knows the Sol Bailey type has already foreseen: Bailey turned clear around in his tracks and became this poor man's cordial shield and champion—with his whole impulsive good heart in his new rôle, and swearing, with strong hand-grip and with the tears of a generous and genuine sympathy and compassion flowing down his cheeks to stand by his imperiled friend to the last, and to devote all his time and energy to saving him; a pleasant task and a holy duty which he would certainly bring to a successful issue if mortal sagacity and a wide and seasoned experience could do it. For the Sol Baileys have hearts that are as soft as jelly; the pains and sorrows of the distressed find instant refuge there and boundless welcome; and if the occupying sorrower is in the way, out he goes, without a thought, to make room for the new one!

Harrison put his arms about his spirit-uplifting friend and hugged him—he couldn't help it; and with grateful tears in his eyes he called him benefactor. Then he put his hands on his shoulders and looked lovingly into his face and added—

"God bless you, Bailey, God bless you! for I never can, adequately. You have made a new man of me, you have saved me from despair, you have filled me with hope and cheer. How good you are!"

"No, I am not good, Harrison, but I am just, and that is better. That wife disappeared—for what? Idle caprice? Oh, never, never. For what, then? For cause. What cause? Because she had done wrong. It is perfectly plain; the logic of it is remorseless. Why did she remain away? Because she dared not return while that embittered man was alive, and she knew it. The argument is unanswerable. She will come mincing back, now, with a lie in her mouth—"

"Oh, dear, I know she will, I know it!"

"But she will find me there—and ready!"

"I know it, I feel it, Bailey, and I am a child to give way to these foolish terrors, with you standing between me and harm. How brave you are, and how noble—I never knew you before, and these people do not know you."

"They'll know me yet, give yourself no concern."

"Indeed they will, I am sure of that. How shall you proceed when she comes?"

"To begin with, I'll never let her come!"

"Ah, that is best of all! There is reason in that, wisdom in it. How will you manage, Bailey?"

Sol Bailey's imagination was white-hot, now, and making 250 revolutions a minute; it was ready and competent to supply him all the appliances he might need for the embarrassment and obstruction of that disloyal woman at half a minute's notice. It began to expand Allen Osgood straight off.

"Easily. I've got two of the best and most experienced professional detectives in the world shadowing her already!"

"What! You've already begun your generous work without even waiting for me to get a chance to thank you?"

"The grass never grows under *my* feet! I turned the matter over in my mind; in ten minutes I knew her for what she was and had been; in ten more I saw what game she was going to play, and in ten more I had telegraphed the detectives to pack up and start."

Harrison was lost in admiration. All he could say was—

"We never knew you, Bailey, we never knew you. These marvelous intuitions—this astonishing penetration—this promptness, this swiftness, this energy! In my life I have encountered nothing that approached it."

"Well, it's my way; I was born to it, I suppose. When a thing is to be done, some people are content to cipher on the hours. I can't; the seconds are the servants I am after."

"I see. I understand, now. It's the difference between efficiency and half-efficiency. In the present instance, if you will allow me to say it, it's the difference between the mail and the telegraph; between the lightning-bug and the lightning."

"I make no pretensions, Harrison, and it may be that you are over-esti—"

"No, I am only just—nothing more. And to think that you have gone right ahead and done this generous thing for me, advancing the money out of your own pocket—"

Bailey laid his hand affectionately on Harrison's shoulder, and said with a benignant smile—

"Ah, well, when my friend's welfare is at stake my pocket is his, not mine."

"Ah, let me shake you by the hand, best friend and truest a man ever had. And let me take a partial example by you: let me be at least just, where you are generous; do not let me be helped at cost of your hurt. This will be an expensive matter; also, your own time and talents are valuable beyond price—draw upon me freely, draw upon me for everything. Let me give you something now."

"No, not now. It is true that the matter is difficult and will become costly as it goes along, but I do not need any money yet, I still have a little left. I will tell you when there is occasion."

"But you *must* take some; I insist."

It turned out to be difficult to persuade Bailey. He was in debt sixty or eighty dollars to the Fund, but was not able to realize it—at least not the whole of it. He knew he had borrowed twenty-two dollars from the first contribution, but as he had paid it back out of the second it seemed wiped out. As to the rest it was well invested and paying high interest, and therefore hardly seemed a debt at all. He was used to being in harder circumstances than these, he was quite comfortable, and not disposed to accept of expense-money until the expense should have been incurred and become a concrete fact. After the manner of his breed he had quite forgotten that a part of his scheme in rescuing and righting the Milliken heirs had been the securing of a commission amounting to the half of the estate for himself and Osgood the rescuers. A member of the Sol Bailey tribe can seldom keep the details of an old scheme in mind after a new one has evicted it from the premises.

However, Harrison forced a hundred dollars upon him, and said it was not a loan and not a part of the outside expenses—no, it was salary, his first fortnight's salary. In all his life Bailey had never earned such a mammoth sum before, even in treble the time. He was dazzled, bewildered, overcome, almost breathless. It was riches, and he was not able to put his thankfulness into words; and said so. Harrison was happy, and said—

"My good friend, my best friend, it is nothing. You are going to save me, I know it, I feel it. You are going to find those people and buy their rights, for half or for less, and I tell you this: of what is left, you shall have half."

Words failed poor Bailey again, and he left the presence drunk with gratitude, and steeped in love and veneration for his benefactor, and unshakeably resolved to labor with all his heart and all his mind in his interest; and to this good and pure and righteous work he solemnly dedicated himself with the gushing enthusiasm of his tribe.

Whenever a true Sol Baliey does a thing, whether good or evil, his next act, usually, is to repent of it; and not mildly and moderately, but in sackcloth and ashes. A true Sol Bailey is the most impressionable of men; and in some ways the most sensitive. He is made up mainly of feeling—gushy, impulsive, unordered and systemless feeling. A happy feeling will transport him to the clouds, but nothing can keep him there; a revulsion is sure to come, and will as surely plunge him Satan's nine-days' flight to perdition and despair. He is a volcano, and is usually in eruption: discharging fire and radiance one day and mud and ashes the next. Or, he is consolidated twins, one inside of the other: when one of them is awake, all is joy; when it is the other's turn, all is black despondency, and miscry of mind. One of our Idiot Philosopher's maxims was, "Do your duty to-day and repent to-morrow." He thought that this was the law of our race, and that men can do hardly any act, even the finest and highest, without getting flayed for it by their insane consciences pretty soon afterward. He was subject to frightful fits of despondency, and while he was in them he suffered like a damned soul, and lamented the lack of physical courage which stayed his hand from ending his life and his distress. When most men have decided upon a thing and done it, they are able to drop it out of their minds and leave it alone, saying, "If it was a mistake, let it go—fussing over it will not mend it"; but the Sol Baileys can't do that. The moment they have done a thing they go to taking it to pieces and examining it; and not with an eye to fortifying their judgment and solidifying the resultant structure, but to hunting out all the doubtful things that may be in it and supplying it with a lot of imaginary ones.

And so Sol Bailey went part of the way home in the clouds and the rest of it down in the mire. Through the window his wife caught sight of him and said with peppery impatience—

"There he comes, with his heart in his socks; what good thing has happened to him *now* to repent of?"

She was a plain woman and practical, she had common sense but nothing above it, and she knew it and made no moan. She considered him a splendid genius, and was proud of him and worshiped him, and believed he would have been a celebrity if he had had a field proper to his size—like London, or some other place where geniuses accumulate and by their superior penetration discover and advertise each other. She admired him without limit, but he was a sore trial to her with his freaks and eccentricities and his sudden and astonishing changes of weather in the matter of moods. She modified his conditions when she could, and comforted him to the best of her ability when she couldn't. She loved him out of a despondency or scolded him out of it, according to circumstances; and in return he was grateful for these helps, and loved her, and valued her above all his other possessions when he had any. She relieved him of his hat and overcoat, now, and his boots; brought his slippers, made him comfortable in his rocking chair by the stove, sat down by him, laid a hand on his knee, and set an alert eye upon those tracts and features of his face where expressions which disagreed with his statements were accustomed to ambush themselves and give him away. He had no secrets from her. He sometimes imagined he had, but found out presently that it was an error; she could read him like a book. Her first remark, now, showed that Sol's projects with Harrison had been communicated to her previously and talked over.

"Now, then, Sol, you are down in the dumps again, and of course there's no occasion for it and no sense in it. You look like all your folks are dead. I know the sign; it means that you have struck splendid good luck and are hunting up some sort of fool excuse to knock it in the head. Go on, now—tell me the whole thing."

Sol began his tale, and got a little way, then she interrupted him: "Wait. You told him you had long been certain that the Milliken woman was his uncle's lawful wife by a secret marriage?

Why, man, when you went out of this house you only suspected it
—nothing more."

Sol was embarrassed.

"We-ll—yes. Yes, now I remember, that is so; I had forgotten
that."

"Very well—what changed your mind? What put that certainty
into your head?"

Sol recovered his confidence.

"It was perfectly natural, Ann. Reasoning it over brought the
conviction. And—"

"Who did the reasoning?"

Sol's animation lost some of its sparkle, and he said diffidently—

"I did it."

"Huh! Go on."

"I—well, I put this and that together—known odds and ends
and details of the woman's conduct, you know—and it was
wonderful the light they threw, and the way they hitched together,
link by link; just a perfect chain, not a link missing: straight, lucid,
logical, convincing; and there she stood revealed, a legal wife, a
disloyal wife, a fugitive from that justice which she dared not face!
Ann, I was astonished, myself."

Ann said drily—

"Very likely. Tell me the process. Put the links together again."

Sol did it with animation, and with a pride which he did not try
to conceal. Then his wife gazed placidly and compassionately into
his face until his eyes drooped and fell.

"Sol Bailey," she said, soberly, almost mournfully, "if I had a
tomcat that could be turned against a suspected sowcat by such
wandering and pointless drivel as that, I would take him out and
drown him. Do you mean to tell me that George Harrison was
convinced by—by—Sol!"

"Well?"

"Had he been drinking?"

"N-no, I—"

"I mean, was he *drunk?*"

"Oh, no—most certainly not."

"Sober—and was convinced?"

"We-ll—yes, he was, Ann; I know it."

"Then he is an idiot. An idiot, or something's the matter with him. Has anything happened to him, do you know? Is something disturbing him? I don't mean his father's death—that couldn't do this. Has he any secret worries, do you reckon?"

"No, not that I know of. Oh, yes—you know Deathshead Phillips has been appearing to him."

"Fudge! I didn't ask you if he was a baby, I'm asking you if you think he has any secret worries such as would trouble a grown person; for upon my word it looks like it. Surely that incredible and impossible private wife couldn't turn his reason upside down like this; it's silly!"

It was an uncomfortable time for Bailey. But he pulled himself together and said—

"Why, Ann, if you'll look at it just from one point of view, you'll see that this wife business is enough to worry him sharply without hunting further."

"What point of view is that?"

"That he believes in that wife. I'll tell you how much that means for him, then you will see that it is competent matter for worry for him, whether it looks silly to another person or not."

He told her of the depths of despair the dread of the poverty threatened by this woman's existence and discovery had cast Harrison into. Then Ann said—

"Well, I see. His fear is built on a phantom and is silly, but I pity him just the same. Misery is misery, it don't make any difference whether God sends it or you dig it out of your own imagination. Well, did you try to comfort him? Did you tell him you had sent that ass of yours to hunt up the woman and quiet her down and strike up a compromise with her?"

Sol colored slightly, and said—

"I didn't name names, but I told him."

"Thanks to goodness you had judgment that time! Allen Osgood —the idea!"

Bailey bridled a little, and said—

"It doesn't become you to disparage him, Ann. He is one of the best detectives that in all my experience I—"

His wife shouted with laughter.

"Detective! Good land, listen at the man. Why, Sol, *you* know he couldn't follow the telegraph wire and find the office. He's lost, by this time—oh, days and days ago!—and you'll have to send out another search-party, the way they do when they're finding the north pole and losing themselves. Sol!"

"Well?"

"Who pays the freight?"

"Expenses, do you mean?"

"Yes."

"Harrison."

"Good—it will give him employment and save the relics of his mind. Is it arranged?"

"Yes."

"Well, I'm glad of that. With all your genius you've got no real business capacity. It was just like you to borrow money out of that missionary fund and start those expenses yourself without ever stopping to think how you—Sol!"

"*Yes*, Ann!"

"You gave me your word you would pay that loan back, straight off and no fooling. Look me in the eye: have you done it?"

"I have."

She kept her gaze on him.

"Sure?"

"Yes, sure."

She was removing her gaze, gradually, doubtfully—now she stopped, then slowly turned it back upon him and fastened it there. Presently the man began to wilt.

"There—I just knew it. Where'd you get the money?"

"B-borrowed it."

"I know, but *where'd* you borrow it?"

"F-from the Fund."

"Borrowed it from the Fund to *pay* the Fund—we-ll, if that ain't Sol Bailey all over! Con-sound you, I never saw such a man!"

"Now don't act like that, Ann—be reasonable; I'm going to pay the whole thing—I am, I give you my word."

"Oh, shucks! don't I know you? I lay you've borrowed from the

Fund to pay the Fund till there isn't any Fund left, and consequently no place left *to* pay the rest with? You know it's so; I can see it as plain—look me in the eye! Isn't it so?"

"Well, er, anyway, I—"

"O-o, my *goodness*—to have to live with a meandering-minded coot who—Sol!"

"Well, *what!*"

"You just march right along this minute and take everything that's saleable in this house, shingles and all, and pay that debt to the last cent—to the last cent, understand, if it takes the clothes off our backs—and don't you *what* me like that again, or I'll give you a talking-to that'll—"

"Ann, *do* give me a chance to get in half a word, can't you? I swear I'm going to pay the entire thing off this very day, to the last red cent, and sell nothing—there, now!"

Ann's eyes snapped derision.

"You will! Lawks! Where'll you get the money?"

Sol drew out his batch of bills and laid it in her hand—exteriorly without emotion, interiorly with consuming exultation. His wife was dumb. She laid the notes out one by one on her lap, absently mumbling and counting: "Five—fifteen—twenty—forty—forty-five"—and so on, till she had piled and smoothed and caressed the last one; then she pulled a profound and impressive sigh, and said, reverently—

"A whole hundred. I have never had so much in my hand at one time before." She counted again, and said, "It's not believable—but it's there. Where'd you get it?"

Bailey answered, with a mask of indifference thinly concealing some more exultation—artificially yawning and stretching, meantime, like a cat that has caught an elephant and would let on that it is merely an incident, nothing more—

"It's my salary."

"Salary!" There was disappointment in the tone.

"Salary"—with another yawn.

"Huh! For a year, I reckon."

"For a fortnight."

"Sol Bailey!" The wife's eyes danced—sparkled—flamed—and

she gripped his arm with a trembling hand. "Oh, how splendid! Salary! All that! Salary for what?"

"To run Harrison's detective work and find that woman and compromise with her and save him from poverty."

"Oh, Sol, it's beautiful; and we so need the money. We'll lay up every cent we can. Ah, we were so poor, but now—" Her eyes filled, her voice failed her for a moment, then she went on. "I always believed somebody would find out how great you are and capable, and now it has come at last, thank God, and my pride is justified—my love was that before, dear old idol of my youth! Ah, how dear you are to me, Sol—am I to you?"

"You know it, sweetheart. Don't you know it?"

She kissed him with a passion which age had not modified, and said she knew it. Which was true; and he had willingly and veraciously said it every day for thirty-three years upon demand; for she had always explained that although she knew it and never doubted it, she also wanted him to *say* it. And say it every day; that she loved the sound of it, and the day was not complete without it.

They held hands and made love a while, recalling hard times patiently borne for each other's sake, and comparing and contrasting them with this gorgeously-salaried moment. Then the wife said—

"We'll save every cent we can, while it lasts. How long will it last, Sol?"

"The salary? Several weeks—or months. One can't tell."

"We'll call it weeks, then, so as to be safe; and if you succeed—but I know you will—it will give you a great name and plenty of work, and we shan't ever know sharp privations and wretchednesses and people's compassion—*that's* the worst!—again."

Bailey patted her on the cheek and said—

"Shall I tell you a little secret, old lady?"

She snuggled to him, alive with interest.

"Oh, do, Sol! What is it? Tell me quick—what is it?"

"Ann, the salary isn't the half of it!"

"What, Sol—there's more?"

"Oceans more!"

She was eager to know. He told her everything; and finished with—

"So that is how we stand. Salary right along. Expenses right along. Draw on him whenever I want to. And when the compromise is made with the heirs, half of what's left of the fortune comes to me—that is, to Allen and me."

It took the woman's breath away for half a minute. Then she said—

"It's a grand estate isn't it, Sol? The village says it's worth—"

"Ann, it's worth more than four hundred thousand. At least a quarter more than that, I believe."

"Why, Sol—but I can't realize it, it's too immense—the riches we'll have, I mean." She fell into a feverish reverie, and clasped and unclasped her hands, nervously and unconsciously, occasionally murmuring, "I hope it's fair to take so much. . . . I hope it is. . . . I wonder if it is?" Presently when she came out of it and her glance fell upon her husband, he sat there with his head bowed upon his breast, the picture of irremediable despair. Her eyes shot out a baleful flash and she said with wrathful energy, *"Now* what's the matter with you!"

The cloud that had settled upon him on his way home had shut down on him again, precipitated by his wife's soliloquy. The thoughts that had waylaid him and harried him then were all back and clawing him and tearing him once more. Their reproachful arguments were as moving as ever, as unanswerable as ever. His conscience was calling him ingrate, blood-sucker, heartless devourer of a generous friend caught at a disadvantage and helpless. The lash presently drove him to speech. The fountains of his great deep were broken up, and he poured out his remorse, bitter, fierce, unsparing, in a torrent that burst along scornful of obstacles, if any there might be; and his wife sat as one under a spell, and listened: at first angrily; then curiously and amusedly; then respectfully; then admiringly; then wonderingly; then reverently; then adoringly; and now in impulsive and unconditional surrender she flung her arms about him and spoke out her feelings—

"Oh, you marvelous creature with the golden tongue and the best heart that ever beat! How right you are, Sol—it *would* be extortion; and he so good and generous. Have it your way; I wanted to take less, myself, but I was too selfish, and kept the thought down and wanted to kill it. How much will it be right for you and Allen to take, Sol?"

His conscience was content and purring, now, and he was floating in tranquil seas of dreamy happiness, his eyes closed, his breast rising and falling to the subsiding storm of his emotions. After many minutes his excitement passed wholly away and he was his normal self again and in condition to consider earthly matters and deliver opinions and judgments concerning them. Ann repeated her question. He deliberated upon it a while, then said—

"Ann, I think a fifth of what remains to Harrison after he gets through will be a plenty, and all that by any fair argument could be required of him or accepted."

She was pleased with this view.

"I think so, too, Sol. In fact I know it; for if what's left is large, the fifth will be riches, and if it's small a fifth cuts it down all he could spare—almost more than he could well spare, maybe. You'll write Allen and tell him you're not going to let it be over a fifth?"

"Right away. And if it isn't satisfactory he can draw out."

"*He* draw out! I think I see him! Expenses paid, whisky and billiards and all—that poor ornery thing, that poor half-done doughnut? You couldn't drive him out with a club."

"I'll draw fifty and send it to him in the letter; and I'll tell him my arrangement about expenses; the two items together will reconcile him, I reckon."

"Don't you doubt it. Less would do it. Look here, Sol, you want to send somebody to superintend that creature—it'll be an economy. Otherwise he'll idle around and spend the money and nothing will come of it."

Bailey was hard to convince, but his wife did not give the contention up until he was convinced. Then he asked—

"Could a competent person be persuaded to leave his affairs and take the post?"

"If you promised him a little of our share of the estate he could. There isn't any doubt about that."

"That's true—of course. But Ann, we've got to make a confidant of him; and suppose after we had told him everything he should refuse?—refuse and then talk. What then?"

Ann considered this, then said—

"Sol, I can fix it so it will be safe and all right. I'll put before him a suppositious case—"

"Supposititious."

"Dang the difference!—supposititious, then; and I'll say, Suppose there was such-and-such an estate, up in Illinois, and so-and-so had such-and-such a chance for a share of it if so-and-so found the lost heirs, and so on: would he go in with so-and-so for such-and-such a share of so-and-so's share, and how much of it would he require?—as a correspondent of ours has asked us to look up a likely person, and all that."

"That's good—that will answer, first rate. You've got a head yourself, Ann."

She answered, placidly—

"I knew that before you did, Sol."

The next problem in due order of succession now offered itself:

"Where are we going to find the right person, Ann?"

That was a serious difficulty. For ten minutes Bailey walked the floor plowing his hair with his fingers, and Ann sat with her chin in her hands and her supporting elbows on her knees. Thus far, there had been no result. Then, from some point a mile away came floating a remark of Dug Hapgood's, privately addressed to a passing friend—

"Say, Billy, going to the sayence to-night? Eleven, sharp!"

Simultaneously Bailey and his wife glanced up at a printed bill on the wall; then at each other and nodded and smiled, as who should say, "That settles it; the very ticket!"

The little placard was nearly two years old, and it said—

Mrs. Charlotte Gunning, Trance-Medium. Late professional assistant of the Fox sisters. Communications from spirits of departed friends. Conveyed through her in the Chinese tongue by the revered sage, Confucius, and translated by her son, in trance, by spirit-inspiration, he knowing no word of that language when in his normal state. The past described, the future foretold. Advice given, problems solved, perplexities removed. Public seances at intervals, at the Ice Cream Parlors, by subscription—entrance 25 cents. Private seances, Two Dollars.

In four seconds Bailey was re-converted to Spiritualism. He had been Charlotte Gunning's first convert when she arrived, nearly two years before, but had soon lapsed, attracted by some other evanescently-inviting way of getting himself saved or damned.

"She's wonderful, Ann, wonderful! The things which that dead Chinaman reveals through her—"

"Oh, don't I know! He's good on the future, and just amazing on a person's past. He'll pick out the right man for us, and don't you doubt it. Sol, we can have them here, say—"

"To-night, Ann, to-night—the sooner the better. Say at nine—a good two hours before the public seance, and while the Chinaman is fresh and not tired."

"That's it! And we'll put before him the supposi—si—"

"—ti—"

"—tious case—"

"—and call game!"

"It's splendid, Sol; go 'long and pay the debt and write the letter and book the Chinaman for business."

And so that matter was settled. Ann was quite right as regarded the Chinaman's surprising knowledge concerning Tom, Dick and Harry's past. His reputation for hindsight was great in the village, and solid. Mrs. Gunning was often able to assist him considerably, for she was always hovering around tables where low-voiced privacies were being retailed in the ice cream parlors. When other people hovered, those talks stopped; but when she hovered they went unrestrainedly on, for her reputation for deafness was as solid as was the Chinaman's for reversed prophecy.

Bailey squared up with the Fund, wrote to Allen Osgood, hired the spiritualists, posted his letter, got one out of the office from Allen, and went back home pleasantly expectant.

In cosy privacy Bailey read Allen's letter aloud to his eager wife:

As early as possible after economically locating myself in Memphis, I cautiously began my inquiries about the abused wife, the ostensible "Mrs. Milliken." The outcome was both melancholy and romantic. It appears that she changed her name to Lucy Wallace and became for a moment a celebrity—

"Lu—cy Wallace!" exclaimed Bailey. "Why Ann, she *was* the Milliken woman—I had clean forgotten it. Don't you remember it?"

"We—ll, no, I believe I don't. I remember the grand noise over her swindle—most do, I reckon—and I remember her name well enough, but if I ever knew she was the Milliken woman—"

"Why, certainly she was! Don't you re—"

"No, I don't! It's fifteen years or more; and it don't signify, anyway. Go on with the letter."

—became for a moment a celebrity, then vanished with thousands and thousands of dollars, and hasn't been heard of since. I found, after sifting around a while, that there was one man who could be more valuable to us than any other in Memphis, perhaps, if he chose —Simon Bunker, post-office clerk in her day, clerk of the county court for the past ten years. I determined that he should so choose. I have succeeded.

"Now, then, Ann, what do you say to that! You didn't think much of that detective, you know."

"And I don't yet"—with a sniff. "Go on with his truck."

I got acquainted with him, and found him a disappointed man—he thinks he's been wronged, and ought to be county judge; moreover he's poor, and I suspect he has had a love-cross away back some time or other. He is a reserved and sour bachelor of 40, and hates women— seems to hate Lucy Wallace particularly. He doesn't say it, but I think it leaks out. You see, people thought he ought to have been smart enough to suspect a rat in her monstrous mail, and catch the rat; they used to talk that way, so he says, and I reckon he visits his spite on her when he might more logically visit it on himself—a confusion of mind more usual in a woman than in a—"

"Allen's just a fool—I always told you so, Sol. It's forty to one the man was in love with that woman, and she shook him and he hates her because he couldn't get her and her swag. Go on with his twaddle."

—man. I wormed my way into his friendship, then into his confidence; then I laid our whole scheme before him, and how you were going to raise money to work with, and then I offered him a sixteenth of your half of the estate and a sixteenth of mine, if we succeeded, and he said he wanted to consider it about half an hour—for he is a careful and cautious man—

"Sol!" This with a suggestion of anxiety in her tone.
"Well, Ann?"
"Have you mailed the letter?"
"Yes. Why?"
"You couldn't get it back, think?"
"No, the mail's gone. Why?"
"Oh, don't you see why?"
"N-no—no, I don't."
She said, dismally—
"Oh, well, it's done, and can't be helped. Go on."
"Why, what—"
"Go *on*, I tell you!"

—then he accepted, and we are all right, Bailey, and things are moving right along. Send some money.

"There, old lady, I reckon you'll confess now that our matters are looking pretty bright, and that poor Allen is something more than a half-done doughnut, after all."

There was no reply; Ann was moving slowly toward the kitchen, deeply pondering, with her fingers nervously gripping and ungripping each other behind her back. Sol moved gaily to the wood-shed to gather chips and split kindlings for her.

Arrived in the kitchen, Ann stood lost in thought a while, cracking and snapping her finger-joints absently, and muttering. "The letter's gone. . . . The man is to get an eighth *of* a fifth. . . . When Allen shows him *that,* in the letter. . . . Offering him an eight of *half* was chuckleheaded enough, after giving away the whole scheme to him, and him the usefulest person in the gang; but when it turns out to be an eighth of a *fifth!* . . . Oh, well"—with a sigh—"it's done, and can't be helped; let it go. That doughnut!"

She had quite forgotten that she had ridiculed the reasonings the scheme was built upon, and wouldn't have respected a cat that could be beguiled by them. She was poor, she had drunk of poverty down to the dregs, poor lady; and to such as she, even the most chimerical and impossible impending money, when diligently dwelt upon and dreamed over, will presently come to look solid and attainable.

We will now go to Memphis.

After Simon Bunker had accepted Allen's proposition, he suggested that the two should now have a frank and free talk. He built up his hickory fire, set his kettle to boil on the hob, brought out his cigars, pulled down the blinds, lit an extra candle or two, and brewed some steaming punches. By this time his desolate little parlor was looking quite cosy and pleasant. He remarked upon this —stopping in the middle of his sentence to listen to the distant and gust-broken boom of the town-clock beating out eleven—then he sat down, handed a punch to Allen, touched glasses with him, passed him a cigar and held the candle while he lit it, then he set a pair of sharp and observant eyes upon his face, and said—

"Now, then, we need to know our people. Tell me all you know about Mr. Bailey."

When he was through, Bunker said—

"He is variegated, it seems."

"Yes. Yes, one may say that, but he has a good head."

"He seems to have a roving and adulterous passion for all breeds of religions and isms and so-on."

"Yes. Yes, he is that way, one must confess."

"What is he at present—religiously?"

"Ah, God knows!"

"Are you sure?"

"Sure of what?"

"Ah, well, it's no matter." He made a mental note: "Waste no jokes on this one." Aloud: "He's pretty weak, isn't he?"

"Weak? Oh, no, I should say not. No, I should say he is anything but that."

Mental note: "His judgment is not mature yet—this one's."
Aloud: "Will he be able to keep us in money?"

"Oh, yes, I think so."

"How does he get it?"

"Collects for charities," said Allen, innocently.

"Charities?"

"Yes, missionaries, and that kind. Borrows from the Fund.
Anyway, he did this time. He told me so."

"But how do they come to let him? Who keeps the Fund?"

"He does."

"Oh, I see." Mental note: "It's a hell of an idea!" Aloud: "Now,
then, about Harrison."

Allen told him all he knew. Bunker studied over the details a
while in silence, then said—

"Harrison had never seen his uncle in life? Are you sure?"

"Quite so. He told Bailey so himself."

"Knew him only by correspondence, you say?"

"Yes. He wrote letters to his brother, Harrison's father, sometimes."

Mental note: "That is valuable." Aloud: "You say Harrison
showed nervousness when Bailey hinted that perhaps the Milliken
woman was the uncle's wife by a private marriage. Was Bailey sure
of that?"

"Oh, quite. And a little while after I got here Bailey wrote me he
had been visiting him several times since and had found him more
and more nervous, and really worried; and Bailey was feeling pretty
certain that it was about the Milliken heirs."

"Isn't Harrison a rather weak man?—or a little broken, perhaps?"

"Oh, mercy no! He is a very strong character. I know him myself
—know him personally."

Bunker, drily: "That settles it."

Allen, pleased: "I'm sure it's very kind of you to think so."

Allen went away comfortable and mellow at midnight. Bunker
resumed his seat and held a conversation with himself:

"It's not a bad scheme at all—if the Milliken 'heirs' are still alive. If they are, I know how to draft an advertisement that will produce them. Also, I know how to establish the secret marriage, and how to make Lucy Wallace divide the estate with me. And not just a part of it, but the whole of it—alas for Harrison! . . . Do I need any outsiders in this business? this young innocent, for instance? or the singular person whom his deaf village-mate, it seems, picturesquely calls 'The Idiot Philosopher'—that whirligig, that weather-vane, that spiritual harlot, that abandoned speculator in religions and isms! . . . Why, yes—yes, for the present I do, at least. Yes, I do—for they furnish the money. Yes, and I can make the young chap useful—I see several ways."

He wrote out the following advertisement, which he had no present intention of showing to Allen or any other interested person; then he went to bed, satisfied and comfortable:

A VAST FORTUNE

to be had for nothing. Sentence annulled by fire. All the court records burnt. Supplementary U.S. Mail please address the Swamp Angel, directing the letter to the latter's real name.

In bed he continued his soliloquy a while: "The burnt-records nonsense will not deceive her, and isn't expected to, but she's sharp enough to know there's something back of it, and she'll write from a false address and inquire. Write? No, she'll do no writing—at first, before I explain; she'll print her letter in capitals, like a child; or she'll telegraph, and dictate her dispatch to the operator, under some pretext or other. Anyway, I shall hear from her if she's alive. The rest will be swift and simple. . . . The thing grows! If it shall turn out that that weakling, Harrison, is really frightened, his fortune is gettable, sure, whether *those* particular 'heirs' are living or not. . . . The advertising is going to be cheap—also universal. One insertion—in one paper—anywhere in the United States— and the thing's done! All the other papers will copy it, and comment on it editorially, and be gay over it, and make lubberly back-settlement fun of it, and gambol around it elephantinely—all free gratis for nothing—and it'll sweep the continent like a prairie fire! Will it find her—if alive? Well, I should say! . . . It's late. Good night, Harrison; sleep well, if you can."

Let us attend the private seance at Bailey's house.

The Gunnings arrived promptly at nine, and were received with the lively and familiar welcome due to old friends—for they were that. They were in a happy mood, and Templeton was very nearly his old gay and sportive normal self once more, for the subscription-seance had listed close upon a hundred names and was therefore a fine success and lucrative. Mrs. Gunning, from her earliest days in Indiantown, had wisely husbanded and fed the popular interest in her public appearances by putting pretty wide intervals between them.

When the friendly shoutings at Mrs. Gunning concerning her health were over and Templeton had popped off the best of the pleasantries he had brought along for the occasion, the seance-table was placed and the seats occupied. The mediums sat side by side, so that they could hold hands, under the table, and talk the deaf and dumb language together unperceived; Sol and Ann sat opposite them. Silence was now requested. It followed; it deepened; it became solemn, impressive, weird, uncanny. At last Mrs. Gunning made some slow and quivering passes about her head and face with her hands, and finished each pass with a snipping of her fingers in the air, as if she were flirting an invisible fluid from them. Then she made the passes over and about her son's head and face. After an interval of some minutes both performers began to nod and sway, and soon the mother's head drooped upon her breast, where it remained for a little while, the son's head following suit. Presently the heads came up; the eyes opened; the expression in them was dreamy and far away. The mother said, in a hollow voice—

"The Sage is present. Speak to him."

Templeton responded, in a low and reverent tone, and bowing slowly and solemnly—

"Hong ting woo—si-washy! We salute you, august master!"

The mother answered, with grave dignity—

"Oomtong hopsing hoangho."

Templeton, with like gravity and dignity, translated: "Approval and thanks."

Ann, speaking with animation in her ordinary voice, said—

"Sol, the more I've seen it the more I can't get over the wonder of it—that when she is in a trance she can hear the faintest word that's said."

"Ann, haven't I told you a dozen times that *she* can't hear, it's the Chinaman that hears."

"Yes, it seems like it must be so, and I know it must be so, because it's the only rational way to account for it, but that makes it all the more wonderful if it *is* so—"

"*If* it's so! What do you say *if* for? Where's any if? Don't we know it's so?"

"How do we know it?"

"I told you once."

"No you didn't."

"I bet I did—but I'll tell you again. We know it because she doesn't hear English, low-spoken, but only Chinese."

That struck Ann.

"Isn't that amazing! Sol—are you funning? Are you trying to fool me?"

He answered, with easy confidence—

"Hmp! you needn't take my word: just pass her a little English and see what she does."

"Plagued if I don't. Er—Charlotte, can I ask you a question or two?"

There was no response. Sol was happy in his triumph, and said teasingly—

"Oh, of course *she* can hear! Say it louder, Ann."

Ann said it louder, then repeated it a little louder still. Charlotte sat unmoved and unresponsive. Ann was charmed and astonished, and gave it up. Then to make the test perfect and splendid, she slipped around and asked Templeton to whisper an easy Chinese word or two in her ear. He did it; she returned to her seat and uttered them very softly—

"Tsung-li yamen!"

Confucius replied promptly—

"Singsong tai-ping yangtzekiang!"

"My land, Sol, doesn't that just beat the band! Talk of miracles —raising the dead with a jab of a saint's jaw-bone ain't a circumstance to it! Say, Templeton, what was it I said to him?"

"You said all is not gold that glitters."

"And what did he say?"

"He said he would make a note of it."

Ann had a suspicion that she had been snubbed. She said—

"Make a *note* of it. Consound him it's older than he is, and he knows it. Sol, I don't know that old carcase, and I don't want any of his familiarities. I'll never speak to him again. He'll make a *note* of it! I lay I'll make a note of *him* if I ever get my hands on him, the dried-up old superannuated pagan ash-cat! and I'll just say, right here—"

"Shantung wai-hei-wei-whooplong!"—solemnly, from the Sage's spirit.

The translation followed at once:

"The noble lady is destined to great riches and a long life, with deserved happiness and honor."

Templeton got through it safely, by covering his face with his hands and bowing low to hide the laughter that was struggling to get free.

"Does he mean that for me, Templeton?" asked Ann, mollified and visibly pleased.

"Yes, for you."

Ann blushed a little, and was embarrassed as to what return to make to that gracious and handsomely-endowed speech, then she said, timidly—

"I am ashamed of myself for mistaking his character so, Templeton. Introduce me to him, please, and thank him for me, and say we'll always be glad and flattered to have him come whenever he can, and make himself at home."

Templeton put it into Chinese, and Ann got up at what she judged to be the right place and gravely made the formal old-fashioned curtsy of the days of her youth to the invisible new acquaintance and guest of her hearthstone.

Bailey was impatient to get to business by this time, and said so;

so the subject was changed. Both mediums were glad, for straight faces are required in their profession, and they were finding it difficult to keep them. Ann said—

"Templeton, the matter stands about like this. A friend of ours has written us and wants advice about a most urgent case, where immense money is involved. There's a long-lost widow and child to be hunted up—private marriage, you know, and all that; it's all a secret—keep it close. This friend wants to find these heirs—the son's about of age, now—"

"And both of them disappeared about—" broke in Sol.

"You wait, Sol. I'm a-talking, and I reckon I'm competent. He wants to find the heirs and work their case through for a little part of their fortune, and he's got one detective on their track already, and wants a smart, bright, trustworthy person to go and help him— and spy on him, too, because he's of the sort that'll bear watching. The idea is, to have Confucius pick out such a person."

Templeton fingered out a sarcastic suggestion on his mother's hand under the table:

"Get Confucius to appoint Dug Hapgood, mother."

She fingered a response:

"Don't joke, I can't stand it; you'll make me laugh and spoil everything; I'm on the point of it all the time. There's immense fun here, but we must save it for home and privacy—then we'll have grand times over it."

Ann continued:

"We are in it a little with this friend, but of course that is to be kept quiet. Our friend is willing to give the man that's picked out a small part of his small part, when he gets it—"

Templeton fingered again—

"When he gets it, mother—not any earlier, you know, because if—"

The mother fingered back—

"Do be quiet! These are the quaintest, innocentest, foolishest good people that ever—"

Ann, continuing—

"And he would like to settle terms with him—find out what he would require, you see—before he's admitted to the secrets. Of

course we are expecting to make you acquainted with any details
you need to know, so that you can deal with Confucius under-
standingly, but we don't want you to tell *him* any more than you're
obliged to, because we haven't any way to keep him quiet, of
course, if he chooses to go and spread it all over America and
Kingdom Come and goodness knows where."

Templeton fingered—

"Mother, if you go and let Confucius find out anything he
oughtn't to know about this most important and—"

She fingered an interruption—

"Don't bother me so! do let her get through with her wearisome
rubbish."

Ann, dribbling composedly along—

"You see, it's best to get his terms first and bind him up tight and
fast. Well—to tell you a little about it, so you'll understand: the
disappeared widow's name *was* Milliken—dear me, what's the
matter!"

"Nothing," said Templeton, faintly, "it's a nervous affection; she
often jumps that way."

"You jumped too," observed Sol, innocently.

"Yes. When we are in the trance state whatever affects one of us
affects the other."

"Now ain't that int'resting!—ain't it, Sol!" exclaimed Ann, with
admiration. "It's like everything about them—just miraculous and
like nobody else." She faced Templeton again, and sailed placidly
along with her tale: "Well, as I was saying, she was privately
married to George Harrison's old uncle in Memphis, and had a
child, and she did something wrong, and her husband would have
killed her if he had got his hands on her, but she escaped and
changed her name to Lucy Wallace and got up the smartest
swindle that ever was, and robbed people of loads and loads of
money and got away with it; and neither hide nor hair has ever
been seen of her since. There's ten years in the penitentiary
hanging over her, and she'll sell out cheap when she's found—and
Sol here is going to find her, to a dead certainty. It's as sure as if she
was in this room!"

The mediums were calm, now; calm, and grave, even to solemnity. The funniness had disappeared from the scheme, and they were feeling troubled, distressed, burdened with vague forebodings and terrors. For a while the chief medium's mind was a chaos of flying and confused and colliding thoughts. What was to be done to meet this danger and thwart it? If left alone these idiots would start a hue and cry that might end by lodging her in the penitentiary. Templeton's mind was not functioning at all, it was paralysed.

His mother presently conquered her bewilderment and became her clear-headed natural self and competent. She rose to the situation and knew what to do—at least the first move. She fingered out this message—

"Describe to Confucius the kind of spy they require. He will appoint *you*. Go ahead."

Templeton exclaimed to himself fervently, "She's *always* wonderful when she's in a tight place"—then swiftly fingered his admiration—

"Mother, you're just a brick!" Then he let fly in Chinese: "Shang-haitientsin hongwo-wallahwallah chin-chow!" Then he translated the substance of the remark: "I have informed the sage that you good friends of ours want a bright, watchful, and perfectly trustworthy person for a secret and delicate service, and asked him to pick out the very best man he knows of, anywhere."

The mother straightened up and set her features for deep reflection—to represent Confucius working out the problem on the inside of her.

"Look at her!" whispered Ann; "Sol, you can just *see* him think, in her. And look at Templeton—ain't it wonderful the way he can jabber out that heathen stuff without knowing a word of it in his natural state."

"Yes, it is, Ann; and what is just as wonderful is the way he can crowd a whole history into hardly more words than it takes to say 'scat.' Hold still—Confucius is going to speak."

The mother murmured—

"Chong-hi chop-chop Templum Gunniwup!"

Templeton translated, without emotion:

"Young, able, perfectest of the perfect, he that is chosen sits with you, and his honorable name is Templeton Gunning."

Bailey was so carried away with delight over this choice that he couldn't keep still, but plunged his hands across the table and wrung Templeton's with enthusiasm, crying out—

"Will you? will you do it? 'George, it's too splendid for anything! You *will*, won't you? Say it, Templeton—say the words, clinch the bargain!"

There was no response. The mediums sat dreamy, tranquil, lost to the world and its concerns, like a couple of Buddhas on duty in a temple. Ann was frightened, and said in a low voice—

"Sol, they're dead!"

"No they're not. I know what's the matter. I'd forgotten. They're loaded for bear—spiritually speaking, you understand— and they're not themselves as long as they're in a trance; but they'll wake right up when Confucius leaves. Watch, now, and see: I remember what to do. Templeton, dismiss the Sage!"

Templeton discharged a flowing Chinese remark; then he and his mother came immediately to life and inquired with great interest if they had had an interview with Confucius, and if it had been satisfactory.

"Oh yes indeed," said Sol; "and it will interest you to know you are personally interested in the result—both of you."

"We?" said mother and son, simultaneously, and apparently a good deal surprised.

Bailey rubbed his hands with the jejune delight the average human being feels when he is first in the field with exclusive news, and said—

"Listen! you'll see."

Then he and Ann, constantly interrupting and correcting each other, eagerly laid bare every detail of the interview, charmed all along with the astonished ejaculations their narrative evoked; and when the end was reached and Templeton's appointment announced, Sol closed with an anxious supplication that the Sage's choice be ratified.

The mediums lost their vivacity, now, and looked grave. Bailey saw this and lost heart. He put his mouth to Charlotte's ear—

"Ah, I was afraid you wouldn't," he yelled, mournfully.

"Wouldn't *what?*"

"Wouldn't ratify the appointment."

Charlotte smiled a resigned and "It's-pretty-evident-you-are-not-abreast-of-the-situation" kind of smile, and said, placidly—

"Why, dear man, we've *got* to. If I want to keep in with Confucius, the ablest percipient in hell, I'm not going to accomplish it by running counter to his wishes, am I? I'll manage the parlors all right. Templeton will go."

To get all the words necessary to fully portray Bailey's happiness would disembowel the dictionary; it is cheaper to leave it to be imagined. Ann now confessed some uneasiness on a certain point: did Confucius get hold of anything that he could tell to improper people and baulk the scheme? and was he leaky? Charlotte explained:

"There's no fear. I've had him in my employ four years, and have never known him to leak a drop. And he couldn't, in this case, even if he wanted to; because he belongs to the Fox sisters and I've bought territory from them and pay them a royalty, and it comes under the patent laws the same as a patent, and if they should work him on my territory I could sue in the Supreme Court and get heavy damages. Well, I've got him for all the Southern States except Texas, and you can make up your mind to it the Foxes are not going down there as long as they can work the Northern States and England."

"Not much!" said Templeton.

Ann was almost satisfied. She hesitated a moment, then ventured to ask—

"Do you think he—does he—ever strike?"

"Why, Ann Bailey, with his character and his reputation he would no more think of it than you would think of doing the most dishonorable thing you could ever imagine."

Ann was content, now, and at peace.

Terms were then discussed. Bailey was surprised and gratified to see how reasonable and unexacting the Gunnings turned out to be, in this matter. Charlotte stipulated for twenty-five dollars a week and expenses for Templeton and such portion of Bailey's apocryphal "friend's" share of the estate—when acquired—as said friend should think fair to give him.

It was now half past ten, and guests and hosts shook hands heartily and parted.

For a time Bailey's mood-mercury remained at 92 in the shade, then the usual revulsion set in and it began to drop. It went steadily down till it struck the frost-line. Meantime Ann was absent in the kitchen setting her dough to rise, and attending to other small duties there. When she had left Sol, he was tramping the floor in jubilant excitement and building air-castles two or three hundred feet high; she was gone fifteen minutes, and when she returned he was slouching wilted in a chair, with his chin on his breast, his joy all dead and gone. She stood erect in the door and gazed long at him, her feelings rising and the clouds gathering in her face. Then she let fly:

"Sol Bailey!"

He moaned, and lifted a haggard countenance.

"Well of all the chicken-hearted, white-livered, chuckle-headed nincompoops in this world, you do take the rag! What in the nation's come over you now!"

In grieved and lifeless accents he explained:

"Ah, Ann, it's the same old thing—'Do your duty to-day and repent to-morrow.' I'm always ruining everything by impulsiveness."

"What have your ruined now?"

"We're going to get the estate—it's perfectly plain—and we could just as well have had half as not, and of *course* I had to go and write that fatal letter and cut our share down to a fifth; and not only to a fifth, but a fifth of what's *left,* instead of a fifth of the whole. It's the most brutal stupidity that ever a—oh, I want to die!"

"T'would do you good, too! Not but what a fifth of what's left is all right, and a plenty for a Christian—and you're sometimes that, when there's nothing fresh going—but because it cuts Allen's share and his pal's down to where it don't amount to enough to keep them from going back on you if they see a tempting good chance. And besides—"

"Oh, don't, Ann, don't; I never thought of that, and it kills me to think what a gushing girl-hearted fool I've been."

"Well, *I* thought of it." She forgot to add "after I had helped you do it, and it was all done and too late." "I thought of it, but of course you had rushed the letter off, the way you always do, without giving a person a chance to turn a thing over and examine it good."

"Oh, I know it, I know it—only too well I know it, and I wish, now—Oh, dear, dear, isn't there something we can do? do try to think of something, Ann—oh, I'm *so* miserable!"

He had reached her pity, and she couldn't scold him any more. She softened, and went about a task she was familiar with from of old—the comforting of her stricken and sorrowing old baby. She sat down on the settee and made him stretch out on it and rest his head in her lap; and while she caressed his hair and his forehead she restored by earnest and patient reasoning his conviction that a fifth of the leavings of the estate was the right and honorable figure, and then persuaded him to hope and believe that Templeton would be able to defeat any games that Allen and Simon Bunker might try to play, and thus secure the fifth undamaged—"and that's a plenty, Sol, and more than we'll ever need, I'll be bound."

Sol was happy again and satisfied, and called her his ever-faithful and capable good angel—which indeed she was. He said he would go right off and report progress to Harrison and brighten him up. He departed in high spirits upon this pleasant errand.

Ann closed the door behind him and observed musingly to herself, "It's just the thing—for Dug says poor Harrison is just regularly infested by that crazy corpse-face these nights, and is deep down in the dumps again. . . . If some other maggot don't get into Sol's head before he gets there. . . . but goodness knows!"

She sighed; which seemed to imply lack of confidence.

The mediums had a low-voiced and earnest talk as they groped down the murky lanes and alleys on their way home. It resulted in this decision—delivered by Charlotte:

"So, as you see, the thing is not so perilous as it looked. Simon Bunker is probably moved by spite against me, for of course he must have been a chief witness in the trial, and it follows that the lawyers cross-questioned him to death, and made fun of him and a public spectacle of him for letting a woman receive a barrel of letters every day from people proposing to learn Sanscrit and Hebrew (!) and he so witless as to be taken in by such fool nonsense as that and never suspect. Of course he would like to fry me over a slow fire; but he's not a fool, and as soon as he searches into this thing and finds there was no marriage he will drop it. But Allen *is* a fool, and *he* won't drop it. Why, Templeton, he may go to advertising for me! That came very near catching me, four different times in the old days, and I can't stand it to go through that misery and terror again. Get in with Allen and prevent the advertising, and there's no penitentiary for me. I shall suffer, suffer, suffer, till I hear from you that you have beguiled him out of advertising. I'll pack your things to-night; you'll start to-morrow."

"Good—I'm ready. But I say, mother, won't the Baileys think it strange if I go away without going to them for final instructions?"

"Go if you have time after I've finished with you myself—after sleeping on the matter; waking on it, I mean, for it isn't soporific in its nature."

"And if I don't have time?"

"What of it? Can't I get their instructions every day in the week, if they've got them in stock, and tell them I'll have them in your possession in fifteen minutes? Won't that satisfy them?"

"Why, ye-s—but telegraphing's expensive."

"Hmp—what's the matter with Confucius?"

"Land, I never thought of that! Oh, you *are* a brick, mother!"

Meantime Sol's brother the Rev. Swinton Bailey was standing a comforter's watch at Harrison's bedside. While, at Sol's house, the private seance was going on, the clergyman, more sanely employed, was adroitly lifting Harrison's mind little by little out of its wearing and degrading absorption in material and sordid cares and interests, and breathing upon it the refreshing snow-summit breath of loftier themes. He beguiled it to the contemplation of beautiful and exalting abstractions: the Universal Brotherhood of Man; Unselfishness; Self-Sacrifice; Man's God-given Supremacy over the Beasts that Perish; the Wonder and Mystery of his Construction; the Nobility of his Character; his final and crowning endowment, the Moral Sense—granted to him alone of Created Beings. Carried above and beyond himself by the grandeur of his subjects and by the sweet and gracious humanity of his object, the clergyman spoke as one inspired; and as his flowing and impassioned periods fell from his tongue he could see the mental glooms that shadowed Harrison's face melt gradually away and the light of a happier spirit steal into their place. Harrison listened like one entranced. It seemed to him that he had not known man before, and was seeing him for the first time in the imposing majesty of his supremacy in God's mighty universe. As pictured now, how nobly endowed he was, with sweetness, love for his enemy, compassion, forgiveness of injuries; in the golden grace of unselfishness how imperially enriched!

In bidding good-night to his benefactor Harrison clung to his hand and repeatedly pressed it and caressed it, saying—

"God bless you for coming; you have flooded my soul with sunshine, you have borne it an eagle's flight above the sordid concerns of life, I know my race as I never knew it before—God bless you, Bailey, you have made a new man of me!"

Meantime Sol had arrived below-stairs finely exalted by the thought of the kindly errand he had come upon; but on the parlor table lay a new book which his brother had just acquired and had deposited there to wait his return from Harrison's chamber, and Sol picked it up to see what it was. He was soon cutting its leaves and devouring its contents. Presently, recollecting his mission, he thrust it into his pocket and started upstairs. He met his brother on the way, and said—

"I've got your book, but I'll return it to-morrow. How is Harrison?"

In a tone of self-complimentary satisfaction which was quite pardonable, the brother replied—

"I found him in the blackest deeps of depression. I'd like you to notice what he's like *now*, Sol."

Sol was not listening; he was brimming with something else. A moment later he burst in upon Harrison and was breezily talking before he was fairly at anchor in a chair.

"How splendid you're looking!" he said, shaking hands cordially. "I say, George, I want to read you something. It's brand new—just come—belongs to Swinton. Dear me, but it's interesting. Listen to this:

[Mark Twain made a note of his intention to insert here an "extract from *Cawnpore*," concerning atrocities performed by soldiers (British) to "avenge the massacre of the women" by rebels during the Cawnpore mutiny in India. He probably meant to present part or all of an account of this action that is in Sir George O. Trevelyan, *Cawnpore* (London, Macmillan, 1865), pp. 355–356. He had previously quoted this passage in *Following the Equator*, II, 238–239.]

Sol laid the book aside, remarking—

"That's Man, all over! I haven't seen anything as typical as that since—" He glanced up, and said to himself, "Why, he's down in the depths again. I wonder what's happened?"

Harrison moaned, and said—

"Bailey, it's all pitiful—so pitiful! And so unnatural, too, so out of character. Look at man, in his right and proper estate: how nobly gifted, intellectually, how graciously endowed with—"

And so forth and so on. This kind of thing was just in Sol's line. Arguing on stately and foggy abstractions was meat and drink to him, and his appetite was always ready and sharp for any meal of the kind that might fall in its way. He sailed gaily and gratefully into the subject of Man "in his right and proper estate," now, and he and Harrison were soon deep in it and each sparring away the best he knew how. They threshed out the detail of man's mentality to the bottom of the stack, both granting his supremacy in that matter, but Sol denying that the other animals were altogether destitute of the reasoning faculty, and maintaining that as far as the ant and his brethren were able to reason at all their processes were the same as man's. Finally Harrison said—

"We have come a good way, Bailey. As a result—as I understand you—I am required to concede that there is absolutely no fence separating man and the beasts that perish."

"Yes, that is it. There is no such fence—there is no way to get around that. Man has a finer and more capable machine in him than those others, but it's the same machine and works the same way."

Harrison said impatiently—

"Then man and the other animals are all alike, as to mental machinery, and there isn't any difference of any stupendous magnitude between them, except in quality, not in kind."

"Yes, that is about the state of it—intellectually. There are pronounced limitations on *both* sides. We can't learn to understand much of their language, but the dog, the elephant, etc., learn to understand a great deal of ours. To that extent they are our superiors. Not our mere equals, you see, but our *superiors*. Come, grant that large fact. You know it's perfectly true, Harrison." Harrison made no answer. "On the other hand they can't learn reading, writing, etc., nor any of our fine and high things, and there we have a large advantage over them."

Harrison spoke up with heat—

"Very well, then, let them have what they've got, and welcome; there is still a wall, and a lofty one: they haven't the Moral Sense. We have it, and it lifts us immeasurably above them."

"What makes you think that?"

Harrison flushed, and an angry light shone in his eye. Evidently the new comforter was knocking the other comforter's work to rags, but he was adorably unheedful of it and guilelessly blind to it. Harrison said, hotly—

"What makes me think it! What else could I think? Now look here—let us call a halt. I have stood the other infamies and insanities, and that is enough: I am not going to have man and the brutes put upon the same level *morally*."

"I wasn't going to do that, Harrison."

The gentleness of the response made Harrison a little ashamed of his warmth, and he said with a repentant touch in his tone—

"Oh, very well, then, go on."

Bailey's eyes beamed gentle acceptance of the unarticulated apology, and he resumed:

"No, it would not be right to put them on the same level morally. Lacking the Moral Sense, the brutes don't know right from wrong, and consequently they can't 'do wrong. We can. Well, then, of course an animal that can't do wrong is as much better and higher and nobler than an animal that can, as an angel is better and higher and nobler than a Pawnee Indian. The angels didn't fall, you know, so they haven't got the Moral Sense yet. So, as I was saying, it would not be right to put brutes and humans on the same level morally. Well, then—"

An explosion of wrath from Harrison made Bailey jump out of his clothes almost.

"Stop where you are! It's enough to drive a healthy-minded person mad, to lie helpless and have to listen to these inane stupidities."

"Why, Harrison," said Sol, wounded, "I wasn't meaning any harm; I couldn't mean any, *you* know that, and—"

"Oh, I know it, I know it, Bailey; and I ought to remember that, and keep my temper down"; and he reached out and repentantly patted the Philosopher on the arm, manfully struggling, at the same time—without possibility of success—against another up-heaval that was climbing up in him. "But—but—without your knowing, half the time, what you are driving at nor where you are traveling to, you do manage to say the damdest exasperatingest things!—*you* know that, Bailey."

Sol answered earnestly and humbly—

"It isn't intentional, Harrison, I know you'll grant that. What I am trying to do is to comfort you and tranquilize you, not disturb you and aggravate you; and when I was saying that about the Moral Sense and how it has pulled us down, I wasn't arguing—I was careful about that, because arguing to a sick man is unsettling —I was only just stating the facts, and—"

"Facts! Oh, great guns, change the subject and give us a rest!"

Poor Bailey was deeply troubled to see his kindly-meant endeavors to bring healing peace and serenity to his friend's harassed spirit so dolorously miscarry, and he wished he could think of something to talk about that would not be so incendiary. He fished around in his mind for a sedative, a pacifying subject, and was guilelessly happy when he presently caught what he was sure was just the thing—Man's Sole and Only Originating Impulse, Selfishness. He had pretty fully argued his doctrine with Harrison a few days before, and he remembered that Harrison had shown interest in it; also, so far as he could recollect, Harrison had not given way to violence in combating it. So, with good hope, he proceeded to break ground upon that topic, with the inquiry—

"Harrison, have you given thought to the Gospel of Self, since the talk we had?" [10]

"Yes, I've been considering that proposition of yours that no act is ever born of any but a selfish impulse—primarily. And meantime I have looked around a little for instances to slay it with."

"Well?"

"Oh, I shall find them, I shall find them. In time, plenty of them."

"Harrison, that's a confession that—"

"Oh, you can call it that if you want to—I don't mind. Along at first I didn't have the luck to look in the right places—but that's nothing, and doesn't prove anything. I examined fine and apparently unselfish deeds in romances and biographies, but—"

"That's it! Under searching analysis the ostensible unselfishness disappeared? It'll do it every time, Harrison, every time; there aren't any exceptions."

Harrison was not disturbed.

"I beg your pardon—not every time," he said. "I've got one here in this book that will demolish that detail."

"It won't; I know it beforehand. State it."

"Very well, this is the way of it. In the Adirondack woods is a wage-earner who is an untrained and self-appointed lay preacher in the lumber-camps. He is of noble character, and deeply religious.

---

[10] In his composition from this point in the story until that at which Harrison is put to sleep by Bailey's oratory, Mark Twain closely followed an early draft of *What Is Man?* See *Writings*, XXVI, 30–34.

By and by there comes to his region, on vacation, an earnest and practical laborer in the New York slums who is a great merchant and is also a leader of a section of the great Unsectarian Union. Holme, the lumberman, is fired with a desire to throw away his excellent worldly prospects and go down and save souls on the East Side. He counts it happiness to make this sacrifice for the glory of God and for the cause of Christ. He resigns his place, makes the sacrifice cheerfully, and goes to the East Side and preaches Christ and Him crucified every day and every night to little groups of half-civilized foreign paupers who scoff at him. But he rejoices in the scoffings, since he is suffering them in the cause of Christ. Bailey, you have so filled my mind with suspicions that I was constantly expecting to find a hidden selfish impulse back of all this, but I am thankful to say I have failed. This man saw his duty, and for duty's sake and no other sake he sacrificed self and assumed the burden it imposed. There, now! What do you say to that?"

"Harrison, is that as far as you have read?"

"Yes."

"Well, we must read further, presently. Meantime, in sacrificing himself—not for the glory of God *primarily,* as he imagined, but primarily to content that imperious master, Self, within him—did he sacrifice anybody else?"

"How do you mean?"

"He relinquished a very lucrative post, and got mere food and lodging in place of it?"

"He did that very thing," said Harrison, with reverent admiration.

"Had he any dependants?"

"Well—yes."

"Mm. In what way and to what extent did his so-called self-sacrifice affect *them?*"

"Well, he was the support of a superannuated father, and—"

"That's *one.* Go on."

"—he had a young sister with a remarkable voice—he was giving her a musical education, so that her longing to be self-supporting might be gratified—"

"That's *two.* Go on."

"He was furnishing the money to put a young brother through a polytechnic school and satisfy his desire to become a civil engineer. That's the list."

"*Three* dependents upon his rich earnings. A helpless old father, a helpless young sister, a helpless young brother. The old father's comforts were curtailed?"

Harrison—a little impatiently:

"Certainly, certainly—of course. It follows necessarily."

"The sister's music-lessons had to stop?"

More impatiently:

"Confound you, you know they did!"

A little of Harrison's patience was beginning to ooze out.

"The young brother's education—well, an extinguishing blight fell upon that happy dream, and he had to go to sawing wood, or screening gravel, or shoveling snow, or tending hogs, to feed the old father and the young sister?"

"Oh, go on; and don't be so damned tedious!"

"Now Harrison, what a handsome job of self-sacrificing he did do! It seems to me that he sacrificed everybody except *himself*. Haven't I told you that no man ever sacrifices himself; that there is no instance of it upon record anywhere; and that when the master, Self, requires a thing of its slave for either its momentary or its permanent contentment, that thing must and *will* be furnished and that command obeyed, no matter who may stand in the way and suffer disaster by it? That man ruined his family to please and content his Self—"

"And help Christ's cause."

"Yes—*secondly*. Not firstly. Though *he* thought it was firstly."

"Oh, all right, have it so if you want to. But it could be that he argued that if he saved a hundred souls in New York—"

"The sacrifice of the family would be justified by that great profit upon the—the—what shall we call it?"

"Investment?"

"Hardly. How would Speculation do? how would Gamble do? Not a single soul-capture was sure. He *played* for a possible thirty-three hundred per cent profit. It was gambling—with his family for 'chips.' However, what we are mainly interested to get on the track of, is, the secret original impulse that moved him to so nobly sacrifice his family in the Savior's cause under the delusion that he was sacrificing himself. What is your guess, Harrison?"

"Never mind my guess. The man's act may have been a mistake, in the circumstances, but if you will read along and find the original impulse that was back of it—since you are not satisfied that the one already furnished was the real one—it may be that you will have to concede that it was a noble and beautiful one."

"It *may* be, you think? Well, it won't be, Harrison; I know that, beforehand. . . . I've found it—it was bound to expose itself sooner or later."

"Go on, then. What was it?"

"Here are the facts: and they lead up to the exposure. He preached to the East Side rabble a season, then went back to his dull and obscure life in the northern wilderness hurt to the heart, his pride humbled. Why? Were not his efforts acceptable to the Savior, for Whom alone (ostensibly) they were made? Harrison, I give you my word, *that* detail is lost sight of, and is not even mentioned—the fact that it started out as a motive is entirely forgotten!"

"Well, then, what was the trouble?"

The exultation and exaltation of the orator who sees victory in sight came upon Bailey, and he rose and walked the floor with measured strides, impressively driving and clinching his argumentative nails one by one and climbing step by step toward a climax which he intended should be the prize effort of his life.

"You ask," he began, "what the trouble was. You shall immediately see—for the authoress quite innocently and unconsciously gives the whole business away. The trouble was this: Holme merely *preached* to the poor; that is not the Unsectarian Union's way: it deals in (to the poor), more immediately imperative things than that, and it did not enthuse over that crude and windy stump-oratory. It was courteous to Holme—but cool. It did not pet him, did not take him to its bosom. Now, then, give sharp attention to this wail from the book, and see if it doesn't point straight at that man's original—and self-seeking—motive: *'Perished were all his dreams of distinction, the praise and grateful approval of—'* Of

whom? The Savior? No, the Savior is not mentioned. Of whom, then? Why, Harrison, *'of his fellow-workers!'* That is to say, the Unsectarian Union. Why did he want that? Because the Self inside of him wanted it, and would not be content without it. That emphasized sentence reveals the secret we have been seeking, the *original impulse* which moved the obscure and unappreciated Adirondack lumberman to sacrifice his family and go on that crusade to the East Side—which said original impulse was this, to-wit: without knowing it he went there to show a neglectful world the large oratorical talent that was in him, and *rise to distinction.*"
Absorbed in his theme, he went on with accumulating energy and fire:

"As I have warned you before, no act springs from any but a selfish motive. Whenever you read of an unselfish act, or of an act of self-sacrifice, or of a duty done for *duty's* sake, take it to pieces and look for the selfish motive. Pretty soon you will get so you can't help doing it, it's so horribly interesting—*fascinating* is the word. The minute you come across a noble deed in a book you will have to stop and take it apart and examine it; the whole interest of the tale fades out at once, and you excitedly get out your vivisection-tools and—"

A long-drawn, peaceful snore broke upon his ear. He glanced up —Harrison was asleep. For a moment he was ashamed and hurt, and a faint blush mounted to his cheek. Then his resentment passed, and he muttered, with the pleased air of one who had started out for a victory and has won it:

"*That* fetched him, anyway!"

It is hard to defeat a man who doesn't know it when it has happened. Bailey sat down and contemplated his conquest with grateful and naïve satisfaction, and pleasantly planned future campaigns for the comforting and tranquilizing of his friend. He believed that if he could come every day and read to him chapters out of what he called The Baylianic Philosophy of Life and which Dug Hapgood had nick-named The Black Gospels, he could soon have him as gay and happy as ever he was in his life. He mentally set down certain of these chapters by title, and resolved to administer them to the perturbed patient:

1. The Mind of Man, merely a machine; working automatically; getting its materials from the outside, never from the inside; incapable of originating a thought of any kind; always a weaver of half-breed originals out of exterior suggestions; controlled and commanded by exterior influences alone, and not subject to the man's authority, nor ever even receiving suggestions from him.

2. Personal Merit. It is non-existent and impossible. A man's qualities are born in him, he does not make them. If he is born an idiot he can't help it, and is not open to contempt for it; if he is born a poet he can't help it and is entitled to no praise for it. If he is born with a rabbit's heart his cowardice is as respectworthy as is the bravery of the man born with a lion's heart; if it is right to despise the one it is right to despise the other.

3. Man, the Creature who never Thinks. Product of circumstances and outside influences solely, never of reasoned intention. Presbyterian merely because he lives among Presbyterians; Catholic because he lives among Catholics; Mormon because he lives among Mormons; Mohammedan because he lives among Mohammedans; monarchist because he lives among monarchists; democrat or republican because his papa was one.

4. Man, the Creature that believes the Truth is Mighty and Will Prevail, and All That. With Instances as above to Prove it By.

5. Man, Sole Proprietor of the Moral Sense, and Similar Assets.

6. Man, the Supreme Achievement—And All That.

Bailey, gently lulled toward slumber by charmed visions of his depressed friend going through an inspiriting course of his Philosophy and coming out of it healed and sparkling and frisky, presently fell asleep. After half an hour he awoke; and being loth to mar the soothing work his humane late labors had accomplished upon his host, he forebore to awake him, but wrote a note briefly reporting the progress made in the Memphis business and the enlarged outlay it would involve, and placed it where Harrison would find it; then he took his way homeward serene in his mind and contented; for he had given blessed sleep to a harassed sufferer, and the thought of this good deed laid upon his spirit a great peace.

CHAPTER [XVIII]

S OL BAILEY's letter reached Allen in Memphis. Meantime he had had nightly talks and hot punches with Simon Bunker, and had had the happiness of being able to report to headquarters that Bunker's heart was with the wronged woman and that his desire to find her and secure to her her rights amounted now to a holy passion. (Allen was young, and in things sentimental the vision of youth sees its object through a prism.) Let the expense-money be supplied liberally and promptly, and success would be certain—in Allen's opinion.

Bailey's letter, coming at this juncture, was a wet blanket. Contemplated soberly, observed practically and without a prism, what might its effect be upon that holy passion? How would Bunker take it? Would he be disgusted with its unfaithfulness to the original arrangement, with its large block of the estate as commission? Would he be affronted by this mean reduction to a trifling fraction of an indefinite remnant of the estate and indignantly retire from the case?

However, he said to himself, this music must be faced: he must go to Bunker and reveal the new conditions and put up with the consequences, howsoever sorrowful and humiliating they might be. He went upon his errand sufficiently heavy-hearted and ashamed.

Bunker listened to his mournful tale without comment, and with a countenance which told poor Allen nothing. Allen's hopes faded gradually and steadily away, and finally disappeared with the conclusion of his story. Fortune and Asphyxia disappeared with them.

Bunker sat thinking—thinking. Allen sat suffering; and it seemed to him that he had not known so deep a silence before in his life, nor such a dismally long one.

At last Bunker brewed the punches, distributed them, and settled himself in his chair. Then, instead of breaking out with the storm of anger and contempt which Allen had supposed was gathering and swelling all this time, Bunker astonished him with a commonplace question uttered in a colorless tone:

"The proposed new arrangement is for you and me the eighth part of an unconcreted and indeterminate fifth—and such money as we shall need for expenses—is that it?"

Allen dropped his eyes and answered:

"Yes."

"Write him and say we accept."

All the clouds flew away, and Allen could have posed acceptably as a statue of Joy. He could hardly believe his ears, the words sounded so good and were such a surprise. His eyes grew moist, and he said with grateful and admiring emotion—

"It is lovely of you, and noble. I can't understand it. I thought you would feel cheated and insulted, and would have nothing more to do with the scheme."

"Oh, no. And there is nothing noble about it—"

"Nor unselfish?"

"No."

"Nor self-sacrificing?"

"No. None of these things. Just the opposite. It is a business move. I do not like a man to play with me when I have been trusting him. And when he does it, and in doing it heedlessly and stupidly relinquishs the advantage of the game to me, I take my revenge. In this case I shall do it with a quite tranquil conscience."

Allen was not able to understand.

"Advantage?" he said. "I believe I do not comprehend. To have our profit cut down to a fractional part of nothing—so to speak—is that an advantage?"

Bunker proceeded to explain.

"Yes. You will presently perceive that it is. But first, we will examine into the morals of the situation. In matters of business, as in all things else, it is best to start from a sound moral basis if we wish to go a course which will leave us no regrets—isn't it so?"

Bunker was proceeding in the right and judicious way; for he had found out that Allen was theoretically a moralist, from early training, whatever he might be in practice. He was persuadable from his theoretical moral side, and it was Bunker's intention to persuade him. Allen promptly agreed with the proposition to get the morals correctly arranged as a beginning; and the proposition itself raised Bunker a peg in his good opinion.

"Very well," said Bunker. "You told me the other night that Mr. Bailey had been teaching you that all impulses are selfish; that some are high and fine, others low; and that of two impulses, one fine and the other base, we should be careful to choose the fine one, and thus train ourselves constantly upward toward higher and higher ideals. It seems sound. Let us accept it and guide ourselves by it."

"Gladly! I believe it is the very rightest way there is, Mr. Bunker."

"Very well. Mr. Bailey examined his impulses in this Milliken matter, and found two—a high selfish one and a low selfish one. The high one was, to rescue this wronged woman's fortune and take half of it for the service performed; the low one was, to serve the usurper and conceal his robbery because the robber was his friend; and the selfishness that is the basis of friendship urged him to stand by the friend when he knew it was a crime to do it. But he nobly chose the high impulse and elected to do battle in the wronged woman's cause. He was right. Wasn't he right?"

"He certainly was, Mr. Bunker; and I had to admire him for it."

"One easily sees that he was right. There is not a flaw in his position."

There was a pause. Allen looked up inquiringly. Bunker added, laying a hand impressively upon Allen's knee, "You perceive what has happened?"

"Er—what is it?"

"He has gone over to the enemy and deserted the friendless woman. He has done the thing which he knew was a crime."

"Why—he has, by George! Upon my word, it is just what he has done. It didn't occur to me, but I see it now."

"He means to beguile the woman out of almost the whole of the estate and turn what he chooses of it over to Harrison, and out of that remnant give you and me a beggarly trifle—we who do the

work. Come—shall we desert the poor woman too, because our pay
is small—"

"No, sir—never!"

"—or shall we keep to the right moral basis, and see her
through—"

"Yes!"

"—and be in at the death, and arrange the terms ourselves, and
personally see to it that she gets her rights and the whole of
them?"

"We'll stand by her to the end, Mr. Bunker! I'm with you!"

They clinked glasses and drank to the honor of the right moral
basis. Then Bunker said—

"Now, then, we must go carefully. That man Bailey is shrewd
and watchful. We must use diplomacy—understand?"

"How do you mean?"

"Suppose we should veraciously report to him every step we
take? What then?"

"Well?"

"We find the woman, and report that."

"Yes?"

"He will arrive on deck straight off, and claim authority to make
the terms with her,—privately and without our help, to the
destruction of her fair rights—on the ground that we are merely
paid subordinates, who did our work with money furnished by him,
as the other side's representative and agent."

Allen was alarmed, and said—

"That won't do, it won't do at all. I get your idea: we must find
money somewhere else—"

"While apparently working for him—on the terms of this letter
of his? Decline his money? Why, he would be suspicious at once,
and put somebody else on the case. We could continue, on our own
hook, but competition in such a matter is not desirable. No, we
must take his money, even if, in order to be perfectly fair, we
should insist upon refunding it afterward."

Allen caught at that, and his doubting conscience rose up and
approved.

"Yes, we'll take it, and pay it back. That will be right. Yes, and
more than right; it will be fine."

"It seems so to me," assented Bunker, smiling on his inside. "Now, as I have said, we must use diplomacy with that man Bailey, for whether he is deep or not, he is sharp and alert. We don't want him following our track, we don't want him to know what our movements are. We'll hunt for the Milliken woman, but we'll not tell *him* so. We'll put him on a wrong scent."

He expected that proposition to trouble Allen, and it did. Allen fidgeted uncomfortably a moment, then said—

"Is—is that necessary?"

Bunker responded, gently and persuasively—

"I won't insist upon it, but if we look into the thing we shall probably find it wise. Our main, chief, overshadowing purpose—our sole purpose, almost—is to right that wronged woman. Isn't it so?"

The question startled Allen, and shamed him. He had been unconsciously losing sight of that large part of the project and allowing his yearnings to dwell upon the minor part, the profit to be fished out of it. But the question brought him back to his bearings, and he said—

"Yes, that is so."

"Very well. When Bailey comes to reflect upon his letter he will be frightened. He will say to himself that he has made a mistake; that he ought to have kept still about the new and shabby terms until his game was secure; that you and I will feel cheated and insulted; that we are merely human, and consequently selfish; that we are in this scheme for the sordid profit we can get out of it; that in our anger we will return his treachery to us with treachery to him, and go on and work the scheme in our own interest while pretending to work it in his. Doesn't that strike you as being about what will pass through his mind?"

"Now that you have mapped it out, I think I see clearly that that is what will happen. Why, certainly. I might have thought of that myself."

"Well, then, what will be the most natural thing for him to do, do you think?"

No obvious procedure occurred to Allen. After puzzling over the matter a little he confessed it, and asked—

"What do you think he will do?"

"Why, there's only one rational thing *for* him to do: he'll send a spy here—to help us!"

"And—watch us?"

"That's it. And report to him every move we make."

"I see—and have Bailey on hand when we find the woman."

"Exactly."

"Of course that would be—"

"Fatal. Necessarily."

Said Allen, anxiously—

"We must do something! What can we do?"

"Throw sand in the spy's eyes. And in his."

Allen was converted; converted, and vastly relieved. Bunker saw it in his face, and was content. Allen was now eager to have the proper protective measures taken, and said so.

"And help take them?" asked Bunker.

"Yes, sir, and help take them."

"Then we'll lay the first brick now. There's the desk. Sit down and answer Bailey's letter. I will dictate."

"I'm ready. Go on."

"Begin, then—to-wit:"

Dear Mr. Bailey: The fifty received. Many thanks. A like sum per week will be sufficient for the present. We are somewhat disappointed in the new terms, but Mr. Bunker argues that on the whole they are just and fair, therefore we accept them, but beg that they shall be formally made permanent and not reduced again.

I have news of the highest interest to report. By a lucky accident we have struck upon a new development in the case, and our plans are all changed. There *was* a banished wife and son, sure enough, but not the pair we were after. The Millikens are entirely out of it. I—

"Dear me, Mr. Bunker, is it really true, or is it only—"

"Never you mind. Go on with your writing. To-wit:"

I will give you all the details as soon as we have gathered them in. Could you send us a capable and trustworthy person to help us? We can get along without him, perhaps, but better with him we think."

"But, Mr. Bunker, that is really inviting the spy, you see."

"Of course. And it's sound business. It's a good suspicion-queller.

If Bailey is meditating a spy this may restore his confidence and put the notion out of his head; and in any case it is better politics to invite him than have him flung at our heads. Sign the letter and send it."

Allen said with admiration—

"I shouldn't ever have thought of those things, I know I never should. You are deeper than I am, Mr. Bunker."

"Thank you for the compliment," said Bunker, blandly; and to himself, "Such as it is."

No one spoke for a while, now. Both men were waiting. Allen was waiting, with a razor-edged curiosity, for Bunker to unfold the new development mentioned in the letter, and name the new heirs, and detail their romantic history, and say whether it was fact or only thrilling and appetising fiction, and plan out the new campaign; Bunker was waiting for Allen to go.

At last Allen felt obliged to say something about it's being late—which it wasn't—and that he thought perhaps he ought to be getting home—which he didn't; and was sorrowfully disappointed when Bunker took these damaged assets at par and rose and shook hands good-night without even a shadow of protest.

While he was departing the spy was arriving; and when he reached his cheap little tavern he found him there and soon learned his errand from his own lips—to-wit, that Bailey had sent him "to help."

Allen made a remark to himself which was sodden with homage for Bunker:

"I'd rather have that man's brains than Stephen Girard's millions!"

Bunker, meantime, was walking the floor and doing some deep and perplexed thinking. It took him an hour or two to tunnel his way through his problem and reach daylight at the other end. Then he snapped his fingers with satisfaction, and said—

"It will answer. Sally Archer's the ticket!"

CHAPTER [XIX]

Next day Allen got word to Bunker that the spy was come, and in the evening he brought Templeton around and introduced him. Bunker was able to seem handsomely surprised at his advent and glad of his coming; and remarked that there was a new development, and capable and trustworthy help would almost surely be needed.

"In fact," he said, "we felt so sure of it that we have already ventured to ask Mr. Bailey for it by letter."

Templeton could hardly conceal his delight at this lucky accident, and said to himself, "But for this, I should have been suspected, almost to a certainty. Why, if Confucius himself had engineered it I couldn't be better fixed. Tra la la—I'm on velvet!" He resolved to laugh the incident over with his mother in a letter before he slept.

The three chatted pleasantly together for an hour or two about the discarded campaign and the prospects of the new one, then Bunker said—

"If I have made myself clear, Mr. Gunning, the Milliken case was quite impossible, promising as it looked in the beginning."

"Yes," answered Templeton, "it was a wrong scent—one realizes it, now."

"I am glad you see it in that light. As a principal, that adventuress is out of the scheme—that is settled; but it is possible that she could be of some value as a witness."

"As a witness?—in a court?—with her record?"

"Hardly!" and Bunker was almost delivered of a laugh. "With a ten-year sentence hanging over her she would decline, with thanks —and right enough. I meant, as a private witness—in our behalf. You see, Sally Archer was hardly gone from Harrison's when the Milliken woman arrived. They would still be talking about Sally there—the house servants would. Well, the Milliken was a servant —you get the idea?"

"Yes—she would gather a good deal about Sally."

"Just so. She might give us points which could help us a good deal in getting on Sally's track, if we could make it worth her while. The Milliken would sell her soul for a dollar and a half," he added in a matter-of-course way which jolted Templeton considerably. "My deputy, Floyd Parker, was a young fellow on the plantation in those days, and thinks he and Milliken are the only whites now alive who know much about Sally and her history out there." He paused, and began to bait a hook for Templeton. When he had gotten it baited to suit him he concluded to ward off suspicion by pretending to fish for Allen with it. He now cast it. "If we could divide forces, now that we are strong, and one of us exclusively devote himself to hunting up the Milliken—" (Templeton's hopes bounded up several feet)—"the other two would not need to bother about her at all, but could concentrate their whole activities upon Sally—Sally the important, Sally the essential! Osgood, you are the man" (Templeton's hopes fell back to the earth)—"will you hunt the Milliken?"

Osgood showed disappointment; he could not have better done the thing desired by Bunker if he had been an old hand in duplicity and was working his art, instead of being a new hand, untrained in tricks, and merely working his sincerities. Templeton saw his disappointment and (as he wrote his mother later) took brilliant advantage of the situation. He spoke up and said:

"Turn her over to me, Mr. Bunker."

In his letter to his mother, that night, he said: "You ought to have been there! He couldn't get out of that hole, there wasn't any way. He not only had to take me up, but pretend to like it. Of course he had wanted to have me on the 'important' division of the hunt, for poor Allen isn't bright and can't be much help to him, and his idea had been to shove him out of the way and keep him obliterated and harmlessly amused while he and I prosecuted the division of the chase which he imagines is the 'essential' division— but I saw my chance and played that great card, and he had to pocket his disappointment. I said I was a beginner and a late-comer, and in all fairness must take a modest place. What could he say to that? Nothing. I had him where he couldn't budge. Yet of course he never suspected the immense size of the card I played in that quiet and unostentatious way; he thought it merely crippled his game, whereas it utterly destroyed it, so far as you and I are concerned. You are permanently safe, mother! All alone I shall hunt you—all solitary and alone. Look sharp, for I'm a wonderful hunter when I get started."

Bunker said to Templeton:

"You've the easiest part of the work, Mr. Gunning. You'll find the Milliken woman in ten days."

Templeton felt himself turn pale, but said as indifferently as he could—

"Is that so?"

"Yes. If she's alive, that is."

Templeton felt relieved. The preceding remark had made him fear that Bunker had some suspicion of his mother's whereabouts and knew she was alive. He said to himself, comfortably, "She'll not be alive to *you*, dear sir." Then Bunker gave him another little shock without being aware of it:

"I'll put you on her track, and if she is alive you'll have her in ten days, sure."

He opened a drawer of his desk and produced his advertisement in which the "Supplementary U.S. Mail" was invited to correspond with the "Swamp Angel," and handed it to the spy.

"Put that in just one newspaper," he said, "a Vicksburg paper, for instance, and you will hear from the Milliken woman inside of ten days. If she's alive."

The spy read it, and was relieved again. He said to himself, "Those are the nicknames my mother referred to, I guess. No harm; it will be a riddle to all but her." Then aloud—

"Why, Mr. Bunker, it doesn't mention the Milliken woman, and so how—"

"Don't you trouble about that. Put it in print and wait—you'll see."

"Just as you say. I'll attend to it."

He allowed Allen to puzzle over it a while, then pocketed it and said he would go and write a letter and send it to the Vicksburg paper. Bunker complimented him on his promptness and energy, and he went away well pleased with his evening and with the way luck was running in his direction. He sent the advertisement, then wrote his mother and enclosed a copy, remarking—

"We've scored again! It's too funny for anything. Everything comes my way, and nobody suspects. It's lovely to be on the inside, this way, and have it all to oneself. I wouldn't be anywhere but here for the world. Ten days! I reckon it will be longer than that before you respond. Then he will think you are dead—you and your poor child. A pity, too, because they so need your private information concerning Sally Archer."

He told her about the Sally Archer scheme and the great confidence Bunker had in it. He closed with—

"I'm on velvet, you see—nothing to do but sit around and draw my pay and watch the game and wait for the Supplementary U.S. Mail to respond. *If* not dead."

Bunker and Allen chatted together a while over the prospect, then Deputy Floyd Parker dropped in, by appointment, and Bunker said—

"What I wanted was, to have you talk with Mr. Osgood, here, about Sally Archer, and the best way to get on her track. As I have already told you, confidentially, he and I—however, you can take him to your room and discuss the whole matter and plan out the search. Have you been mulling it over any?"

"Yes, I've made a start. If you'd like to come with us—"

"I'll come presently. No—you come to me when you are through. Did you find any letters of about that date?"

"Yes, here are eight, and I can get more if you want them."

"No, these will do, no doubt."

Parker and Allen moved down the hall and entered a room; Bunker stood listening. He heard a door close, then he closed his own and eagerly took up the letters, and began to glance through them.

"They will answer," he said. "Yes, they will answer. A good, firm, business-like hand. Harrison was at his best in those days."

He sat down and took a pen and began to carefully copy one of them. He finished his work and compared it with the original, nodding approvingly, and saying, "It's no trick at all; even a novice could counterfeit a hand like that."

The letters were written on foolscap, with a red line down the left-hand side of the page. Bunker now forged a couple, dated them back seventeen and sixteen years, and signed the late Harrison's name to them. They began with "Dear Bro.," and consisted mainly of colorless commonplaces; they had the air of "duty" letters. That kind lack juice. These lacked it, except that there was one drop in each. This—in one:

> "I was a fool to marry the woman, and it was largely your fault that I did it. In a single day I repented. I have never acknowledged the marriage, and I never will. The birth of the child has not changed my feeling; your pleadings are wasted; I never change. She is Mrs. Milliken, and Mrs. Milliken she will remain; therefore please learn to write that name, and stop referring to her as my wife."

This—in the other:

> "The 'celebrity' and her 'nephew' are my wife and child. They decamped a couple of months ago; they couldn't stand mc nor I thcm. She provoked me one shade beyond endurance, and I did a thing which—well, I was branding Tom, a runaway, and she interfered and I branded *her*. Scold, if you like—circumstance and opportunity were more to blame than I. It got me rid of the pair, and I am content. Two or three times she threatened to go to law and make me acknowledge her. I am shut of *that*, now—for good and all. She will not venture to show her face in these parts again."

"Come in!"

It was Floyd Parker.

"Sit down. Go on. Tell me."

"Well, I've mapped it out for him, and made it sufficiently difficult to keep him busy and entertained—and harmless."

"Right."

"He has the several places where Sally tarried after she left, and twice as many where she didn't tarry—"

"That's the idea, exactly! But you left out New York and the pest house?"

"Certainly. He can trace her three years, but not the fourth; I have arranged for that."

"Very good. They've been dead—how long is it?"

"About eleven years. I say, Simon, that's a good boy—dreadfully simple, but he hasn't the least harm in him, except what other people put there."

"Why, hang it, Floyd, that describes the most of us—don't you know that? Was there any harm in you and me when we were boys together? Did we take to crookednesses of our own volition, or wasn't it by the devilish training of resentments nursed and mulled over for wrongs done us?"

A cynical smile flitted across Parker's face, but he said nothing.

"Where would you be, now, but for this old scoundrel that's dead?" Bunker got up and began to walk the floor and gesticulate. "Yes, where would you be? Why, you'd be in your father's shoes—rich, and president of the bank he left behind him."

Parker made no response.

"And where would I be? Wasn't I prospering until he got his fangs into me? And didn't he strip me bare? Why, even to my poor swamp paradise, which *he* hadn't any use for! And isn't he the reason that for five years you were a sot, and that the girl that should have been your wife died of a broken heart?"

He paused, but Parker said nothing. Bunker resumed, still walking, still punctuating and italicising with his hands:

"And wasn't he the reason that every time the people might have promoted me a grade or two the old shame of my post-office stupidity was resurrected and laughed about and my chance spoiled? But for him my life would not be the half-success it is—I should be away up! Isn't it so?"

Another pause, and no response. Bunker—raising his voice:

"Floyd! I have done things, and you have done things, which, if anybody besides you and I knew them—Why, if we had the money he robbed us of—Floyd, every cent of it has got to come out of that estate, let the means and methods be what they may—*Why* don't you say something!"

Parker's hard face cracked slightly in several directions and let out an ironical laugh; a laugh of the sort that blows a chill upon sentiment. It was followed by words in keeping with it, chaffingly uttered:

"Sit down, Simon, and cool-off your soul."

Bunker's face flushed, and he seemed on the point of saying something hot; then he jerked his chair into position and flung himself into it, saying, in a tone of disgust—

"Oh, well, I'm a fool, of *course*. Go on, I know what you're going to say."

Parker responded with mocking urbanity—

"No, I should not put it as strong as that; I should not say 'of course'—no, not quite that; I think the most I should say—Look here, Bunker, let's be serious. Come—are you willing to talk on that basis?"

"Am *I* willing! Have I been otherwise?"

"Very well, for the sake of argument, let us suppose you haven't. Shall *I* be serious?"

"Yes, go on."

"All right, then. Drop sentiment, and come down to business. Now, *you* know me, and I know you. It's all right for you to hatch out a lot of excuses to rob the estate—it's your nature; it's my nature to rob it without any. It's your nature to want to humbug yourself when you are starting out on an indiscretion, you were born so and you can't help it; it's my nature to go right ahead and commit the indiscretion and not worry about reasons for it. Born so. Why, man, if we hadn't been born with a predisposition to rascality, those little cheatings and overreachings and ill-usings couldn't make rascals of us. Sho! all you wanted was a chance! Chance to develop and be your predestined self. The same with me. We've had it. The result is before you. Now then, let's be honest, just this once, dear, dear old friend and pal, and recognize this plain unadorned fact: we wish to rob that estate, we *mean* to rob that estate, we don't care what the means are nor who it hurts, old Harrison's treatment of us isn't our inspiration, sentiment is clean away outside of it, we'd skin it, by God, if it belonged to an orphan asylum, and you *know* it; come out and *say* it, like a man!"

Bunker broke into a laugh, and Parker followed suit. Then Bunker said—

"Well, the truth is, it's as you say; but somehow I never could seem to go into an impropriety without shoring myself up with a kind of a justification, you know."

"That's all right, it's your nature. But you've confessed; sentiment has had its innings; the atmosphere is purged of humbug, now, the decks are cleared for action, our spirits are up, we're ready for business. Satisfied?"

"I am."

"All right—play ball!"

Bunker drained his glass, smacked his lips, and said—

"Very well. Now, then, listen to the scheme—I didn't half fill it out last night—I might say I didn't even skeletonize it. I've made Osgood and the spy believe that Sally is the wronged wife and the person we really want—"

"Yes, I got that from Osgood."

"—whereas, of course—"

"Yes, I know. We want the Millikens. Allen told me about the enigmatical advertisement that is to fetch them. He was miserably sorry you didn't explain it."

"Yes, no doubt. Now then, we shall hear from them inside of ten days—"

"If—"

"Oh, yes, I know: if they're alive. Confound that if, it *is* a most troublesome one. But anyway—"

"Go on—leave the if out."

"In that case I'll have a talk with her, and establish the marriage, and the estate is hers, *sure*—subject to our lien on it. See it?"

Parker wrinkled his brows in thought, a while, then said—

"Well, no. I don't quite see it. With that ten years hanging over her, how is she going to venture before a court and—"

"Oh, no, no, there'll be nothing of that kind. This isn't a matter for courts."

"What, then?"

"It's only for that Indiantown heir, George Harrison."

"How do you mean?"

"Prove the marriage to *him* privately."

"Good. But by whose evidence?"

"Hers."

"Good again. But *he* will carry it into court, of course."

"Not if he is the man I take him to be. I have pumped young Allen pretty thoroughly, and I conclude that Harrison is a most strangely and unaccountably scarable man—for a grown person. Afraid of shadows—a man with a lofty and blameless reputation, a sort of idol and model of all the moralities and virtues, in the eyes of the community, and would rather lose a leg than come down a peg from that high place. Prove the marriage, and that is the kind of a man to step down and out without a word."

Parker did some more thinking; then said—

"Has the man no protectors?"

"A young son, and the son's law-partner; but he doesn't seem to have business-confidences with anybody but a flighty nondescript with a rather suggestive nick-name—the Idiot Philosopher."

"Yes. Curious bird. Osgood threw in a word or two about him. Go on with the scheme. Tell me—how are you going to prove the marriage to Harrison? That done, how are you going to prove to him, to his entire satisfaction, that this woman is the right one, and not a substitute?"

"Why, if she's dead, we've got to *get* a substitute; but in either case the identification is easy and sure. Read these."

He handed the new letters to Parker, whose face, for the first time since his arrival in the room, broke up in a smile of a genial and undevilish sort.

"Forgeries!"

"That's it."

"Good enough, too; but the paper and ink—however, that's all right; you know how to take the freshness out of them."

"I do."

"Well, they'll do for private exploitation with Harrison and the woman, I reckon—they don't have to be perfect for that."

"They'll do; and if—"

Parker cut him short with a burst of admiration:

"O come, this is *great!* why, this is a master-stroke!"

"What—the brand?"

"Yes."

"A pretty unassailable sort of an identifier, isn't it?"

"Well, I—should—*say!* It's grand! How did you find out she was branded?"

"I didn't."

Parker glanced up wonderingly, admiringly—

"Do you mean to say—"

"I just do. Invented the idea myself."

"By George!" Parker reached for his hat, put it on, then took it off ceremoniously. "I uncover to you. It would have been a pity if you had entered the ministry, because—"

"Thanks. These flatteries—"

"O, opulently endowed! O, incomparable rascal! Why, Bunker, it's genius; that's what it is, it's genius. You can put the brand on *any* woman you please, and there she is!—old Harrison's widow, and no way to get around it."

"That's the idea," said Bunker, well pleased.

"Well—well—well—it does beat anything that ever—But look here, you don't say *where* she was branded."

"Because women are so various in the matter of taste—in brands. It is best to let them choose the part of their person they prefer to have it on."

"Another stroke of genius! Upon my word, Bunker, there's not two men in a million that could have thought of a delicate shade like that. Why, you know, it's just immense!"

"Glad you like it, Floyd. It did seem to me it was rather neat."

"Neat! it isn't syllables enough by fourteen. Shakspeare himself couldn't discount it, the best day he ever saw. Come—here's success to the conspiracy; drink hearty. Now a word more, and then I'll go. What's my part to play?"

"A quiet trip to Indiantown."

"To look the ground over and study the situation and Harrison?"

"That's it. Have you ever been there?"

"No."

"Good. Know anybody there?"

"No."

"Good again. You'll have to go disguised; like enough the spy and Allen have described us casually in their letters home. Where'll you hail from, and what will you be?"

"Mm—let me see. Specially I need to know Harrison—"

"Yes."

"Well, I'll think up something that will answer; something of a simple and quiet sort. Fortune-teller is my best card, perhaps—I'm used to it. How does it strike you?"

"Just [the] thing, it seems to me, for you can find out the past of the principal villagers from Gunning and Osgood."

"Very well, I will pump them a day or two and then disappear."

CHAPTER [XX]

A week later. Ann Bailey had been out slumming around among the very poor. Formerly she had been able to contribute only sympathy and affection and encouragement, and sick-nursing, and help in the kitchen and at the wash-tub—it was all she had to contribute; but in these latter days she was having prouder and happier times, for now she could spend a little money on these people, and she got great satisfaction out of this. Her clothes were plain and cheap, but they were new, and that novelty was precious to her, and a happiness. Her heart was singing. She entered her house by the back way and the kitchen, and stopped in the door that opened into her parlor. Stopped and began to gaze. Her husband sat by the stove, with an open letter in his hand and misery in his face. He was lost to the world, he was not conscious of Ann's presence. She still gazed, and gazed, while the waters of her wrath rose; presently the dam burst:

"Sol Bailey!"

It brought him to, with a wrench.

"Gracious, Ann, *why* do you—"

"Never you mind the why's of it; what I want to know is, what *new* streak of good luck has gone and happened, to make you look like that?"

"I don't know why you should think good luck could have such a—"

"Because it always does. There wasn't *ever* such a misconstructed man in the world, I do believe. If ever you're set up and gay, it's over something for a sane person to cry about, and if ever you're—come, out with it, Sol Bailey, what's happened?"

She flung off her things and came and sat down by him.

"Now then," she said, "go on. Tell me about it."

"It's this letter, Ann," said Bailey, with a dreary sigh. "All our dreams are gone to ruin—it's from Allen."

Ann's face grew grave.

"Ah," she said; and then "ah," again, after a pause; and fell to nervously clasping and unclasping her hands, a sign that she was troubled. Presently she said, not very resignedly—

"Oh, well, it was to be expected."

"What was, Ann?"

"Why, that the one-eighth of a *fifth,* and the fifth a fifth of an uncertain remnant at that, would knock the whole thing into flinders and they wouldn't accept. Oh, hang it, I just *knew* it, I *felt* it! why *did* we ever go and do that fool thing!" and she was near to crying.

"Yes, but Ann, they *do* accept."

"*No!*—you don't mean it!" and she flung her arms around Sol and gave him a passionate hug. The next moment she burst out on him and said, "Then what in the nation are you sweating about, you turnip?"

Sol said, reproachfully—

"Ann, you always go off like that, and you don't give a person a chance. If you would wait and hear it all, then you would see it's as I said."

"Ruined?"

"Yes."

"Well, then, go on. Prosperity's new, it ain't a habit yet—a body can break it, I guess." Then she added, mournfully, "Go on; I'm used to trouble, I reckon I can stand it."

"Poor old girl, I'm just as sorry; I love you, dear," and he patted her head.

"Say it again, Sol, it heals all a body's sores—life can't ever get quite dreary as long as that music's in it." Sol said it again, with another love-pat, and Ann said—

"I can hear the bad news now, and not turn a hair. Take hold of my hand. Now go on, Sol."

"Well, it's like this, Ann. There's two letters. Here's the other one. One accepts, and wants help. That's good luck, as long as we were sending it anyway; and it says they were after the wrong pair, but they're after the right pair now—and *that's* all right; but the other letter is later, and says that the fresh pair have been gone eleven years, and Allen says it may take two or three years to run them down, and maybe they'll never find them at all, and if they do, they may find them dead. And so, you see, it's just a wild-goose chase, Ann—we'll never never find them, and everything's gone to smash, I just know it. Oh, dear, it was only a dream, just a beautiful dream, and it's a wreck."

"Thank goodness!" Ann said it with fervor.

"Thank goodness, Ann?" said Sol, with surprise. "What about?"

Evidently Ann's troubles were all gone.

"Let me get a drink; land, my throat is that dry!" She got her drink and returned. "Now then," she said, "I was right, in the first place. Whenever you are hit with the dumps, Sol, it means good luck. What are those expenses yonder in Memphis?"

"Four or five thousand dollars a year."

"Your salary is half as much?"

"Yes."

"What is prob'ly George Harrison's income from the estate?"

"At ten per cent, which is about right, forty thousand a year."

"Now then, Sol Bailey, you listen to me, and have some sense. Are these expenses going to crush George Harrison?"

"Sho! of course not."

"Suppose we should find the heirs next week, and they should stand out for nine-tenths, and just would *have* it, spite of anything we could do? Is there anything to hender it?"

"Why—no, I reckon not."

"Well, then, where'd *we* be, with our one-eighth of a one-fifth of what's left? What *is* one-eighth of nothing, Sol Bailey?"

"Well, the fact is—"

"And what is one-eighth of one-fifth of nothing, when *we* don't get the nothing, but have to divide it, and subdivide it, and split it up and—and—Sol Bailey, don't you see?"

Bailey was in a whirl of half-comprehension, half-bewilderment.

"See—see what, Ann?"

"Why, this. If they take years to find those people, it's good luck for George Harrison—his income goes on—and your salary goes on, and that is good enough luck for *us*. I hope they'll never be found, for that good soul's sake!"

"So do I! So do I, Ann, I see it now—what a head you've got!"

"I was born with it," said Ann, giving it an appreciative toss. "Now then, go straight and cheer that man up. Tell him the search has got to go on, now that it's started and other parties interested in it and bargained with, but there isn't the least likelihood that that pair's ever going to be found—not inside of five years anyway, maybe ten."

"I'll do it! It will make him the happiest man in the world. Ann, you are the most wonderful woman to dig through a cloud and find the sunshine on the other side that ever was—give me a kiss."

He found Harrison melancholy, despondent, miserable, and for fifteen minutes he rained upon him the refreshing shower of his news; then in a passion of gratitude Harrison shook him by both hands and said—

"I was dead, and you have brought me to life again—what a friend you are, Bailey! I don't know how to thank you."

"Oh, never mind about—"

"Bailey! found or not found, your salary goes right on just the same, as long as I've got the money to pay it with. No, no, no, not a word, I won't hear it. I *will* have it so, and it's a contract. Tell your wife so, from me—a good woman, if ever there was one. Going? Don't. Stop to supper—do; there'll be others."

Bailey was persuadable, for he liked talk and company, and the Harrison table was good. The evening passed off happily. The conversation was of a cheerful sort, and for once there were no chance remarks about murders and murderers to send cold chills down Harrison's back. When he found himself alone at half past ten, he looked so restful and at peace that old Martha noticed it and said it did her good to see it. Then she went on talking while she set things to rights.

"I been down to de village safternoon, en I seen Marse Tom en Miss Helen, en dey couldn't come up to-day; but Marse George, dey's a-thinkin' 'bout you all de time, en a-praisin' you up, en dey ain't nobody got no mo' lovin' chillern den what *dem* is. Marse George, you orter be mighty happy."

"I know it, Martha, I know it; and to-night I am."

"Well, suh, you looks it—hit do jist do a body's heart good to see it. I wisht it was mo' oftener. But nemmine, hit gwyne to come, don't you be 'fraid 'bout dat. En ain't *dey* happy! oh, it's jist pooty to see 'em. En Miss Helen—lawsy me, de way she look in Marse Tom's eyes an wusshup—dat's it, wusshup—dat's de right name of it. En Marse Tom he's jist de same 'bout her—plumb crazy. Oh, yes indeedy, if dey's anybody in de worl' got a right to be happy thoo en thoo, hit's you, Marse George—en thank Gawd you *is*; it make yo' face fa'rly shine!"

She gossiped cheerily along at her work, dropping in a word about this and that and the other villager and his small affairs and working up the effects with an eye to George's further uplifting and refreshment; and when at last her tasks were finished and she took her leave she recognized that his spirits were many points higher than they had ever registered since the old master's death, and she was proud of her share in bringing about that result.

"She's a good old soul," Harrison said to himself. "If I could only feel like this, all the time! And why shouldn't I? Troubles are only mental; it is the mind that manufactures them, and the mind can forget them, banish them, abolish them. Mine shall do it. Nothing is needed but resolution, firmness, determination. I will exert it. It is the only wisdom. I will put all these goblins, these unrealities behind me, I have been their slave long enough; if I have done wrong I have atoned for it, I have paid the cost and more, I have sweated blood, I have earned my freedom, I have earned peace and a redeemed and contented spirit, and why should I not have them? I will lift up my head, it is my right. I am honored and esteemed by all. Yes, by all. I can say it truly. There is not a person in the community who does not look up to me and—"

There was a knock on the front door. Harrison stepped to it and opened it, and found Jasper standing there in the humble attitude of his caste, with his ancient slouch hat in his hand.

"Kin I see you a minute, seh?" he asked.

Harrison said, with ruffled dignity—

"Where are your manners, you dog? Take yourself to the back door."

He closed the front one in Jasper's face and returned to his seat. Presently Jasper entered by the back one, without knocking, came forward, and began:

"I wanted to ast you, seh—"

"Take your hat off!"

"I begs yo' pahdon, seh—I fo'got, deed I did, seh, I's in sich trouble en so worrited."

"Now then, go on. And cut it short. What is it you want? Wait —put that stick on the fire."

Jasper dropped his hat on the floor and obeyed. But the stick slipped from his hands, and scattered the coals in every direction. While he brushed them up George scolded his clumsiness and superintended his work, correcting, fussing, finding fault, and giving new orders before the mulatto could finish the old ones. At last there was an end, and George said—

"I think I never saw such an awkward brute."

Jasper explained.

"I ain't allays so, Marse Hahson, but I been laid up in de bed considable many days, en I's stiff en ain't got de full use er myseff."

"What laid you up?"

"De constable, he done it. He gimme thutty-nine."

"You needed it, I reckon. Step out back and fetch in an armful of wood, then tell me what your business is, here—and be quick about it, you hear? it's getting late."

This all seems harsh, coming from so kind-hearted a man as Harrison was, but it was merely custom, the habit of the time, in dealing with the colored man, and had less depth to it and feeling in it than a stranger to the country would have supposed. The whites imagined that the negroes did not mind it. They judged by the negro's outside, and forgot to inquire within. Jasper brought the wood and piled it, and Harrison said—

"You were out without a pass—was that it?"

"Yes, seh."

"How was that?"

"You know, seh, I's de Squiah's g'yardener, en so now dey ain't nobody to gimme a pass."

"Then you're here without one! Speak up—is that so?"

Jasper—humbly:

"Yes, seh. I ain't got no fren's, en—"

"I'll have you jailed to-morrow! Upon my word, the impudence of a free nigger beats anything that ever—look here, my man, what's your business here? Come, speak out—speak out."

Jasper dropped on his knees and put up his hands and began to plead.

"Oh, marse Hahson, if I can't git nobody to he'p me I doan' know what gwyneter become er me. Workin' in de greenhouse ain't gwynter save me if I ain't got no pass. Dey'll drive me outen de State, en if I's to try to stay dey'd take en sell me, en if I resis' dey'll lynch me, caze I ain't got no fren's en nobody to stan' by me. Won't *you*, marse Hahson?—won't you stan' by me?"

"What!"

"You's de mos' pow'ful genlman in de whole deestrick, now; you's de only one dey dasn't stan' out agin, de only one dat kin say 'You keep yo' han's off'n him' en dey dasn't say a word. Don't you reckon, seh—"

"No—I don't. I don't like the law that sells and banishes free niggers, but if the people wish to enforce it it is their right, and as a Christian citizen it is my duty to bow to their will and not obstruct the law in its course."

Jasper rose slowly up, and stood on his feet. Harrison turned his eyes away, and stroked his jaw nervously and uncomfortably with his hand; he was not proud of himself. There was a pause, then the negro said—

"Ain't dey noth'n better'n bein' a Christian, seh?"

"You blasphemous scoundrel! You—"

"I means, *dat* kind of a Christian, seh."

Harrison turned an outraged eye upon him and motioned toward the door with his hand, saying sharply—

"I've had enough of this—quite enough; I don't like your tone; there's the door; move along!"

Jasper picked up his hat and stood fumbling it, with his head bowed, Harrison watching him with rising choler. After a moment or two the drooping head came up—and the hat was on it! Harrison could not speak. He could only stare, and wonder if this miracle of insolence was real, or only a fantastic delusion. Jasper turned slowly away, saying, absently—

"Po' Jake Bleeker. If de law would let a nigger testify in a cote—"

Any reference to the tragedy which had wrecked Harrison's life was enough—it took the man all out of him, it filled his imagination with formless shapes and ghastly terrors. He rose up sick and trembling, steadying himself with his hand on his chair-back, and said, with a weak counterfeit of mere curiosity—

"Wait a moment. What's that?"

Jasper moved a step, saying—

" 'Tain't no matter, seh." Still moving: " 'Course de law—"

"Wait, I tell you," said Harrison. "This is a matter of interest to every public-spirited citizen; nothing concerning it—however seemingly trivial it may seem—is unimportant. What are you hinting at? Suppose niggers could testify—what then?"

Jasper's hat was still on. Harrison ignored it. Jasper turned toward him, and said—

"Marse Hahson, you reckon dey's any doubt dat de Squiah done it?"

Harrison answered with as easy a confidence as he was able to assume—

"Oh, no, there seems to be none. No, none at all, I am afraid."

He wished the mulatto would not keep his eyes bent on him so steadily; the effect was uncomfortable.

"Dey say de Squiah tole Miss Helen he never done it; dey say he tole her dat de man 'at done it was a stranger in de place. Does you reckon dat could happen, seh?"

"Why, yes. Why, certainly, it *could* happen."

Jasper was silent a moment, then he said—

"I hearn a man say he reckon it could a been a stranger, en said he b'lieve it *was*, en said he wisht he could find dat man."

Harrison could not say anything; the remark made him shiver. The silence that followed oppressed him; it seemed to bear down on him like a weight. Presently Jasper said, in an indifferent tone—

"I reckon marse Tom would, too, becaze he's gwyne to marry in de fambly."

Harrison—relieved:

"Ah, yes, yes, indeed he would!"

"'Course—hit stan' to reason. En you'd like to find de man, too."

"Ye-s."

In an instant Jasper snatched him by the shoulders and whirled him in front of the mirror.

"*Dah he is!*"

Harrison's terror paralysed his voice for a moment, then it freed itself in a passion of fright and indignation mixed, and he broke away, panting, and stood at bay and began to pour out a torrent of threats and curses and insults upon the mulatto, who listened with the look of one who is hearing pleasant music; listened intently, tranquilly, contentedly: then, in the midst of it all, he fished around in his coat pocket in a leisurely way and got out a white handkerchief with two holes in it and blood stains upon it, and shook it out and held it up by two corners!

The tornado stopped, and Harrison sank into a chair, white and breathless, and dumbly staring. Jasper folded the handkerchief carefully, slowly, elaborately, and returned it to his pocket. Then he nodded toward Harrison and said—

"*You is my meat.*"

Harrison moaned in his misery, but no words came. He realized that a formidable disaster had befallen him. How formidable it might be he could not estimate, it was but matter for guesswork as yet, and his brain was too much stunned to work capably, now, upon the materials at hand. It tried to guess, of course, but its efforts were so dominated by fright that they were the opposite of tranquilizing. Presently these thought-processes suffered an interruption which changed their drift and raised the temperature of Harrison's blood by several degrees: the negro coolly sat down in his presence! This was too much. For a moment Harrison forgot all other things in the indignation bred in him by this monstrous insult, and he straightened up and said—

"How dare you? Get up!"

For all reply the negro got out the red-stained mask again, and spread it upon his knees. In an instant Harrison had snatched it and sprung toward the fire with it; but in the next moment his wrists were prisoners in the vise-like grip of the yellow athlete's brawny hands. He struggled, and raged, and wept—a vain waste of wind and strength, it was but a case of rabbit and wolf; Jasper held him, waited, and said nothing. When he saw that his prey was exhausted, he crushed him into his chair, freed him, and said, picking up the fallen mask and pocketing it—

"Set dah en pant whilst I talks to you, Hahson."

Harrison allowed this fresh affront to pass; there could be no profit in discussing it, in the circumstances.

"Now den, in de fust place, some niggers is fools. De mos' of 'em is. Well, I ain' no fool. You gwyneter fine it out 'fo' I's done wid you. I's gwyneter ast you some questions. Answer 'em right out squah en plain—I ain' gwyneter 'low no foolin'. You knowed de hankcher was missin'?"

"Yes."

"Didn't you reckon it was cur'us it didn't turn up at de inques'?"

"Yes."

" 'Course! What did you reckon was de reason?"

"Thought an enemy had it."

"*White* enemy?"

"Yes."

The negro chuckled.

"You ain' *got* none! Hain't it so?"

"Well—yes. I believe it is."

"Den it was a dam fool reason. He'd a brung it to de inques', so's he kin git revenge. But *I* never brung it to de inques'. Does you know de reason?"

"No."

"Becaze I warn't ready. Does you know why I brung it now?"

"No."

"Becaze I *is* ready."

"I don't know how you are more ready now than you were on the fourth of November. I don't see any reason for it."

"Den I's gwyneter tell you. Nigger evidence ain't no good in cote?"

"N-no." Harrison felt a sinking sensation at the pit of his stomach.

"I had to rummage out de *white* witness, en I done it!"

Harrison sank back with a gasp, and a half-smothered "Ah, my God!" He looked so ghastly that Jasper jumped for water and sprinkled some in his face, thinking he would die if help was not promptly afforded. He watched his patient with absorbing interest and solicitude until he saw him revive, then he resumed his talk and his tortures.

"Does you know, Hahson, if I couldn't *make* dat white man tell what he seen en what he hearn dat night, he wouldn't go a step to de cote? Becaze—well, *I* knows why. You's pow'ful strong en 'spectable en looked up to, Hahson, you's got a mighty good name in dis town."

The persecutor chuckled again.

"But *he* knows I kin fetch de white folks dat'll jail him down dah in de Souf any time I says de word, en so if I tell him to go to de cote en swah agin you, he *got* to."

Harrison was about to pluck up a little imitation spirit and cast contempt upon this possibly imaginary witness, when Jasper added, in an indifferent tone—

"But I ain' gwyneter sen' him to no cote."

Joyful words! So joyful that Harrison was half afraid, for a moment, that he had mis-heard. But before he could reassure himself and utter his gratification, Jasper was speaking again. What he said dismissed the fickle sunshine and brought the clouds once more.

"Dat man ain' gwyne to no cote, Hahson—not if I knows it. You b'longs to me, now. You's my proppity, same as a nigger, en I ain' gwyneter was'e you. By God, I kin hang you any minute I wanter! Git up en fetch yo' marster a dram!"

Through Harrison's half-paralysed brain flitted the shameful reflection, "Slave of an ex-slave! it is the final degradation; there is nothing below this." It is win or lose, now—this moment will never come again; he must act a man's part, now—resist, free himself, risk his life on it, or remain a slave! He said in his heart he *would*, and bravely raised his eyes; they met the stern gaze of the master, wavered there a moment, then fell. He was conquered, and knew it. He rose, and passed unsteadily by his tamer, and at the other end of the room began his menial labors.

"Make it strong—you heah? En put sugar in it."

Harrison's eye fell upon the gun—double-barrelled—loaded for robbers. He glanced cautiously around, hopeful, excited, trembling from his hair to his heels: Jasper's back was to him! stirring the toddy noisily with one hand, he reached for the gun with the other, got it and faced about, cocking it. Jasper heard the clicks, turned, and looked down the barrels. Harrison pulled the triggers. Jasper burst into an unfeeling laugh.

"I never see sich a fool," he said; "didn't you reckon I knowed de gun was dah—right whah anybody kin see it? I done fix' dat gun befo' de constable laid me up. Been yo' ole father, *he'd* a foun' it out, but I could 'pen' 'pon you, *you* doan' take notice er noth'n. I drove pins in de nipples en filed 'em down. Stan' her up in de cornder. When I's done wid you you kin have some mo' guns if you want 'em—dey ain't gwyne to worry *me* none. *You's* gwyne to p'oteck me, yo' own seff—you'll see; yes, en you's gwyneter be mighty k'yerful uv me, too, *dat* you is. Fetch de dram!"

He tasted it. "Put in some mo' sugar." He tasted again. "Put in mo'—dah, dat's enough." He had his feet in Harrison's chair. "Whah is yo' paper en pen? Git 'em. Git a cheer. Now, den, you write what I tells you. En don't you try to come no games, er I'll make you sorry."

George wrote from Jasper's dictation, doctoring the English as he went along:

> "This is my body-servant, Jasper. Let him pass at all hours of the day and night. I make myself responsible for his behavior.
> *George L. P. Harrison.*"

Jasper folded the pass and put it in his pocket.

"Now den," he said, "write agin." He furnished the words. The pen dropped from Harrison's paralysed fingers.

"Write *that?* Oh, my God," he cried, "I can't—I can't!"

"You can't?" said Jasper, dispassionately.

"How *can* I? Have some mercy! What are you going to do with it?"

"Gwyne to make you *safe*—dat's de idear. Hit'll go to dat witness —alonger dish-yer hankcher dat I's got. If anything happen' to me, *he'll* know what to do wid it. If noth'n don't happen to me, he on'y jist hide it en wait, en keep mum. Well, dey ain't noth'n gwyne to happen to me. You's gwyneter take pow'ful good k'yer o' dat, *I* bet you!"

"Yes, I will, with my hand on my heart I promise I will and—"

"*I* doan' want none o' yo' promises," said Jasper, scornfully, "I wouldn't give a dern for 'em."

"I'll do anything you say—anything, *everything* you tell me to—"

"Mp! Dey ain't no 'casion for you to tell me dat, I 'low to *make* you."

"—but spare me this—I can't, oh, I *can't* write it!"

Jasper got up and moved lazily away, remarking in a careless tone—

"Dat's all right—dat's all right."

"Wait!" cried Harrison in a panic; "oh, don't go! Where are you going?"

"Whah is I gwyne? You knows mighty well whah I's a gwyne, Jawge Hahson."

"Stop, for God's sake, don't go! I'll write it—I will, I will!"

"Well, den, *do* it. En I can tell you dis: if I starts *agin*—"

"There it is! it's written. Now be kind, be merciful; I've signed away my life, my good name, my liberty, all my spiritual riches—"

"En you's a slave!—dat's what you is; en I lay I'll learn you de paces! I been one, en I *know* 'em; slave to de meanest white man dat ever walked—en he 'uz *my father;* en I bought my freedom fum him en paid him for it, en he took 'vantage of me en stole it back; en he sold my mother down de river, po' young thing, en she a cryin' en a beggin' him to let her hug me jist once mo', en he wouldn't; en she say 'cruel, cruel,' en he hit her on de mouf, God damn his soul!—but it's my turn, now; dey's a long bill agin de low-down ornery white race, en you's a-gwyneter *settle* it."

He held up the fateful paper and contemplated it a long minute, his nostrils faintly dilating; and when at last he ceased from this contemplation he was visibly a changed man. The meek slouch of the slave was gone from him, and he stood straight, the exultation of victory burning in his eyes; and not even his rags and tatters could rob his great figure of a certain state and dignity born in this moment to it of the pride of mastership and command that was rising in his heart. He *looked* the master; but that which had gone from him was not lost, for his discarded droop and humble mien had passed to his white serf, and already they seemed not out of place there, but fit, and congruous, and pathetically proper and at home.

He resumed his chair and sat dreaming, musing, and unconsciously fondling and caressing the puissant bit of paper that had lifted him so high and brought that other man so low. Harrison was submerged in thinkings, too. Presently he stirred, and something like a moan escaped him. It roused Jasper, who said—

"Hahson?"

Harrison—wearily, sadly:

"Yes?"

"Yes?" (mimicking him). "Is dat yo' manners?"

Harrison looked up, inquiringly.

"I—I don't understand."

"You don't? Well, den, I'll learn you. Does servants say Yes, to dey marster, and stop dah?"

The word stuck in Harrison's throat; it refused to come.

"Hahson!"

By this help he got it out:

"Yes . . . sir?"

"Now den, don't you fo'git again. I lay if you do I'll make you sorry. You's a servant—you unnerstan'?—en I's gwyneter make you know yo' place en *keep* it. Say it agin!"

"Yes, sir."

"Dat's all right. Practice! You heah?"

"Yes, sir."

The mulatto's eyes spat fire for a while, filling Harrison's soul with nameless fears and discomforts, and he wished he could forecast this exacting master's requirements and save himself sorrow by meeting them before the orders came. He was alert, now, and pitifully anxious to do almost anything that could protect him from the pain and shame of uttered insults.

"Hahson?"

Harrison—with a timorous eagerness:

"Yes, sir?"

"Hain't I a talkin' to you?"

"Yes, sir."

A pause—with a penetrating look of inquiry and disapproval. Then—

"*Well* den!"

"I—I'm afraid I don't understand, sir. I—"

"Does servants *set down* when dey marsters is talkin' to 'em?"

Harrison rose and stood, with the red sign of humiliation stealing into his gray and tired face. Jasper contemplated his serf's misery with deep and healing satisfaction: studying it, weighing it, measuring it, so to speak, his mind traveling back over bitter years and comparing it with the thousand instances wherein he himself had been the unoffending victim and had looked like that, suffered like that. Then he began to speak.

"Hahson, hit do me good to look at you like dat. My father serve' me so, many's de time, en I not doin' any harm, no mo' dan what you is. En him a white man, en treat my po' little mother so, en rob' me like a thief—I hope he's a-roastin' in hell! Hahson?"

"Yes, sir."

"You's white, en I's gwyneter take it outer *you*. You en de res'. Ev'ry time I gits a chance. Now den, I done made my plans, en I's gwyneter tell you. I been run outer two States, or dey'd a sold me to de nigger-traders or lynch' me. Some folks hint aroun' dey gwyneter drive me outer *dis* one. Lemme see 'em try it!—it'll cost *you* heavy. Dey hints if I don't go, dey gwyneter put me on de block en sell me. Lemme see 'em try it!—it'll cost *you* heavy. Dey hints if I resis' dey gwyneter lynch me. Lemme see 'em try it! Let 'em try jist *one* un um—en straight off dish-yer paper goes to Miss Helen!"

"Oh, for God's sake! Oh—"

"Shet up! Git up off'n de flo'!—a-clawin' en a-wallerin' aroun' like a cat in a fit; you oughter be 'shame' er yoseff, en you a grown pusson. Dah, now, set on de flo' if you can't stan' up—dad burn you, you ain' got no mo' grit 'n a rabbit. I reckon you's a right down coward, Hahson. Fac' I knows you is; for *I* knows you—knows you by de back, same as de gamblers knows de k'yards. Stop dat whinin' en blubberin', Hahson; stop it! you *heah* me?"

Jasper sat looking down at him in measureless contempt. Presently he took up his discourse again.

"Hahson, made de way you is, *you* ain't in no danger—not de least."

"Oh, I am so thankful for—"

"Thank yo'seff! Dat's whah it b'longs. *You* ain't gwyneter git yo'seff in no danger—lawd, I knows *you*. Becaze you knows better'n to let anybody do *me* any harm, bless yo' soul you does! Now, den, you listen. Hahson, I can't stay wid you to-night, caze I got to go en give de white witness de hankcher en de paper en 'splain to him what to do case any harm come to me whilst I's in dis deestrick; but I's a-comin' back in de mawnin', en den I's gwyneter stay wid you all yo' life. When dey's anybody aroun', I's yo' servant, en pow'ful polite, en waits on you, en waits on de table, en wah's good clo'es, en runs arrants, en sleeps over yo' stable, en gits ten dollars a week; en when dey ain't nobody aroun' but me en you, you's *my* servant, en if I don't sweat you!—well, nemmine 'bout dat, *I'll* show you! Hahson?"

"Yes, sir."

"You ain' got no manners."

"I know, but I can soon—"

"Learn? You better bet you kin—if you knows what's good for you. Hahson?"

"Yes, sir."

"When I's a waitin' on de quality, you keep yo' eye on me, en notice de way I does, en de way I 'spress myseff, en de way I bows, en all dat; den you study it by yo'seff, en practice. You ain't fitten for shucks de way you is, becase you ain't had no breedin', but I's gwyneter make you wuth two dollars a week befo' I's done wid you. Does you unnerstan' de whole plan, now?"

"Yes, sir."

"Gimme de fust week. Ten dollars. Don't you fo'git 'bout de clo'es, ner 'bout de stable—you heah? Git up en open de do' for me."

When he was gone Harrison put his face in his hands and sobbed, moaning and muttering, and saying, "Oh, my God, I cannot bear it, the burden is too heavy; *why* was I born with a man's form and a rabbit's heart? why haven't I the courage to kill myself? who but I would keep a life that is become an agony?"

CHAPTER [XXI]

A T DAWN in the morning Jasper arrived at Harrison's kitchen with a banjo, a jewsharp, a mouth-harp, and not much other baggage. He uncovered the fire, built it up, brought in a load of wood, fetched a bucket of water from the well, filled the kettle, hung it on the hook, found the breakfast coffee in the mill, and was beginning to grind it when old Martha entered from her room to see who was making the noise. She threw up her hands in astonishment, and said—

"Well, fo' de lan' sake if it ain't you! What brung *you* heah, Jasper?"

"What brung me? Bless yo' soul, honey, I's de new servant."

"No!—you don't say!"

"True for a fac', my darlin'. Marse Hahson done hire me las' night."

"Well—well—well—*is* dat so? Now ain't you in luck, sho' nuff?"

"Deed I is, en so is you. Caze you ain' got no sweetheart, en I's gwyneter cote you—dat I is, honey. You's de gal for me!"

"Shet up yo' impudence, er I'll take en bat you over de head, you long-laigged yaller-jacket! I's ole enough to be yo' mother."

Then they broke out and laughed a rollicking laugh in cordial admiration of their powers of repartee, and Jasper plunged at Martha saying he was just "honing" for a kiss, and a three-minute struggling and scuffling and laughing followed, which ended in Jasper's getting the kiss and a sounding cuff; then Martha wiped her eyes on her apron and said—

"*Allays* a humbuggin' en a carryin' on, I never see sich a nigger; hain't you ever serious *no* time?"

"What I gwyneter be serious 'bout? I ain't only thutty-five; what *I* got to be serious 'bout?"

"Nemmine, nemmine, Jasper, you wait ontel you's fifty, de way I is—"

"Den I'll be serious de way *you* is, you ole cat!"

"Jasper, what you needs is some trouble; I lay dat'll take de friskies outen you when it come—you'll see."

"G'long wid you! Trouble! didn't dat constable take de hide off'n me?"

Martha set her hands on her hips and gave him a look that was full of pity of his ignorance.

"Took de hide off'n you! What's dat! 'Tain't nothin'. Who gwyneter mind a little thing like dat? You doan' know nothin' 'bout real trouble; you wait ontel you has some *real* trouble, den you'll know!"

"Well, den, what you *call* real trouble?"

"A heart dat's broke! dat's what's real trouble. If you'd a had a

father to lose, er a mother to lose. . . . Look at marse George.
Dah's trouble! Jasper, mo'n half de time he jist can't res', on
accounts er ole marster a-dyin."

It seemed to impress Jasper, and he said—

"Well, I reckon it is turrible hard. But Martha, he was sich a *ole*
man. I's pow'ful sorry for marse Hahson, but if he ain't got no
troubles but dat—"

"Can't you see, yo'seff, dat it's enough? He couldn't stan' no mo'
if he *had* 'em, you yaller fool!"

"Well, *I* ain't sayin' he could, I 'uz on'y jist sayin' he—"

"Shet up, you doan' know nothin' what you talkin' 'bout. You
wait tell you's had trouble; up to den you can't talk nothin' 'bout it
but foolishness."

"Martha, how kin you say dat? Hain't I *seen* people dat's had it?
Look at Bridget; look at de Squiah—my, dat's trouble, sho-nuff
trouble. You see, if marse Hahson had troubles like *dem*—"

It went to Martha's compassionate old heart, and she said—

"Oh, yes, Gawd knows he ain't had no troubles like *dem* po'
creturs has. 'Twould kill marse George, he got sich a good heart en
so sof'. Why Jasper, jist *hearin'* 'bout what de Squiah done 'most
killed him. Laws, it make me feel turrible down, talkin' like dis.
Wake up de banjo."

"Camptown Races?"

"Dat's it. Go it!"

Pul-lunky plunk-plunk plunk-plunk. Jasper poured out the gay
song in great style, and when the chorus came round, Martha, all
enthusiasm, added the rich voice that is the birthright of her
race.

> "I's boun' to run all night,
>   I's boun' to run all day,
> I bet my money on de bobtail nag,
>   If somebody bet on de bay."

Other songs followed, and rattling dance-tunes, and light-
hearted laughter; and Harrison recognized the voices, and one of
them carried dread and misery to his heart. An hour passed, and

Martha said she must carry up the shaving-water now, and set the table; but Jasper said—

"What you talkin' 'bout? What is I for?"

"Why, bless you, Jasper, I clean fo'got you's hired. Ain't dat good! 'Tain't gwyneter be lonesome en mo'nful in dis kitchen no mo', now. I's pow'ful glad, Jasper. Heah—take de hot water. You got a good marster, now—jist as kind. He'll cuff you roun' a little when he's cross, but don't you mind, 'tain't much, en he don't mean nothin' by it."

Jasper answered bravely—

"I doan' k'yer noth'n for cuffin', I kin stan' all he'll gimme."

He departed with the water. Martha liked that reply of his; it showed the right spirit, the spirit of a slave, and made her doubt if free niggers were quite as black as they had been commonly painted—for certainly here was one that was rational, and worthily constructed. She felt sure that Jasper's sunny spirit would have a good influence upon the master, and that the importing it into the shadowed homestead would turn out to have been a fortunate idea on the master's part. She recognized, too, that there was profit for herself in the arrangement—her labor-burdens eased, and lively company at hand in place of loneliness. Jasper was gone ten minutes.

"What kep' you so long?" she asked, when he returned.

Jasper's white teeth radiated a gleaming smile, and he answered—

"Well, he's feelin' prime, smawnin', en hatter jist let go en talk, he couldn't he'p it, he feelin' so gay."

"Dah, now!" exclaimed Martha, "hit's jist as I's a-sayin' no longer ago 'n dis minute. Las' night he was a feelin' jesso, en I turn' in en cher'd him up good, en I says to myseff, hit ain't takin' all *dis* time to tote up dat shavin' water, I lay Jasper's a cherin' him up some mo'—warn't I right, hey, warn't I?"

"Dat you wuz, sho's you bawn; he's jist gay, now, *I* tell you!"

This was not true. However, Martha, innocently taking it at par, laughed out her happy thankfulness over it, and said—

"I jist know'd how 'twould be. Jasper, I do b'lieve befo' you's done wid marse George he's gwyneter be a diff'nt man to what he was."

He responded, with modest confidence—

"*I* bet you!"

She rewarded him with a buttered biscuit hot from the reflector. His eye chanced to fall upon the breakfast dishes, and he felt a sense of disappointment. He said—

"Martha, is *dat* all?"

She chuckled, and answered—

"Bless yo' soul, honey, hit shows you doan' know what sorrer is. *He* doan' eat nothin'. My, if a body could *git* him to!"

Jasper—argumentatively, persuasively—and with a watering mouth:

"Martha, hit's diff'nt, smawnin', you know. He's a feelin' like a bird. Hain't dat gwyneter raise his appertite, don't you reckon?"

"Well, well, well, what *is* de matter of me! gracious I never thought. 'Course it will! Jasper, how much you reckon you kin 'suade him to eat?" and she began to load up her pans and ovens again, in great excitement and joy, Jasper helping, without invitation.

"Pile 'em in, pile 'em in," he said, with fervor, "doan' you 'feered, Martha, you ain' gwyneter see 'em no mo'."

"We-ll, if dat ain't de bes' news I ever—Lan', Jasper, why dis is enough for a hoss!"

"His very words! Martha, he *said* he could eat a hoss!"

"Dem's blessed words, Jasper, jist blessed—*I* doan' wanter heah no mo' blesseder ones. Laws, if he kin on'y git away wid dis stack it'll be de makin' of him."

Jasper—with placid conviction:

"Look yo' las' on it, honey—look yo' las'."

Some little time afterward Jasper was sitting solitary in the dining room—at the head of Harrison's table. The snowy table-cloth was almost hidden under its prodigal freightage of hot and appetising good things; the coffee pot was steaming, and a generous hickory fire was sending a sheet of flame up the chimney. Jasper was listening—listening with evil satisfaction to a descending step on the stair, a slow and lifeless step, a weary and halting step. And now Harrison appeared. Wan, old, gaunt, broken, humble—he seemed rather a spectre than a man. Jasper's mind slipped back over long years, and he saw the duplicate of this apparition: himself. It was when he went to his father to ask for a new bill of sale in place of the one which had burned up with his cabin, and his father mocked him, laughed in his face and said, "Out of my presence, you bastard, and keep mum, or I'll sell you South, as I did your sniveling mother!"

The mulatto sat studying the meek apparition, and musing, with a hardening heart. This was a Harrison, *that* was a Harrison—the hated blood was in his own veins! The thought stung him, galled him. He spoke up sharply—

"Hahson!"

Harrison—timidly:

"Yes, sir."

"You's makin' a po' start. You's kep' me a waitin'. I ain' gwyneter have it!"

"I—"

"Shet up, when I's a talkin'. Got no mo' manners 'n a animal. You wait till somebody asts you to mix in." He paused, to see if Harrison's judgment would fail him again, but it didn't. "Now den, git to work. En doan' you wait for me to give you de orders; you watch en 'scover what I wants befo' I tells you."

Harrison poured the coffee, then furnished beefsteak, spare-ribs, home-made sausages, corn-pone, biscuits, winter-stored vegetables —one after the other, with encores, and in generous quantity—and kept a sharp lookout, as commanded, saying nothing, and moving constantly and with his best briskness, for this devourer was more than a mere man, he was a mill. When about half of the food had been devoured there was a light knock on the door, and by force of habit Harrison called out before he had had time to think—

"Come in!"

Jasper scowled darkly upon him and said—

"Has anybody ast you to make yo'seff so dam brash?"

"Oh, I beg pardon, sir."

"De do's bolted. I done it." He got up with deliberation and said, "Hit's Martha. She's comin' in wid de batter-cakes." He had risen from his chair. He pointed to it, and added: "Set down here. I's servant, now—you is marster; you *un'stan'?* Doan' you fo'git yo'seff, less'n you wanter be sorry. Look cherful! you heah?"

Harrison took the seat, and Jasper went to the door. Martha, entering, said, reprovingly—

"What you fasten de do' for?"

Jasper chuckled, in what seemed to be a sort of embarrassed but pleasant confusion, and explained.

"Nev' you mine 'bout de do', honey: marse Hahson feelin' prime, smawnin', en tellin' 'bout de times when he's young; en he say shet de do', 'tain't suitable for ladies to heah. Bless you, he's feelin' dat gay—look at him laugh!"

Harrison, obeying a threatening side look, delivered himself of a ghastly travesty of a laugh which sent a shudder through Martha, and would have made her drop her platter of cakes but that it was already reaching the refuge of Jasper's hands. Martha soliloquised audibly, and unconsciously—

"De Lawd God!" and stood staring, rather vacantly yet admiringly, while Jasper, all smiling servility, most politely helped the master to one cake and purposely dropped another in his lap, at the same time whispering, "Raise hell 'bout it! you *heah?*"

"Curse your lumbering awkwardness, *now* look what you've done!" responded the obedient master.

Jasper mimicked the proper consternation while he nervously and clumsily repaired the mishap, meanwhile whispering " 'Buse me, 'buse me, Hahson—keep it up!" and Harrison, obeying, poured out severities the best he could, and trembled to his marrow in apprehension of what he might have to pay for them. Martha chimed in—

"Give it to him good, marse George, hit boun' to do you good, stirrin' yo'seff up like dat; tain't gwyneter do *him* no harm, en he 'zerve it, anyway."

Privately she was puzzled at Harrison's haggard appearance, and could not understand why he should look like that, now when he was so gay—so unnaturally gay that he was even obliged to break out in tales not proper for ladies to hear, to get relief, an extravagance of high spirits which he surely had never risen to before. She was minded to speak of this curious thing, and inquire if the gayety was solid and real; but she glanced at the table and held her peace. She remarked to herself:

"I reckon he's all right. He's et enough to bust a tavern."

She passed out, and master and servant changed places again.

"Pass 'em, pass 'em along!" cried Jasper, indicating the tower of hot batter-cakes, "en de m'lasses; I's pow'ful hongry, yit; I ain't had no sich breakfus' as dis sence de cows come home."

But there was a brisk stamping of feet at the front door, now, and Jasper jumped from his seat and thrust Harrison into it just in time. Dug Hapgood burst in with an eager shout—

"Say, George, there's a stranger at the tavern. Get it? *stranger,* I said. Been there a couple of days. How he managed it without me finding it out, blamed if *I* know." He was busy shedding his wraps, and quite unaware that Jasper was obsequiously receiving them and hanging them up. But he noticed the mulatto now, and shouted in great surprise, "Why, what in the nation are *you* doing here?" Jasper grinned in a flattered and thankful way and answered,

"Marse Hahson done hire me, Misto Dug."

"Well, by gracious if that ain't just like you, George Harrison! There ain't anybody too low down for you to come up to the rack and give him a lift when he's in trouble, even a free nigger! I just honor you, George Harrison, I do, that's the fact." He went forward blinking the sympathetic water out of his eyes, and wrung Harrison's hand cordially. "George derned if I don't think you are just a brevet angel, that's what *I* think—just a noble generous tadpole-angel, as you may say, and likely to sprout legs any time and feather-out and jine the choir. Shake again!" He turned to Jasper: "Looky here, yaller-belly, do you know you've had a mighty close shave? You bet you! Why, George, it was all put up yesterday to run him out of the State to-night—sho! what am I talkin' about; you found it out and that's why he's here. Now how in the nation *did* you, and you shut up in the house all the time?"

Jasper cut in, and saved Harrison the necessity of answering:

"I foun' it out myseff, Misto Dug, en come en tole him, en he up 'n say 'You's my nigger, now—jist let 'em tetch you!' he says."

"Well, George, I'll say it again, you're the bravest devil that ever was, when you want to be. You're the only man in the whole deestrict that could a saved this cuss, and the only one that's good-hearted enough. Jasper!"

"Yes, seh."

"Are you grateful?"

" 'Deed I is, Misto Dug."

"All right, then; some niggers ain't." His eye fell on the table, and his mouth watered. "That looks good. Pity to let *that* go to waste. George, I'll see what I can do, if you don't mind," and he sat down and began an assault on the remaining half of the breakfast that meant victory and annihilation, Jasper serving him with zeal and exterior eagerness accompanied by a running fire of curses inside his breast. "Say, George, he's a whole team and a yeller dog under the wagon, when it comes to telling fortunes. Bowles says he lays over Confucius, oh, to hell and gone! Says he told *him* things in his life he hadn't thought of for so long he'd about forgotten them. And he told my fortune, too, and it's plumb wonderful the way he does it. It's a new way: just looks in your hand, and there it's all wrote out and he can read it like print—everything you've ever done or going to do. Say, George, he told Frances Osgood's fortune, and in one place he looked awful sorrowful, and says 'You've had a dreadful calamity in your life, poor lady,' and put her hand away and didn't want to go on; but she made him, and then he started in and told her all about the fire where she lost her twin and you lost your house and family, just as straight as if he'd been there and seen the whole thing himself—ain't it wonderful!" A potatoe, impaled on a fork, was approaching his mouth, which was falling open in welcome and anticipation. It stopped where it was, and the mouth began to close. These were signs that a vast idea had been born to Dug. He laid the potatoe down and said impressively—

"George!"

"Well?"

"He's the very man!"

"How the very man?" said Harrison, wearily.

"To root out the bottom facts of Jake Bleeker's murder."

It made Harrison gasp, it hit him with such power and suddenness.

"Bottom facts?" he said, as indifferently as he could, "what bottom facts?"

"Well, I'll tell you. You see, he could get right down into the details. There *ain't* any details, up to now. This cuss could lay it all just as bare as your hand. By gracious, it's a grand idea!" He sprang from the devastated table and began to throw on his things. Harrison shouted—

"Stop! what are you going to do?"

"Going to have him come here tomorrow afternoon and—"

"Oh, stop, *stop*, I tell you!"

But Dug was gone. Harrison plunged toward the door, but Jasper stepped in his way and said—

"Stay whah you is. Hain't you ever gwyneter git any sense? S'pose you stop dat deef jackass—how you gwyneter 'splain it? Does you want to raise a lot er s'picions? Let de man come. I's gwyneter be in dat closet dah, en notice what he say. He ain't gwyneter jail you en spile yo' good name en yo' power, not if *I* knows it—I can't 'ford it. If he gits down to de bottom facks, I's gwyneter buy his mouf shet, en you's gwyneter pay de bill. Cler up de table—hustle! Stack up de dishes; I's gwyneter tote 'em to de kitchen en git some mo' grub, dad burn dat greedy gut!"

Dug spread the news of Jasper's redemption, and it made a sensation in the village, which had had nothing to buzz about and get excited over for some little time. It was diligently discussed. Harrison's judgment was discounted, and his conduct in some degree censured; but his courage was frankly admired and extolled, and there was none but had a fervent word of praise for the nobility of his nature and the never-failing goodness of his heart. His act would have heavily damaged any other citizen, but it raised Harrison a shade in the public reverence and affection, and was recognized as a natural and proper thing for him to do. When some persons did things, the public customarily hunted for a doubtful motive, and generally believed it had found it; in Harrison's case it always premised a good motive, and of course it always found it.

What one expects to find and wants to find is easy to find, as a rule. Reputation is a formidable force in this world.

People flocked to Harrison's house all day; partly to recognize his pluck and praise it, and partly out of curiosity to see Jasper, gardener, perform as a house servant. Their praises were vinegar to Harrison's wounds, and the pain was the greater for that Jasper was there to see and enjoy the sufferings the others did not suspect and could not see. Everybody was surprised and a little disappointed to find that Jasper did not seem very much out of place in his new office, and many were candid enough to say so, and fling him a compliment as well. Tom and Helen were of these. Tom said, heartily—

"You are performing really well, Jasper, and I mean what I say. All you've got to do is to behave yourself, and show yourself worthy of what my father has done for you, and you'll have in him a protector that is not afraid to stand by you against the whole town."

Jasper was so moved, and so grateful for these gracious words that Tom was quite touched, and gave him a dime, which he gave to Harrison that night, at the same time mimicking the son's manner and paraphrasing his speech:

"You's p'fawmin' real good, Hahson, en I means what I says. All you got to do is to behave, en show yo'seff wuthy of what I's went en done for you, en I's gwyneter be a p'tector dat'll—yah-yah-yah! I couldn't scasely keep fum laughin' to heah dat goslin' talk 'bout you p'tectin' *me!*"

Frances Osgood was there in the afternoon, and shook George by the hand, and said—

"George, you are so different from other people! Happiness, good fortune and an applauding conscience make some persons hard or indifferent, but they only furnish you new impulses toward—"

"No, Frances, no, you—"

"There, I will spare you, but I had to say it, because I feel it. If Alison and the children could come back now from the grave, how proud they would be of you, and what love and worship they—"

Jasper was hearing all this and storing it up for sarcastic use. He was always hovering in Harrison's neighborhood when it was handy to do it; partly to listen, but mainly because his listening sharpened his slave's miseries.

Ann Bailey cordially endorsed Frances Osgood's remarks, and so did Sol and his brother the minister; the widow Wilkinson and Axtell the consumptive joined the group and added their praises, and General Landry and Asphyxia Perry did likewise while Tom and Helen listened in charmed contentment and pride, all unaware that these compliments which were heaven to them were hell to Harrison; unaware, too, that he would have to hear them again, toward midnight, with Jasper to serve them up, in a new edition revised and improved.

Three Thousand Years
Among the Microbes

"Three Thousand Years Among the Microbes" was written at Dublin, New Hampshire, between 20 May and 23 June 1905. During that time Mark Twain worked rapidly and exuberantly. On 11 June he wrote to his daughter Clara that he had reached page 240 of the manuscript and exulted, "It beats the record (oh, all to smash!)"[1] Five days later he reported to F. A. Duneka of Harper & Brothers, "I am deep in a new book which I enjoy more than I have enjoyed any other for twenty years and I hope it will take me the entire summer to write it."[2] But by 24 June he had apparently emptied the tank of his inspiration. He informed his friend Joseph H. Twichell, "I began a new book here in this enchanting solitude 35 days ago. I have done 33 full days' work on it. To-day I have not worked. There was another day in this present month wherein I did no work—you will know that date without my telling you."[3] The date was that of his wife's death, which had come on 5 June of the preceding year. This story, like other selections in this volume, was written with pleasure but written nevertheless under the shadow of disaster.

There is no evidence that Mark Twain took up work upon the manuscript again after the 24th; probably he had already written all of it that now exists. According to A. B. Paine, "He tired of it before it reached completion. . . . Its chief mission was to divert him mentally

[1] Mark Twain to Clara Clemens, 11 June 1905; copy in MTP.
[2] Mark Twain to Frederick A. Duneka, 16 June 1905; copy in MTP.
[3] Mark Twain to Joseph H. Twichell, St. John's Day [24 June] 1905; copy in MTP.

that summer during those days and nights when he would otherwise have been alone and brooding upon his loneliness." [4] Paine called the work "a fantastic tale" and "a sort of scientific revel"; he also commented, "It was a satire, of course—Gulliver's Lilliput outdone—a sort of scientific, socialistic, mathematical jamboree." [5] The narrator, a cholera germ who in a previous existence has been a human being, comes to the world of the microbes to escape the tainted atmosphere of his former country, a land of get-rich-quick opportunism. But with irony Mark Twain then shows "Huck," as the narrator comes to be called, elaborating a foolish dream of an imaginary fortune in gold and persuading even himself that it is a reality. "Huck" illustrates the author's gospel of selfishness as he schemes to keep all of the dream gold for himself rather than share it with his partners. Like other one-horse individuals, he is ready to lie and cheat and steal when tempted beyond his limit. The story breaks off after he has revealed his own corruption. Were it not for Mark Twain's statement in 1906 that he had left the manuscript half-finished, one might even say that at this point the narrative ends, for there is a sense of finality in "Huck's" moral disintegration. Although Mark Twain made many notes for the story, on sheets of small note-pad paper, they do not reveal any further intention for the plot; rather, they suggest that in any continuation he would have used this book as a vehicle for further satire on a variety of topics, including stock market manipulations, Tammany Hall, the Russo-Japanese War, and imperialism. Two brief fragments satirize, respectively, pension frauds and "Kitchen Science." The latter fragment, which shows "Huck" cynically adopting a religion that will not, he believes, require of him any charities or sacrifices, logically follows the "ending" mentioned above. However, it was not included in a typescript that was prepared under Mark Twain's direction, and he probably did not intend to use it. The typescript was made by Jean Clemens, who followed the holograph but occasionally changed or omitted words or phrases. Since there is no evidence that these alterations were intended by Mark Twain, the holograph has in such cases been credited with primary authority. The typescript has, however, been considered reliable for its indication of the sections of the manuscript that Mark Twain meant to include and of his intended ordering of them, for in these

---

[4] *MTB*, III, 1238–1239.
[5] *MTB*, III, 1238.

matters his daughter followed his directions, which appear as marginalia in the holograph.

The chapters have been numbered as he designated them; there are two runs of XI–XIV. However, the narration is continuous throughout the manuscript, and there seems to be no warrant for omitting or changing the order of either of the two sequences. His two prefaces have also been presented as he wrote them.

3,000 Years Among the Microbes

BY A MICROBE

With Notes Added by the Same Hand
7,000 Years Later

Translated from the Original Microbic
By
MARK TWAIN

1905.

PREFACE.

ALTHOUGH THIS WORK is a History, I believe it to be true. There is internal evidence in every page of it that its Author was conscientiously trying to state bare facts, unembellished by fancy. While this insures irksome reading, it also insures useful reading; and I feel satisfied that this will be regarded as full compensation by an intelligent public which has long been suffering from a surfeit of pure History unrefreshed by fact. Among the thousands of statements put forth in this Work there are but two that have a doubtful look, and I think these divergences—if they are divergences—are forgivable for the reason that there are indications that the Author made them with regret and was afterward pursued by remorse for having made them at all. But for this pair of slight and indeed inconsequential blemishes, there had been no occasion for apologies from me.

The Translator.

PREFACE.

I HAVE TRANSLATED the author's style and construction, as well as his matter. I began by reforming these, but gave it up. It amounted to putting evening dress on a stevedore and making him stand up in the college and lecture. He was trim, but he was stiff; he delivered strict English, polished English, but it seemed strained and artificial, coming from such a source, and was not pleasant, not satisfactory. Elegant, but cold and unsympathetic. In fact, corpsy. It seemed best to put him back into his shirt-sleeves and overalls, and let him flounder around after the fashion that he was used to.

His style is loose and wandering and garrulous and self-contented beyond anything I have ever encountered before, and his grammar breaks the heart. But there is no remedy: let it go.

The Translator.

His title-page is incorrect.

xxxxx. But really no one was to blame, it was an accident.

I.

xxxx.

THE MAGICIAN's experiment miscarried, because of the impossibility of getting pure and honest drugs in those days, and the result was that he transformed me into a cholera-germ when he was trying to turn me into a bird.[6]

---

[6] Mark Twain at first wrote that the change had been effected by Mary Baker Eddy, who, annoyed by "a certain doubtful statement" of the narrator, had "applied her supernatural powers to the turning of [him] into a cholera germ." Later he deleted this passage and inserted what appears above.

* NOTE, *7,000 years later*. I had been a microbe 3,000 years (microbe-years) when I resolved to do this Narrative. At first I was minded to save time and labor by delivering it into the mechanical thought-recorder, but I gave up that idea because I might want to deal in some privacies—in fact I should *have* to do it—and a body might as well publish a secret and be done with it as put it into a machine which is ready to reveal its privacies to any thief that will turn the crank, let the thief's language and nationality be what they may. So I decided to write my book in my own tongue. Not many sooflaskies would be able to read it if they got hold of it; besides, I was beginning to forget my English, and this labor would presently bring it back to me as good as new, no doubt. B.*b*.B.

At first I was not pleased. But this feeling did not last. I was soon interested in my surroundings, and eager to study them and enjoy them. I was peculiarly well equipped for these pleasures, for certain reasons: to wit, I had become instantly naturalized, instantly endowed with a cholera germ's instincts, perceptions, opinions, ideals, ambitions, vanities, prides, affections and emotions; that is to say, I was become a real cholera germ, not an imitation one; I was become intensely, passionately, cholera-germanic; indeed, I out-natived the natives themselves, and felt and spoke and acted like those girls of ours who marry nobilities and lose their democracy the first week and their American accent the next; I loved all the germ-world—the Bacilli, the Bacteria, the Microbes, etc.,—and took them to my heart with all the zeal they would allow; my patriotism was hotter than their own, more aggressive, more uncompromising; I was the germiest of the germy. It will be perceived, now, that I could observe the germs from their own point of view. At the same time, I was able to observe them from a human being's point of view, and naturally this invested them with an added interest for me. Another thing: my human measurements of time and my human span of life remained to me, right alongside of my full appreciation of the germ-measurements of time and the germ span of life. That is to say, when I was thinking as a human, 10 minutes meant 10 minutes, but when I was thinking as a microbe, it meant a year; when I was thinking as a human, an hour meant an hour, but when I was thinking as a mircrobe it meant 6 years; when I was thinking as a human, a day meant a day, but when I was thinking as a microbe it meant 144 years; when I was thinking as a human, a week meant a week, but when I was thinking as a microbe it

meant 1,008 years; when I was thinking as a human, a year meant
a year, but when I was thinking as a microbe it meant 52,416
years. When I was using microbe-time, I could start at the cradle
with a tender young thing and grow old with her: follow her
fortunes second by second, minute by minute, hour after hour; see
her bud into sweet maidenhood, see her marry an idolized husband,
see her develop into the matron's noble estate, see her lovingly watch
over her millions of babes, see her rear them in honesty and honor,
see her mourn the loss of millions of them by early death, see her
rejoice over the happy nuptials of more fortunate millions of them,
see old age and wrinkles and decrepitude descend gradually upon
her, and finally see her released from the griefs and the burden of
life and laid to rest in the hallowed peace of the grave, with my
benediction and my tears for farewell—all this in 150 years by
microbe-count, about 24 hours by human time.

II.

THE ERRING magician introduced me into the blood of a
hoary and mouldering old bald-headed tramp. His name is Blitzowski—if that isn't an alias—and he was shipped to America by
Hungary because Hungary was tired of him. He tramps in the
summer and sleeps in the fields; in the winter he passes the hat in
cities, and sleeps in the jails when the gutter is too cold; he was
sober once, but does not remember when it was; he never shaves,
never washes, never combs his tangled fringe of hair; he is
wonderfully ragged, incredibly dirty; he is malicious, malignant,
vengeful, treacherous, he was born a thief, and will die one; he is
unspeakably profane, his body is a sewer, a reek of decay, a charnel
house, and contains swarming nations of all the different kinds of
germ-vermin that have been invented for the contentment of man.
He is their world, their globe, lord of their universe, its jewel, its
marvel, its miracle, its masterpiece. They are as proud of their
world as is any earthling of his. When the soul of the cholera-germ

possesses me I am proud of him: I shout for him, I would die for him; but when the man-nature invades me I hold my nose. At such times it is impossible for me to respect this pulpy old sepulchre.

I have been a microbe about 3 weeks, now. By microbe-time it is 3 thousand years. What ages and ages of joy, prosperity, poverty, hope, despair, triumph, defeat, pain, grief, misery, I have seen, felt, experienced in this lagging and lingering slow drift of centuries! What billions of friends I have made, and loved, and clung to, only to see them pass from this fleeting life to return no more! What black days I have seen—but also what bright ones!

III

WHEN I BECAME a microbe, the transformation was so complete that I felt at home at once. This is not surprising, for men and germs are not widely different from each other. Of germs there are many nationalities, and there are many languages, just as it is with mankind. The germs think the man they are occupying is the only world there is. To them it is a vast and wonderful world, and they are as proud of it as if they had made it themselves. It seems a pity that this poor forlorn old tramp will never know that, for compliments are scarce with him.

IV

OUR WORLD (the tramp) is as large and grand and awe-compelling to us microscopic creatures as is man's world to man. Our tramp is mountainous, there are vast oceans in him, and lakes that are sea-like for size, there are many rivers (veins and arteries) which are fifteen miles across, and of a length so stupendous as to make the Mississippi and the Amazon trifling little Rhode Island brooks by comparison. As for our minor rivers, they are multitudinous, and the dutiable commerce of disease which they carry is rich beyond the dreams of the American custom-house.

Well, and why shouldn't our tramp seem imposing and majestic to us little creatures? Think what a wee little speck a man would be if you stood the American Continent up on end in front of him. Standing there with his back to the waves,—standing there on the arching roof of the continent's big toe, (Cape Horn), he would naturally lift his eyes skyward; and how far up that dimming huge frontage would his vision carry? Half way to the knees? No. Not a tenth of the distance! Evanishment would quickly supervene, the colossus would be swallowed up and lost in the sky! If you should stand one of us microscopic specks upon the roof of our tramp's big toe and say "look up"—well, you'd have the same result over again.

There are upwards of a thousand republics in our planet, and as many as thirty thousand monarchies. Several of these monarchies have a venerable history behind them. They do not date back to the actual moment of Blitzowski's birth, for a human child is born pure of disease-germs, and remains pure of them for a matter of three or four hours—say eighteen or twenty years, microbe-time—but they do date back to the earliest invasions, and have sturdily maintained and preserved their regal authority in full force through all vicissitudes from that remote period until now, a stretch approximating four and a half million years. In one case *the same dynasty* holds the throne to-day that established it twenty-five hundred thousand years ago. This is the Pus family,—Pus being the family name, just as Romanoff is the family name of the Czars; the official title is, His August Majesty Henry, D.G. Staphylococcus Pyogenes Aureus * CMX—that is to say, he is the One Hundred and

---

* Latin. "D.G.," (Deus gratias,) means *by the grace of God.* The long word means *pus-tank.* The next word—when used in a scientific sense—means *principal;* politically it means *imperial;* in the slang of the common people it means *brick,* and is a term of admiration. Aureus means *gold.* Hence the title, when occurring in a State paper, could be translated *Henry by the grace of God Imperial Pus-Tank,* while in the endearing speech of the common people it would be shortened to *Henry the Gold Brick.*

Ten Thousandth monarch of the Pus lineage that has occupied that throne. They have all used the one name, HENRY. In this they have been imitated by the Princes of Reuss, of Germany: all Princes of Reuss are named Henry. Reuss is a fine old royal house, and its blood can be traced back, right alongside the Guelf and the Hohenzollern to the dim antiquity of ten centuries ago.

The English monarchy—the *real* English monarchy—has been in existence about 840 years; its 36 reigns have averaged about 23 years each. Pretty nearly the same average obtains here. At least it is so with the great monarchy of which I have been speaking—the greatest, in population, and the most ambitious, in all Blitzowski. In my 3,000 years here I have walked, uncovered and sincerely sorrowing, at the end of the funeral pageants of 121 sovereigns of this venerable line, and have been permitted to assist in the rejoicings which followed the coronations of their successors. It is a stern and noble race, and by diplomacy and arms has pushed its frontiers far. Wherever it has deprived a conquered nation of its liberties and its religion it has replaced these with something better. It is justly claimed for this great House that it has carried the blessings of civilization further than has any other imperial power. In honor of this good work many of our microbe nations have come to speak of pus and civilization as being substantially the same thing.*

---

* NOTE: *5,000 [Years] Later.* The microbe's name for himself is not Microbe, it is *Sooflasky.* It would bankrupt the Unabridged to furnish definitions enough to damage *all* its meanings and make you afraid of the word forever after. Oh, that worthless, worthless book, that timid book, that shifty book, that uncertain book, that time-serving book, that exasperating book, that unspeakable book, the Unlimited Dictionary! that book with but one object in life: to get in more words and shadings of the words than its competitors. With the result that nearly every time it gets done shading a good old useful word it means everything in general and nothing in particular. When, in my human life, we first borrowed the word *unique*, for instance, it was strong and direct, it meant *sole, only,* the *one and only* "joker"—not another one in the pack; the *one and only* existent example of whatever thing the user of the word was referring to: then the Dictionary took hold of it, and hitched to it every careless user's definition of it that it could hunt out—and look at that whilom virgin now! I am not as particular as I might be, perhaps, but I should not like to be caught going around in public with that trollop.

Now as to that word Sooflasky. Straitly translated, it means in Blitzowski what the word Man—as chief creature in the scheme of Creation—means in the human World: that is to say, The Pet, The Chosen One, The Wonderful One, The Grand Razzledazzle, The Whole Thing, The Lord of Creation, The Drum Major, The Head of the Procession. The word Sooflasky means all that, includes all those shades. To construct an English equivalent that would hold them all and not leak was exceedingly difficult, for me, but I believe

Bullyboywithaglasseye came nearest. I often applied it to my fellow-microbes, from the very first, and they liked it. Partly because it was long and fine-sounding and foreign, and partly because of the modified translation I furnished along with it. I told them it was the form employed by our best Major Molar poets, and meant "the Deity's Delight." On these terms I worked it into universal use among the grateful clergy, the poets, the great orators, and the rest of our best people. Quaintly and prettily accented, and delivered lingeringly and lovingly and impressively in a sermon, or with fire and thunder and gush in a great oration, it is certainly one of the nobbiest things I know of. But the first time I heard it wafted from the pulpit it took me unprepared, and it was all I could do to keep from being over-affected by it.

I often used the term Microbe, applying it freely to myself and to the others; and this without offence. If I had explained its real meaning—its mean little patronizing microscopic meaning—there would have been trouble, but I did not do that. I saved myself early. I said it was Major Molar for "the Creature With The Moral Sense," and was the cold scientific term employed to technically describe the Lord Paramount of Animated Nature. There are times when guff is better than fact, and you get more for the price.

"*The* Creature With The Moral Sense." The *the* got them—the *the* captured them—the *the* took them into camp. You know, I thought it would. To be *a* "the" is something, to Man and Microbe; but to be *the* "the"—oh, well, that is a bait which they can't resist at all. I was always a daring person, I never could help it, and I played that 'ansome title on them for a compliment. They did the natural thing, the thing which the honestest of us does when he is on uncertain ground: they looked wise and unsurprised, and let on to know all about it. Without doubt they thought I had brought that jewel from some deep well of erudition in the Major Molar. If they thought that, one thing was sure: they wouldn't expose their ignorance by *asking* me. No, they would keep still; they wouldn't even risk asking if it was a custom there to keep such things in wells.

My instinct was right; that is to say, my knowledge was right—my knowledge of the furtive and cautious ways of Man and Microbe: they didn't ask any questions. Not public ones, at any rate. One inquirer did approach me, but he came privately. He wanted to talk frankly and freely, he said, but hoped I would let the conversation be and remain confidential. He said—

"I will be candid, for I am inviting candor. You supposed, of course, that your '*the* Creature With The Moral Sense' was not new to us, but it was; our calm manner of receiving it was a deception; we had never heard of it before. It has gone into currency; it is accepted, and purred over, and I think it is safe to say that everybody is vain of it, the learned and the ignorant alike. So—"

"Dear sir," I said, with some complacency, interrupting, "I was not altogether deceived—I was doing a little pretending on my own account; I perceived that the restricting of the Moral Sense to the Bullyboywithaglasseye was a new idea to them, and—"

"Oh, bless you, no!" cried he, "not *that*. That was not new."

"Ah-h," said I, a little squelched, "what was it that was new, then?"

"Why, the *the*—used as you used it. You see, that emphasis was the striking thing. I mean, the way you *said* it. It made it sound like a title of honor, a compliment. Making a compliment of it was a new idea, you see. We haven't ever doubted that the Moral Sense is restricted to the Higher Animals, but— look here, give me some help. Our idea of the Moral Sense is, that it teaches us how to distinguish right from wrong; isn't that your idea of it, the Major Molar idea of it?"

"Yes."

"Also, it enables us to find out what is right, and *do* it."

"Correct."

"Also, it enables us to find out what is wrong, and do *that.*"

"Correct."

"Also, without *it* we couldn't find out what was wrong, and therefore couldn't *do* wrong. There wouldn't *be* any wrong; everything we did would be right. Just as it is with the Lower Animals."

"Correct, again."

"Rationally stated, then, the function of the Moral Sense is to *create* WRONG —since without it all conduct would be right."

"Correct."

"It creates wrong, points it out, and so enables us to *do* it."

"Yes."

"Therefore the special and particular office of the Moral Sense is to suggest, instigate and propagate wrong-doing."

"Also, *right*-doing, dear sir—admit it, please."

"Excuse me, we could do that *without* it. But we couldn't do *wrong* without it."

"Very true. But dear sir, to be *able* to do wrong is a high distinction—it lifts us far above the other animals. It is a good deal of a distinction, isn't it?"

"Yes: the distinction between a dial and a tin watch."

x x x He went away pretty sour. All the same, the *the* was planted, and it stayed. Ever since then, these nations look complacently down upon the Lower Animals because they can't do wrong, and complacently up at themselves because they *can.* The Microbes are my own people, and I loyally and patriotically admire them and am proud of them; yet I know in my secret heart that when it comes to reasoning-power they are not really a shade less comical than Man. *B.b.B.*

P.S., 2,000 years still later. That note was an error. I had not given the matter sufficient thought at that time. I am aware now that the Moral Sense is a valuable possession, indeed inestimably valuable. Without it we could not be what we are. Life would be monotonous, it would consist of sleeping and feeding, only, it would have no lofty ambitions, no noble ideals, there would be no missionaries, no statesmen, no jails, no crime, no soldiers, no thrones, no slaves, no slaughter,—in a word, no Civilization. Without the Moral Sense, Civilization is impossible. *B.b.B.*[7]

I have often been in the actual presence of our Emperors. More, I have been spoken to by them. This great honor has never been vouchsafed to any other foreigner of my degree in all the vast stretch of time during which the present Family has occupied the

---

[7] This note of the narrator appears in the holograph on inserted pages 15A– 15L. The paper of these pages—light buff, laid, size 5¾" x 9"—is that which Mark Twain used while composing the latter part of the story, beginning with p. 199 and continuing to the end of the holograph. For the rest of the part preceding p. 199, he used a cream colored paper, laid, size 5¾" x 8⅞". Apparently he went back to add the above note after he was more than half way through the story.

throne. It was accorded only once before, in all history. That was
nearly three million years ago. There is a monument, to preserve
the memory of it. It is rebuilt every five hundred years, by
voluntary contributions exacted by the State. This is in obedience
to an edict promulgated by the emperor of that ancient day and
dynasty, who was of a lofty nature and noted for his benevolence.
It is a matter of pride to me to know that the subject of that
distinction was of my own race—a cholera germ. Beyond this fact
nothing is known of him except that he was a foreigner. From what
part of Blitzowski he came, history does not say, nor what procured
him the memorable honor which the emperor bestowed upon
him.

Foreigners are not hated, here; I may say they are not even
disliked—they are tolerated. The people treat them courteously,
but are indifferent to them. They look down upon them, without
being distinctly conscious of it. Foreigners are regarded as inferiors
everywhere under the Blitzowski skies. Substantially that, though
there are some exceptions. One at least—Getrichquick, the principal republic. There, a third-rate foreign microbic celebrity easily
outranks a first-rate native one, and is received with a worshipful
enthusiasm which astonishes him away down in his private soul,
and he gets more champagne than he gets beer at home. In a
Blitzowskan monarchy it is the other way: there, a Getrichquick
first-rate ranks as a fifth-rate. But he is solaced: he is a shade
prouder of being fifth-rate there than first-rate at home.

Everywhere throughout the planet of Blitzowski the foreigner
ranks as an inferior, except—as I have just said—in the mighty
Republic of Getrichquick, universally known as the greatest of all
the democracies. It occupies a prodigious domain. Under its flag is
the whole of Blitzowski's stomach, which is the richest country, the
most fertile, the most productive and the most prodigally and
variously endowed with material resources in all the microbic
world. In that world it is one of the two or three conspicuously
great centres of trade. Its commerce, both domestic and foreign, is
colossal. Its transportation-facilities are quite extraordinary; these
make it a distributing-centre of imposing importance. In manufactures it heads all the countries in Blitzowski. It imports raw

materials from the North and ships the manufactured product to all the great nations lying toward the South. For ages it was selfish; it cared for the prosperity and happiness of its own people only, and steadily refused to extend its dominions in the interest of remote and suffering little nations. Many of its best people were ashamed of this. They saw great Heartland sending the refreshing blood of her gracious Civilization to many a dark and neglected nation rotting in debasing indolence and oriental luxury upon the confines of Blitzowski and requiring nothing in return but subjection and revenue; they saw imperial Henryland, far away in the desolate North gradually and surely spreading its dominion down the planet's flat expanse from the Shoulder Range to the lofty land of the Far South—the "Majestic Dome" of the poet and the traveler—distributing happiness and pus all the way, and in return requiring nothing of the benefited peoples except what they had; they saw these things and were ashamed. They were ashamed, and they rose and fought that policy at the polls and replaced it with a higher and holier one, which they baptised with the noble name of Benevolent Assimilation. It was an epoch-making achievement. It lifted Getrichquick out of her obscure and selfish isolation, the moment she was worthy, and throned her in the august company of the Pirate Powers. This was in very recent times—hardly three hundred and fifty thousand years ago, indeed. Far away, in the midst of the shoreless solitudes of the Great Lone Sea [8] was a collection of mud islets inhabited by those harmless bacilli which are the food of the fierce *hispaniola sataniensis,* whose excretions are the instrument appointed to propagate disease in the human trigonum. This archipelago was benevolently assimilated by the puissant Republic. It was first ingeniously wrested from its owners, by help of the unsuspicious owners themselves, then it was purchased from its routed and dispossessed foreign oppressors at a great price. This made the title perfect, even elegant. Also it added a Great Power to Blitzowski's riches and distinctions of that sort. The new Great Power was really no greater than it was before; the

---

[8] The holograph here reads "Great Stale Sea"; however, Mark Twain recorded in his working notes his intention of changing this name, wherever it appears in the story, to "Great Lone Sea." This later intention has been followed.

addition of the mud-piles was about the equivalent of adding a prairie-dog village to a mountain range, but the artificial expansion produced by the addition was so vast that it may justly be likened to a case of "before and after": the great Captive Balloon of Paris lying flat and observed of no passer-by, before filling, and the same balloon high in the air, rotund, prodigious, its belly full of gas, the wonder and admiration of a gazing world.

The native bacilli of the islets are of the kind called "benevolent" by the Blitzowski scientist. That is to say, they are not disease-producers. They are unusually little creatures. I have seen several of them. They were hardly more than five feet in diameter. I mean, as seen by my present eye—the eye of a microbe. Ordinary bacilli can be seen by a human being with a microscope magnifying ten or twelve hundred times; but he would not be able to see these little creatures without magnifying them considerably more than that. If you bunch a million ordinary bacilli together on a glass slide they will appear to the naked human eye like a minute stain, but I doubt if a similar crowd of these little Great Lone Sea islanders could be detected at all by the naked human eye. Yes, they are small, like their archipelago, but to hear the Republic talk about the combination, you would think she had been annexing four comets and a constellation.

The first of my imperial masters I was privileged to see was Henry the Great. Not the first one bearing that title—no, I do not mean that; mine was the 861st Henry the Great. By law and usage he was called Seiner Kaiserlichedurchlaustigstehochbegabtergottallmächtiger Eight-Sixty-One des Grossen. It sounds like German, but it isn't. Many of the 861 Greats earned the envied title by begetting heirs in a time of scarcity, several earned it by generalship in war and other forms of massacre, others earned it by illustrious achievements in the line of Benevolent Assimilation, still others by acting as the Church's harlot, others still by enriching the nobility with State lands and with large pensions and gratuities bilked from the public till; the rest earned it by sitting still, looking wise, accepting the credit of the great achievements of their ministers of State—and *not meddling*. These latter are held in imperishable honor by the grateful nation. They have their monuments. Built by the people, by voluntary contributions—real voluntaries. And rebuilt by the people whenever time moulders them to ruin.

As I have already remarked, my own Henry the Great was No. 861. This was about 3,000 years ago—when I first came. That I should have the distinction of appearing before the emperor was a most extraordinary thing. Because I was a foreigner, and (at that time) not noble. My scpt—the Cholera Microbes—is one of the Malignant Septs, therefore nobilities may be chosen from it, but I myself was neither noble nor received by persons of noble degree. So it naturally made a great sensation when I was commanded to the presence.

The event came about in this way. By some strange circumstance the egg of an American flea got into Blitzowski's blood and was hatched out and drowned. Then it became fossilized. This was about four million years ago, when the tramp was a boy. On earth I was a scientist by profession, and I remained one after I was transformed into a microbe. Paleontology was a passion with me. I was soon searching for fossils. I found several new ones, and this good fortune gave me the entré into scientific society. Local, I mean. It was humble and obscure, but in its heart burned the same passion for science that was consuming my own.

NOTE. *Seven Thousand Years Later.*[9] Many things have gone from my memory in the 7,000 years that have passed since then, but I still remember little incidents connected with my introduction to that pleasant comradeship. We had a little banquet, a very modest one, of course, for we were all poor and earned our living by hard work in common handicrafts, but it was very good, what there was of it. Exceedingly good, I may say. The word is not too strong, for we were more used to fasting than feasting. We had both kinds of corpuscles, and they were served up in six different ways, from soup and raw down to pie. The red ones were a little high, but Tom Nash made us all laugh by wittily saying it wasn't any matter, because the *bill* was so low that—that— well, it has gone from me, but I still consider it one of the wittiest things I have ever heard in my life. And he said it offhand—he did not have to stop and think, just flirted it out without any study, and perfectly easy and composed, the same as if he might be saying any little thing; and he . . . but *was* it Tom? . . . Ah, well, it could have been Sam Bowen . . . or maybe John Garth or Ed. Stevens. . . . Anyway it was one of them, I remember it

[9] At this point in the holograph, at the top of page 27A, Mark Twain noted, "Tom Nash—no, get another name." However, he did not make the intended change, and this name, as well as the names of other persons he had known during his early years in Hannibal, remain in the text.

perfectly. Yes, it was a quite memorable event, for young fellows like us. Ah, little did we suspect that we were making history! But we were. Little did we foresee that our poor little banquet was going to live forever in song and story, and in text-book and grave chronicle, and that my most careless words were destined to be remembered, and treasured and reverently repeated until the last germ shall fall silent and be gathered to his rest. I think the finest part of my speech was where I said, in concluding a lofty and impassioned tribute to the *real* nobility of Science and her devotees, "Ah, gentlemen," I said, "in the—the . . . in the—." I will look it up, in one of the Universal Histories. Here it is: "Ah, gentlemen, in the laboratory there are no fustian ranks, no brummagem aristocracies; the domain of Science is a republic, and all its citizens are brothers and equals, its princes of Monaco and its stonemasons of Cromarty meeting, barren of man-made gauds and meretricious decorations, upon the one majestic level!"

Of course the boys did not understand the references, and I did not explain at that time, but it was a grand peroration and the eloquence of it carried them clear off their feet. Eloquence is the essential thing in a speech, not information. B.b.B.

I no longer regretted lost America, I was among friends, admirers, helpers, and was happy.

In all ways I was enviably situated in those days. I lived in the country, in a dozing village, an easy distance from the capital, and had for neighbors a kindly and innocent peasantry whose quaint habits and quainter speech I loved to study. There were some billions of them, in the village and around it, yet they seemed few and scattering, for billions count for nothing among germs. The region was healthful and attractive; on every hand a receding and diminishing perspective of fair fields and gardens and parks, threaded with limpid streams and musical with the songs of birds, stretched away to a stately mountain rampart which lifted its rugged and broken sky-line against the western horizon—a prospect ever serene, contenting and beautiful, and never curtained, never blotted out, for in Blitzowski there is no night. What would be the blackest darkness to a human eye is noonday—a noonday as of fairyland, soft and rich and delicate—to the microbe's. The microbe's mission is urgent, exacting, he seldom sleeps, until age tires him.

What would my rugged mountains be, to the human eye? Ah, they would hardly even rank as warts. And my limpid and sparkling streams? Cobweb threads, delicate blood-vessels which it could not detect without the aid of the microscope. And the soaring arch of my dream-haunted sky? For that coarse eye it would have no existence. To my exquisite organ of vision all this spacious landscape is *alive*—alive and in energetic motion—unceasing motion—every detail of it! It is because I can see the individual molecules that compose it, and even the atoms which compose the molecules; but no microscope is powerful enough to reveal either of these things to the human eye. To the human mind they exist only in *theory,* not in demonstrated fact. The human mind—that wonderful machine—has measured the invisible molecule, and measured it accurately, without seeing it; also it has counted the multitudinous electrons that compose it, and counted them correctly, without having seen one of them; certainly a marvelous achievement.

Take a man like Sir Oliver Lodge, and what secret of Nature can be hidden from him? He says: "A billion, that is a million millions, of atoms is truly an immense number, but the resulting aggregate is still excessively minute. A portion of substance consisting of a billion atoms is only barely visible with the *highest* power of a microscope; and a speck or granule, in order to be visible to the naked eye, like a grain of lycopodium-dust, *must be a million times bigger still.*"

The human eye could see it then—that dainty little speck. But with my microbe-eye I could see *every individual* of the whirling billions of *atoms* that *compose* the speck. *Nothing is ever at rest*—wood, iron, water, everything is alive, everything is raging, whirling, whizzing, day and night and night and day, nothing is dead, *there is no such thing as death*, everything is full of bristling life, tremendous life, even the bones of the crusader that perished before Jerusalem eight centuries ago. There are no vegetables, *all things are* ANIMAL; each electron is an animal, each molecule is a collection of animals, and each has an appointed duty to perform and a soul to be saved. Heaven was not made for man alone, and oblivion and neglect reserved for the rest of His creatures. He gave them life, He gave them humble services to perform, they have performed them, and they will not be forgotten, they will have their reward. Man—always vain, windy, conceited—thinks he will be in the majority there. He will be disappointed. Let him humble himself. But for the despised microbe and the persecuted bacillus, who needed a home and nourishment, he would not have been created. He has a mission, therefore—a reason for existing: let him do the service he was made for, and keep quiet.

Three weeks ago I was a man myself, and thought and felt as men think and feel; but I have lived 3,000 years since then, and I see the foolishness of it now. We live to learn; and fortunate are we when we are wise enough to profit by it.

V.

In matters pertaining to microscopy we necessarily have an advantage, here, over the scientist of the earth, because, as I have just been indicating, we see with our naked eyes minutenesses which no man-made microscope can detect, and are therefore able to register as facts many things which exist for him as theories only. Indeed, we know as facts several things which he has not yet divined even by theory. For example he does not suspect that there is no life but *animal* life, and that all atoms are *individual animals*, each endowed with a certain degree of consciousness, great or small, each with likes and dislikes, predilections and aversions— that, in a word, each has a *character*, a character of its own. Yet such is the case. Some of the molecules of a stone have an aversion for some of those of a vegetable or any other creature, and will not associate with them—and would not be allowed to, if they tried. Nothing is more particular about society than a molecule. And so there are no end of castes; in this matter India is not a circumstance.

I often think of a talk I once had upon some of these things with a friend of mine, a renowned specialist by the name of Bblbgxw, a name which I have to modify to Benjamin Franklin because it is so difficult for me to pronounce that combination right; but that is near enough anyway, because when a foreigner pronounces it it always sounds a little like Franklin, when it doesn't sound like Smith. As I was saying, I was discussing those things with him, and

I still remember some of the remarks he made; others have faded out of my memory, but no matter, I wrote down the talk at the time, and will insert that record here:

THE RECORD.

FRANKLIN is a Yellow-fever germ, but speaks a broken and fiendishly ungrammatical thyroid-diphthyritic which I am able to follow, and could follow better if his accent were less homicidal. I wish he knew Latin—however, he doesn't. It is curious, the way these bacilli stick to their own tongues and avoid foreign ones. And yet it is not so very curious, perhaps, seeing there is such a multitude of foreign tongues in Blitzowski that a learner hardly knows where to begin on them. As for me, I have a talent for languages, and I like to learn them. The time-cost is nothing to me. I can learn six in an hour, without difficulty. (Microbe-time, of course, confound these troublesome time-tables!)

I may well say that, for they make my head ache. I have no trouble with *microbe*-time, for I have used no other, nor had occasion to use any other, for several centuries; and so the familiarity with human time which I once possessed has ceased to be a familiarity, and I cannot now handle its forms with easy confidence and a sure touch when I want to translate them into microbe-equivalents. This is natural. Since ever so long ago, microbe time has been *real* to me, and human time a dream—the one present and vivid, the other far away and dim, very dim, wavering, spectral, the substantiality all gone out of it. Sometimes I shut my eyes and try to bring back the faces that were so dear to me in my human days in America. How immeasurably remote they are, and vague and shadowy, glimpsed across that gulf of time—mere dream-figures drifting formless through a haze! Indeed, all things are dim to me, I think, that lie beyond it. Why, when I first began to write this little statement a half a second ago, I had to keep stopping to dig down into my memory for old forgotten human measurements of time that I had not used nor thought of for lifetimes and lifetimes! My difficulties were so great and my mistakes so frequent and vexatious that for comfort's sake and accuracy's sake I stopped writing, and labored out a tabulated

translation of microbe time-divisions into human ones for my guid-
ance and protection. Like this:

TIME—EQUIVALENTS.

Human.					Microbe.
¼ of a second is (roughly) .	.	.	.	. . . .	. 3 hours.
½ " " " " "	.	.	.	. . . .	. 6 "
1 second " "	.	.	.	. . . .	. 12 "
2 " " "	.	.	.	. . . .	. 24 "
15 " " "	.	.	.	. . . .	. 1 week.
30 " " "	.	.	.	. . . .	. 1 fortnight.
60 " " "	.	.	.	. . . .	. 1 month.
10 minutes " "	.	.	.	. . . .	. 1 year
1 hour " "	.	.	.	. . . .	. 6 years
1 day " "	.	.	.	. . . .	. 144 "
1 week " "	.	.	.	. . . .	. 1,008 "
1 year " "	.	.	.	. . . .	. 52,416 "

A Pause for Comment.
Record Suspended, Meantime.

As far as the table deals in seconds and minutes it is inexact.
The microbe month is *more* than 60 human seconds; it is 1 human
minute, and 12 seconds over. But I use the rough measurement
because it is handy, and near enough for all ordinary purposes. I
wanted to translate a microbe hour into its human equivalent, but
it kept shrinking and diminishing and wasting away, and finally
disappeared from under my pen, leaving nothing behind that I
could find again when I wanted it. As nearly as I could get at it, a
microbe hour seemed to be the fiftieth part of human second. We
will let it go at that. I used to be the best mathematician in Yale
when I was in the class of '53, and to-day I am considered the best

one in Blitzowski—that is, in microbe mathematics—but I can do nothing with human mathematics now. I have tried lately to get back the art, but my memory refuses. In the Yale days I was perfect in it; indeed I was called wonderful. Justly, too, perhaps, for people used to come from great distances to see me do eclipses, and occultations of Venus, and such things. I could do twelve simultaneously, blindfold, and keep the run of them all, just in my head. It was in those days that I invented the logarhythyms, but I cannot even spell it without embarrassment now, let alone put up a hand in them that a soph can't beat. Great days—yes, they were great days. They will come no more. In this pathetic life all things pass, nothing abides. Even the human multiplication table has gone from me—almost utterly. It has been more than seven thousand years since I could say it beyond 4 times 9 is 42. But it is no matter, I shall never need it after I get done writing this. And besides, if I should need multiplications in this, it may be that I can use the local multiplication table and then translate it into human. No— that will hardly answer, everything is so small here, as compared with human dimensions. It is not likely that 4 times 9 in microbe would amount to enough in English to be worth while. It would not convey enough of the idea for the reader to get it.

Having clarified the atmosphere on the time-limit and removed the confusions and perplexities that were vexing it, I will now return to the conversation I had with Franklin.

The Record Resumed.

"FRANKLIN," I asked, "is it certain that each and every existing *thing* is an individual and alive—every *plant*, for instance?"

"Yes," he answered.

"And is each molecule that composes it an individual too, and alive?"

"Yes."

"And is each atom that composes the molecule an individual also, and alive?"

"Yes."

"Now then, has the whole plant—a tree, for instance—feelings, sympathies and so on, *as* a tree?"

"Yes."

"Whence do they come?"

"They are imparted by the combined feelings and sympathies that exist separately in the molecules that compose the tree. They are the tree's soul. They make the tree feel like a tree instead of like a rock or a horse."

"Have rocks, trees and horses any feelings that are common to the three?"

"Yes. The feelings which are the product of oxygen are shared in greater or lesser degree by all three. If the chemical compounds of a rock were the same as those of a tree and in the same proportions, it wouldn't look like a rock, nor feel like a rock, and—"

"Well?"

"Well, it wouldn't *be* a rock. It would be a tree."

"I do believe it. Tell me: Inasmuch as oxygen enters into the composition of pretty much everything that exists, it would interest me to know if it imparts a *special and particular feeling*—a feeling not imparted to a creature by any other kind of molecule?"

"Indeed it does. Oxygen is *temper,* and is the sole source of it. Where there is but little of it there is but little passion; where there is more of it, there is more temper; where there is more still, still more temper; add still more oxygen, degree by degree, keep on adding, and you warm that temper up and up, stage by stage, till by and by you reach the ultimate of fury. Some plants are very quiet and peaceable —you have noticed that?"

"I have."

"It is because they contain but little oxygen. Others contain more, others more still. Some are more heavily charged with oxygen than with any other chemical. We know the result: the rose is sweet-tempered, the nettle is hasty, the horse-radish is violent. Observe the bacilli: Some are gentle—it means lack of oxygen. Then look at the tuberculosis-germ, and typhoid: loaded to the mandibles with oxygen! I have some temper myself, but I am thankful to say I do not act like those outlaws. When I am at my angriest, I am still able to remember that I am a gentleman."

Well, we are curious creatures. Sometimes I wonder if there *is* anybody who is not a self-deceiver. He believed what he was saying, he was perfectly sincere about it; yet everybody knows that when a yellow-fever germ's temper is up, there is no real difference between him and an insurrection. He evidently expected me to concede that he was a kind of a saint, and so I had discretion enough to do it, for I take no pleasure in mutilations, and I am going to be unusually anxious for trouble before ever I throw out any remark that is likely to stir up *his* oxygen. Presently, I said—

"Tell me, Franklin, is the ocean an individual, an animal, a creature?"

"Sure."

"Then water—any water—is an individual?"

"Sure."

"Suppose you remove a drop of it? Is what is left an individual?"

"Yes, and so is the drop."

"Suppose you divide the drop?"

"Then you have two individuals."

"Suppose you separate the hydrogen and the oxygen?"

"Again you have two individuals. But you haven't water, any more."

"Of course. Certainly. Well, suppose you combine them again, but in a new way: Make the proportions equal—one part oxygen to one of hydrogen?"

"But you know you can't. They won't combine on equal terms."

I was ashamed to have made that blunder. I was embarrassed; to cover it, I started to say we used to combine them like that where I came from, but thought better of it, and stood pat.

"Now then," I said, "it amounts to this: water is an individual, an animal, and is alive; remove the hydrogen and *it* is an animal and is alive; the remaining oxygen is also an individual, an animal, and is alive. Recapitulation: the two individuals combined, constitute a third individual—and yet each *continues* to be an individual."

I glanced at Franklin, but . . . upon reflection, held my peace. I could have pointed out to him that here was mute Nature explaining the sublime mystery of the Trinity so luminously that even the commonest understanding could comprehend it, whereas many a trained master of words had labored to do it with speech and failed. But he would not have known what I was talking about. After a moment, I resumed—

"Listen—and see if I have understood you rightly. To-wit—All the atoms that constitute each oxygen molecule are separate individuals,

and each one is a living animal; all the atoms that constitute each
hydrogen molecule are separate individuals, and each one is a living
animal; each drop of water consists of millions of living animals, the
drop itself is an individual, a living animal, and the wide ocean is
another. Is that it?"

"Yes, that is correct."

"By George, it beats the band!"

He liked the expression, and set it down in his tablets.

"Franklin, we've got it down fine. And to think—there are other
animals that are still smaller than a hydrogen atom, and yet *it* is so
small that it takes five thousand of them to make a molecule—a
molecule so minute that it could get into a microbe's eye and he
wouldn't know it was there!"

"Yes, the wee creatures that inhabit the bodies of us germs, and
feed upon us, and rot us with disease. Ah, what could they have been
created for? they give us pain, they make our lives miserable, they
murder us—and where is the use of it all, where the wisdom? Ah,
friend Bkshp, we live in a strange and unaccountable world; our
birth is a mystery, our little life is a mystery and a trouble, we pass
and are seen no more; all is mystery, mystery, mystery; we know not
whence we came, nor why, we know not whither we go, nor why we
go. We only know we were not made in vain, we only know we were
made for a wise purpose, and that all is well! We shall not be cast
aside in contumely and unblest, after all we have suffered. Let us be
patient, let us not repine, let us trust. The humblest of us is cared for
—oh, believe it!—and this fleeting stay is not the end!"

You notice that? He did not suspect that he, also, was engaged in
gnawing, torturing, defiling, rotting, and murdering a fellow-creature
—he and all the swarming billions of his race. None of them suspects
it. That is significant. It is suggestive—irresistibly suggestive—insist-
ently suggestive. It hints at the possibility that the procession of
known and listed devourers and persecutors is not complete. It
suggests the possibility, and substantially the certainty, that man is
himself a microbe, and his globe a blood-corpuscle drifting with its
shining brethren of the Milky Way down a vein of the Master and
Maker of all things, Whose body, mayhap,—glimpsed partwise from
the earth by night, and receding and lost to view in the measureless
remotenesses of Space—is what men name the Universe.

VI.

"WELL, FRANKLIN," I said, "Carpe diem—quam minimum credula postero." *

* Latin. It means, "Be thou wise: take a drink whilst the chance offers; none but the gods know when the jug will come around again."

He was very much pleased when I translated it for him; and got me to write it down in his tablets, so that he could make an illuminated motto of it and stick it up in his parlor like a God-Bless-Our-Home and have its admonition ever under his eye, for he was profoundly struck by its wisdom. While I was complying, he took *two* drinks. I did not say anything, but it seemed to me that when it came to wisdom he already had enough for the practical purposes of this brief life.

I excused myself from going to the door with him—being shy, for I had long been intolerably renowned and sought after. He understood, for he could see, himself, that the usual multitude had massed itself, black and solid, for hundreds of yards around, hoping to get a glimpse of me. He took a snap with his instantaneous multograph, looked at the record, and called back to me that the number of persons present was 648,342,227,549,113. It interested him, and he put up his hand and flung back, with a flirt or two of his fingers, the sign-language remark, "This is the penalty for being illustrious, magister!"

Oh, dear, how many million times I have heard and seen that shop-worn remark since I became famous. Each person that utters it thinks he's the first that thought of it; thinks it's a cute phrase and felicitous, and is as vain of it as if he had cornered the fourth dimension. Whereas it is the *obvious* remark; any person who was alive and not in the asylum would think of it. It is of the grade of the puns which small wits make upon people's names. Every time they are introduced to a person named Terry they dazzle-up like the sun bursting out of a cloud and say, "I am not going to hurt you, don't look so *terrified*!" and then they almost perish with cackling over that poor little addled egg that they've laid. Why doesn't it occur to them that in the very nature of things Terry has seen it laid every day since he was born? Twain . . . Twain . . . what was his other name? Mike? I think it was Mike, but it was long ago, centuries ago, that I used to hear of him in that almost forgotten world that I used to inhabit; and I read his books, too, but I do not remember what they were about, now . . . no, it wasn't books, it was pictures . . . pictures or agriculture . . . agri . . . yes, it *was* agriculture, I remember it perfectly, now. He was a Californian, and his middle name was Burbank; he did miracles in the invention and propagation of new and impossible breeds of flowers and fruits and timber, and became known all over the world, and was finally hanged, many thought unjustly. He was coming out of a saloon sometimes one day, and one of the times that he was coming out of it a stranger was introduced to him, and dazzled-up like the sun bursting out of a cloud, and shouted, "Aha! he-he! he-he! if a man require thee to go with him a mile, go *with* him, Twain!" and Twain shot him in five places and he crumpled up on the sidewalk and died, many people looking on, and some regretting it. The whole State joined in an effort to get the death-sentence commuted to a term in Congress or jail, I do not remember which it was, now, and the governor was quite willing if the agriculturist would say he was sorry, but he said he could not tell a lie, and some believed him, because he had once chopped down a cherry tree because he couldn't; and then it came out that he had already killed dozens of persons of every sex for making that remark and had concealed it for one reason or another, and so it was judged best, on the whole, to let the sentence stand, although everybody, even Grovenor Rossfelt, President of the United States, conceded that such people were not necessary.

Well, certainly memory is a curious machine and strangely capricious. It has no order, it has no system, it has no notion of values, it is always throwing away gold and hoarding rubbish. Out of that dim old time I have recalled that swarm of wholly trifling facts with ease and precision, yet to save my life I can't get back my mathematics. It vexes me, yet I am aware that everybody's memory is like that, and that therefore I have no right to complain. There was an odd instance of it the other day: Wzprgfski * the historian was

* Pronounced Tolliver.

here, and was telling about ancient times, and all of a sudden the bottom fell out of the back end of his memory and spilt every proper name he ever knew. During the interval that the infirmity lasted, he was short on generals, poets, patriarchs and all the rest of his venerated celebrities, and long on lies and legends and battles and revolutions and other incorporeate facts only. Presently he got his proper-name memory back, then another piece of bottom fell out and spilt a hatful of verbs. When it happened he was just starting to say, "And so, in the fulness of time Ggggmmmdw.* . . ." But there he

* Pronounced nearly like the Welsh name Llthwbgww.

went aground; the word he wanted was gone. I had to supply it myself and start him along again. It was *hfcñzz*. With that umlaut over the *n* it means "began to disintegrate;" without the umlaut, the word is an active transitive past participle, and means that the disintegration has been completed; thus it means—substantially—that the man is *dead*: but not exactly that, but not *really*, because in Blitzowski, as I have previously remarked, there is no such thing as death. The umlauted word is restricted to poetry; but even in poetry it does not mean that life has *ceased*; it has *departed*—that is all; we do not know its new habitat, but we know it is still with us, still near us. Of the molecules which constituted its late dwelling and gave it motion and feeling— that is to say, *life*—many have wandered away and joined themselves to new plasmic forms, and are continuing their careers in the bodies of plants, birds, fishes, flies, and other creatures; in time the rest will follow, till the last bone has crumbled to dust, in the far future, and dismissed its atoms, each to seek its kind and go on with its functions indefinitely. And so our people here have no word to signify that either a person or his spirit is *dead*, in our sense of that term; no, his oxygen molecules are gradually deserting and wandering away, in groups and companies, to furnish temper to the horse-radish, the tiger and the rabbit, each in the degree required; his hydrogen, (humor, hope, cheer) as fast as it is released, will carry its happy spirit whither it is needed, and will lift up the drooping flower and whatever other thing is despondent; his glucose, his acetic acid, his— well, everything he has got will go out and seek and find a new home, and each will continue its vocation. Nothing will be lost, nothing will perish.

Franklin realizes that no atom is destructible; that it has always existed and will exist forever; but he thinks all atoms will go out of this world some day and continue their life in a happier one. Old Tolliver thinks no atom's life will ever end, but he also thinks

Blitzowski is the only world it will ever see, and that at no time in its eternity will it be either worse off or better off than it is now and always has been. Of course he thinks the planet Blitzowski is itself eternal and indestructible—at any rate he says he thinks that. It could make me sad, only I know better. D. T. will fetch Blitzy yet, one of these days.

But these are alien thoughts, human thoughts, and they falsely indicate that I do not want this tramp to go on living. What would become of me if he should disintegrate? My molecules would scatter all around and take up new quarters in hundreds of plants and animals; each would carry its special feelings along with it, each would be content in its new estate, but where should *I* be? I should not have a rag of a feeling left, after my disintegration—with his—was complete. Nothing to think with, nothing to grieve or rejoice with, nothing to hope or despair with. There would be no more *me*. I should be musing and thinking and dreaming somewhere else—in some distant animal, maybe—perhaps a cat; by proxy of my oxygen I should be raging and fuming in some other creature—a rat, perhaps; I should be smiling and hoping in still another child of Nature—heir to my hydrogen—a weed, or a cabbage, or something; my carbonic acid (ambition) would be dreaming dreams in some lowly wood-violet that was longing for a showy career; thus my details would be doing as much feeling as ever, but I should not be aware of it, it would all be going on for the benefit of those others, and I not in it at all. I should be gradually wasting away, atom by atom, molecule by molecule, as the years went on, and at last I should be all distributed, and nothing left of what had once been Me. It is curious, and not without impressiveness: I should still be alive, intensely alive, but so scattered that I would not know it. I should not be dead,—no, one cannot call it that—but I should be the next thing to it. And to think what centuries and ages and aeons would drift over Me before the disintegration was finished, the last bone turned to gas and blown away! I wish I knew what it is going to feel like, to lie helpless such a weary, weary time, and see my faculties decay and depart, one by one, like lights which burn low, and flicker, and perish, until the ever-deepening gloom and darkness which—oh, away, away with these horrors, and let me think of something wholesomer!

My tramp is only 85; there is good hope that he will live ten years longer—500,000 of my microbe years. So may it be.

The Ancient Record Continued.

VII.

As soon as I was sure Franklin was out of sight I stepped out on the balcony: looked surprised to find that people were waiting in the hope of getting a glimpse of me—fell into an attitude of embarrassment and consternation which is very effective in Kodak-snaps and illustrations, and which I have perfected by practice before the glass —then I allowed the usual thunder-crash of salutation and welcome to astonish me into another and quite stunning attitude of surprise— surprise mixed with almost childish gratification—really a most fetching thing when it is done well—then I scudded away like a dear little shy maid who has been caught with nothing on but a blush, and vanished into my quarters, thus making the most taking and delightful effect of all, for it always leaves the mighty multitude rent with storms of happy and grateful laughter, and they shout "oh, isn't he *too* sweet for anything!"

Oh shocked and scornful reader, be gentle with me! Can't you see *yourself* in that disgraceful picture? For it *is* you. There has never been anybody who would not like to be in that place; there has never been any one who would throw away the chance to occupy it if he had it. The baby microbe shows off before company; the microbe lad shows off, with silly antics, before the little bacillus girls; also he plays pirate, soldier, clown—anything to be conspicuous. After that— well, after that, his appetite for notice and notoriety remains— remains always—but he lyingly and hypocritically lets on that he has lost it. He hasn't lost it, he has only lost his honesty.

Now then, be gentle with me, for that is all that I have lost; all that you and I have lost. Otherwise we are what we were when we were babies and used to crow and cackle and carry on in mommer's lap and glance at the company to collect the applause. The company were poignantly ashamed of the baby, and you have been as poignantly ashamed of me—that is, you thought you were ashamed of

me, but that was not so—you were ashamed of yourself, as exposed in
me.

We can't help our nature, we didn't make it, it was made for us;
and so we are not to blame for possessing it. Let us be kind and
compassionate toward ourselves; let us not allow the fact to distress us
and grieve us that from mommer's lap to the grave we are all shams
and hypocrites and humbugs without an exception, seeing that we
did not make the fact and are in no way responsible for it. If any
teacher tries to persuade you that hypocrisy is not a part of your blood
and bone and flesh, and can therefore be trained out of you by
determined and watchful and ceaseless and diligent application to
the job, do not you heed him; ask him to cure himself first, then call
again. If he is an honorable person and is meaning well, he will give
the medicine you have recommended to him an earnest and honest
and sincere trial, but he will not call again.

For centuries I have held unchallenged the reputation of being a
celebrity who is so shy and modest by nature that he shrinks from
public notice and is pained by it. Very well, I have earned it. By
thoughtful and deeply-reasoned arts. I have played my game every
day for a lengthy procession of centuries, and played it well; I have
my reward. I have copied the way of the kings; they do not make
themselves common to the public eye. A king's most valued and
valuable asset is public notice. Without it the chief charm of his
difficult and burdensome office would be wanting, and he would
mourn and sigh, and wish he could trade his post for one with more
show to it and less work to do. Tradition puts this frank retort into
the mouth of old Henry MMMMMDCXXII, surnamed The
Untamed: "Yes, I *am* fond of praises, processions, notice, attentions,
reverence, fuss and feathers! *Vanities*, are they? There was never a
creature, particularly a god, that did not like them."

I started to tell how I came to be celebrated, but I have wandered
far from my course. It is partly because I have long been unused to
writing, and thereby have lost the art and habit of concentration.
And so I scatter too much. Then there was another difficulty: I
wanted to write in English, but could not manage it to my
satisfaction, because the words, the grammar, the forms, the spelling
and everything else connected with the language had faded and
become unfamiliar to me. And the phrasing! Phrasing is everything,
almost. Oh, yes, phrasing is a kind of photography: out of focus, a
blurred picture; in focus, a sharp one. One must get the focus right—

that is, frame the sentence with exactness and precision, in his mind
—before he pulls the string.*

* Alas, alas! Well, I was certainly pretty young when I wrote that, away
back yonder, ages ago; pretty young and self-satisfied. It makes me ashamed.
Still, I believe I will let it stand. Why should I care? it is not giving *me* away,
it is giving away a silly youth who *was* me, but is no more me now than is the
once-sapling the present oak. B.b.B.

(*End of Extract from the Ancient Record.*)

VIII.

I T SEEMED best to fall back on the microbe tongue, and so I
did it. I went back to the start and put this History into that
language, then laboriously translated it into English, just as you see
it now. It is very good, not many could do it better, yet in brilliancy
and effectiveness it is but the lightning-bug to the lightning, when
compared with the microbic original. Among microbe authors I
hold the belt for phrasing, and I could hold it in English if I was a
mind to take the trouble.

The way I came to be celebrated was this. When I first arrived in
Blitzowski I was poor and a stranger; and as all could see that I was
a foreigner, my society was not sought after. I took cheap board
with a humble family * and by their kindly help I was enabled to

* Named Taylor, but spelt different.

hire a hand-organ and a monkey. On credit. On a royalty. I was
very industrious, performing all day and studying the family's
language all night, with the children for teachers, for they never
slept, there being no night for them; and indeed none for me
except the conventional one invented by myself.

At first I gained but few pennies, but I soon struck a good idea. I
began to sing. In English. It was not very good singing, and was
avoided; but only for a little while; for when the germs noticed that

I was using a strange tongue, and one which they had never heard before, they were interested. I sang "Sally in Our Alley" and "I don't 'low no Coon to Fool roun' Me," and other simple anthems, and then the crowds began to follow me around, and couldn't get enough.

I prospered. By the end of the first year I was past master in the family's language, then I went to work on a new one. I was still so American that that microbe year of ten minutes and twelve seconds seemed astonishingly brief; but after that, each year that went by seemed considerably longer than its immediate predecessor. This constantly lengthening process continued for ten years; after that, the microbe year was become fully as long to me as the half of any American year had ever been. The older crops of Taylor children had grown so, meantime, that several of the girls were 40 and marriageable. A microbe girl at 40 is about where an American girl is at 20 or 25, for the climate is wonderfully healthy and the food nutricious, and many a person lives to be 150, which is a shade more than an entire human day.

Yes, I had prospered. But Sally and the Coon-song were beginning to show wear and invite rocks; so, out of prudence I reorganized my program and pulled off another prosperous ten with "Bonny Doon" and "Buffalo Gals Can't You Come out To-night." Microbes like sentimental music best.

Pretty early I had to explain what *kind* of a foreigner I was. This was a delicate business. I could have told inquirers the truth, of course, for I was in practice, but there would have been no takers. I could market a lie if I built it with judgment, but to say I was an American and came of a race of star-bumping colossi who couldn't even see an average microbe without a microscope, would have landed me in the asylum.

The local name of the cholera microbe is *Bwilk*—a word equivalent to the Latin word *lextalionis,* which means—well, I don't remember, now, what it means, but bwilk is a good name and much respected here. I found that there was no one in our neighborhood that had ever seen a native of the Major Molar, or knew what the language of that region sounded like. The Major

Molar is Blitzowski's furthest-aft tooth on the port side. In the dentine of that tooth there are some exceeding delicate nerve-threads that traverse it horizontally, crossing the cane-brake of perpendicular ones at right angles, and I pretended that I was a native of one of those—the north-west one. After I had said it and it was too late to mend the statement, I remembered that Blitzowski's Major Molar was at the dentist's—awaiting redemption and not likely to get it, for Blitzowski is not given to paying for services or redeeming undesirable securities so long as he can dodge. But no one noticed, and my statement passed. Some good-hearted people thought it a pity that a respectable race should be so straitened as to be obliged to live in such a remote and desolate country. This touched me deeply, and I took up a collection for them.

I was fond of the Taylor children, they had grown up under my eye, many crops of them had been dear little pets and housemates of mine from their cradle-days, and it caused me a pang when they began to leave the safe haven of their home and embark upon the uncertain sea of matrimony. In the case of the boy-microbes, I did not so much mind it, but it was very hard to lose the girls, indeed I could hardly bear to think of it. And to make it the harder, the first to give her heart away was my favorite. This was Maggie (my love-name for her, and used by none but her and me). I gave her that sacred name out of the secretest chamber of my heart, when she was a little thing; and in after-years when she came to have a budding sense of the sweetest and tenderest of all the passions and I told her why that name was the name of names to me, her eyes filled and she expressed with a kiss the pitying words her quivering lips could not frame. The marriage made a great gap in the family, for 981,642 of her sisters were married at the same time, and many brothers—over a million, I do not remember the exact number, but I think I am within 30 or 35 of it. None can know the desolation of a day like that who has not lived it. I had an honored place at the wedding solemnities, and assisted in deepening their impressiveness by singing one of the dear old early songs; but when I tried to sing the other one the strain upon my feelings was too great and I broke down. Neither could Maggie bear it. From that day to this I have never been able to sing "I Don't 'Low No Coon" through to the end without my voice breaking.

That wedding carried my mind back to other scenes and other days, and filled it with images painfully sweet and unforgetable. Turning the pages of my mouldy diaries now, to refresh my memory for these chapters, I find this entry, whose pathos moves me still, after all these centuries:

May 25, Y. H. 2,501,007. Yesterday, Maggie's wedding. Last night I dreamed of that other Maggie, that human Maggie, whose dear face I shall look upon no more in this life. In that sweet vision I saw her as I had seen her last—oh, dream of loveliness, oh, radiant creature, oh, spirit of fire and dew, oh, fairy form, transfigured by the golden flood of the sinking sun! . . . God forgive me, I hurt her with a cruel speech! How could I commit that crime! And how had I the heart to note unmoved the reproach in those gentle eyes and go from that sweet presence unforgiven?

I wrote that passage 7,000 years ago. There is a very curious thing connected with it: I have had that same dream, its glory unfaded, its pain unsoftened, once in every century since that recorded date—and always on the 24th of May of the hundredth year. When this had recurred two or three times I took courage to hope it was a sign—a sign that it would continue to recur after the lapse of each century; when it had blessed me five times I felt sure it would continue; after that, I never had a doubt. So sure was I, that when the sixth century drew toward its close, I began to tally off the decades, then the years, the months, the days, with ever increasing impatience and longing, until the hallowed day came and again upon my slumbering mind the beautiful vision rose. I have always watched with confidence for the dream since, as each century waned toward the memorable date, and in no instance have I been disappointed. Always in the dream I hear distant music— distant and faint, but always sweet, always moving: "Bonny Doon." It was Margaret's favorite, therefore it was mine too.

There is one very curious effect: in the dream the beautiful human girl is as beautiful to me as she was when I was of her own race. This is quite unaccountable, there is no way to explain it. Do I become human again, in the dream, and re-acquire human notions of what is beautiful and what isn't? Really it has a plausible look, yet it is pretty fanciful, pretty far-fetched, not very persuasive, not very likely, when one examines it soberly. When I am awake, my standards of beauty and and loveliness are microbic, and microbic only, and this is natural. When I am awake and my memory calls up human faces and forms which were once beautiful to me, they are still beautiful, but not with the beauty that exists by grace of *race*-ship—no, it is merely the sort of beauty which I see in a flower, a bird, or other comely thing not of my own kind. To the young gentleman-caterpillar no human being nor any other creature approaches in charm and beauty and winsomeness the lissome and rounded young lady-caterpillar whom he loves. What is Cleopatra to him? Nothing. He would not go out of his way to look at her. To him she would seem fluffy, gross, unshapely, she could not fire his passions. To the vain and happy mother-octopus, the bunch of goggled and squirming fringes which she has given birth to is beautiful beyond imagination, she cannot take her eyes off it, whereas I would not give a damn for a ton of them. Indeed, to me any octopus is insufferable, and I would not live with one for anything a person could give me. This is not unreasoning prejudice, it is merely nature. We do not invent our tastes in this matter, they come to us with our birth, they are of the many mysteries of our being.

I am a microbe. A cholera microbe. For me there is comeliness, there is grace, there is beauty findable, some way or some where, in greater or lesser degree, in every one of the nationalities that make up the prodigious germ-world—but at the head I place the cholera-germ. To me its beauty has no near competitor. I still remember that in the human world each of the nationalities had a beauty of its own: there was the Italian style, the German style, the French, the American, the Spanish, the English, the Egyptian, the Dahomian, the red Indian, the East Indian and a thousand other styles, civilized and savage, and I also remember that each thought its own style the finest and best—a condition which is repeated here in Blitzowski, from one end of him to the other. From the scrapings of his teeth you can gather, oh, such an array of self-complacent tribes! and from the rotting dollar-bill in his pocket you can accumulate another swarm; and I give you my word that every naked savage in the lot would pass indifferently by Maggie Taylor, the germ-belle of Henryland, if she were still existent, and go into ecstasies over the imagined beauty of some frumpy squaw of his own particular breed who could no more stir me than a cow could. I speak from experience. With my own eyes I have seen a he-buccalis maximus lose his mind over a she-one, accidentally encountered, while right in sight were a dozen surpassingly lovely little cholera-germ witches, each and every of them more tantalizingly delicious to look at than her comrades, if possible. Of course, to my mind that spirilla was a fool; and of course, to his mind I was another one.

It is the way we are made, and we can't help it. I have never married, I shall never marry. Is it because I lost my heart irrecoverably when I lost it to Margaret Adams in America three thousand years ago? It must be so. I think it is so. Once in every century she comes to me in my dream, clothed in immortal youth and imperishable beauty; and in the dream she is as erst my idol, and I adore. But when the dream passes, I am myself again and she but a dim and fair unthrilling memory; I am myself again, and my worship of the budding and beautiful of my own loved microbic race comes back to me, and I know that for another century I shall have no homage for any charm but that which looks out from the blue eyes and plays in the winsome smile of the college-maid whose high privilege it is to carry in her veins the blood of the cholera-germ—oldest and noblest and most puissant of all the race of germs, save only the Plague-Bacillus, at sound of whose mighty name the nations uncover!

I cannot be sure of my human dear one's age, for it was long ago, but I think she was eighteen or nineteen. I think I was three or four years older than she was, but I find myself unable to be exact about it, all such things are so dim in my memory now. I have an impression that the first Napoleon was reigning at the time, or that he had lately fallen at Marathon or Philippi, whichever it was, for I am clear that a world-convulsing event was filling all men's mouths

then, and I think it must have been that one. I remember that I
had just graduated—class of '53 *—a vast event for me, and not

* NOTE. *Seven thousand years later.* This is the second time this statement has crept in, I do not know how. I wrote it, but I think it is untrue.
I do not think I was ever at Yale, except to receive honorary degrees. B.b.B.

lightly to be misplaced in my memory I should think, and *that* was
the year that General Washington went North to assume command of the Hessians, the only time I ever saw him, so far as I
remember. I depend mainly on historical events to preserve my
connection with my human life, because they stay with me better
than minor happenings do, on account of their prominence and
importance, and because I have a natural fondness for history and
an aptness for mastering its details which Professor Tolliver regarded as quite remarkable, a verdict which greatly pleased me,
since history was that learned and illustrious germ's specialty.

I must explain that that "Y.H.," in the above diary-date stands
for "year of the Henriad." It was like this arrogant House to cancel
and wipe out the preceding ages when it captured the throne, and
second-stage history with a new Year One. Speaking as a microbe,
and with a microbe's ideas of propriety, I think it was not seemly.
Indeed I had felt the same way before I was ever a microbe, for I
was among the dissenters when the American Revolution ended
successfully and Sir John Franklin and his brother Benjamin got the
Diet of Worms to establish a new Year One and name the months
Germinal, and *Fructidor,* and all that nonsense. Such tremendous
readjustments of time should be the prerogative of religions only, I
think. Religions achieve real and permanent epochs, whereas no
political epoch can be of that character, the very law of all political
entities being change, change, unceasing change,—sometimes ad-
vancement, sometimes retrogression, but never rest, never repose,
never fixity. Religions are of God, and they come from His hand
perfect, therefore unimprovable, but policies are of men and
microbes, and unstable, like their creators. Evolution is the law of
policies: Darwin said it, Socrates endorsed it, Cuvier proved it and
established it for all time in his paper on "The Survival of the
Fittest." These are illustrious names, this is a mighty doctrine:

nothing can ever remove it from its firm base, nothing dissolve it, but evolution.

IX

THOSE TAYLOR weddings are a land-mark in my career. It was there that I met a teacher of music whom I was permitted to call Thompson, his right name being too difficult for me. He was a cream-ripening bacullus of good character and considerable education, and was attracted by my singing, because it was so different. He came of his own accord and introduced himself. It made me happy beyond words, for I had long been starving for intellectual companionship. We soon became intimates. He was not a person of importance, therefore he could not advance my material interests, but he introduced me to educated friends of his, and that was service enough. Among these were some humble scientists. Was I happy now? Indeed I was, and most grateful. We were young, and full of enthusiasm; we lost no opportunity of being together. We foregathered as often as the bread-and-butter requirements of our several trades permitted, and in happy comradeship we searched after Nature's secrets.

Sometimes we stole a day from shop, counting-room, hand-organ, etc., and made excursions—botanical, insectivorous, mammiferous, piscatorial, paleontological, and the like, and every now and then, as the years danced by on joyous wing, we had the luck to make quite fortunate discoveries. This went on for ten years. Then all of a sudden came the discovery of discoveries—the fossil flea heretofore mentioned.[10]

---

[10] After this sentence Mark Twain noted in the holograph, at the top of p. 83, "Withdraw—beginning here," and on an inserted page wrote, "Skip to page 102 and go ahead." Chapter X begins on page 102. The deleted section, pp. 83–101, presents a farcical account of the discovery and digging out of the fossil flea and also mentions the fossilized brontosaurus, discovered in Wyoming, which had been reconstructed and exhibited by the Metropolitan Museum of New York. Mark Twain satirizes the tendency of science to theorize on the basis of insufficient evidence: "It seems odd, now, that we all thought the Brontosaurus was a pre-Adamite cow. . . ." (p. 97).

X.

W<small>E BOYS</small> had good times in those days. I say boys, because we still felt like boys, and because the term had stayed with us, from old habit, after we had crossed the strictly "young-chap" (boy-) frontier; and naturally enough, for we had crossed it without noticing it. We had been training together ten years. I was 78 (microbe-time), but looked just as I had looked 30 years earlier when I first arrived: that is to say I looked my human age of that date—about 26 or 27. Their age was about 50 when we first met, and they had then looked as humans of 25 to 28 look; the 10 years they had since added, showed: one could see that they had grown older. In my case no shade of change was detectible. My sojourn of 30 years had seemed a life-long stretch of time, to me, yet exteriorly it had not aged me by a day. My face, my figure, my strength, my young vivacity and animation—all these had kept their youth. The boys wondered, and so did I. I puzzled over it privately a good deal. Was there something human left in me? I had been a microbe a considerable part of a human day; could it be that my consciousness was keeping microbe time and my body keeping human time? I couldn't tell, I didn't know anything about it; and moreover, being happy,—and just a little frivolous by nature, perhaps—I didn't care. The mystery of my stuck-fast youth was a valued riddle for the boys: whenever they ran out of science-conundrums they could always fall back upon that and subject it to a new discussion.

Naturally they wanted me to help them do the theorizing, and naturally I dearly wanted to, for the echte [11] scientist would rather theorize than eat; but I was reluctant. To be fair and honest I should have to do as the scientist always does—I should have to honorably contribute to the discussion every fact within my possession which could by any possibility be related to the matter;

---

[11] Mark Twain here uses this word from the German language in the sense of "genuine."

and so I should be obliged to reveal the secret of my earlier existence, and frankly furnish all the particulars. It is not easy to exaggerate the embarrassment of the situation. I wanted to keep the respect of my comrades: to tell them a colossal lie would not be a good way to do that, and certainly the chances were a thousand to one, in my opinion, that they would put just that estimate upon my statement.

Well, we are mere creatures of Circumstance. Circumstance is master, we are his slaves. We cannot do as we desire, we have to be humbly obedient and do as Circumstances command. Command— that is the word; Circumstance never requests, he always commands: then we do the thing, and think *we* planned it. When our circumstances change, we have to change with them, we cannot help it. Very well, there came a time when mine changed. The boys began to get suspicious of me. *Why* did I always shirk, and fumble, and change the subject whenever they wanted me to help theorize upon the mystery of my persistent youthfulness? They took that up, and began to whisper apart. When I appeared among them no face lighted with a welcome for me, I got perfunctory greetings in place of the old hearty ones, the group soon broke up and went away and I was left solitary and depressed. I had been happy always, before; I was always miserable, now.

Circumstances had changed. They commanded a change on my part. Being their slave, I had to obey. There was but one course to pursue if I would get back the boys' confidence and affection: I must frankly empty my human history into the debated mystery and take the consequences. Very well, I shut myself to think out the best way to proceed in the matter. Ought I to make my statement to the comradeship assembled in a body, or would it be wisest to try my history on a couple of the boys, make converts of them, if possible, and get their help in converting the rest? After much thought I inclined toward the latter course.

There were twelve of us. I will remark here that we were all of "good stock," to use the common phrase. We were nobodies, we were not noble, but by descent we were of the blood twelve of the great families or classes from which all the monarchies in Blitzowski drew their hereditary aristocracies. Not one of us had a vowel in his name, but our blood entitled us to acquire vowels, whereas this was not the case with persons of meaner extraction. Mainly, vowels went by favor, of course,—among the high-up,— as in all aristocracies, but minor persons of the Blood could acquire them by merit, purchase, the arts of corruption, and so forth. There was a mighty hunger for these gauds and distinctions, but that was natural, and is one of the indications that the difference between microbes and men is more a matter of physical bulk than anything else.

There was hardly a name among us that I could pronounce, on account of the absence of vowels, and the boys had a deal of trouble in managing my microbe-name, for I used an alias, painstakingly invented by myself, to cover accidents; I had said I was a native of the Major Molar, and so, as that was a far-off and quite unknown country it was rather necessary to have a name that would inspire confidence in the hearer—that is to say a name strange enough to properly fit a strange country. I made it out of a Zulu name and a Tierra del Fuegan name combined, and it consisted of three clucks and a belch, and was one of the most trying names I have ever struck. I could not pronounce it twice the same way myself; and as for the boys they presently gave it up, and only used it, after that, to swear with. They asked me to give them an easier one, and I gave them "Huck," an abbreviation of my American middle name, Huxley. On their side, and to show their thankfulness, they allowed me to change their names, too. I invoiced 45 literary ones, favorites of mine, and after considerable drill we selected the eleven which they could pull off with least danger to their jaws. I here append them; and with each name, the strain of great ancestral blood, or branch of it, that flowed in the veins of the owner; also, family crest:

LEMUEL GULLIVER. *Dot-Pyogenes. Head of the Pus-breeders.* Crest, *Single dot.*

LURBRULGRUD. *Pair-Dot, Diplococcus,* branch of Suppuration family. Crest, the printer's *colon.*

RIP VAN WINKLE. *Sarcina branch: cuboidal masses.* Crest, *a window-sash.*

GUY MANNERING. *Streptococcus. Erysipelas.* Crest, a *looped chain.*

DOGBERRY. *Acute pneumonia* branch. Crest, *a lance.*

SANCHO PANZA. *Typhoid.* Crest, *jackstraws.*

DAVID COPPERFIELD.[12] Branch—with cilia. Crest, *a radish, with roots adhering.*

COLONEL MULBERRY SELLERS. Branch—with spores. *Lockjaw.* Crest, *a broken needle.*

LOUIS XIV. *Consumption.* Crest, *a ruined spider-web.*

KING HEROD. *Diphtheria.* Crest, *Morse alphabet, wrecked.*

HUCK.[13] *Asiatic Cholera.* Crest, *Group of earth-worms.*

DON QUIXOTTE. *Recurrent Fever.* Crest, *maze of hair-snakes.*

Nobody knows the origin of these illustrious crests, there is no record of the great events which they were intended to commemorate and preserve from oblivion; the events occurred such ages and ages ago that history cannot remember them, and even legend itself has forgotten them. Now then, for an odd thing! I distinctly remember that under the microscope, in the earth, each of these families of microbes *looks like its crest,* whereas when you observe them here, with the microbe eye, they are strikingly beautiful in form and feature, and have not even a remote resemblance to their crests. This is certainly very odd, and to my mind it is most interesting. I think that as a coincidence it ranks away up. There was a time, long ago, when I came near to telling the boys about this curious thing, I was so anxious to examine it and discuss it with them, but I restrained myself. It would not have been prudent. They were a sensitive lot, and I doubt if they would have been pleased. Another thing: they—

But never mind that, for the present; I must get back to the real business of this chapter. In the end, I concluded to take a couple of the boys into my confidence, and let the others wait a while. I chose Gulliver and Louis XIV. I would have preferred Guy Mannering and David Copperfield, for certain reasons, but we were not living

[12] Mark Twain first wrote "Nicholas Nickleby," then "Meg Merrilies," but deleted both of these names.

[13] Mark Twain first wrote "Mark Twain" (page 111 of the holograph); he then deleted that name and inserted "Huck."

in a republic, and I had to think a little about etiquette and precedence. In Gulliver's veins was a quarter of a molecule of the blood of the reigning House, the imperial Henries; and although the imperial Henries did not know it and would not have cared for it if they had, Gulliver cared for it and kept himself—and others—reminded of it. So I had to choose Gulliver, and choose him *first*. Louis XIV had to come next. This was imperative, on account of his great blood—what he had of it. Of course if we had had a Plague bacillus—but we hadn't, so there is no occasion to go into that. Gulliver was clerk in a feed-store, Louis XIV was a pill-constructor in the pharmacy.

I invited that pair to my poor quarters, and they came. It was the evening of the day of the splendid discovery of the monster flea—the discovery of the point of his prodigious claw, to be exact. It was a good time, for our enthusiasm over the discovery had drawn us together again, and we had been like our old selves once more. For days I had been on the point of calling Lem and Louis, but had lost courage every time I had tried to do it, but now I knew the conditions were favorable, and I struck while the iron was hot.

The boys came, and they came in good spirits. I gave them an old-time welcome which touched them, and even brought the moisture to their eyes. I chunked up the poor little cheap fire and made it look its cheerfulest, and we bunched ourselves in front of it with lighted pipes, and with hot punches thereto.

"Oh, come, this is great!" said Louis "this is like old times!"

"Here's to their resurrection!" cried Gulliver; and "drink hearty!" cried I, and we did accordingly.

Then we chatted along, and chatted along, stowing the liquor between paragraphs, for punctuation, until we were become properly mellow and receptive, then I broke ground.

"Boys," I said, "I'm going to make a confession." They glanced at me with interest, not to say apprehension. "You have all wanted me to take a hand and help unriddle the mystery of my arrested development in the matter of age-indications, and I have avoided that subject—not out of perversity, I give you my word, but for a better reason, which I mean to lay before you to-night, and try to convince you that my course was fair and justifiable."

Their eyes beamed gratification, and their tongues put it into cordial words:

"Shake!" they said, and we shook.

"Without a doubt you have all suspected that I had invented an elixir of life, and was preserving my youth with it. Isn't it so?"

They hesitated, then said it was so. They said they had been forced to that conclusion because all their other theorizings had come to nothing. Then they quoted a remark of mine which I had long ago forgotten: a hint which I had thrown out to the effect that perhaps an elixir might be distilled from the chyle in the veins of a ram which—

"Well, you know," continued Louis, who had instanced the remark, "you did throw that out. When you wouldn't talk any more, we took hold of that hint and tried to get at your secret for ourselves. We believed, for a time, that we had succeeded. We made the elixir, and tried it on a lot of decrepit and tottering bacilli, and at first the results were splendid. The poor old things brisked up in a surprising way, and began to go to balls, and do the trapeze, and win foot-races, and show off in all sorts of antic improprieties, and it was the most pathetic and ridiculous spectacle of the century. But all of a sudden every lunatic of them collapsed and went to rags and ruin."

"I remember it! Was it you boys that got up the famous sheep-elixir that made such an immense noise for a little while?"

"Yes," said Lem Gulliver, "and we believed you could correct it and perfect it for us if you would, and it grieved us to think you were keeping such a sublime secret to yourself, when the honorable traditions of science required you to reveal it and confer it free of reward upon the public."

"Boys," I said, "I am going to ask you, for old friendship's sake, to believe two things, taking them from my lips without other evidence of their truth. First, that I invented no elixir of life; second, that if I had invented one I would have given it freely to the public. Do you believe?" They answered up promptly:

"By the beard and body of Henry the Great, 861, we do, Huck,[14] and are *glad* to! Shake!"

---

[14] Mark Twain first wrote "Mark" (page 120 of the holograph); he then deleted that name and inserted "Huck."

Which we did.

"Now then," I said, "I will ask you to believe one more thing—which is this: *I don't know the secret of my persistent youth myself.*"

I saw the chill descend upon them. They gazed steadily at me, sorrowfully, reproachfully—until my eyes fell. I waited—and waited—hoping that in charity they would break the miserable silence, but they would not. At last I said—

"Friends, old comrades, hear me, and be kind. You do not believe me, yet upon my honor I have spoken the truth. And now I come to my confession—according to the promise which I made. Possibly it may throw light upon this mystery—I hope it may. I believe there is light in it, but I am not certain, and, as a scientist, I am not permitted to accept anything, howsoever plausible, which cannot meet and conquer the final test, the test of tests—*demonstration*. The first article of my confession is this: *I was not always a cholera-germ.*"

The surprise of it made them gasp—I had suspected it would. But it lifted the solemnities a bit, and that was a good thing.

[XI]

Yes, it did that. That remark delivered a blast of ozone into the atmosphere. It was a remark that would fresh-up the curiosity of any person that ever lived. Naturally you couldn't throw it at a pair of trained scientists and not get attention. The new, the unheard-of, the uncanny, the mysterious—how the dullest head welcomes them! The old mystery was riches, here was the match of it, piled on top of it. The scientist is not permitted to exhibit surprise, eagerness, emotion, he must be careful of his trade-dignity—it is the law. Therefore the boys pulled themselves together and masked their eagerness the best they could. There was a studied scientific pause, then Louis, in a voice trembling with calm, opened the engagement—

"Huck, have you spoken figuratively, or are we [to] take that statement on a scientific rating?"

"Scientific."

"If you were not always a cholera-germ, what were you be-fore?"

"An American."

"A what?"

"American."

"This seems—well, it seems vague. I do not understand. What is an American?"

"A man."

"Er—that is vague, too. Lem, do you get it?"

"Search me!" He said it despairingly. Louis returned to the inquest:

"What is a man, Huck?"

"A creature you are not acquainted with. He does not inhabit this planet, but another one."

"Another one!"

"Another one!" echoed Gulliver. "What do you mean by that, Huck?"

"Why, I mean what I said."

He chuckled amusedly, and said—

"The Major Molar a *planet!* Well, that *is* good, upon my word. Here they've been trying for centuries to track-out and locate the original habitat of the modesty-germ, and . . . *say,* Huck, *that's* settled!"

It irritated me, but I kept the most of my temper down, and said:

"Lem, I never called it so. I wasn't referring to the Major Molar, at all."

"Oh, is *that* so! Say, Huck—"

"I don't know anything *about* the Major Molar, and I don't *care* anything about it. I was never there in my life!"

"What! you were nev—"

"No! I never was. I—"

"Sho! where'd you get that heart-breaking name?"

"Invented it. My real name doesn't resemble it."

"What is your real name?"

"B. b. Bkshp."

"Why, Huck," said Louis, "what did you want to tell so many lies for? What was the good of it?"

"I *had* to."

"Why?"

"Because if I had told the truth they would have put me in the asylum, thinking I was out of my head."

"I don't see how that could happen. Why should the truth have such an effect?"

"Because it would not have been understood, and would have been considered a lie. And a crazy one, at that."

"Come, Huck, you are straining your fancy. I guess you wouldn't have been misunderstood. You—"

"Oh, I like that! Only a minute ago I told *you* two or three truths and you didn't understand me. And when I said I came from another planet, Lem thought I was talking about the Major Molar, that humble little backwoods province! whereas I was referring to —to—hang it, I meant what I *said*—another *planet*. Not Blitzowski, but *another* one."

Then Gulliver broke in:

"Why, you muggins, there *isn't* any other. Lots of germs like to play with the *theory* that there's others, but you know quite well it's only theory. Nobody takes it seriously. There's nothing to support it. Come, Huck, your attitude is distinctly unscientific. Be reasonable—throw that dream-stuff out of your system."

"I tell you it *isn't* dream-stuff; there *is* another planet, and I was reared to maturity in it."

"If that is so, you must know a good deal about it. And perhaps you'll enrich us with as much of it as—"

"You needn't mock! I *can* enrich your knowledge-treasury as it was never enriched before, if you will listen and reflect, instead of making fun of everything I say."

Louis said—

"It isn't fair, Lem. Stop chaffing. How would you like to be treated so?"

"All right. Go on, Huck, tell us about the new planet. Is it as big as this one?"

I found I was going to laugh; so I pretended some smoke went down the wrong way, and this enabled me to cough past the danger-point. Then I said—

"It is bigger."

"Bigger, your granny! How much bigger?"

It was delicate ground, but I thought it wisest to go right on.

"It—well, it is so much bigger that if you were to mislay this planet in it and didn't tie a string to it or mark the place, it would take you a good four thousand years to find it again. In my opinion, *more* than that."

They stared at me a while most thankfully, then Louis got down on the floor so that he could laugh with spacious enjoyment, and Gulliver went behind the door and took off his shirt and brought it and folded it up and laid it in my lap without saying anything. It is the microbe way of saying "that takes the chromo." I threw the shirt on the floor, and told both of them they were as mean as they could be.

That sobered them, and Lem said, "Why, Huck, *I* didn't suppose you were in earnest," and Louis sat up on the floor and began to wipe the tears away, and said, "I didn't either, Huck—I *couldn't*, you know—and it came so sudden, you see."

Then they took their seats again, and tried to look repentant, and *did* look sorry, and Lem asked me to bite off another piece. If it had been almost any one else I would have struck him, but a prudent person doesn't hit one of those deadly pus-breeders when arbitration will do. Louis reproved Gulliver, then the pair set themselves to work to smooth my feathers down and get me in a good humor again; and the kind things they said soon had that effect, for one can't pout long when voices beloved for ten years are playing the old tunes on his heart—so to speak, for the metaphor is mixed. Soon the inquest was going along again, all right. I furnished several minor planetary facts, then Louis said—

"Huck, what is the actual size of that planet, in straight figures?"

"Figures! oh, I couldn't ever! There isn't room enough in this one to hold them!"

"Now there you go again, with your extrav—"

"Here! Come to the window—both of you. Look. How far can you see, across that plain?"

"To the mountains. Sixty-five miles."

"Come to this opposite side. Now how far do you see?"

"There being no mountain-barrier, we can't tell. The plain melts into the sky; there's no way to measure."

I said—

"Substantially, it's limitless receding and fading spaciousness, isn't it?"

"Just so."

"Very well. Let *it* represent that other planet; drop a single mustard seed in the middle of it, and—"

"O, fetch him a drink!" shouted Lem Gulliver; "and fetch it quick, his lie-mill's a-failing him!"

There spoke the practical mind, the unsentimental mind—the railroad mind, it may be called, perhaps. It has large abilities, but no imagination. It is always winter there. No, not just that—call it about the first week of November: no snow, only threats; cloudy, occasional drizzles, occasional wandering fogs drifting along; all aspects a little doubtful, suspicious, counseling wariness, watchfulness; temperature not vicious, not frosty, only chilly; average, about 45 F. It is the kind of mind that does not invent things itself, and does not risk money and worry on the development of another man's invention, and will not believe in its value until other people's money and labor have proved it; but it has been watching, all the time, and it steps promptly forward, then, and is the first to get in on the ground floor and help rake in the profits. It takes nothing on trust, you can't get it to invest in a dream at any discount, nor believe in it; but if you notice you will find that it is always present when the dream comes true—and has a mortgage on it, too.

To Lem Gulliver my planet was a dream, and would remain one, for the present. But to Louis, who had sentiment and imagination it was a poem, and I a poet. And he *said* that handsome thing, too. He said it was plain that I was endowed with a noble and beautiful gift, and that my planet was a majestic conception, a grand and impressive foundation, so to speak, lying ready for the architect's hand; and he said he believed that the genius that could imagine such a foundation was competent to build upon it a very palace of enchantment—a tumult of airy domes and towers, without, a golden wilderness of wonders within, where the satisfied soul might wander and worship, unconscious of the flight of time, uncon—

"O, rats!" said Lem Gulliver, breaking in, "that's just your style, Louis XIV—always jumping in to build a cathedral out of a hatful of bricks. Because he has spread out a big foundation, that's enough for you, you can already see the summer-hotel he's going to put up on it. Now I am not made in that way; I'm ready and willing to take stock in that joint *when* it's built, but—finance it at this stage? oh, I think I *see* myself!"

"Oh, yes," retorted Louis, "that *is* your style, Lem Gulliver, we all know it, and we know what comes of it, too. You are always keeping us back, with your doubts; you discourage everything. If Huck can go on as he has begun, it will be the sublimest poem in all the literatures; and anybody but you would believe that the mind that was able to imagine that mighty foundation is able to imagine the palace too, and furnish the rich materials and put them divinely together. Lie-mill, indeed! You may live to see the day when you will wish God had given *you* such a mill, Lem Gulliver!"

"Oh, go it! all down but nine, set 'em up on the other alley! I'm crushed—I'm routed; but all the same, I copper the hotel—at the present date. If you think he's got the materials for it, all right, it's your privilege; but as for me, I reason that when a person has laid down a foundation the size of that one, it isn't argument that it's a sample, it's argument that you've got his pile. He's empty, Louis—you'll see."

"I don't believe it. You're *not* empty, are you, Huck?"

"Empty? No. I haven't begun, yet."

"There, now, Lem Gulliver, what do you say to that?"

"I say his saying it is no proof. Let him start-up his mill again, that's all. Let him venture!"

Louis hesitated. Lem noticed it, and said, mockingly—

"You're right, Louis, I wouldn't over-strain him."

"I wasn't hesitating on account of fear, Lem Gulliver, and you needn't think it. I was recognizing that it wasn't fair. He is entitled to a recess, to recuperate in. Inspirations are not a mechanical affair, they do not come by command. It may well be—"

"Oh, don't apologize. It's all right; he's empty. I'm not wanting to crowd him. Give him a rest; let him recuperate. It's just as you say: inspirations are not mechanical things—no, they are spiritual. Pass him the jug."

"I don't need it," said I, recognizing that I ought to come to Louis' help. "I can get along without it."

Louis brightened up at that, and said—

"*Do* you think you can go ahead, Huck? do you think you can?"

"I don't only think it, I know it!"

Lem chuckled derisively, and told me to fetch on my "empty-ings."

[XII]

So the inquest began again. I was asked to describe my planet. I said—

"Well, as to shape, it is round, and—"

"*Round?*" said Gulliver, interrupting. "What a shape for a planet! Everybody would slide off—why, a cat couldn't stay on it! *Round!* Oh, cork the jug—*he* doesn't need any inspiration! Round! Say, Cholera—"

"Let him alone!" cried Louis, sharply. "There's neither right nor dignity in criticizing the fanciful creations of poesy by the standards of cold reason, Lem Gulliver, and you know it."

"Well, that *is* so, Louis, and I take it back. You see, it sounded just as if he were throwing out a straight fact, and so—well, it caught me off my base."

"I *was* throwing out a fact," I said. "If it must pass as poetry I can't help that, but it's fact, just the same, and I stand by it and stick to it. Louis, it *is* fact, I give you my word of honor it is."

It dazed him. He looked a good deal jumbled up, for a while, then he said, resignedly—

"Well, I feel all adrift. I don't quite know what to do with a situation like this, it's clear out of my experience. *I* don't understand how there could be a round planet, but I believe you *think* there is such a thing, and that you honestly believe you have been in it. I can say that much, Huck, and say it sincerely."

I was pleased, and touched, and said—

"Out of my heart I thank you for that, Louis. It cheers me, and I was needing it, for my task is not an easy one."

This was too sentimental to suit the pus-germ, and he said—

"*Dear* girlies! Oh—oh—*oh,* it is *too* touching! Do it some more."

I do not see how a person can act like that. To me it is a mark of coarseness. I coldly ignored it, I would not condescend to notice it. I reckon that that showed him what I thought about it. I now went calmly on with my work, just as if I was not aware that there had been any interruption. I judged it cut him, but I was cold and stern, and did not care. I remarked that my planet was called the World; that there were many countries and oceans spread over its vast surface—"

"O, hold on!" said Gulliver. "Oceans?"

"Yes—oceans."

"And they are facts too, are they?"

"Certainly."

"Well, then, perhaps you will be good enough to tell me how *they* stay on? What keeps them from spilling off?—those that are on the under side, I mean—in case there *are* any on the under side —and certainly there ought to be, to keep up the uniformity of insanity proper to such a crazy invention as that."

"There *isn't* any under side," I said. "The world keeps turning over in the air all the time."

"Turning over—in the air! Come—is that introduced as a fact, too?"

"Yes—and it is a fact."

"Turns over in the air, and doesn't fall! Is that it?"

"Yes."

"Doesn't rest on anything? Is that it?"

"Yes."

"What's it made out of? Is it gas, in a soap bubble?"

"No. Rocks and dirt."

"Turns over in the air, doesn't rest on anything, is made out of rocks and dirt, and doesn't fall! Seems too good to be true! What's the reason it doesn't fall?"

"It is kept in its place by the attraction of other worlds in the sky; and the sun."

"Other worlds!"

"Yes."

"Well! So there's more, then?"

"Yes."

"How many?"

"Nobody knows. Millions."

"Millions! Oh, sweet Maria!"

"You can make as much fun as you want to, Lem Gulliver, but all the same it's true. There are millions of them."

"Say—couldn't you knock off a few? just a few, you know, for cash?"

"I've told you—and you can believe it or not, just as you please."

"Oh, I believe it—oh, yes indeedy! I could believe a little thing like that with both hands tied behind me. Are they big, Huck, or little?"

"Big. The world is a puny little thing compared to the most of them."

"How handsome of you to allow it! Now *that's* what I call *real* magnanimity. It humbles me. I bow to it."

He was going on with his mean sarcasms, but Louis was so ashamed of him, and so outraged to see me treated so ungenerously when I was evidently speaking the truth, or at least speaking what I believed to be the truth, that he cut in and shut Gulliver off in the midst of his small-arm gun-play.

"Huck," he said, "what are the components of the World, and their proportions?"

"Offer an amendment!"—this from the tiresome pustule—"call it the Bubble. If it flies, that's what it is; if it's solid, it's a lie; either a lie or supernatural. Supernatural lie, *I* think."

I took no notice of his drivel, I would not stoop to it. I addressed my answer to Louis:

"Three-fifths of the World's surface is water. Seas and oceans. That is to say, salt water and undrinkable."

Of course Lem broke in:

"Oh, my land, *that* won't do! it would take ten million mountain ranges of pure salt to keep it up to standard, and *then* it wouldn't. Come—what *makes* it salt? That's it. Out with it—don't stop to invent. What *makes* it salt?"

I simply answered—

"I don't know."

"Don't *know!* The idea! Don't know!"

"No, I don't. *What makes your Great Lone Sea rancid?*"

I scored, that time! He couldn't say a word. It crumpled him up like sitting down on a plug hat. I was tickled to the pericardium; so was Louis, for it was a corker, now I tell you! You see, Science had been fussing for ages over the riddle of what supplies the waters of the Great Lone Sea; the riddle of whence they could come in such miraculous quantity was persistently and exasperatingly insolvable —just as was the case with earthscience in its effort to find the source of the sea's salt-supply.

After a little, Louis said—

"Three-fifths of the surface is a mighty quantity. If it should overflow its banks there would be a catastrophe that would be remembered."

"It did it once," I said. "There was a rain-storm which lasted forty days and forty nights, and buried the whole globe out of sight, mountains and all, for eleven months."

I thought the pathos of the stupendous disaster to life would stir them; but no—with the true scientist, science always comes first, the humanities later. Louis said—

"Why didn't it *stay* buried? What reduced the water?"

"Evaporation."

"How much of it did evaporation carry off?"

"The water covered mountains six miles high, which overlooked ocean-valleys five miles deep. Evaporation carried off the upper six miles."

"Why didn't it get the rest? What stopped it?"

I had not thought of that before, and the question embarrassed me. But I did not show it, beyond a catching of the breath, and maybe an anxious look in the face, and before these had time to rouse suspicion I had scraped up an emergency-answer:

"*There,*"—with a just-perceptible pressure on the word—"*there* the law of evaporation is restricted to the upper six miles. Below that line it can't work."

The boys looked at me so sadly, and withal so reproachfully, that I was sorry for myself, and dropped my eyes. There was one of those oppressive silences, for a time,—the kind, you know, that start at a weight of 30 pounds to the square inch and add 30 per second—then Lem Gulliver fetched a deep sigh and said—

"Well, it certainly is the insanest country that ever *I've* struck. But I make no moan; I'm getting hardened to its freaks. Hand me another, Huck. Sock it to me! One—two—three—let her go, Gallagher! *Say*—three-fifths is salt water; what's the next detail?"

"Ice and desert. But there's only one-fifth of that."

"*Only!* Only's good! *Only* one-fifth ice and desert! Oh, *what* a planet! *Only* one-f—"

The scorn of it was unendurable, it scorched me like fire. In a fury I threw up my hand—he stopped—and almost to my tongue's end leaped the words—

"Look at *your* planet! A third of it is—" [15]

But I caught myself in time. Slowly I closed my mouth, slowly I lowered my threatening hand. I was bred in an atmosphere of refinement, I was refined by nature and instinct, and I could not sully my lips with the word. We are strange beings, we seem to be free, but we go in chains—chains of training, custom, convention, association, disposition, environment—in a word, Circumstance— and against these bonds the strongest of us struggle in vain. The proudest of us and the meanest meet upon a common level, the

---

[15] Cancelled word was "guts."

rankless level of servitude. King, cobbler, bishop, tramp—all are slaves, and no slave in the lot is freer than another.

I was burning, I was blazing! I had been caring nothing for my lost World; at bottom I was even despising it, so loyal was I in my admiration for the planet which was become so dear to me by reason of my microbe blood; but this scorn of that lost home of mine turned me into its champion, and I jumped to my feet, white to the lips with anger, and burst out with—

"Silence, and listen! I have spoken the truth—and only the truth, so help me God! That World *is*, as compared with your planet, as is that horizonless plain yonder to a grain of sand! And yet it itself is nothing—less than nothing—when its littleness is brought into contrast with the vast bulk of the millions of suns that swim those seas of space wherein it paddles lonely and unnoticed, save by its own sun, its own moon. And what is a sun, and what is a moon? I will tell you. That sun is a hundred thousand times the bulk of that World; it is made of white fire, and flames in the far zenith 92,000,000 miles away, and pours its floods of light upon the World all the day; and when the black darkness of the night comes, then comes the moon, drifting through the distant blue, and clothes the World in mellow light. *You* know no night, and you know no day that is like the World's day. You know a light that is lovelier than these—be grateful! You live in an eternal day of soft and pearly light through which trembles and shimmers unceasingly the dainty and delicate fires of the opal—be grateful! it is your possession, and yours alone—no light that shines on any other land is like it; none possesses its charm, its witchery, none is so gentle, so dreamy, so charged with healing for the hurt mind and the broken spirit.

"There that little World—so unimaginably vast, compared with yours!—paddles about in a shoreless solitude of space; and where are those millions of others? Lost!—vanished! invisible, when the great sun rides in the sky; but at night—oh, there they are! colossal black bulks, lumbering by? No!—turned to mere glinting sparks by distance!—a distance not conceivable by such as you! The vault is sown thick with them, the vault is alive with them, trembles with them, quivers with them! And through their midst rises a broad belt of their like, uncountable for number—rises and flows up into the sky, from the one horizon, and pours across and goes flooding down to the other—a stupendous arch, made all of glittering vast suns diminished to twinkling points by the awful distance—and where is that colossal planet of mine? It's *in* that Belt—somewhere, God knows where! It wanders there somewhere in that immeasurable ocean of twinkling fires, and takes up no more room and gets no more notice than would a firefly that was adrift in the deeps of the opal skies that bend over imperial Henryland!

"Now then, take it or leave it! I've told you the truth, and there's not a force in this planet that can make me take back a word of it!"

All aglow with enthusiasm, Louis burst out—

"By God, there stands the palace!—I believed he could build it!"

"And by God, there stands the supernatural lie!—I *knew* he could hatch it!"

[XIII]

By now it was two o'clock in the morning, and my little thought-recorder girl—always punctual to the minute—entered and broke up the sitting. The boys rose to go, but they said they didn't want to, and they said it with the most evident sincerity, too. Louis said it was inspiring and uplifting to listen to such a poem, and Lem Gulliver said with fervency, he wished he had my talent, so help him God he would never speak the truth again. I had never seen them so moved. Louis said my art was perfect, and Lem said the same. Louis said he was going to practice it himself, and Lem said he was, too; but both said they could never hope to get up to my plane. They both said they had had a wonderful evening. These great praises made me feel so happy that I seemed [to be] walking on air, and I had no words to thank the boys enough for them. What a change it was from that long season of aching depression and disfavor! My atrophied nerves cast off their apathy, and along them raced and rioted fresh new life and pleasure; I was like one risen from the dead.

The boys wanted to rush away to the fossil-mine and tell the whole thing to the nine others—just what I was hoping for! My original scheme would succeed, now—these missionaries would convert the rest of the comradeship, and I should be in full favor again, I felt sure of it. And now they did me a parting honor: by their own invitation we stood up and clinked glasses, shouting—thus:

Louis. "To Old Times Come Again—to stay!"

Lem. "Bumpers! no heel-taps!"

Huck. "And God bless us all!"

Then they sallied out unsteadily, arm-locked, and singing a song I had taught them in those same Old Times—a song disused this many a heavy day—

"Goblskvet liikdwzan hooooclk!" *

* Trans. "We won't go home till mor-or-ning—
Till daylight doth appear!"

In the enthusiasm born of our great fossil-find, we had agreed to dig right along, twenty-four hours in the day, and day after day indefinitely, in order that we might get as far along as possible with the excavating before the news should get abroad and the interruptions begin; but I was deep in a History of the World which I was dictating, to the end that my knowledge in that matter might not fade out and be lost, and I was minded to finish it, now, and make good my share of the flea-mine agreement when it was done. The history of Japan would complete the formidable enterprise; I would put that together at the present sitting, then I should be free and could devote my energies to the fossil flea with a contented spirit and an undivided mind. Meantime the missionarying would be going on, out there at the mine, and might I not venture to hope that by the time I appeared there the conversions would have been accomplished—provided I strung out the story of Japan pretty elaborately? Seemed so to me.

By good luck the thought-recording machine was out of order; it would take a little time to fix it. It would take more if I taught

Catherine of Aragon how to do it herself—so I adopted that plan. She was a dear little thing, with a pretty good head, and quite teachable; for whereas she was a "benevolent" microbe—that is to say, a daughter of the people, the masses, the humble hard-workers, the ill-paid, the oppressed, the despised, the unthanked, the meek and docile bulwark of the Throne, without whose support it would tumble to ruin like the card-house it really was—whereas, as I say, she was of this breed and therefore an ass by right of birth, and by old heredity entitled to be profoundly stupid, she was not stupid at all. She wasn't, because, by reason of an ancestral adventure of ancient date, part of a drop of cancer-blood had trickled down to her which should have trickled down to somebody else, and that little stain was worth much to Catherine. It lifted her mentalities away above the average intellectual level of her caste, for the cancers are bright, and have always been so. The other aristocracies breed a bright specimen now and then, but with the cancers, and with the cancers only, brightness is the rule.

Catherine was a neighbor's child, and she and her *Geschwister* were contemporaries and comrades of our earliest Taylor-litter—I mean the one I first knew. Both of these litters had been my teachers in the local tongues, and in return I had conferred English (pretending it was Major Molar) upon hundreds of kids belonging to the two batches—a *sort* of English, at any rate, and not really bad for "benevolents"—but Catherine learned it the quickest of them all, and was a daisy at it. Indeed, she spoke it like a native. I always used the English language when talking with her, in order to keep her in practice and keep myself from forgetting it.

I did not choose that name for her—Catherine of Aragon. I should not have thought of such a thing, for it was quite unsuitable, she was so little. In a World-microscope she would not have showed up at all until she was magnified eighteen hundred diameters. But when she did show up she would command exclamations of delight and admiration, for the Observer would have to grant that she was very very pretty—pretty as a diatom. No, she chose the name herself. She lit upon it one day when we were doing the History of England, and she was quite carried away by it and said it was the sweetest thing out of doors. She had to have it, she couldn't do without it; so she took it. Her name, before that, was Kittie Daisybird Timpleton, and quite suited her petite and dainty figure and exquisite complexion and frivolousness, and made her look charming. In replacing unpronounceable native names with easy human ones I always tried to select such as would not invoke prejudice and uncharitable comment by being in violent contrast with the style of the persons decorated with them.

But she wanted to be Catherine of Aragon, and was ready to cry about it, so I had to let her have her way, though,—so applied,—it had no more fitness nor point than there was in Lem Gulliver's latest nick-name for me, which was Nancy. Lem Gulliver is vulgar, and resents refinement, and thinks any person who is refined is effeminate.

However, she wanted it, so I yielded and let her have it. It was just an accident that she ever heard of Catherine of Aragon. It happened one night when I was dictating historical thoughts into the Recorder. You do not dictate *words*, you understand, but only thoughts—*impressions*—and they are not articulated; that is to say, you do not frame the impressions into words, you deliver them in *blocks*, a whole chapter in one blast—in a single second, you know —and the machine seizes them and records them and perpetuates them for time and eternity in that form; and there they are, and there they glow and burn forever; and so luminous are they, and so clear and limpid and superbly radiant in expression that they make all articulated speech—even the most brilliant and the most perfect —seem dull and lifeless and confused by comparison. Ah, if a person wants to know what an intellectual aurora borealis is like, with the skies all one tumultuous conflagration and downpour of divine colors and blinding splendors, let him connect-up a Recorder and turn on one of those grand poems which the inspired Masters of a million years ago dreamed into these machines!

Yes, you sit silent and dictate to the machine with your soul, not with your mouth; but sometimes you utter a chance word without being aware of it, you are so absorbed. And so that was the way Cat got her new name. I was doing impressions of Henry VIII, and was so stirred by some of his cruelties toward his first queen that I unconsciously exclaimed, "Alas, poor Catherine of Aragon!"

That I should break out in *speech* while dictating, was such a surprise to Kittie that it knocked the self-possession out of her and she stopped turning the crank to look at me and wonder. Then the stately flow and music of the name knocked it in again and she exclaimed with emotion—

"Oh, how sweet, oh, how recherché! Oh, I could die for such a name as that! Oh, I think it is *so* chahming!"

Do you notice? Just a dear little bundle of self-complacencies and affectations,—that was what she was. A single speech is enough to expose her. Even the word "die" is an affectation, for she couldn't *think* die; she was a microbe, and could only think "disintegrate." But you would not catch *her* saying she could disintegrate for such a name as that; no, it would not be foreign enough, not affected enough.

Well, that was some time ago, when we were doing "England, From Brutus to Edward VII." Now then, when she came in, that morning, and interrupted that nice time I was having with Lem and Louis, I noticed an astonishing change in her: she was grave, dignified, calm, reposeful—all her notice-begging fussy little airs and graces and simperings and smirkings were gone, her chewing-gum corals were gone, her brass bracelets were gone, her glass aigrette was gone, the manufactured waves were gone from her hair, the spit-curl was gone from her forehead, her gown was dark and plain and neat, simplicities and sincerities sat upon her everywhere, and looked out of her eyes, and found unconscious utterance in her words and her tones when she spoke. I said to myself, "Here is a mystery, a miracle: lo, Kittie Daisybird Templeton is no more, the bogus Catherine of Aragon is no more: this is that bogus Catherine transmuted into the true metal, and worthy to wear the name!"

While she tinkered at the machine, repairing it under my instructions, I inquired into the cause of the transformation, and she explained the matter at once—simply, frankly, unembarrassedly, even with a sort of glad and grateful eagerness, as it seemed to me. She said she had picked up the book called "Science and Wealth, With Key to the Fixtures," with the idea of finding out, for herself, what there was about it to make the new sect, popularly and ironically called the Giddyites, set so much store by it—with the unexpected result that within ten minutes a change began to take place in her—an etherealizing change—a change which was volatilizing her flesh and turning it to spirit. She read on and on, the transforming process continued; within the hour it was complete, and she was all spirit, the last vestige of flesh was gone. I said—

"Catherine, you don't look it; there must be some mistake."

But she was quite sure there was not; and she was so earnest about it that I could not doubt, and did not doubt, that she believed what she was saying. To me it was a delusion; an hour or two earlier I would have *said* so, and risen superior to her, and looked down upon her compassionately from that high altitude, and would have advised her to put the foolish and manifest fraud out of her head and come back to common sense and reasonableness. But not now. No. An hour or two ago and *now*—those were two quite different dates. Within that brief space I had suffered a sea-change myself. I had seen a certainty of mine dubbed a delusion and laughed at by a couple of able minds—minds trained to searchingly and exhaustively examine the phenomena of Nature, and segregate fact from fancy, truth from illusion, and pronounce final judgment —and these competent minds had puffed my World away without a moment's hesitancy, and without the shadow of a misgiving. They thought they knew it was an illusion. I knew it wasn't.

The list of things which we absolutely know, is not a long one, and we have not the luck to add a fresh one to it often, but I recognized that I had added one to mine this day. I knew, now, that it isn't safe to sit in judgment upon another person's illusion when you are not on the inside. While you are thinking it is a dream, he may be knowing it is a planet.

I was well satisfied in my mind that Catherine was the prey of an illusion, but I had no disposition to say so, and so I didn't say it. My wounds were too sore for that, as yet. But I talked her new condition over with her, and she made the matter very interesting. She said there was no such thing as substance—substance was a fiction of Mortal Mind, an illusion. It was amusing to hear it!

Whose illusion? Why, anybody's that didn't believe as she did. How simple—and how settling! Oh, dear, we are all like that. Each of us knows it all, and *knows* he knows it all—the rest, to a man, are fools and deluded. One man knows there is a hell, the next one knows there isn't; one man knows high tariff is right, the next man knows it isn't; one man knows monarchy is best, the next one knows it isn't; one age knows there are witches, the next one knows there aren't; one sect knows its religion is the only true one, there are sixty-four thousand five hundred million sects that know it isn't so. There is not a mind present among this multitude of verdict-deliverers that is the superior of the minds that persuade and represent the rest of the divisions of the multitude. Yet this sarcastic fact does not humble the arrogance nor diminish the know-it-all bulk of a single verdict-maker of the lot, by so much as a shade. Mind is plainly an ass, but it will be many ages before it finds it out, no doubt. Why do we respect the opinions of any man or any microbe that ever lived? I swear [I] don't know. Why do I respect my own? Well—that is different.

Catherine said there was no such thing as pain, or hunger, or thirst, or care, or suffering of any kind: these were all fictions of the Mortal Mind; without the presence of substance they could not exist, save as illusions, therefore they had no existence in fact, there being no such thing as substance. She called these fictions "claims"; and said that whenever a claim applied, she could drive it away in a moment. If it was a pain, for instance, she had only to repeat the formula of "the Scientific Statement of Being," as set down in the book, then add the words "there is no such thing as pain," and the detected fiction vanished away. She said there was no so-called disease and no so-called pain in all the long roll of microbic ailment-fictions that could not be routed and dismissed by the method above described. Except teeth-claims. They were fictions like the rest, but it was safest to carry them to the dentist. This was not immoral, not irreligious, for it was permitted by the finder of the Giddyite religion, who took her own teeth to the painless-gas establishment, and in that way made the departure from principle holy.

Catherine said cheerfulness was real, and depression of spirits a fiction. She said there was not a care, not a sorrow, not a worry left in her soul. She looked it; I had to confess it!

I asked her to put the principles of her sect into a few clear sentences, so that I could understand them and keep them in my head, and she did it, quite without effort:

"Mortal Mind, being the idea of Supreme Refraction exhibited and sanctified in the Bacterium in correspondence and co-ordination with Immortal Mind in suspension, which is Truth, All-Good follows, of necessity, precipitating and combining with the elements of the Good-Good, the More-Good and the Ultimate or Most-Good, sin being a fiction of Mortal Mind operating upon Absence of Mind, nothing can be otherwise, Law being Law and hence beyond jurisdiction, wherefore the result is paramount—and being paramount, our spirits are thus freed from Substance, which is an Error of Mortal Mind, and whosoever so desires, can. This is Salvation."

She asked me if I believed it, and I said I did. I didn't really believe it, and I don't now, but it pleased her and was a little thing to say, so I said it. It would have been a sin to tell her the truth, and I think it is not right to commit a sin when there is no occasion for it. If we would observe this rule oftener our lives would be purer.

I was greatly pleased with this conversation, because it contained things which seemed to show that the microbe mind and the human mind were substantially alike and possessed reasoning powers which clearly placed them above the other animals. This was very interesting.

I had an opportunity, now, to look into a matter which had been in my mind a long time—the attitude of the microbe toward the lower animals. In my human state I had wanted to believe that our humble comrades and friends would be forgiven and permitted to be with us in the blessed Land of the Hereafter. I had had difficulty in acquiring this belief, because there was so much opposition to it. In fact I never did get it where it would stick. Still, whenever and wherever there was a friendly dog wagging his affectionate tail, and looking up at me with his kind eyes and asking me to swap love for love with him; or a silken cat that climbed into my lap, uninvited, for a nap, thus flattering me with her trust; or a gracious horse that took me for a friend just by the look of me and pushed his nose into my pocket for possible sugar and made me wish he could impart his nature to my race and give it a lift up toward his own—whenever these things happened they always raised that hope in me again and set it struggling toward concrete belief once more.

When I talked with opposers about this, they said—

"If you admit those because they are innocent of wrong by the law of their make, as you say, what are you going to do about the mosquito, the fly, and those others? Where are you going to draw the line? They are all innocent alike; come—where are you going to draw the line?"

It was my custom to say I didn't draw it at all. I didn't want the fly and his friends, but no matter; what a man could stand here he could stand there, and moreover there was a high matter concerned —common justice. By even the elemental moralities, it would be unjust to let in any creature made honor-worthy by deriving its spirit and life from God's hand and shut any other out.

But it never settled it. The opposer was human, and knew he was right; I was human, and knew I was right. There isn't anybody that isn't right, I don't care what the subject is. It comes of our having reasoning powers.

Once I carried the matter to a good and wise man who. . . .

XIV.

I T WAS a clergyman. He said—

"Let us proceed logically; it is the law of my training, and is a good law. Helter-skeltering is bad: it starts in the middle and goes both ways, it jumbles the points instead of ranking them according to seniority or importance, it gets lost in the woods and doesn't arrive. It is best to start at the beginning. You are a Christian?"

"I am."

"What is a creature?"

"That which has been created."

"That is broad; has it a restricted sense?"

"Yes. The dictionary adds, *'especially* a living being.' "

"Is that what we commonly mean when we use the word?"

"Yes."

"Is it also what we *always* mean when we use it without a qualifying adjective?"

"Yes."

"Used without qualification, then, a dog is a creature?"

"Certainly."

"A cat?"

"Yes."

"A horse, a rat, a fly, and all the rest?"

"Of course."

"What verse is it which authorizes the missionary to carry the gospel to the pagans?—to the willing and to the unwilling alike."

" 'Whatsoever ye would that men should do unto you—' "

"*No!* It is infinitely broader: 'Go ye into *all the world* and preach the gospel to *every* CREATURE.' Is that language plain and clear, or is it foggy and doubtful?"

"Plain and clear, I should say. I cannot see anything doubtful about the meaning of it."

"How would you go about doctoring the meaning of it so as to make it apply to man only, and shut out the other creatures? What art would you employ?"

"Well, the arts of shuffling and indirection, adroitly used, could accomplish it, but I like it best as it is. I would not wish to change it."

"You are aware that the plain meaning stood at its full value, unchanged and unchallenged, during fifteen hundred years?"

"I am."

"You are aware that the intelligence of the Fathers of the Church ranks as high to-day as does the intelligence of any theologian that has followed them, and that they found no fault with that language and did not try to improve its meaning?"

"Yes."

"You are aware that the change is a quite modern freshet of intelligence, and that up to so late a time as three centuries ago the Christian clergy were still including the dumb animals in the privileges of that great commandment, and that both Catholic priest and Protestant were still preaching the gospel to them, in honorable obedience to its uncompromising terms?"

"I am aware of it."

"In commanding that the gospel be carried to all the World and preached to every creature, what was the object in view?"

"The salvation of the hearers."

"Is there any question that that was the object?"

"None has been suggested. It has not been disputed."

"Then not two, but only one inference is deducible from the language of that commandment when it is spared jugglery and is conscientiously examined: that *all* of God's creatures are included in His merciful scheme of salvation. Heaven will not look strange to us; the other animals will be there, and it will look like home, and *be* home."

This was a rational view, at last, a just view, a fair and righteous view, a generous view, and one in accord with the merciful character of the Creator. It removed all my doubts, all my perplexities, it brought conviction to me, and planted my feet upon solid ground. The clergyman was right, I felt it to my marrow, and in the best words I could command I tried to make him understand how grateful I was to him. My feelings were revealed in my words, and *they* at least were eloquent I knew, whether the words were or not, for he was much moved. I wished he would say that pleasant sentence over again, and over again, and still again, it had been so contenting to my spirit; and really, he seemed to divine that thought of mine, for without my saying anything he uttered it at once, and with emphasis—

"Yes, *all* the creatures! Be at rest as to that—they will be there; no creature designed, created, and appointed to a duty in the earth will be barred out of that happy home; they have done the duty they were commissioned to do, they have earned their reward, they will all be there, even to the littlest and the humblest."

"The *littlest*." The words sent a subtle chill down my hot veins.

Something rose in me: was it a shadowy doubt? I looked up vacantly, muttering absently—

"The disease-germs? the microbes?"

He hesitated—some little time; then changed the subject.

Well, as I have said before, the matter of whether our humble friends go with us to our happy future home or not had never lost its interest with me, and so I thought I would introduce it, now, and talk it over with Catherine. I asked her if she thought the dogs and the horses and so on would go with us microbes and still be our pets and comrades. It raised her interest at once. She said I knew she had formerly belonged to the most widely spread of all the many religions of the planet—the Established Church of Henryland—and didn't I know that that question was always being privately discussed and fussed over by the membership whenever the authorities were not around? didn't I know that?

Yes, oh, yes, I said, certainly I knew it, but it had escaped my mind. It would have hurt her if I had told her I hadn't even heard of it before, but I think it is not right to hurt a person who is not doing any harm. Lem Gulliver would have told her, for he has no moral sense; it is nothing to him whether he does right or doesn't. It is the way he is made, and so it may be that he is not responsible for it. But I do not do right because I am responsible, and I do not do right because it is right to do right, I think it is a low motive; I do it because—because—well I have a lot of reasons, I do not recollect which ones are the main ones now, but it is of no consequence, anyway. She said she felt a strong interest in the subject, and had very decided notions about it—that is, she *had* had—and would gladly state them for me—that is, her present ones. But not in her own language, for that was not allowed; members of her sect must not exhibit religious matters in their own words, because they would be incompetently put together and would convey error. Then she began, and went along so trippingly that I saw she had her Book by heart:

"As concerns this question, our inspired Founder instructs us that the fealty due from the Ultimate in connection with and subjection to the intermediate and the inferential, these being of necessity subordinate to the Auto-Isothermal, and limited subliminally by this contact, which is in all cases sporadic and incandescent, those that ascend to the Abode of the Blest are assimilated in thought and action by the objective influence of the truth which sets us free, otherwise they could not."

There she stopped. Apparently I had wandered, and missed a cog somewhere, so I apologised and got her to say it again. She said it the same way. It certainly sounded straightforward and simple, yet I couldn't seem to get it, quite. I said—

"Do you understand it, Catherine?"

She said she did.

"Well, I *seem* to, but I can't make sure. Which ones do *you* think it is that ascend to the Abode of the Blest?"

"We are not allowed to explain the text, it would confuse its meaning."

"Well, then, don't do it. I do not pretend to revere it, still I would not like that to happen to it. But you can tell me this much, anyway, without doing any harm. (You needn't speak, you know, just nod your head; I'll understand.) Which ones is it that could not?—could not *otherwise*, I mean? It seems to be the sporadics, but it looks as if it might be the incandescents. *Is* it the sporadics? Don't speak, just nod. Nod, or shake, according to the facts."

But she refrained. She said it would amount to explaining, and was not allowable.

"Well, are they *animals*? Surely you can tell me that, Catherine?"

But she couldn't. She was willing to say the formula over again, and as many times as I pleased, but the rules were strict, and would not allow her to add to the formula, or take from it, or change the place of a word, the whole being divinely conceived and divinely framed, and therefore sacred.

It seemed to me that it would have been a good idea to apply this sensible rule to the other Scriptures and paralyse the tinkers with it: the ones that squeezed the animals out of that good and merciful text.

"Well," I said, "say it again, and say it slow. I'll tally-off as you unwind; that is, when I think you've let out as much of an instalment as I can handle without help, I'll give notice and you'll shut down till I take up the slack and stow it, then you'll let out another one—and so on, and so on, till I've got it all. The instalment plan is the best, with this line of goods. Remember—don't rush—slow and careful is the thing. Now then—ready? Play ball!"

"Which?"

"Oh, that's a technicality. If means, Begin. Once more—ready? Unwind!"

She understood, this time, and performed perfectly. Pretty metalically, as to sound, pretty dead-level and expressionless, like a phonograph saying its prayers, but sharp and definite, and quite satisfactory:

"As concerns—this question—our inspired Founder—instructs us that—the fealty due from—the Ultimate in connection with—and subjection to the—intermediate and the inferential, these—being of necessity sub—"

"Halt! I do believe you've dealt me a sequence. Let me look at my hand."

But it was a disappointment. Good cards, but no two of the same suit. Still, it was a hand that might be patched, perhaps. "Intermediate—Inferential"—that really looked like a pair. I felt encouraged, and said:

"Go on, Catherine, I'll draw to fill. Give me three."

But she is not educated, and she did not understand. But I did not explain; I said the laws of the cult didn't allow it. This was a sarcasm, but it didn't penetrate. I often fired little things like that at her, but only because she was sarcasm-proof, and they wouldn't hurt. I have a good deal of natural wit, and when a person is that way, he enjoys to listen to himself do it. If such a person gets the right encouragement, there is no limit to how high up he can develop. I think it was owing almost entirely to Uncle Assfalt that I got mine developed so high. He loved to hear me, and that made me keep working at it. The time that I said that about the cow that—that—well, the rest of it has gone out of my memory, now, I can't recollect what it was she did, but it was that funny it seemed like Uncle Assfalt was never going to get done laughing over it. He fairly rolled on the floor in agonies. I said—

"Never mind the three, Catty, it's another technicality. This instalment is a failure; let us try another. Go ahead."

But it was another failure. It was just a snow-flurry on a warm day: every flake was distinct and perfect, but they melted before you could grab enough to make a ball out of them. So I said—

"We will try another way. Sometimes, you know, if you dart a swift glance over a tough foreign sentence you capture the general meaning of it, whereas if you stop to meddle with details you're gone. We'll try that method. Now then—no commas, no dashes, no pauses of any sort: start at the beginning and buzz the whole incantation through just in one solid whiz—swift, you know— Empire Express—no stop this side of Albany. One—two—three— let her *go!*"

My, it was a grand effect! Away off you could hear it coming— next it was in sight and raging down the line like a demon chasing a Christian—next second, *by* she plunges, roaring and thundering, and vomiting black smoke—next, round the corner and out of sight! Apparent dividend: scurrying leaves, whirling dust, a shower of cinders. Even these settle and quiet down, after a little, and then there isn't anything left at all.

When the furniture stopped whirling around and there was only one Catherine instead of a ring of Catherines, I said I was willing to surrender if I could march out with my side-arms. Then, being defeated, I felt malicious, and was going to say I believed the Founder had a "claim," and that it was a mental one, but I didn't say it. It would only hurt Catherine, and she couldn't defend herself, because she wasn't built like some, and hadn't any wit; and so it would not be generous in me to say it. Put *me* in *her* place, and I would be back before you could wink, with a withering "Perhaps it's *you* that's got the claim!" But not many would think of that. They would think of it next day, but that is the difference between talent and the imitation of it. Talent thinks of it at the time.

I could see that Catherine was disappointed about the failure; she had a great affection for her new cult, and it grieved her to see it miss the triumph she had expected it was going to achieve—I thought I could read this in her face, poor thing—so I hadn't the heart to confess I was permanently done trying to strike oil in that formation: I let on that by and by when I got leisure I was going to torpedo that well, and was feeling sure I should turn loose a gusher —a thousand barrels a day, I said; and when I saw how glad it made her, I raised it to four thousand, the expense being the same. I told her to empty the incantation into the recorder—which she did at once—and leave it there. I said I thought that what it needed was, to be *disarticulated,* and resolved into its original elements; that the way it was now, the words broke up the sense—interrupted the flow of meaning, you see—jumbled it all up, you understand, when there was no occasion; the machine would mash the words together into a pulp, and grind the pulp around the way an arastra does with pulverised ores from the mill, and when you come to clean up at the week-end, there you are! there's your virgin gold, caught tight and fast in the amalgam! there's your clean and clear four dollars' worth, a thousand carats fine, *rescued!* Every yellow grain captured, safe and sound, and nothing left behind but eleven tons of slush! It's four dollars, and every dollar worth a hundred cents on the scales; it's not coined, but that's nothing, you've got the full-par *impression,* and when you've got that you've got the whole thing: mint it if you want to, it's your privilege: coin it and stamp Henry's head on it, and it's worth par all over Henryland, but leave it as it is and it's worth par from one end of Blitzowski clean to the other!

Well, it pleased her so, that I wished I had made it nine dollars. For a moment I thought I would do it, but I had scruples about it and refrained. It would be 76 cents a ton, and I knew you couldn't get that out of *that* kind of rock—no, not even with the cyanide. Presently I sighed, and Catherine wanted to know, right away, what was troubling me; she was just that quick in her sympathies, now that her new religion was giving her a chance to stop thinking about her own troubles—in fact she hadn't any, any more, she said. I said—

"I was wishing I had *somebody* that would talk to me about whether the animals are going up there with us or not. You, see, Catty—"

She made a spring for the window, and cried out—

"Countess! Yonder is Rev. Brother Pjorsky drowsing on the fire-plug. Would you mind asking him to step in here a minute as you pass by him?" Then she returned to her seat, saying, "He'll love to talk with you about it. And he is very nice, too. You remember him, don't you—the time he came here once and took up a collection? No? It was years ago, I thought you would remember it. He is about the same as a priest, but he isn't that—they don't have priests in his sect, but only Brothers, as they call them. He used to be my spiritual father before I was orthodox; or maybe it was before that —or perhaps it was before that again; I remember it was somewhere along there; and so—"

"Why don't you keep a list?"

"List of what?"—proceeding toward the window.

"Salvation-trains. You ought to have a time-table."

"Why?" Oh, that vacant Why! I did hear it *so* often! She could overlook more points than—oh, well she was absolutely immune to wit, it was wasted on her. "There—she's waking him—she's telling him, now. . . . He's nestling, again, but it's all right, he'll come when his nap's out; he won't forget."

"Nap? I thought a microbe never slept. They don't in the Major Molar."

"But he is different. We don't know how to account for it. Nobody knows. It beats the scientists. He is not a native; he comes from the jungles of Mbumbum—emphasis on the antepenultimate —it's a wee little isolated tribe, and almost unknown—its name is Flubbrzwak—"

"Land! what's the matter?" she exclaimed.

I said I was sorry I made her jump; then I explained that I had had a stitch in the side; and it was quite true, too; I did have one once—it was in America, I remember it quite well, though nothing came of it. But that name! It certainly gave me a start, for this is the rare and mysterious microbe that breeds the awful disease called the African Sleeping Sickness—drowses the victim into a dull and heavy lethargy that is steeped with death; he lies there week after week, month after month, his despairing dear ones weeping over him, shaking him, imploring him to wake, beseeching him to open his eyes, if only a moment, and look into theirs once more—just once more—one little look of love and blessing and farewell. But let their hearts break!—it is what the malady was invented for; he will never wake any more.

Isn't it curious and interesting?—the fact that not a microbe in all this microbe-stuffed planet of Blitzowski ever suspects that he is a harmful creature! They would be astonished and cruelly hurt if you should tell them such a thing. The Nobles eat the Ignobles— that is all right, it was intended they should, and so there is no wrong in that, and they would tell you so; in turn, the Ignobles eat *them*, and neither is *that* objectionable; both races feed on Blitzowski's blood and tissue, and that also is proper, foreordained and void of sin; also, they rot him with disease, they poison him, but *that* they do not know, that they do not suspect. *They* don't know he is an animal, they take him for a planet; to them he is rocks and dirt and landscape and one thing and another, they think he has been provided for them, and they honestly admire him, enjoy him, and praise God for him. And why not? they would be ingrates and unworthy of the blessings and the bounties that have been lavished upon them if they did otherwise. Without being a microbe I could not feel this so deeply; before I was a microbe I do not believe I felt it at all. How alike we all are! all we think about is ourselves, we do not care whether others are happy or not. When I was a man, I would have turned a microbe from my door hungry, anytime. Now I see how selfish I was; now I should be ashamed to do such a thing. So would any person that had any religion. The very littleness of a microbe should appeal to a person, let alone his friendlessness. Yet in America you see scientists torturing them, and exposing them naked on microscope slides, before ladies, and culturing them, and harrying them, and hunting up every way they can think of to extirpate them—even doing it on the Sabbath. I have seen it myself. I have seen a doctor do it; and he not cold from church. It was murder. I did not realize it at the time, but that is what it was, it was murder. He conceded it himself, in light words, little dreaming how mighty they were: he called himself a germicide. Some day he will know to his sorrow that there is no moral difference between a germicide and a homicide. He will find that not even a germ falls to the ground unnoticed. There is a Record. It does not draw the line at feathers.

She said he belonged to the sect of the Magnanimites, and that it was a very good sect, and this Brother as good as the best. She said he and she had always had a fondness for each other when she used to be a Magnanimite, and that that feeling still continued, she was glad to say. She said the countess was orthodox, because she was a kind of a sort of a Noble by marriage, and it would not be good form for her to travel the side-trails to the Abode of the Blest, but she was a good creature and liked the Brother, and he liked her. On she rattled:

"She's a foreigner—the countess. She's a GRQ, and—"

"What's a GRQ?"

"Getrichquick—and she was a lady there; though here, people of her family's condition, being SBE's would have to stick to their proper place, and so—"

"What's an SBE?"

"Soiled-Bread Eater."

"Why *soiled* bread?"

"Because it's earned."

"Because it's *earned?*"

"Yes."

"Does the act of earning it soil it?"

It made her laugh—the idea that I, a grown-up, could be ignorant of an ABC fact like that!—but I detected a sudden happy hunger in her eye which we are all acquainted with, and which I was not sorry to see there: it comes when we think we have discovered that we know something the other person doesn't, and are going to have a chance to unload information into him and surprise him and make him admire us. It wasn't very often that Catherine dropped a *fact* that was new to me, but she often threw an interesting new light upon an old one if I kept shady and allowed her to think the fact itself was a valuable contribution to my treasury. So I generally kept shady. Sometimes I got a profit out of this policy, sometimes I didn't, but on the whole it paid.

My question made her laugh. She repeated it—apparently to taste again the refreshing ignorance of it:

" 'Does the act of earning it soil it?' Why, don't you know—"

She stopped, and looked a little ashamed. I said—

"What's the trouble?"

"You are joking with me."

"Joking? Why should I be joking?"

"Because."

"Because what?"

"Ah, you know very well."

"I don't. I give you my word."

She looked straight in the eye, and said—

"If you are joking, I shall see it. Now I will ask you in earnest, and I think you ought to answer in earnest: Have you ever heard of a nation—a *large* nation—where earning the bread didn't soil it?"

It was my turn to laugh! I started to do it, but—Something moved me to wait a minute; something which suggested that maybe it was not so foolish a question as it seemed. I mused for a while. Great nations began to drift past my mind's eye—habitants of both the planets—and I soon reached a decision, and said—

"I thought it was a foolish question, Catherine, but really it isn't, when a body examines it. I reckon we are pretty full of notions which we got at second hand and haven't examined to see whether they are supported by the statistics or not. I know of a country— through talking with natives of it—where the dignity of labor is a phrase which is in everybody's mouth; where the *reality* of that dignity is never questioned; where everybody says it is an honor to a person that he works for the bread he eats; that earned bread is noble bread, and lifts the earner to the level of the highest in the land; that unearned bread, the bread of idleness, is tainted with discredit; a land where the sayers of these things say them with strong emotion, and think they believe what they say, and are proud of their land because it is the sole land where the bread-earners are the only acknowledged aristocracy. And yet I do see, that when you come to examine into it—"

"I know the land you mean! It's GRQ! Honest—isn't it GRQ?"

"Yes, it is."

"I recognised it in a minute! The countess is always talking about it. She used to love it when she lived there, but she despises it now, and says so, but I reckon she has to talk that way to keep people from doubting that she's been changed and is a real, actual

Henryling, now—and you know, she *is* a real one, realer than the born ones themselves, I know it by the way she talks. Well, she told me about the dignity-of-labor gospeling, and says it's all sham. She says a mechanic is the same there as anywhere. They don't ask him to dinner—plumber, carpenter, blacksmith, cobbler, butler, coachman, sailor, soldier, stevedore, it's all the same all around, they don't ask *any* of them. The professionals and merchants and preachers don't, and the idle rich don't invite *them*—not by a dam sight, she says, and—"

"H'sh! I'm astonished at you!"

"Well, she *said* it, anyway; and she said *they* don't give a dam whether—"

"*Will* you be quiet! You *must* stop this habit of picking up and fetching home every dreadful word you—"

"But she *said* it—I *heard* her say it! The way she said it was this: she fetched her fist down—so!—and said 'By—' "

"Never *mind* how she said it! I don't want to hear it. You are certainly the most innocent animal that ever was. You don't seem to have any discrimination—everything that gets in front of your rake is treasure to you. I think there was never such a random scavenger since language was invented. Now then, let those words alone; just let them alone, and start over again where they side-tracked you."

"Well, I will, and I'm sorry if I've done wrong, I wasn't meaning any harm. The rest that she said was, that if the banker's daughter married the plumber, and if the multimillionaire's daughter married the editor, and if the bishop's daughter married the horse-doctor, and if the governor's daughter married the coachman, there was hell to pay!"

"Now *there* you go, again! I—"

"Why, that's what she said."

"Oh, *I* know it, but—"

"And she said there's families that are so awful high-up and swell, that they won't let their daughters marry any native at all, if they can help it. They save them up till a foreign bacillus with a title comes along; then if they can agree on the price they make the trade. But they don't have auctions, she says. Not public ones. She's as nice as she can be, and it's most interesting to hear her talk.

She's good-hearted and malicious and all that, and is never borous, and makes plenty of friends—and keeps them, too. She's got a heart of gold, and false teeth and a glass eye, and I think she's perfect."

"Those are the marks. I should recognize them anywhere."

"It's nice to have you say that. And I thought you would. There's a good deal to her. I think she's awfully interesting. She's morganatic."

"Morganatic?"

"Yes. That's what she is—morganatic."

"How do you make that out?"

"Well, it's what they say. Not she herself, but the others. Neighbors, you know. That's what they say. Morganatic."

"Yes, but *how?*"

"Well, her mother was a vermiform appendix—"

"Oh, good land!"

"It's what they say, anyway. They don't know who her father was. Only just her mother. She was a vermiform appendix. That's what they say. Morganatic."

"How in the nation is *that* morganatic?"

"Irregular, you know. They all say it's irregular for a vermiform appendix to have a family anyway, to *begin* with, for it's never happened before, and doctors didn't believe it *could* happen till it *did* happen; and then to go and have it irregular besides—well, it's morganatic, you see. That's what they all say. Morganatic. Some say it's *more* than morganatic, but I reckon it's not so much as that, do you think?"

"Why, hang it there's nothing morganatic about it—nothing that resembles it. The whole thing is insane—absolutely insane. Now how can these germs be cruel enough to ruin the countess's character in this wanton way?"

"Ruin her character? What makes you think it hurts her character?"

"But doesn't it?"

"Why no. How could it affect her character? *She* wasn't to blame. *She* hadn't anything to do with it. Why, she wasn't any more than just *there*, when it happened. I reckon another minute and she'd have been too late."

"What an idea! Hanged if you can't make the most unexpected turns, and pop out in the most unexpected places that ever I—and there's no such *thing* as understanding these mixed up and helter-skelter and involved statements of yours—why, they fuddle a person all up, they make him dizzy, he can't tell them from sacred passages out of Science and Wealth itself, the style is so astonishingly replicated!"

I was so sorry it escaped me! But for only half a second. Why, she was beaming with gratitude! It wasn't a sarcasm to *her*. It fell short—away short! She took it for a compliment. I hastened to get back on our course and said—

"I am very glad it didn't hurt her character; and very sincerely glad to come across *one* civilization which places shame where it belongs, instead of emptying its brutal scorn upon the innocent product of it. So these good and just people respect the countess, do they?"

"Oh yes, they do, as far as *that* incident is concerned. In fact it is a valuable thing to her, because it gives her distinction."

"How?"

"Why, she's the only appendicitis there is. There's plenty *inside* of people, in the hospitals and around, but she's the only one that's outside; the only one that's been *born*, you know.—Irregular, and pretty morganatic, and all that, but never mind, when all's said and done, she's the *only* one in history, and it's a gigantic distinction. I wish I was it, myself."

"Oh, Great Sc—"

XI [16]

S HE CLATTERED right along, paying no attention to my attempt to invoke the Great Scott. Also she followed a slovenly fashion of hers, of throwing a back-handspring clear over thirty yards of general conversation and landing right-side-up in front of an unfinished remark of an hour before—then she would hitch-on to

---

[16] Mark Twain numbered two chapter sequences as XI–XIV (see headnote); the second sequence begins here.

it, and come lumbering along with it the same as if there hadn't
been anything obstructing the line, and no interruption to its
progress—

"So you see, there *isn't* any big nation, after all, where it doesn't
soil the bread to earn it, notwithstanding you stood out so
stubbornly that it wasn't so." (I hadn't done anything of the kind,
but I knew it would save time and wind to leave it so, and not
argue it.) "The countess says it's all a sham, in GRQ, and of course
if there was a big nation anywhere where it *wasn't* a sham, it would
be there, which is a republic and a democracy, and the greatest one
on the planet, and everybody letting on to be equal and some of
them succeeding, God only knows which ones, *she* says! She says
the sham starts at the top and runs straight to the bottom without a
break, and there isn't a da—" ("Look out!" I said)—"isn't a person
in the land that can see it. That's what *she* says—all blind-fuddled
with bogus sentiment.

"Ranks—grades—castes—there's a million of them! that's what
she says. Mesalliances! why, she says it's just the natural native
home of them, on account of there being so many more ranks and
aristocracies there than anywhere else. She says there's families that
the very President isn't good enough to marry into—at least *until*
he's President. They're nearly always SBE's—tanners, or rail-
splitters, or tailors, or prohibitionists, or some other low trade, and
they've got to climb *away* up above that before they can crowd into
those families—and by that time, you know, it's too late, they're
already coupled. *They* consider it climbing, she says, and everybody does. They admire him—admire him immensely—for what
he is *now*, don't you know—admire him for the respectability he's
climbed up to. They don't say, with swelling pride and noble
emotion, 'Look at him, the splendid SBE—he's a rail-splitter!' No,
they say, with swelling pride and noble emotion, 'Look at him—
away up there!—and just think, he used to wasn't anything but a
rail-splitter!' And she says he's not ashamed of what he was, and no
occasion to, it's a distinction and a grand one, now that he's where
he *is*; and you'd think he would make tailors and tanners and rail-
splitters out of his boys. She says she thinks they do, but she don't
remember any instances.

"So there 'tis, and I reckon you've got to come down."

"Come down?"

"Yes. Come down and acknowledge it."

"Acknowledge what?"

"That *earned* bread is soiled bread—everywhere on the planet of Blitzowski, republics and all. It's the soiled bread that *makes* a nation; makes it great, makes it honored, makes it strong, props up its throne and saves it from the junk-shop, makes its waving flag a beautiful thing to see, and bring the proud tears to your eyes to look at it, keeps its da—keeps its Grand Dukes out of the hog-wallow, the jail and the alms-house—if you sh'd sweep the SBE's and their dirty bread away there wouldn't be a solitary valuable thing left in the land! and yet, by God—"

"Oh, for goodness sake!—"

"Well, that's what *she* said. She said, 'By—' "

"*Will* you hush! I tell you—"

"But she *said* it—the countess did. She put up her hand—away up so, with her fist clinched and her eyes snapping, and rips out the doggondest, consoundedest, allfiredest, thunderblast of—"

Thank heaven there was a knock on the door! It was the good Brother, the impressive Sleeping-Sickness germ.

He had a gentle way with him, and a kind and winning face, for he was a Malignant; that is to say, a Noble of the loftiest rank and the deadliest, and the gentle bearing and the kind face are theirs by nature and old heredity. *He* was not aware that he was deadly; he was not aware that *any* Noble was deadly; he was far from suspecting the shocking truth that *all* Nobles are deadly. I was the only person in all Blitzowski that knew these terrible facts, and I knew it only because I had learned it in another World.

He and Catherine gave each other a pleased and affectionate greeting, she going on her knees to him, as etiquette required, she being an SBE and he of dizzily lofty blood, and he patting her bowed head lovingly, and telling her she might rise. Which she did, and waited so, until he told her she could sit. He and I exchanged stately bows, each repeatedly waving a reverent hand toward a chair and accompanying each wave with a courtly "After you, m'lord."

We got it settled presently, by the two of us chairing ourselves with carefully exact simultaneousness. He had a slender long box with him, which Catherine relieved him of—curtsying profoundly.

Ah, he knew things, the wise old gentleman! He knew that when you are in doubt it is safest to lead trumps. He could see that I was of a great blood; I *might* be a Noble, so he treated me as one, without asking any awkward questions. I followed his lead: I made him a Duke, without asking him anything about it.

He was munching an SBE which he had captured as he came along—eating it alive, which is our way—and its cries and struggles made my mouth water, for it was an infant of four weeks and quite fat and tender and juicy, and I hadn't tasted a bite since the boys left at 2 A.M. There was enough of it for a family, therefore no occasion for etiquetical declining and polite lying when he offered me a leg; I took it, and it seemed to me that I had never tasted anything better. It was a *pectin*—a spring pectin—and I think them quite choice when they are well nourished.

I knew Catherine was hungry, but this kind of game was not for her: SBE's eat Nobles when they get a chance—war-prisoners or battle-slain—but SBE's don't eat each other, and she was an SBE. It was a good meal, and we threw the remnants to the mother, who was crying outside. She was very grateful, poor thing, though it was but a trifling kindness, and we claimed no merit for it.

When the Brother learned that I longed to have our humble friends and helpers, the lower animals, accompany us to the Happy Land and partake of its joys with us, it went to his heart. He was deeply moved, and said it was a most noble and compassionate feeling, and that he shared it with me to the uttermost. That was good and strong and cheering language; and when he added that he not only longed for the translation of the animals but believed it would happen and had no shadow of a doubt that it *would* happen, my cup of happiness was full! I had never lacked anything but a support like this to clinch my own belief and make it solid and perfect, and now it *was* solid and perfect. I think there was not a happier microbe than I, at that moment, from Henryland to GRQ, and from the Major Molar to the Great Lone Sea. There was but one question left to ask, and I asked it without fear or misgiving—

"Does your Grace include *all* the creatures, even the meanest and the smallest—mosquito, rat, fly, *all and every?*"

"Yes, *all and every!*—even the invisible and deadly microbe that feeds upon our bodies and rots them with disease!"

x x x x The stars represent the time it took me to get my breath back. Yes, yes, yes, how strangely we are made! I had always *wanted* somebody to say that, and round-out and perfect the scheme of justice, making all innocent and duty-doing life partakers of it, and I had long ago (unsuccessfully) offered an upright and kind-hearted clergyman an opportunity to do it, yet now that somebody *had* said it [at] last, it nearly paralysed me!

The Duke saw it. I couldn't help it—he saw it. I was ashamed, but there it was; so I didn't make any excuses, or venture any lies, I just stood pat. It's the best way, when you know you are caught and there isn't anything you can do. But the Duke was handsomely magnanimous about it; he dealt in no upbraidings, no sarcasms, he did a better thing—he dealt in reasonings: reasonings supported by facts. He said—

"You make a limit, you draw a line; do not let that trouble you, there was a time when I did it too. It was when I lacked knowledge —that is, full knowledge; it was incomplete—like yours. Yours is about to be amended, now—and completed—by me. Then you will see the right, I know you need have no doubts as to that. I will show you the facts. Arguments carry far, but nothing but facts carry home. There are plenty of evidences on view in this room that you are a student of science, m'lord, but you have revealed the fact—unintentionally—that there is one great field of science— bacteriology—which you have neglected—which, at any rate, you have not made yourself altogether familiar with. Is it so?"

Well, what was I to say? As to *World*-bacteriology, I was the expert of experts—I was a past master—I knew more about it in a week than Pasteur ever knew about it in a year. I couldn't tell the Duke that—he wouldn't know what I was talking about. As to bacteriology here in this planet—the infinitely microscopic microbes that infest *microbes*—land, I knew nothing about it! I had sometimes lazily wondered if they were minute duplicates of the World-microbes, and had the same habits and devoted themselves to the same duties, but I had never felt interest enough in the matter to think examining into it worth the trouble. On the whole I thought I would tell the Duke I didn't know anything about germs and such things, and that is what I did.

It didn't surprise him any—I could see that—and it hurt my pride a little, but I stood it and made no moan. He got up and arranged one of my microscopes—remarking casually that he was a bacteriologist of some reputation—by which he meant that he was *the* bacteriologist of the planet—oh, I know *that* tune!—and I know how to dance to it to the singer's satisfaction, too—which I did, in the old shop-worn way: I said I should consider myself the most ignorant of scientists if I was not aware of *that* pretty well-known fact. Then he got a glass slide out of his grooved box—which I had recognized, early, as a slide-box—and put it under the microscope. He worked the screws and made the proper adjustment, then told me to take a look.

Oh, well, there's no use—I *was* astonished! It was one of those old familiar rascals which I had had under the microscope a thousand times in America, and here was his unspeakably littler twin exactly reproduced, to the last detail. He was a pectin—a spring pectin—a baby one, and most ridiculously like the mammoth one (by comparison) which we had just eaten! It was so funny that I wanted to make a joke about him; I wanted to say, let's get that little speck out on a needle-point and make a gnat eat him, then give his remnants to his mother! But I didn't say it. It might be that the Duke was not witty: well, you don't charm *that* kind by reminding them of their defect and making them ashamed and envious. So I held in, but it strained me some.[17]

---

[17] At this point Mark Twain wrote and deleted: "(Insert here, some bacteria—*any* bacteria of this breed—or *any* breed—engraved with the venal circle and magnified 10 or 1200 times.)" He did not delete the comment: "Mustn't have such pictures—they would destroy the illusion."

XII

H E M A D E a sketchy little introductory layout in the professorial style, in which he generalized, as in an impressionist picture, the great lesson which he was going to particularize for my instruction; then he got down to his work. At this point he discarded the local vernacular, and thenceforth employed the highest and purest dialect of the black plague, which he spoke with a French accent— I mean, it sounded like it. It had long been the court language, all over Blitzowski, and was now becoming the language of science, because of its peculiar richness in several high qualities; among them, precision and flexibility. I will remark, in passing, that in this tongue, the scientific family-name for *all* germ-forms is *swink*. Every microbe is a swink, every bacterium is a swink, and so on; just as in the World every German, Indian, Irishman, and so on, is a *man*.

"Let us begin at the beginning," he said. "This mighty planet which we inhabit, and in which we have set up our democracies, our republics, kingdoms, hierarchies, oligarchies, autocracies and other vanities, was created for a great and wise purpose. It was not chance-work, it proceeded, stage by stage, in accordance with an ordered and systematised plan.

"It was created for a purpose. What was that purpose? That We might have a home. That is the proper expression—a home, not a mere abiding place, stingy of comforts. No, the design was, a home rich in comforts, and in intelligent and hard-working subordinates to provide them for us. No microbe fails to realize this, no microbe forgets to be grateful for it. If the microbe is also a little vain of his high position, a little vain of his august supremacy, it must be allowed that it is pardonable. If the microbe has by his own unanimous consent gilded himself with the large title of Lord of Creation, it must be allowed that that also was pardonable, seeing that it was safer to *take* the title than go before the country with the matter and possibly fail to get elected.

"Very well. The planet was to be created—for a purpose. Was it created—and then the microbe put into possession of it at once? No, he would have starved. It had to be prepared for him. What was the process? Let us *make* a little planet—in fancy—and see.

"Thus. We make some soil, and spread it out. It is going to be a garden, presently. We make air, and put into it moisture; the air and the moisture contain life-nurturing foods in the form of gases —foods for the plants which we are going to raise. We put into the soil some other plant-foods—potassium, phosphorous, nitrates, and such.

"There is plenty of food; the plant eats, is energised, and springs from the soil and flourishes. Presently the garden is wealthy in grains, berries, melons, table-vegetables, and all manner of luscious fruits.

"There being food now for the Lord of Creation and for the horse, the cow and their kind, and for the locust, the weevil, and the countless other destructive insects, we create *them* and set them to the table. Also the tiger, the lion, the snake, the wolf, the cat, the dog, the buzzard, the vulture and their sort?

"Yes, we create them, but it is not a fortunate time for them, because they cannot live on garden-stuff. They have to sacrifice themselves in a great cause. They are martyrs. Though not by request. Being without food, they die.

"At this point we create the *swinks,* and they appear on the scene —with a stupendous mission. They come in countless multitudes, for much is required of them. What would happen if they did not come?

"Why, the catastrophe of catastrophes! The garden would use up and exhaust the supply of essential foods concealed in the soil—the nitrates and the rest of that nutritive menu; then it would have nothing left to live on but the slim menu furnished by the air— carbon dioxide and such—and so it would get hungrier and hungrier, and weaker and weaker, then it would gasp out its remnant of life and die. With it all the animals would perish, the Lord of Creation along with them, and the planet would be a desolate wilderness, without song of bird, or cry of predatory creature, or whir of wing, or any sign of life. The forests would wither and pass away, nothing would be left of all the fair creation but limitless expanses of rocks and sand.

"Is the humble swink important in the scheme, then? Ah, yes— beyond question! What shall we call him? What shall be his title, since he is unmicrobically modest, and has not selected one himself? Let us name him in accordance with the plain facts. He is the Lord Protector of the Lord of Creation, and ex-officio Redeemer of his Planet. Let us now examine his procedure and his methods.

"He arrives on the scene in his due order and at the proper and appointed time. The microbe is well, and well fed; the same is the case with the cow, the horse and the other creatures that can live on vegetable products, but there is a wilderness of tigers, dogs, cats, lions, and other meat-eaters dying, because there isn't meat enough to go around. The swink attacks the carcases and their previous excretions, feeds upon them, decomposes them, and sets free a lot [of] oxygen, nitrogen and other things necessary to the plant-table; the plant-leaves seize upon these foods—with the exception of the nitrogen, which it must get later through the labors of other breeds of swinks.

"Very well, the country is saved. The plants get their foods back again, and thrive. They digest them, building them into albumins, starch, fats and so on; these go back to the animals, who feed upon them and thrive; in digesting them *they* build them into various food-forms; some of these pass to the air in their breath and are re-captured by the plant-leaves and devoured; some of them go from them in their excretions and are recovered by the swink and returned to the plants; when the animals die the swink rots him and sets free the rest of the plant-foods and *they* go back to the garden.

"So, the eternal round goes on: the foods fat-up the plants; they go from the plants to the animals and fat *them* up; the swink recovers them and sends them back to the plants' larder; the plants eat them again, and again forward them to the animals. Nothing is lost, nothing wasted; there's never a new dish, and never *has* been one; it's the same old sumptuous but unchanging bill of fare, and not only the same bill, but the very same old *food* which was set upon the table at creation's first meal, and has been warmed over and chewed and re-chewed, and chewed and chewed and chewed and chewed and chewed again and again and still again and yet again at every single meal that life in any form, in land and water and air has ever sat down to, from that original first day to this.

"It is a marvelous machinery, an amazing machinery; the precision of it, the perfection of it, the wonder of it—put it into your own words, I have none that are sublime enough!

"Remove the swink from the scheme, and what have you? Rocks and sand! Rocks and sand, stripped bare; the forests gone and the flowers, the seas without a fish, the air without a wing, the temples without a worshiper, the thrones empty, the cities crumbled to dust and blown away. And the armies, and the banners, and the shouting—where are they? Do you hear a sound? It is only the wandering wind, the lamenting wind; and do you hear that other sound?—

> " 'The old, old Sea, as one in tears,
>   Comes murmuring with foamy lips,
>   And knocking at the vacant piers,
>   Calls for his long-lost multitude of ships!'

"x x x x We will look at this swink, this giant. Catherine, bring a tin cup. A pint tin cup. Now fill it with wheat—level full. There—it represents a pound, avoirdupois by immemorial tradition. There are 7,000 grains. Take 15 of them, crush them in the mortar. Now wet the pulp, and make a pill of it. It is a small pill, isn't it? You could swallow it without difficulty? Let us suppose it hollow—with a hole in it, pierced by the most delicate needle-point. Let us imagine it the house of the swink, and summon him and his to come forth. Go on with the fancy: behold, he comes—the procession moves! Can you see so minute a creature? No—you must imagine him. Count!

"One—two—three—Three *what*? Individuals? No! It would take a year. You must count him—how? By armies—only by armies—each a million strong. Count!"

"One—two—three." I was counting. I went on counting—counting—counting—monotonously. I got to the forties.

"Go on!"

I got to the seventies.

"Go on!"

I got to the nineties.

"Go on!"

I reached a hundred.

"Stop! There he stands, a hundred million strong—his mass, the mass of a calomel pill! Take off your hat—make reverence: you stand in the presence of his sublime Majesty the Swink, Lord Protector of the Lord of Creation, Redeemer of his Planet, Preserver of all Life!

"Will he be forgiven, and changed to a spirit, and allowed to ascend with us to the Land of Rest—to fold his tired hands and labor no more, his duty done, his mission finished? What do *you* think?"

XIII.

A T LAST my spirit had found perfect repose, perfect peace, perfect contentment—never again to be disturbed, never again to be tossed upon waves of doubt, I hoped and believed. The Lower Animals, big and little, would be *spirits* in the Blessed Land, as intangible as thought; airy, floating forms, wandering hither and thither, leagues apart, in the stupendous solitudes of space, seldom glimpsed, unremarked, inoffensive, intruding upon none—ah, why had not some one thought of this simple and rational solution before? In the human World even the most fastidious churchman would hail with joy and thankfulness the translation of my poor old tramp to the Blessed Land from a repentant deathbed, quite undisturbed by the certainty of having to associate with him there throughout eternity. In what condition? frowsy, drunk, driveling, malodorous?—proper comrade for a disease-germ? No: as a *spirit*— an airy, flitting form, as intangible as thought; in no one's way, offending none. Yet the same charitable churchman who could forecast the tramp as a spirit and purified of offensiveness, could never in all his days happen to hit upon the logical idea of also forecasting the *rest* of the ruck of life as spirits. Plainly a thing not difficult to do after practising on Blitzowski and getting reconciled[18] to the process.

Something roused me out of this reverie, and I found that the Duke was talking. Something like this:

"We have seen that the swink—and the swink alone—saved our planet from denudation and irremediable sterility in the beginning; saved Us and all subordinate life from extinction; is still standing between Us and extinction to-day; and that if ever he deserts Us, that day is Our Doomsday, that day marks the passing of Our Great Race and of Our Noble Planet to the grave of the Things That Were.

"Is that humble mite important, then? Let us confess it: he is in truth the *only* very important personage that exists. What is the suit of clothes which we call Henry the Great, and bow before, reverent and trembling? What are the tribe of kings, and their grandeurs? What are their armies and their navies? What are the multitudinous nations and their pride? Shadows—all shadows— nothing is real but the swink. And their showy might? It is a dream —there is no might but the might of the swink. And their glories? The swink gave them, the swink can take them away. And their riches, their prosperities—

"Let us look at that. There are some strange resemblances between Our Grand Race and those wee creatures. For instance, We have upper classes—so have they. That is a parallel, as far as it goes, but it is not a perfect one, for the reason that Our aristocracy is useful and not often harmful, whereas their aristocracy are disease-germs, and propagate deadly maladies in Our bodies.*

---

* Listen to that, now! He was a disease-germ himself, and didn't suspect it. The girly innocence of these poisonous Toughs is almost unthinkable.

"But the next parallel has no defect. I refer to their lower classes —their laboring poor. They are harmless. They work, they work intelligently, they work unceasingly. We have seen that they save

---

[18] Alternate word in the text: "hardened."

Us and Our planet; very well, they also create Our wealth for Us, they prepare it for Our hand, We take it and use it.

"For instance. No method of separating the linen fibres in the flax from the wood fibres has yet been devised which dispenses with the aid of the swink. He holds the patent upon that essential. He has always been boss of the whole rich linen industry of this planet; he is still boss of it; he keeps the mills going; he pays the wages, he attends to the dividends. He bosses the sacking industry, too; helps to get the jute ready. The same with other fibre-products of several kinds.

"Swinks of various breeds help in a multitude of Our commercial industries. The yeast-swink helps in every kitchen and every bakery on the planet. You get no good bread without him. He conducts Our wine-business, strong-liquor business, beer-business, vinegar-business, and so on, for Us, and does it on a mighty scale. It is by his grace that those generous floods are poured down the throats of the nations, and the dividends handed over by the train-load to the capitalist.

"He sees to it that your butter is good; and your cream, your cheese, and all sorts of boarding-house essentials.

"When the tobacco leaf sprouts, the swink is there—on duty, and faithful to his trust. He will never leave that leaf until he has helped it with his best strength and judgment through every one of its curing-processes; and when it reaches your mouth the flavor and the aroma that make it delicious to your taste and smell, and fill your spirit with contentment and thanks, are *his* work. He oversees, and superintends, and makes profitable beyond the dreams of the statistician the entire tobacco-industry of this great planet, and every day the smoke of the burnt offerings that go up in praise and worship of this unknown god, this god whose labors are not suspected and whose name is never uttered by these ignorant devotees, transcends in volume all the other altar-smokes that have gone skyward during the preceding thirty years. Pray correct me if I seem to fall into error at any time, for we are all prone to do this when stirred by feeling.

"These are great services which we have been tallying off to the credit of Our benefactor, the humble swink, the puissant swink, the all-providing swink, the all-protecting swink. Is the tale finished? Is there yet another service? Yes—and a greater still. This:

"In their time, the trees and the plants fall, and lie. The swink takes hold. He decomposes them, turns them to dust, mingles them with the soil. Suppose he didn't do this work? The fallen vegetation would not rot, it would lie, and pile up, and up, and up, and by and by the soil would be buried fathoms deep; no food could be grown, all life would perish, the planet would be a lifeless desert. There is but one instrument that can keep this vast planet's soil free and usable—the swink."

"Oh, dear me," I muttered to myself, "the idea of ruling God's most valuable creatures out of heaven, and admitting the Blitzowskis!"

"There. Let us finish. We complain of his aristocracy—his disease-germs. All We can think about, when the swink is mentioned, is his aristocracy's evil doings. When do We ever speak of the laboring swink, Our benefactor, Our prosperity-maker? In effect, never. Our race does not even know that he *is* Our benefactor, none knows it but here and there a student, a scholar, a scientist. The public—why, the public thinks *all* swinks are disease-breeders, and so it has a horror of all the race of swinks. It is a pity, too, for the facts and the figures would modify its hostilities if it had them and would examine them.

"When the plague-swink starts upon a raid, the best he can do, while it lasts, is to kill 2½ per cent of the community attacked—not the nation, merely the few communities visited. Nowadays, I mean. He did a larger trade in bygone ages, before science took hold of his case. He kills 2½ per cent; then he has to lie still for years. The cholera-swink does even a slenderer business; then he also must postpone his next raid for years. Both of these are harshly talked about and dreaded. Why? I don't know. None but mere outlying corners of the planet ever see either of them during entire life-times. Meantime the laborer-swink is supporting all the nations, prospering all the nations—and getting neither thanks nor mention."

He dropped into the vernacular:

"Take all the other disease-germs in a mass, and what do they accomplish? They are responsible for ten graves out of a hundred, that is all. It takes them half a lifetime to bring down the average sooflasky try as hard as they may; and all that time his brother swink the laborer has been feeding him, protecting him, enriching him—and getting neither thanks nor notice for it. To use a figure, the swink gives the public a thousand barrels of apples; the public says nothing—not a word; then it finds a rotten apple in the cargo, and—what does it do *then,* Catherine?"

"Raises—"

"Shut up!" I shouted, just in time.

"It's what the countess says, I heard her say it myself. She said—"

"Never *mind* what she said; we don't want to hear it!"

XIV.

I WAS CHARMED with the Duke's lecture. Its wonders were new to me, and astonishing. At the same time, they were old to me, and not astonishing. In the World, when I was studying micrology under Prof. H. W. Conn, we knew all these facts, because they were all true of the microbes that infest the human being; but it was new to me to find them exactly duplicated in the life of the microbes that infest the human *being's* microbes. We knew that the human race was saved from destruction in the beginning by the microbe; that the microbe had been saving it from destruction ever since; that the microbe was the protector and preserver and ablest propagator of many of the mightiest industries in the Earth; that he was the personage most heavily interested in the corporations which exploited them, and that his expert service was the most valuable asset such corporations possessed; we knew that he kept the Earth's soil from being covered up and buried out of sight and made unusable; in a word, we knew that the most valuable citizen of the Earth was the microbe, and that the human race could no more do without him than it could do without the sun and the air.

We also knew that the human race took no notice of these benefactions, and only remembered the disease-germ's ten per cent contribution to the death-rate; and didn't even stop with that unfairness, but charged *all* microbes with being disease-germs, and violently abused the entire stock, benefactors and all!

Yes, that was all old to me, but to find that our little old familiar microbes were *themselves* loaded up with microbes that fed *them*, enriched them, and persistently and faithfully preserved them and their poor old tramp-planet from destruction—oh, that was new, and too delicious!

I wanted to see them! I was in a fever to see them! I had lenses of two-million power, but of course the field was no bigger than a person's finger-nail, and so it wasn't possible to do a considerable spectacle or a landscape with them; whereas what I had been craving was a thirty-foot field, which would represent a spread of several miles of country and show up things in a way to make them worth looking at. The boys and I had often tried to contrive this improvement, but had failed.

I mentioned the matter to the Duke, and it made him smile. He said it was a quite simple thing—he had it at home. I was eager to bargain for the secret, but he said it was a trifle and not worth bargaining for. He said—

"Hasn't it occurred to you that all you have to do is to bend an X-ray to an angle-value of 8.4, and refract it with a parabolism, and there you are?"

Upon my word, I had never thought of that simple thing! You could have knocked me down with a feather.

We rigged a microscope for an exhibition at once, and put a drop of my blood under it, which got mashed flat when the lense got shut down upon it. The result was beyond my dreams. The field stretched miles away, green and undulating, threaded with streams and roads, and bordered all down the mellowing distances with picturesque hills. And there was a great white city of tents; and everywhere were parks of artillery, and divisions of cavalry and infantry—waiting. We had hit a lucky moment; evidently there was going to be a march-past, or something like that. At the front where the chief banner flew, there was a large and showy tent, with showy guards on duty, and about it were some other tents of a swell kind.

The warriors—particularly the officers—were lovely to look at, they were so trim-built and so graceful and so handsomely uniformed. They were quite distinct, vividly distinct, for it was a fine day, and they were so immensely magnified that they looked to be fully finger-nail high.*

* My own expression, and a quite happy one. I said to the Duke—
"Your grace, they're just about finger-nailers!"
"How do you mean, m'lord?"
"This. You notice the stately General standing there with his hand resting upon the muzzle of a cannon? Well, if you could stick your little finger down against the ground alongside of him, his plumes would just reach up to where your nail joins the flesh."
The Duke said "finger-nailers was good"—good and exact; and he afterward used it several times himself. In about a minute a mounted General rode up alongside of the other one and saluted, and the Duke said—
"There, now—with the horse to help, this one's nearly a nail and a third high."

Everywhere you could see officers moving smartly about, and they looked gay, but the common soldiers looked sad. Many wife-swinks and daughter-swinks and sweetheart-swinks were about—crying, mainly. It seemed to indicate that this was a case of war, not a summer-camp for exercise, and that the poor labor-swinks were being torn from their planet-saving industries to go and distribute civilization and other forms of suffering among the feeble be-nighted, somewhere; else why should the swinkesses cry?

The cavalry was very fine; shiny black horses, shapely and spirited; and presently when a flash of light struck a lifted bugle (delivering a command which we couldn't hear) and a division came tearing down on a gallop it was a stirring and gallant sight, until the dust rose an inch—the Duke thought more—and swallowed it up in a rolling and tumbling long gray cloud, with bright weapons glinting and sparking in it.

Before long the real business of the occasion began. A battalion of priests arrived, carrying sacred pictures. That settled it: this was war; these far-stretching masses of troops were bound for the front. Their little monarch came out now, the sweetest little thing that ever travestied the human shape, I think; and he lifted up his hands and blessed the passing armies, and they looked as grateful as they could, and made signs of humble and real reverence as they drifted by the holy pictures.

It was beautiful—the whole thing; and wonderful, too, when those serried masses swung into line and went marching down the valley under the long array of fluttering flags.

Evidently they were going somewhere to fight for their country, which was the little manny that blessed them; and to preserve him and his brethren that occupied the other swell tents; and to civilize and grab a valuable little unwatched country for them somewhere. But the little fellow and his brethren didn't fall in—that was a noticeable particular. But the Duke said it was without doubt a case of Henry and Family on a minute scale—*they* didn't fight; they stayed at home, where it was safe, and waited for the swag.

Very well, then—what ought *we* to do? Had we no moral duty to perform? Ought we to allow this war to begin? Was it not our duty to stop it, in the name of right and righteousness? Was it not our duty to administer a rebuke to this selfish and heartless Family?

The Duke was struck by that, and greatly moved. He felt as I did about it, and was ready to do whatever was right, and thought we ought to pour boiling water on the Family and extinguish it, which we did.

It extinguished the armies, too, which was not intended. We both regretted this, but the Duke said that these people were nothing to us, and deserved extinction anyway for being so poor-spirited as to serve such a Family. He was loyally doing the like himself, and so was I, but I don't think we thought of that. And it wasn't just the same, anyway, because we were sooflaskies, and they were only swinks.

XV.

THE DUKE presently went away, and left my latest thought simmering in my mind—simmering along in the form of reverie: "it wasn't just the same, anyway, because we were sooflaskies, and they were only swinks." There it is: it doesn't make any difference who we are or what we are, there's always *somebody* to look down on! somebody to hold in light esteem or no esteem, somebody to be indifferent about. When I was a human being, and recognized with complacency that I was of the Set-Aparts, the Chosen, a Grand Razzledazzle, The Whole Thing, the Deity's Delight, I looked down upon the microbe; he wasn't of any consequence, he wasn't worth a passing thought; his life was nothing, I took it if I wanted to, it ranked with a mark on a slate—rub it out, if you like. Now that I was a microbe myself I looked back upon that insolence, that pert human indifference, with indignation—and imitated it to the letter, dull-witted unconsciousness and all. I was once more looking down; I was once more finding a life that wasn't of any importance, and sponging it out when I was done with it. Once more I was of the Set-Aparts, the Chosen, a Grand Razzledazzle, and all that, and had something to look down upon, be indifferent about. I was a sooflasky; oh, yes, I was The Whole Thing, and away down below me was the insignificant swink—extinguishable at my pleasure— why not? what of it? who's to find fault?

Then the inexorable logic of the situation arrived, and announced itself. The inexorable logic of the situation was this: there being a Man, with a Microbe to infest him, and for him to be indifferent about; and there being a Sooflasky, with a Swink to infest him and for the said Sooflasky to be indifferent about: then it follows, for a certainty, that the Swink is similarly infested, too, and has something to look down upon and be indifferent to and sponge out upon occasion; and it also follows, of a certainty, that below that infester there is yet another infester that infests *him*— and so on down and down and down till you strike the bottomest bottom of created life—if there is one, which is extremely doubtful.

However, I had reached down to comfort, at any rate, and an easy conscience. We had boiled the swinks, poor things, but never mind, it's all right, let them pass it along; let them take it out of *their* infesters—and those out of *theirs*—and those again out of *theirs*—and so on down and down till there has been an indemnifying boiling all the way down to the bottomest bottom, and everybody satisfied; and glad it happened, on the whole.

Well, it's a picture of life. Life everywhere; life under any and all conditions: the king looks down upon the noble, the noble looks down upon the commoner, the commoner at the top looks down upon the next commoner below, and he upon the next, and that one upon the next one; and so on down the fifty castes that constitute the commonalty—the fifty aristocracies that constitute it, to state it with precision, for each commonalty-caste is a little aristocracy by itself, and each has a caste to look down upon, plum all the way down to the bottom, where you find the burglar looking down upon the house-renting landlord, and the landlord looking down upon his oily brown-wigged pal the real estate agent—which is the bottom, so far as ascertained.

XVI

I GLANCED over my paper on the currency, and found it lucid, interesting, and accurate.[19] It had been written long before. In those early days in Blitzowski I made it a point to put upon paper the new things I learned, lay the thing away, then take it out from time to time in after years and examine it. There was generally something to correct—always, I may say; but in the course of time I got all errors weeded out. This paper on the currency had been through that mill. I found it satisfactory, and gave it to Catherine to put away again.

---

[19] In the holograph the following section, from the beginning of this chapter to the end of the narrator's paper on the currency, is on inserted pages 285-A–285-M. These pages were written in June 1905, as a part of *Three Thousand Years Among the Microbes*. They are on the kind of paper that was used in the holograph beginning with p. 199; also they and the other pages of the holograph are written with the sidewise placement (lines across the length rather than the width of the sheets) that Mark Twain used with a curious consistency in 1905 and probably at no other time. In composing the section on the currency, he may have consulted notes or even a draft (though none has been found) that he had perhaps written earlier—possibly in 1896, when free silver and coinage were of national interest. A notebook entry of July 1896 presents sequences of word-rhymes similar to those which appear as the rhymed names of coins in the narrator's paper: "lash, trash, *cash, mash,* flash, *clash,* dash, brash, crash. . . ." (Typescript 30 (II), p. 43).

That was 3,000 years ago. Ah, Catherine, poor child, where art thou now? Where art thou, thou pretty creature, thou quaint sprite! Where is thy young bloom, thy tumultuous good heart, thy capricious ways, thine unexpectednesses, oh thou uncatchable globule of frisky quicksilver, thou summer-flurry of shower and sun-shine! You were an allegory! you were Life! just joyous, careless, sparkling, gracious, winning, worshipful Life! and now— thou art dust and ashes these thirty centuries!

This faded old paper brings her back. Her hand was the last that rested upon it. She was a dear child; and just a child—it is what she was; if I knew the place her fingers touched, I would kiss it.

There was a time when a pair of young adventurers, exploring a solitude, found a spot which pleased them, and there they began a village, and it was Rome. The village grew, and was the capital of kings for some centuries; and made a stir in the world, and came to be known far and wide; and became a republic, and produced illustrious men; and produced emperors, next, some of them tolerably tough; and when Rome was seven or eight hundred years old, Jesus was born in one of her [20] provinces; by and by came the Age of Faith, and the Dark Ages, and the Middle Ages, extending through a procession of centuries, Rome looking on and superintending; and when she was eighteen hundred years old, William the Conqueror visited the British isles on business; and by and by came the Crusades, and lasted two centuries, and filled the world with a splendid noise, then the romantic show faded out and disappeared, with its banners and its noise, and it was as if the whole thing had been a dream; by and by came Dante and Boccacio and Petrarch; and after another by and by came the Hundred Years' War; and after a while Joan of Arc; and soon the Printing Press, that prodigious event; and after another while the Wars of the Roses, with forty years of blood and tears; and straight after it Columbus and a New World; and in the same year Rome decreed the extirpation of the witches, for she was more than twenty-two hundred years old, now, and tired of witches this good while; after that, during two centuries not a lantern was sold in

---

[20] "Its" is written here as an alternate.

Europe and the art of making them was lost, the tourist traveling at night by the light of roasting old mothers and grandmothers tied to stakes 32 yards apart all over the Christian world, which was gradually getting itself purified and would eventually have accomplished it if some one had not chanced to find out that there wasn't any such thing as a witch, and gone and told; two centuries have dragged by since; Rome, that was once a fresh little village in a solitude, is more than twenty-six hundred years old, now, and is named the Eternal City, and what were her palaces in Christ's time are mouldering humps of weed-grown bricks and masonry in ours, and even Columbus's lonesome continent has put on some age, and acquired some population, and would be a surprise to him if he could come back and see the cities and the railroads and the multitudes.

Musing over these things made it seem a long, long time since the two adventurers had started that village and called it Rome; and yet, I said to myself, "it isn't as long a stretch of centuries as has passed over my head since that girl took this old manuscript from me and put it away; I wish I knew the place her fingers touched."

It is a good chapter, and I will insert it here. Its facts about the money of that day will be valuable in this book.

THE CURRENCY.

IN ONE matter of high importance civilization in Blitzowski can claim a distinct superiority over the civilizations of the World. Blitzowski has, by ancient *Bund,* a *uniform* currency. You don't have to buy a supply of foreign pocket-change when you are preparing for a voyage, nor get your letter of credit made out in currencies you are not familiar with. The money of all the countries goes at par in all the other countries.

When the idea was first suggested it was received with great doubt, for it proposed the simplifying and sanitation of a most crazy and intricate puzzle. Every nation had its own currency, and so had every little tuppenny principality, and the same deplorable condition of things prevailed which must necessarily prevail wherever that kind of a chaos exists. It is illustrated by the experiences of a great-great-grandfather of mine who found himself traveling in Germany, one time.

There were 364 sovereign princes doing business in that State in those days—one per farm. Each had a mint of his own; each coined five or six hundred dollars' worth of money every year and stamped his picture on it; there were 3,230 different breeds of coin in circulation; each had a home-value of its own, each had a name of its own. No man in the country could name all the names, nor spell the half of them; every coin began to lose value when it crossed its own frontier, and the further it went the faster it melted.

My ancestor was an Assfalt, and he was a General, because he had been on the governor's staff when he was young, to fill a vacancy that had three weeks to run. He was in Germany for his health, and by the doctor's orders he had to walk five miles and back every day. Upon inquiry, he found that the cheapest course was nothe-east-and by-nothe, nothe-east-half-east, because it took him across only five frontiers; whereas if he got careless and fell off a point to starboard it took him across seven, and a point to port was worse still, because it took him across nine. These latter were much the best roads, but he was not able to afford them, and had to stick to the muddy one, although it was bad for his health, which he had been sent there on purpose to improve. Any other person would have perceived that the cheap road was really bad economy, but you couldn't ever beat a simple proposition like that into an Assfalt.

He was summering in the capital village of the Grand Duchy of Donnerklapperfeld at the time, and he used to load up with twenty dollars' worth of the local coin every morning, and start, right after breakfast—every alternate day, with a new suit of clothes on, costing about twenty dollars and worth eight and a half. It was an outrage, that price, but he had to buy of the Duke, who was able to have everything his own way, and didn't allow any other tailor to keep shop there.

At the local frontier, 300 yards from the inn, the General had to pay export duty on his clothes, 5 per cent ad valorem. Then they let him through the gate and a uniformed foreigner on the other side of it halted him and collected 5 per cent import duty on the same, and charged him an exchange-discount on his foreign money—another 5 per cent.

The game went right along, like that. He paid export and import duty at every gate, and one discount for exchange-tax each time: two dollars per gate, 5 times repeated. The same, coming back; twenty dollars for the trip. Not a copper left; and yet he hadn't bought a thing on the road. Except just privileges and protection. He could have gotten along without the privileges, and he didn't really get any protection—not from the government, anyway.

Every day ten dollars went for exchange, you see. The General was reconciled to that, but he considered that the daily ten that went for duties was a pure extravagance, a sheer waste; because it ate up the clothes every two days and he had to buy another suit.

Assfalt was there 90 days. Forty-five suits of clothes. But I am a protectionist—which he wasn't—and I think that that was all right; but when you start out with a fat and honest dollar and have it melt entirely away to the last grease-spot just in shaves on exchange, I think it's time to call a halt and establish an international currency, with dollars worth a hundred cents apiece from the North Pole to the South, and from Greenwich straight around, both ways, to 180. Such is Blitzowski style, and nobody can better it, I reckon.

The coin unit of the planet is the *bash,* and is worth one-tenth of a cent, American.

There are six other coins. I will name them, and add their (closely approximate) American values:

Basher—10 *bash.* Value, 1 cent.

Gash—50 *bash.* Value, our nickel.

Gasher—100 *bash.* Value, our dime.

Mash—250 *bash.* Value, our quarter.

Masher—500 *bash.* Value, our half dollar.

Hash—1,000 *bash.* Value, our dollar.

Then comes the paper. It begins with the dollar bill, and runs along up: 1 hash, 2 hash, 5 hash, 10 hash, 20 hash, 50 hash.

Then the name changes, and we have the

Clasher—100,000 *hash.* Value, 100 dollars.

Flasher—1,000,000 *hash.* Value, 1,000 dollars.

Slasher—100,000,000 *hash.* Value, 100,000 dollars.

The purchasing power of a *bash,* in Henryland, equals the purchasing power of a dollar in America.

In the beginning there was a good deal of trouble over selecting the names for the money. It was the poets that made the difficulty. None but business men had been put upon the commission appointed to suggest the names. They put a great deal of time and labor upon the matter, and when they published their proposed list everybody was pleased with it except the poets. They fell foul of it in a solid body, and made remorseless fun of it. They said it would forever mash all sentiment, all pathos, all poetic feeling out of finance, because there wasn't a name in the lot that any language, living or dead, could find a rhyme for. And they proved it. They flooded the land with impassioned couplets whose first lines ended with those coin-names, and went all right and rich and mellow all down the second till they struck the home-stretch, then they pulled a blank, every time, and nobody won out.

The commission was convinced. They decided to sublet the contract to the poets, and that was wisdom; the poets selected the names *bash, mash,* and so on, after a good deal of wrangling among themselves. The names were accepted by the commission and ratified by a referendum, and there they stand, to this day, and will abide. They are excellent for poesy, the best in existence, I think. Compare them with other financial nomenclature, and see:

sovereign,	piastre,	florin,
gulden,	nickel,	groschen,
centime,	obolus,	ruble,
eagle,	shekel,	shinplaster,
doubloon,	bob,	pfennig,

and so on. On a financial epic for a chromo—impromptu, mile heat, single dash—a single sooflaski poet could take the field all by himself against the combined talent of Christendom, and walk over the course in an awful solitude, warbling his gashes and mashes and hashes and ashes just as easy!—and annex that chromo—and where would the others be, I ask you? Still back in the first quarter somewhere, trying to blast rhymes out of that obstinate list, and not the least chance in the living world!

At this point Catherine reminded me that my Advanced Class in Theological Arithmetic would be arriving right after breakfast, and that breakfast was already on the fire. There was no time to spare; so she set herself to the crank and I ground the History of Japan Down to Date into the recorder, and was not sorry to see my gigantic History of the World complete at last. It began with an impressionist cloud which I could make nothing of when I reversed the machine to see how Japan had panned out. The rest was clear, but that was a fog. Then Catherine took the receiver, and recognized that it was that passage from Science and Wealth— boned. Boned of its words and compressed into unarticulated thought. It was a good kind of a nut, in its way, and I left it there for the future history-student to whet his teeth on.

I was impatient to get out to the fossil-field, now, and see what sort of luck my "poem" was having with the boys in full congress assembled; so I thought I would turn my class in Theological Arithmetic over to my assistant and start for the field at once. I had to stay, however; the assistant disappointed me. He was out at the field himself, as it turned out; he was out there listening to the wonderful tale and getting quite carried away by it. He had the soul of a poet, he was born for enthusiasms, and he had an imagination like that microscope I have just been talking about. He was good and true and fine, and by nature all his leanings were toward lofty ideals. It will be perceived by this that he was no twin of his brother, Lem Gulliver. The name I had given him was a pretty large compliment, but it was the right one—Sir Galahad. He didn't know what it stood for, any more than Lem knew what *his* name stood for, but I knew, and was satisfied with my work as a god-father.

Sir Galahad had been my favorite pupil from the beginning, and my brightest. He had risen by his own merit to his high place as my right hand in my little college—if I may call my modest school by so large a name. He was as fond of morals as I was, and as fond of teaching them. I found it safest to be present when he was leading certain of the classes—not because I doubted his honesty, for I didn't, but because it was necessary to put a shrinker upon his imagination from time to time. He never said anything he did not believe to be true, but he could imagine *any* extravagant thing to be true that came into his head; then he immediately believed it was true, and straightway he would come out flat-footed and *say* it was true. But for this infirmity he would have been great—absolutely great—in his class-expositions of certain of our high specialties. It was a charm and a wonder to hear him discourse upon Applied Theology, Theological Arithmetic, Metaphysical Dilutions, and kindred vastnesses, but I could listen with all the more comfort if I had my hand on the air-brake.

When at last I got out to the fossil-mine that afternoon I found the work at a stand-still. All interest was centred in the romance which Louis and Lem had brought from me: the lie, as Lem called it, the poem, as Louis called it. It had made a rousing stir. For hours, now, the boys had been discussing it, some taking Lem's view, some taking Louis', but nobody taking mine. But everybody wanted to hear me tell the rest, and so I was pretty well satisfied with the situation. I began by explaining that in the World, Man was the Great Inhabitant, enjoying there the same supremacy enjoyed in the planet Blitzowski by the Sooflasky. I added—

"The individuals are called Human Beings, the aggregate is called the Human Race. It is a mighty aggregate; it numbers fifteen hundred millions of souls."

"Do you mean that that is all there *are*—in the entire planet?"

The question burst in about that form from the whole clan in one sarcastic voice. I was expecting it, and was not disturbed by it.

"Yes," I said, "it's all there are—fifteen hundred millions."

There was [a] general explosion of laughter, of course, and Lem Gulliver said—

"Why, my land, it doesn't even amount to a family—I've got more blood-kin than that, myself! Fetch the jug, his factory's running dry!"

Louis was troubled—disappointed—my poem wasn't keeping up to standard, in the matter of grandeur; I could see it in his face. I was sorry for him, but I wasn't worrying. Louis said, reluctantly—

"Think, Huck. There's a discrepancy. It is careless art, and no occasion for it. You see, yourself, that so trifling a group is quite out of proportion to the vastness of its habitat; here it would be swallowed up and lost in our meanest village."

"I guess not, Louis. I'm not careless—it's you. You are premature with your conclusion. The returns are not all in yet—there's a detail lacking."

"What detail?"

"The size of those Men."

"Ah—their size. Aren't they like us?"

"Why, yes, they *look* like us, but only as to shape and countenance, but when it comes to bulk—well, that is a different matter. You wouldn't be able to hide that Human Race in our village."

"No? How much of it, then?"

"Well, to be exact, not any of it."

"Now *that's* something like! You are working up to standard, Huck. But don't go too far the other way, now. I—"

"Let him alone, Louis!" said Lem; "he's got his old works going again, don't discourage him, give him full swing. Go it, Huck, pull her wide open! Your reputation's a suffering: you might as well die for a sheep as a lamb—tell us we couldn't even hide *one* of those bullies in our village!"

"Sho," I said, "you make me smile! his mere umbrella would spread from your North Pole far and away below your Equator, and hide two-thirds of your wee Planet entirely from sight!"

There was an immense excitement.

"Shirts! shirts!" the gang shouted, springing to their feet, and the shirts began to sail about me and fall upon me like a snow-flurry.

Louis was beside himself with joy and admiration, and flung his arms about me, murmuring, half-choked with emotion—

"Oh, it's a triumph, a triumph, the poem is redeemed, it is superb, it is unapproachable, its sublime head strikes the very zenith—I *knew* it was in you!"

The others carried on like mad for a while screaming with care-free fun and delight, electing me by acclamation Imperial Hereditary High Chief Liar of Henryland, With Remainder to Heirs Male in Perpetuity, then they began to shout—

"Dimensions! dimensions! hooray for His Nibs, give us his particulars!"

"All right," I said, "any you want. To start with,—supposing this planet of yours wore clothes, I give you my word I've seen more than one Man who couldn't crowd into them without bursting them—yes, sirs, a man who could lie down on Blitzowski and spread over both sides and stick over at both ends."

They were perfectly charmed, and said that *this* kind of lying was something *like,* and they could listen to it by the week; and said there wasn't a liar in all history that could come up to my knee; and why did I go and hide this splendid talent, this gorgeous talent all this time? and now "go ahead—tell some more!"

I was nothing loath. I entertained them an hour or two with details of the Monster and of his World, naming nations and countries, systems of government, chief religions, and so on— watching Lurbrulgrud out of the corner of my eye all the time, and expecting to hear from him by and by. He was one of your natural doubters, you know. We all knew he was taking notes privately—it was his way. He was always trying to ambush somebody and catch him in contradictions and inveracities. I could see that the boys didn't like it this time. They were plainly annoyed. You see, they thought it very handsome of me to make up all those variegated and intricate lies for their amusement, and it wasn't fair to expect me to remember them, and get called to book for them. By and by, sure enough, Grud fetched out his notes, set his eye upon them, and opened his mouth to begin. But at a sign from the others, Davy Copperfield covered it with his hand and said—

"Never you mind; you hold your yawp. Huck doesn't have to make good. He has given us a wonderful exhibition of what imagination can do when there is genius behind it, and he did it to let us have a good time, and we've had it—is that the straight word, boys?"

"It is *that*—every time!"

"Very well then—hold your yawp, I say it again—you can't spring any traps here, you can't fetch him to book."

"And that's the word with the bark on it!" said the boys. "Take a walk, Grud!"

But I interposed, and said—

"No, let him ask his questions—I don't mind. I'm ready to answer."

They were quite willing, in that case. They wanted to see how I would come out.

"Hold on!" said Lem Gulliver. "There's going to be some bets on this game. Ask your first question, Grud, then stop."

Grud said—

"Huck, along in the beginning you threw out a good deal of brag about the Cuban War, as you called it. You furnished some amusing statistics of that skirmish; will you be kind enough to repeat them?"

"Stop," said Lem. "Two to one on each separate statistic; two bash to one he fails on each. Come—who puts up?"

The boys looked unhappy and didn't say anything. Of course Lem jeered; that was the way he was made. It angered Louis, and he sung out—

"I take you!"

"Hanged if I don't, too!" piped up Sir Galahad.

"Good! Any more?" No answer. Lem rubbed his hands together in malicious glee, and said, "Here—the same odds that he doesn't answer *any* question right, in the entire list! Come—what do I hear?"

I waited a moment, then said—

"I take you."

The boys broke out in a rousing shout and kept it up till Lem's temper was pretty thoroughly tried, but he knew better than to let it slip—oh, no, that would have been nuts for the boys—*any* boys. He allowed the noise to quiet down, then he said—

"*You* take it! *You* do! I like your discretion. Go ahead with your answer."

The boys bunched their heads together over Grud's notes, and waited eagerly. I said—

"We sent 70,000 men to Cuba—"

"Score one!—for Huck!"

That was from the boys.

"We lost of them, killed and wounded together, 268."

"Score two—for Huck!"

"We lost 11 by disease—"

"Score three—for Huck!"

"—and 3,849 by the doctors."

"Score four—for Huck!"

"We mustered-in 130,000 men besides the 70,000 we sent to Cuba—kept them in camp in Florida."

"Score five—for Huck!"

"We added the entire 200,000 to the pension roll."

"Score six—for Huck!"

"We made a major general out of a doctor for gallantry at the great battle of San Juan—"

"Score seven—for Huck!"

"—in sending his pills to the rear and saving life with the bullet."

"Score eight—for Huck!"

"Huck, you furnished some medical statistics of what you called the Jap-Russian War—whatever that may be. Please repeat them."

"Of 9,781 sick Jap soldiers brought from the front in one batch to Japan for military hospital treatment, only 34 died."

"Score nine—for Huck!"

"Of a single batch of 1106 wounded Jap soldiers brought to Japan for military hospital treatment because their wounds were too serious for treatment in the field hospitals, none died. All got well, and the majority of them were able to return to the front and did so. Of the 1106, three had been shot through the abdomen, three through the head, and six through the chest."

"Score ten for Huck! And ten thousand for the Japanese military medical service!"

"Huck, in speaking of the American Medical Service—"

"Wait—I did not speak of it. We haven't any. We have never had any, at any time. What I said was, that the *people* call it the Medical Service sometimes, sometimes they call it The Angels of Death, but they are not in earnest when they use either of the terms. We have a Surgical Service, and there is none better; but the other industry is in two divisions, and has no general name covering both. Each is independent, performs a special service, and has a name of its own—an official name, furnished by the War Department. The War Department calls one of them the Typhoid Service, the other the Dysentery Service. The one provides typhoid for the Reserves-Camps, the other provides dysentery for the armies in the field. At another place in my informations I also told you that the lessons of the Cuban War were not lost upon the Government. Immediately after that conflict it reorganized its military system and greatly improved it. It discarded soldiers, and enlisted doctors only. These it sends against the enemy, unencumbered by muskets and artillery, and carrying 30 days' ammunition in their saddlebags. No other impedimenta. The saving in expense is quite extraordinary. Where whole armies were required before, a single regiment is sufficient now. In the Cuban War it took 142,000 Spanish soldiers five months to kill 268 of our defenders, whereas in the same five months our 141 doctors killed 3,849 of our said defenders, and could have killed the rest but they ran out of ammunition. Under our new system we replace 70,000 soldiers with 69 doctors. As a result we have the smallest army on our planet, and quite the most effective. I wanted to lay these particulars before you because, while they are not required by your list of questions, they throw a valuable general light upon the whole body of interrogatories. Pardon me for interrupting the game with this excursion. Now go on with your questions."

But by this time a decided change had come over the boys, and they burst into an excited chorus of—

"Wait! wait, we're coming in!"

And very eager they were, too, and began to get out their money and push it under Lem's nose, boldly offering to take the whole of the 182 remaining questions on Lem's original proposition. But he declined. He had already lost 20 bash to Louis and 20 to Galahad, and matters were getting pretty serious for him. Yes, he declined. He said—without any considerable sugar in it—

"You had your chance, you didn't take it, you're out, and you'll *stay* out."

Then they got yet more excited, and offered *him* two to one. No —he wouldn't. They raised it. Raised it to 3 to 1; 4 to 1; 5 to 1; 6—7—8 to one! He refused. They gave it up, and quieted down. Then I said—

"I'll give you 50 to 1, Lem."

By George, *that* raised a shout! Lem hesitated. He was tempted. The boys held their breath. He studied as much as a minute. Then he said—

"No-o. I decline."

It fetched another shout. I said—

"Lem, I'll do this: two to one I miss on no detail of the 182. Come—if I miss on a single detail, you take the whole pot; isn't that a fat enough thing for you?—a seasoned old sport like you? Come!"

The taunt fetched him! I was sure it would. He took me up. Then he set his teeth, and held his grip, till I had scored 33 without a miss—the boys breathing hard, and occasionally breaking out into a hasty burst of applause—then he let fly in a rage and swore there was chicane here, and frothed at the mouth, and shook his fist in my face and shouted—

"This whole thing's a swindle—a put-up swindle! I'll pay the others, but not you. You got those lies by heart and laid for me, and I was too dull to see it. You knew I'd offer bets, and you laid for me. But you'll get nothing by it, I can tell you that. Betting on a sure thing *cancels the bet,* in *this* country!"

It was a handsome triumph for me, and I was exceedingly comfortable over it. The boys cried—

"Shame, shame, you shirk!" and were going to force him to hand over my winnings, but I saw my chance to do some good by setting a moral example. To do it might be worth more to me, in the way of trade, if it got talked about among families interested in morals, than the money; so I made the boys let him alone, and said—

"I can't take the money, boys, I can't indeed. My position does not permit me to gamble; indeed it requires me to set my face against gambling. Particularly in public, and I regard this occasion as in a sense public. No, I cannot accept the pot; to me, situated as I am, it would be tainted money. I could not conscientiously use it, except in the missionary cause. And not even in that cause, except under certain restrictions. In my discourse upon the World I spoke of the long and bitter war of words which was waged in America over tainted money and the uses which it might be legitimately put to. In the end it was decided that no restriction at all could properly be put upon its use. For that reason I left the country, and came here. I said these parting words; said them in public: 'I go,' I said— 'to return no more; I renounce my country; I will go where it is clean, I cannot live in a tainted atmosphere.' I departed—I came hither. My first breath of the atmosphere of Blitzowski convinced me that I had made a signal change, my friends and dear comrades!"

The boys took it for a compliment—I had judged they would—and they gave me three times three with enthusiasm, and followed it with a rousing *chckk* (tiger). Then I proceeded.

"Where I disagreed with that verdict of my then-countrymen was upon a detail which persons less inflexibly, less inveterately moral than myself might regard as a quibble. I took the stand that all tainted money lost its taint when it left the hand that tainted it, except when employed abroad to damage a civilization superior to our own. I said, do not send it to China, send it to the other missionary fields, then it will go clean and stay so. I mentioned to you the country called China this afternoon, you may remember.

"No, I cannot take these tainted stakes, because now I am out of reach of China. I never intended to take then anyway; I was only betting for amusement—yours and mine. And I did not win them; I knew, all the time, I wasn't winning them, and wouldn't be entitled to them."

"Hel-lo! how do you make that out?" the boys exclaimed.

"Because it's as Lem said—I *was* betting on a sure thing. Those were merely *facts,* not creations of fancy—merely common historical facts, known to me this long time; I couldn't make a mistake in them, if I tried."

That was a sly and well-considered attempt to undermine and weaken the boys' obstinate conviction that my World and all my details were smart inventions—lies. I glanced at their faces—hopefully; then my spirits went down—I hadn't scored; I could see it. Lem was feeling happier and more respectable than had been his case a little while before, but it was observable that he had his doubts as to my having come into our contest with honest cards unstacked. He said—

"Huck, honor bright. Didn't you cram? Didn't you get that raft of details by heart for this occasion?"

"Honor bright, I didn't, Lem."

"All right, I believe you. Moreover I admire you; and that is honest. It shows that you have a splendid memory and—what is just as valuable—a recollection that answers up promptly when required to produce a thing,—a recollecting-faculty which always instantly knows just which pigeon-hole to find it in. In many a case the professional liar lacks the latter gift, and it beats him in the end, to a certainty; his reputation begins to dwindle, it fades gradually out, and you cease to hear of him."

He stopped there, and began to put on his shirt. I waited for his head to come through, supposing he would finish then. But apparently he had already finished, for he did not say anything more. It took me several seconds to realize that there was a connection between his random remarks about professional liars and me. Yes, there was a connection, I could perceive it now. And he had been paying me a compliment. At least that was his idea of it. I turned to the boys, intending to let them help me enjoy the joke, but—ah, well, they hadn't seen any. They were admiring, too—on the same basis. It was certainly a discouraging lot! The laugh I was arranging turned into a sigh.

Presently Sir Galahad took me aside, and said—trying to suppress his excitement—

"Tell me confidentially, master, I will keep it honorably to myself: *was* it lies, or was it really facts—those wonders, those marvels?"

I replied sadly—

"Why tell you, my poor boy? you would not believe me; none believes me."

"But I *will!* Whatever you tell me, I will believe. It is a promise —and sacred!"

I hugged him to my breast, and wept upon him, saying—

"No language can tell how grateful I am for this! for I have been so depressed, so discouraged, and I was hoping for so different a result. I swear to you, my Galahad, I have not made one statement that was not true!"

"Enough!" he said, with fervor, "it is enough; I believe it, every word. And I long to hear more. I long to hear all about that stupendous World and the Humming Race, those sky-scraping monsters that can step from one end of this planet to the other in two strides. They have a history—I know it, I feel it—an old and great and stirring history—would Grak * I knew it, master!"

* One of the principal deities.

"You shall, my precious boy—and at once. Go to Catherine of Aragon, tell her to reverse the recorder, and turn the crank. The entire history of the World is in it. Go—and Grak bless you!"

Straightway he was gone. It was his way, when he was excited.

When I got back to the boys, Lem Gulliver was already busy with a scheme. I sat down and listened. His idea was to get up a company and put my Lie on the market. He called it that. He said there wasn't anything on the planet that could compete with it for a moment. It could absorb all the little concerns in the business, on its own terms, and take the entire trade. It would be a giant monopoly, and you wouldn't have any trouble about the stock, indeed you wouldn't. No trouble about it, and no uncertainties; just get up a little inexpensive syndicate among ourselves, and water the stock, and—

"Water your granny!" said Grud, "it's all water, *now*; you can't find a solid place in a million tons of it. How—"

"Never you mind," said Lem, "you wait—you'll see. All we want is to start right, and she'll go like a hurricane. First, we want a name for her—a grand name; an impressive name—come, make a suggestion, somebody."

"Standard Oil."

I offered that.

"What's Standard Oil?"

"The most colossal corporation in the World, and the richest."

"Good—that's settled. Standard Oil she is! Now then—"

"Huck," said Grud, "you can't market a lie like that, all in one hunk. There isn't any nation that can swallow it whole."

"Who said they could? They don't have to. They'll take it on the instalment plan—there don't any of them have to take any more of it than they can believe at a time. Between rests."

"Well, I reckon that'll do—it looks all right, anyway. Who'll work the flotation?"

"Butters."

"What—that bucket-shop dysentery-germ?"

"Plenty good enough, all the same. He knows the game."

"So he does," said Davy Copperfield; "but would you let him keep our capital in his safe?"

"No. Keep it in the stove, and have two firemen, in two watches, four hours off and four on."

"Well, I reckon that'll answer. But wouldn't Butters feel humiliated?"

"The Butterses ain't that kind."

Hang them, they were actually getting ready to chip in! I never saw such a volatile lot; you could persuade them to anything in five minutes. Their scheme would absolutely destroy me! Parents would not send their young sons to my Institute to be taught morals by an incorporated liar.[21] If the Standard Oil should fail of success, my ease and comfort would be gone, there would be nothing left but the organ, the monkey, and bitter hard toil with little rest.

I was in a sort of panic, and well I might be. I must stop this disastrous scheme at once.

How? by persuasion? Not on your life! Golden dreams are not blown out of frenzied heads by *that* process. No—there is a way— one way, and only one, not two: you must see that golden dream and raise it—raise it to the limit!

---

[21] On a page of working notes, Mark Twain wrote what follows as matter "to be interlarded":

About the middle of the second decade I began to teach morals. The additional money thus earned furnished me some lacking little comforts which were very welcome. I painted my sign myself, on a square of tin, and at first I displayed it on my back when I was around with my organ, but for some reason it did not draw; so then I nailed it on the house door:

INSTRUCTION GIVEN IN
Political Morals
Commercial Morals
Ecclesiastical Morals
and
Morals

Pupils applied at once, and I soon had my classes going. Many of the people said my morals were better than my music, if anything. It sounds like flattery but they were in earnest, I think. I generally found the people to be straight-speakers.

My mind was working with a rush, by now—working full head —you could hear it rumble. Swiftly I turned over this, that and the other project—no good! . . . Time was flying! But at last, just in the nick of time I struck it, and knew I was saved! My anxiety, my worry, my terror, vanished; and I was calm.

"Boys," I said,

XVII.

Then I stopped.

That is the way to get the attention of a fussy and excited young crowd. Start to say something; then pause; they notice *that*, though they hadn't noticed your words—nor cared for them, either. Their clack ceases; they set their eyes upon you, intently, expectantly. You let them do that for about eight seconds, or maybe nine, you meantime putting on the expression of a person whose mind has wandered off and gotten lost in a reverie. You wake up, now, give a little start,—that whets them up! you can see their mouths water. Then you say, quite indifferently, "Well, shall we be starting along?—what time is it?" and the game is in your hands.

It's a disappointment. They are sure you came within an ace of saying something important, and are trying to keep it back, now— out of prudence, maybe. Naturally, then, they are eager to know what it was. You say, oh, it wasn't anything. Of course, then, they are just bound to find out; so they insist and insist, and say they won't stir a step until you've told them what it was. Everything is safe, now. You've got their whole attention; also their curiosity; also their sympathy; they've got an appetite. You can begin. Which I did. I said—

"It's really of no consequence, but if you want to hear it, you shall; but don't blame me if it isn't interesting; I've already indicated that it isn't. That is, *now*."

"What do you mean by *now*?" said Davy Copperfield.

"Well, I mean it *would* have been interesting if—well, it was a scheme I happened on when I was on my way out here this afternoon, and I was rather full of it for a while, for I thought maybe we could scrape together a little capital among us, and—and —I confess it looked pretty promising, but—well, it isn't any matter *now*, and there's no hurry, there isn't a person that knows how to find it but me—I'd give him ten years and he couldn't find it!—so it's perfectly safe; it'll keep, and in a year or two or three when we've got the Standard Oil on its legs and going, we—gee, but that's a good name! It'll make it go—you'll see. If we hadn't anything but just that name it would be enough. I feel just as certain that three years from now—or maybe four,—the Standard Oil—"

"*Hang* the Standard Oil—stick to the scheme!" cried Lem Gulliver, with peppery impatience; "what *is* the scheme?"

"That's it!" they all chimed in together, "fetch it out, Huck, *tell* us!"

"Oh, I've no objection to telling you, for it'll keep, years and years; nobody knows where it is but me, and as for *keeping*, the best thing about gold is—"

"*Gold!*"

It took their breath, it made them gasp.

"Gold!" they shouted, hot-eyed, dry-throated, "Where is it? tell us where! stop fooling around and get to the point!"

"Boys, be calm, do not get excited, I beg of you. We must be prudent; one thing at a time is best. This will keep, I assure you it will. Let it wait—that is wisest; then, in six or seven years, just as soon as the Standard Oil—"

"Thunder and blazes, let the Standard *Oil* do the waiting!" they cried. "Out with it, Huck. Where is it?"

"Ah, well," I said, "of course if it is your unanimous desire and decision to postpone the Standard Oil utterly until after we—"

"It is! it is!—utterly, entirely, never to be touched until we've made that scoop, and you give the word. Go ahead now and tell us —tell us everything!"

I recognized that the Institute of Applied Morals was saved.

"Very well, then, I will place the thing before you, and I think you will like it."

I bound them to secrecy, with proper solemnities, then I told them a tale that crisped their hair, it was of such a heating nature. The interest was intense. Sometimes they breathed, but generally they forgot to. I said the Major Molar was a section of a curving range of stupendous brown cliffs which stretched away, no one knew how far—thousands of miles. The rock was a conglomerate of granite, sandstone, feldspar, pitchblend, lapis lazuli, 'dobies, verde antique, freestone, soapstone, grindstone, basalt, rock salt, epsom salts, and every other ore that contains gold, either free or in a matrix. The country was exceedingly rough and forbidding and desolate, and it had taken me several months to explore a hundred miles of it, but what I had seen of it had satisfied me. I had marked one place, in particular, where I would sink a shaft some day if I lived and ever got hold of capital enough for the job. And now, in my belief, that happy day was come. Were the boys content with the scheme?

Were they! Oh, well!

So *that* was settled. The enthusiasm was away up—away high up—up to the topmost top. Standard Oil was flat. We went home gay.

The truth was, I couldn't really tell whether the scheme was worth anything or not. Still, I had pretty fair hopes. I got them from putting this and that together and drawing an inference. Blitzowski had almost certainly seen better days, at some time or other, for he had the dentist-habit. Among the poor and defeated, none but people who have been well off, and well up, have that expensive habit.

I was satisfied with the way I had played that game. People who are on fire with a splendid new scheme are cynical and chilly toward a new one if you spring it on them suddenly and beseech them to look at it. It is best to be indifferent, and disinclined, then they get an appetite, and do the begging themselves.

XVIII

C ATHERINE SAID she had turned the crank a while for Sir Galahad and he went wild with delight and astonishment over my History of the World, then he rushed away with the Recorder and said he was going to shut himself up with it at home and master its entire contents before ever he rested.

I had saved my College of Morals, by interposing a gold mine between it and the dangerous Standard Oil; it was only an emergency-gold mine, I only invented it to stop that gap; but now that it was invented, and the boys joyfully insane about it, I must stand by it or invent something still richer and better, to take its place. I thought over a lot of substitutes, such as emerald mines and opal mines, and diamond mines, but I had to give them up, Blitzowski would turn out to be quite barren of those things, for sure. I fell back on the gold. I got to working up a hope. The more I worked at it, and coaxed it, and reasoned with it, the less and less chimerical it seemed. It is the right way to do with a hope; it is like any other agriculture: if you hoe it and harrow it and water it enough, you can make three blades of it grow where none grew before. If you've got nothing to plant, the process is slow and difficult, but if you've got a seed of some kind or other—any kind will answer—you get along a good deal faster. I had one. It was a dream. I planted the dream. It turned up in my memory just at the right time. I believe something in dreams. Sometimes. I had not believed in this one when it happened, but that was because I hadn't any use for it then. It was different, now. A dream that comes only once is oftenest only an idle accident, and hasn't any message, but the recurrent dream is quite another matter—oftener than not it has come on business. This one was that kind. I wondered, now, that I hadn't had this thought at the time. It was a good dream, and well put together.

First I dreamed that I was patiently chewing my way through a very long and delicate nerve in one of Blitzowski's back teeth—lower jaw—and feeling him rock and sway mountainously in response to the pain; this went on for some weeks, and at last I fetched out into a vast cavity, a cavity of imposing grandeur, with walls that stretched up and up and up through an ever-dimming twilight until lost in the ultimate thick darkness, for his mouth was shut at the time.

By and by the dream came again. But this time I found the stupendous Cave filled; Blitzowski had been to the dream-dentist.

After an interval it came a third time. In my dream the plug was transparent. It was disposed in three vast strata, each about a third of a mile thick, (microbe measure). The top one was dove-colored, the next one had the tint of oxydized silver, the bottom one was yellow.

I called up those dreams, now, and studied them; a little doubtfully at first, but under painstaking and intelligent cultivation they improved. In the end, the crop arrived at puberty, and was satisfactory. I was in a condition of mind bordering on enthusiasm. The mine was there, sure—pretty dreamy, yes, pretty dreamy, but there, anyway; I could *see* it! just as if it were before my eyes: top stratum, a third of a mile deep—cement; next stratum, amalgam; bottom stratum, gold! good, straight, honest dentist's gold, 23 carats fine!

And as for the quantity. I fell to measuring it—for fun. Very soon the towering figures began to take hold of my imagination! How natural that was! It is the way we are made. I began in fun; in fifteen minutes I was sobering down to earnest. And how natural *that* was, too! In the alembic of my fancy—without my noticing it, so absorbed was I in my ciphering—my dream-gold was turning into the real metal, and my dream was turning into a fact. At least into a persuasion. Very well, it didn't take the persuasion long to harden into a conviction. So there is where I had presently arrived: I was convinced that the dream was a straight and honorable and perfectly trustworthy photograph of an existent actuality. Which is to say, all doubts and questionings had sifted out of my mind, by now, and disappeared, and I was believing, up to the hilt, that that mighty treasure was really yonder and waiting for us in the sub-cellar of Blitzowski's tooth. Between believing a thing and thinking you *know* it is only a small step and quickly taken. I soon took it, and was prepared to say to all comers, "It isn't a mere probability, I *know* the gold is there." It's the way we are made. We could be better made, but we wouldn't be interesting, then.

By my stingiest and most conservative and exacting measure-ment, I was obliged to admit that that wad of gold was not a shade less than half the bigness of a human buckshot! It was titanic—colossal unthinkable—it was absolutely breath-taking! Yet there it was—there were the figures—there was no getting around them.

What might I compare this astonishing deposit with? Klondike? It made me smile. Klondike was but a peanut-pedlar's till, alongside of it. The Big Bonanza, then? Let us consider. The Big Bonanza was discovered in Nevada seven years before I was born—a stupendous body of rich silver ore, the like of which had never been heard of in the world before. Two day-laborers discovered it, and took into partnership in the secret a saloon keeper and a broker; they bought the ground for a song, and in two weeks they were hundred-millionaires. But the Big Bonanza was nothing—you might say, less than nothing—compared with the measureless mass of wealth packed away in the deeps of Blitzowski's tush. A speck of gold worth 2,000 *slasher* would not be detectible under a human microscope until magnified seventeen hundred and fifty-six diame-ters. Let some one else go on now, and cipher out the whole value of that tooth, if desired, it makes me tired.

The spectacle of this incredible wealth dazed me, I was like one drunk—drunk with delight, with exultation! I had never had any money before, to speak of, and I didn't know what to do with it, it was a positive embarrassment—for some minutes. I had never cared for money before, but now I cared for it. So suddenly as this I was changed like that! We *are* strangely made!

What would the boys say when I told them! How would they feel, what would they say, when they pulled their stampeded wits together and realized how limitlessly rich they were! Oh, how *would* they feel when they realized that they couldn't possibly spend their yearly income, even though they should hire the imperial Henryland Family to help!

I was impatient to summon them and tell them the great news. I reached out my hand to touch the bell—

Wait! Something in me seemed to say, don't be precipitate—reflect!

I obeyed the mysterious impulse, and reflected.

x   x   x   x

I reflected hard, for an hour. Then I sighed, and said to myself "It is only fair; it is I that discovered the mine; if it had not been for me it would never have been discovered at all; it would not be just for them to have a twelfth apiece, and I no more."

I reflected further, and decided to keep half, and let them have the other half among them. It seemed to me that that was right and fair, and I felt quite satisfied.

I was going to ring, now—

That warning stopped me again.

x   x   x   x

I reflected another hour. Then I saw that they could never use so much money—it would be impossible. A third of the property would be quite sufficient for them, modest as were their needs, unfamiliar as they were with m—

I reached for the bell.

x   x   x   x

After a season of deep reflection I recognized that they would never be able to spend judiciously any more than a fourth of that mass of riches—

x   x   x   perhaps not even a tenth. Indeed, with so much as a tenth, would not the poisonous spirit of speculation enter insidiously into them? would it not undermine their morals? had I a *right* to place such a temptation before such young and inex—

x   x   x   ah, no, no, I must not betray them, I must do my duty by them, I should never be able to sleep again if I should be the instrument of their moral ruin. Oh, the bare thought of it is more than I—

x   x   x   Yes, it would be best for them that I keep the gold. No harm would come to them then, and the reflection that I had saved them pure would always be my sufficient reward—I could ask no other, no sweeter, no nobler.

x   x   x   But I would not allow them to go wholly shareless in this good fortune that was come to me; no, they should have part of the amalgam mine. They should do the work on both mines, and have part of the amalgam for their labor. I would determine what part, upon further reflection. And they could have all the cement.

I then went to bed.

APPENDIX

The Passenger's Story.

I T WAS on an American liner—couple of years ago. I was a second cabin passenger. It was after midnight, and very dark—and misty and damp. There was some sea on. I was on the upper deck, away aft, snuggled under the lee of the canvassed rail on the starboard side, doing nothing. That is, *thinking*. Nobody stirring; the whole deck was a solitude. By and by two dim figures came down the port side talking and they stopped and stood there, about opposite me and went on with their talk. One had a heavy voice, the other one had an ordinary voice and a little hacking cough. I couldn't tell what the men were like—except that both were large —they were just shapeless blots in the gloom. The bass voice said—

"But I've always had a good word for *dogs* ever *since*, when I hear people talking against them; because *that dog* saved my life."

(*Hack-hack.*) Is *that so?*

Yes, he *did.* And my whole *crew*, too—14 *men.* Do *you* like *dogs?*

(*H-h*). *Like* them? Well I should *think* so.

All *right*, then. Where *was* I?

(*H-h*) Becalmed in the Indian ocean.

I *know.* But where had I got to about the *dog?*

H. Why, you *started* to tell how you *got* him; but you switched off onto—

O, yes, I remember, now. He came aboard at the dock, racing

around with his nose down, hunting for somebody that had been there—his master, I reckon—and the crew captured him and shut him below, and we sailed in an hour. Well, sir, he was just a darling, that dog. Inside of a week he was the pet of the whole crew. He was brim full of play, and fun and affection and good nature. They bedded him like the *aristocracy,* and there warn't a *man* but would divide his dinner with him; and he *was* the lovingest creature and the *gratefulest* you ever *saw.*

Well, that night that I was telling you about, it was *warm,* and *still* and *drowsy* and *lazy;* and the sails hung *idle,* and the deck-watch and the lookout and everybody *else* was sound *asleep.* Well along about an hour after midnight there was a *tremendous* scratching and barking at my door, and *I* jumped *out* and that dog was just *wild* with excitement, and rushed off and just as good as *told* me to come *along,* and come *quick.* Well, sir, she was *afire* down in the *hold,* and he had *discovered* it. Down I plunged, and *he* went raging off and waking up the *others.*

That *was* the closest fit! Remember the *powder*-kegs I told you about? Why in another two *minutes* the fire would a *had* 'em and we'd a been blown into the *sky.*

H. Good *dog*—*splen*-did dog!

I had the powder out of danger in half a *second,* and *here* came the men *tearing*—and *white?* Why

[A page of the manuscript is missing.]

was in the boat but *me,* and the flames were soaring up and lighting the whole *ocean,* I tied the dog to the foot of the *main*mast and then got in my*self* and took the *tiller* and said "All *ready*— give *way."*

Why, they all shouted at once—"*What?*—going to leave the *dog?*"

I said, Did you hear the *order?* Give *way.*

Well the *tears* begun to run down their *faces.* And they said, Why he saved our *lives*—we *can't* leave him. I said—

You don't know what you're *talking* about. He'd be more in the way than a family of *children*—and he can *eat* as much as a family of children, *too.* Now men, *you know me*—and I pulled a *revolver*

[A page of the manuscript is missing.]

tugged at his *rope,* and begged and moaned and yelped—why it was as plain as if he was *saying,* Oh, *don't* leave me, *please* don't leave me, *I* haven't done any harm. And then presently the fire swept down on him and he sent up two or three *awful* shrieks and it was all *over.* And the men sat there sobbing and crying like children.

H. Is that *true?*

"True as *gospel.*"

H. It was the vilest murder that ever was *done*—and I hope you will land in hell before you are an hour *older.*

I heard a blow struck, then another and *another;* the ship gave a heavy *lurch* and the two vague forms came

The Mad Passenger

THE DINNER was a failure. While it was still unfinished the company began to [1] break up and slip out, one after another; and presently none was left but the stranger at my side and me. We were sipping black coffee and smoking. The stranger said, with a sigh—

"Ah, well, that is the way with them. They are mad—that captain and that mate."

"Mad?"

"Well, on the way to it. I have noticed it for days."

"I think, myself, that they are disturbed about something, but I don't see any suggestion of madness about it."

"But you haven't been around. You have been shut up a good deal lately and haven't seen what has been going on. Let me tell you a few things." He was speaking in a low voice. A rattling of dishes attracted his attention—a steward was clearing the other end of the table. "Come to my cabin—this place lacks privacy. Bring your coffee."

It was a roomy and comfortable cabin, and had a good lamp in it, also a locker and a swinging table. He locked the door and we sat down. He began to speak again—still in a guarded voice, a precaution not needed, now, and so I judged that it was habit or nature that made him do this.

"These new people have got a name for me which you may not

---

[1] In revising "The Great Dark," Mark Twain retained the words up to this point but deleted all of what follows.

have heard; they call me the Mad Passenger. I do not mind this insult, I give you my word. It is a secret bitterness to me, true, but as it hasn't its source in malice, but only in ignorance it is of course not blameworthy. O dear, think of the irony of it—they call me mad—*they!* Do you know what these people are doing? They've got a chart of *Dreamland,* and they are navigating this ship by it!"

I tried to look incredulous. He laid his hand on my arm and said with great earnestness—

"You don't believe me. It was not to be expected that you would. But I have said only the truth. I have seen the chart myself; and I have peeped in through the chart-room window when no one was near, and seen them working over it and trying to compass-out a course over it. It is perfectly true. Along at first, any one could go and look; but not now. They don't allow any but themselves to enter that place; and they've curtained the window. You see now, don't you, why they flew out so at the purser and the girl?"

"Well—er—"

"Dear me, it's an amazing thing, when you come to think of it. It's a chart of one particular part of Dreamland—Jupiter. No, not Jupiter—Saturn. No, I'm wrong again. I can't call the name to mind, now, but I know many of the details, land and sea; in fact am tolerably familar with them, for I have often been there in dreams, with the Superintendent. It may be that you have been there, too, and will remember whether it is a planet or a fixed star, if I mention a detail or two. On the chart are countries called England, America, and so on, and an ocean called Atlantic. Come—does it suggest anything? Can you help?"

It troubled me. It was a confusing situation. I said—

"Yes, I have been there. It is called the World, and—"

"That's it, that's it! It had slipped my memory for the moment—"

"But dear sir, are you *sure* it is a part of Dreamland?"

He looked frightened; and edged away from me a little, and sat apparently dazed and ill at ease. I didn't know anything to say, so there was an uncomfortable silence. Presently he said, haltingly and timidly—

"You—you won't be offended—but—but are you mad, too? They all are."

I said to myself, "It is of no use to struggle. Something has happened to me, I don't know what. It seems manifest, from all sorts of evidences, that I have been under a delusion since I don't know when. Years, no doubt. I think I have lived in dreams so long that now that I have at last got back among realities I have lost the sense of them and *they* seem dreams, too." I wished I knew of some good way to get back this man's confidence; no doubt he could wake up my dead memory for me and bring to life in it things of interest to me and thus save me from surprising Alice with my ignorances at every turn. Presently I ventured this—

"No, I am not mad, but a thing has happened to me which is nearly as serious. I can trust you, I think, and I will. Will you let me tell you something in strict confidence—something which I have confessed to no one, not even my wife?"

It pleased him to the marrow—I could see it.

"It is good of you to show me this distinction; but you have always been good to me, these twenty-two years—I say it gratefully. Whatever the secret is, I promise to keep it faithfully."

"I believe you will. It is this. I have lost my memory."

"Lost—your—memory?"

"Lost it wholly."

"Why—it is terrible. Was it from the fall?"

"Fall? Have I had a fall?"

"Yes. Ten or eleven days ago."

"I remember nothing of it."

"Yes, you slipped and fell on the deck,—there was a heavy sea at the time. I was with you. I helped you up, and you laughed and said you were not hurt but your clothes were wet and you would go and change them. I haven't seen you since to speak with you till to-day; but George always said you were well, when I inquired, but chose to keep to your quarters most of the time."

"It must have been the fall. I remember everything that has happened today, but not a single previous experience of my whole life."

"Dear me, it is a fearful thing, an amazing thing."

"And a misery beyond imagination. My wife knows that something has happened to me, but she does not suspect the serious extent of it. Of course I wouldn't have her know, for anything. She terrifies me by reminding me of things which I ought to be familiar with, then I have to scramble out of the scrape the best I can; and of course I do it awkwardly. But I am safe now. When I want to get over one of those obstacles I shall come to you. You will post me?"

"Gladly. Nothing has happened to you in twenty-two years that I am not acquainted with. We shall have no trouble."

"This makes me easy. You will tell me my history. It ought to interest me, for every detail of it will be new. And you must tell me about yourself, too. She spoke of you to-day, and I supposed I was hearing of you for the first time."

"*Isn't* it astonishing!"

We had a long talk together and he told me a great deal of my history, and I found it curious and entertaining; and he told me a great deal about Alice, whom he had known ever since she was three years old. He posted me in the details of the devouring of Captain Hall's boy by the spider-squid, and in other matters which I needed to know in order not to be embarrassed when trading reminiscences with my family and the servants.

We became comrades, and I came to like him better and better every day. I spent an hour or two in his cabin daily, and he an hour or so in my quarters. Alice had always liked him very well; and now he was become very near to her, for outside of our family he was the only relic left of her former life and its lost and lamented comradeships. He had a name of a jaw-breaking sort, but no one called him by it in these recent days; even the family and our servants had dropped it for the one used by the rest of the ship. This was "M.P.," (mad passenger.) It was simple and easy. He was sane, I thought, but as long as the ship thought differently, the title was well enough, and did no harm.

After a couple of weeks I noticed that when I wanted him and couldn't find him in his cabin there was no occasion to go groping everywhere—he was pretty sure to be in one certain place. On the forecastle—sitting on the mizzen-hatch. Sitting there and peering wistfully out ahead through the gloom, and looking melancholy. At last, one day in his cabin I asked him why he did that. A pathetic expression came into his face, and he muttered an ejaculation or two in his own strange language, then said in English—

"I am looking for my country."

"Your country?"

"I have done it every day for twenty-two years. It is long to wait, long to wait!"

The poor devil. It was sort of heart-breaking to hear him.

"What country is it? Where is it?"

He told me the tough name of it—it was an Empire of some sort —then added—

"It isn't anywhere in particular—it floats."

"Floats?—isn't fixed, isn't anchored?"

He smiled, and said—

"Why should it be? It isn't Dreamland. Of course it floats."

"Tell me about it. It must be dreadful there. In the eternal night."

"No, it isn't. It is a fair land, and beautiful. And it is not night there, but eternal day—a mellow rich light, and enchanting; for it circles forever and ever around outside the Great White Glare, and just the right distance away from it—like the other wandering Empires. Tradition says one vaguely glimpses one or another of them now and then at intervals of a century or two.

"It is curious. What keeps your Empire just the right distance away?"

"Attraction and repulsion. But for the attraction it would drift into the darkness; but for the repulsion it would drift into the Glare —and then!"

"I wish I could see that country. Do you expect to see it again?"

A passion of longing lighted his face for a moment, then faded out and he said despondently—

"No, it is too good to hope for. At first I hoped—all the first years. But that is all gone by, now—oh, yes, that is all over, years and years ago; I watch for it now from old habit, not from hope."

He was silent awhile, then sighed and added, "But it is better so, perhaps. My girl-wife has broken her heart with waiting, no doubt; my little child is a woman, now—she would not remember me. She was half as old as your little Bessie—yes, and like her a little, and had the same cunning ways; and sometimes there flashes into Bessie's face an expression when we are playing together that is exact! When I see that, I have to put the child down and go away; I cannot endure the joy of it—and the pain. But let us talk of other things. Say something—anything! Ask me a question."

"I will. Of course I have forgotten about your coming aboard the ship; how did it happen?"

"Curse that day—forever! I had a great yacht, and I used to take my family and friends with me and make cruises out into the cold weather and the darkness; and once we walked the deck a good while laughing and chatting; then a storm began to brew and the snow to fly, and they all went below to arrange for some games and prepare something hot and wait a quarter of an hour for me. We were shortening sail, and I wanted to superintend a little. I was standing astern, backed up against the taffrail and staring up toward the flapping kites—which I could not see for the gloom— when your ship's invisible bowsprit swept past me, and the dragging bight of the main-brace caught me around the body and carried me off my feet. I seized it and saved myself; the bowsprit dipped me into the sea, but when it rose again I was astride it, and my yacht had vanished in the blackness and the storm."

"You never saw it again?"

"No, never. And now I was among strangers; we did not know each other's language, of course, and I could not explain how I got there; but they were friendly to me and hospitable. They taught me the language; they taught me how to divide time, and measure it off into seconds, minutes, hours, days, weeks, months, years, and a hundred other strange and interesting things; and so, as I was always something of a scholar, these twenty-two years have not been dull and stupid to me. But I would they could have had less of heart-break in them!"

It was a pathetic history, and I was touched by it. I was moved to try to say some hopeful things to the poor exile, but he courteously put all that aside, and said he found it wholesomest to keep the subject out of his mind when he had the opportunity to do it—and that was only when he had a chance to talk. Talk could deal with other matters, and was a good medicine. So then we drifted into a discussion of language, its curiosities and peculiarities, and it presently came out that in his tongue there were no exact equivalents for our words *modesty, immodesty, decency, indecency, right, wrong, sin.* He said that in most details the civilization of his country was the counterpart of that which prevailed among the highest civilizations of dreamlands like the World, and that a citizen of that unreal planet would be quite at home in his Empire, and would find it quite up to date in matters of art, erudition, invention, architecture, etc.

That seemed strange, but he said there was properly nothing strange about it, since dreamlands were nothing but imitations of real countries created out of the dreamer's own imagination and experience, with some help, perhaps, from the Superintendent of Dreams. At least that was his belief, he said, and he thought it reasonable and plausible. He had noticed that in Jupiter, Uranus, and in fact in all other dream-countries he found things about as they were at home, and apparently quite real and natural as long as the dream lasted. In the World, it was true, there were a few details that it had a monopoly of, but they were not important, and not pleasant.

"For instance?"

"Well, for instance they have what they term Religions; also curious systems of government, and an interesting but most odd code of morals. But don't you know about these things? Haven't you been there with the Superintendent? Come in!"

It was the children. They had come with Germania to be entertained.

M. P. was good at that. He told them a quaint and charming tale whose scene was laid in his lost country, then he and I had a game of romps with them. In the course of the romps Bessie hurt herself, and in her anger she tried to break things, and did break a glass. I said—

"Tut-tut, why did you do that, Bessie?—it's wrong."

"No-no, not wrong," said M. P.; "don't call it that."

"What then?"

"Inexpedient."

I remembered. It was the nearest that his native tongue could come to furnishing an equivalent for our word "wrong."

He petted Bessie into a good humor, then set the children to rummaging the drawers of his bureau and the compartments of his locker. In one of these latter they found a microscope. M. P. began to arrange it for an exhibition, and a curious feeling came over me. It seemed to me that I had seen the same thing done before; even that I had done it myself—in a dream. It was a strange sensation, and troubled me. Then M. P. put a drop of water on a glass slide, threw a circle of white light under it from the reflector, screwed the lens down tight against it, and soon the children were exclaiming over the hideous animals they saw darting about and fighting in the bit of moisture.

I dropped into a whirl of thinkings and dim and shadowy half-reminiscences, and wholly lost myself. After a while the children reached up and kissed me good-bye—I was hardly conscious of it—and then they went away with the nurse and with M. P., who said the sea was rising and he would help them home and then come back. I presently got up to stretch my legs, and noticed a portfolio lying in the open locker. Pictures, I judged, for M. P. was a good amateur artist—there were several small portraits and photographs of his wife and children pinned to the wall which were his own work, he had told me. I opened the portfolio and found a number of pictures; pictures of himself, his family, and many lady and gentleman friends: in some cases beautifully clothed, but in most cases naked!

I heard him coming. I put the book away, and prepared myself to look like a person who had not discovered a disgraceful secret and who was not shocked. I arranged a pleasant smile and—

Dying Deposition

In "Which Was It?" the deposition of the dying Andrew Harrison is taken, to be presented at the trial of the squire. This fragment Mark Twain apparently intended to bring into that story in a later part that he never wrote. The confession (or accusation) of Andrew can perhaps be viewed as an invention of his crazed imagination. However, an alternate possibility is that Mark Twain at one time planned to reveal at the end that the squire and not George Harrison had, after all, dealt the killing blow to Jake Bleeker. The squire is called Brewster, as he was in an early-written part of "Which Was It?"

I, ANDREW BAYLISS HARRISON, being of sound mind and possessed of all my faculties; and being near to death, and desiring to depart this life at peace with all and with my conscience, do make oath and depose as here followeth:

I was indebted to Walter Brewster in the sum of five thousand dollars, representing four thousand dollars, borrowed money and two and a half years' interest at ten per cent. In his house on the 27th of October I handed him the money in bank bills and received back my promissory note, which fluttered from my hand, I being old and feeble and my hands unsteady, and fell upon the fire and was burnt before it could be rescued. He said it was no matter, there was now no longer any evidence of debt against me. But I said I would rather have another note, canceled, to keep with my papers. He said very well, perhaps it would be best, and sat down and took up his pen, and just then his slave-woman Liza came and whispered to him and he said he must go, but would send me the canceled note—would that do? I said yes, perfectly; and went away.

But it did not come, that day, nor the next, nor the next. I was not troubled; but now I heard it reported that he was beginning to drink again, and this made me uneasy, and I went to his house on the 1st of November and again on the second, but on both occasions he was reported out. The next day, the 3d, he sent for me. He received me coldly, and asked me sternly when I was going to pay that money. I was astonished, and said he well knew I paid it six days ago. He affected to be angry and said he would have none of this trifling; that he had trusted me, mistaking me for an honest man, and had returned my note to me upon my assurance that I had the money ready and would fetch it; and said that before sunset he must have a new note payable at one day's notice and secured by a mortgage on the mill. I was in great trouble, and did not know what to do; for all these days I had kept my dilemma from my son George, being ashamed to tell him of my carelessness and of my perhaps unnecessary uneasiness. But I was astonished and outraged, now, and said I would expose this base trick to George and to all the world. He said I was a fool; who would believe such a fantastic story? I said all would; for my family had never been liars; I might be weak and foolishly trustful, being used to deal with honorable men, but the community had never known one of us to speak an untruth—a reputation which would stand me in good stead now. That seemed to strike him; he reflected; then began to threaten—to kill me, to kill George, if I did not comply with his demand. He had been drinking; I was at his mercy; I must promise, he said, or I should not leave his house alive. I promised. I gave the note, and went away, to have the mortgage drawn and executed; I sent it to him, according to my promise; for I had never broken a promise, and could not begin now, in my old age. But toward nine that night I was at his house again—sent for by him. He received me in his bedroom up stairs, and his manner was pleasant and friendly. He asked if I had told George or any one. I said no, I was too ashamed. Banish the shame, he said, a little hilariously—his bottle and hot water were on the table: "Tom and Helen have made it up again," he said, "the two families are one, now; here are the papers, canceled and no longer harmful; I will give them to Helen as a betrothal present. Are you satisfied?" "Perfectly," I said. He mixed toddies, and said we must celebrate. This we did, and continued it, I being full of joy over this happy turn in our fortunes and nothing loath. About eleven, it being very still, we heard a slight noise down stairs. "A burglar," he said, and took up his cane, and started, on tip-toe. I said "Don't go in the dark," and took up the candle. "What?" said he, "carry a light and be a target?—leave it." I left it, and followed, tip-toeing after him. Below, the room was open; in the middle of it a man stooping, with his back to us, and a candle near, on a chair. We could not see what he was doing. He turned—it was Jake Bleeker. Brewster strode toward him in a fury, with his cane raised. Jake shouted in fright— words I did not understand—and dropped on his knees and put up his hands, begging for his life, and said he was only playing a little joke—a trick. Brewster said, "I will kill you!" "Don't!" I begged; but the cane was descending—there was a wild shriek—it struck. I fled—the back way, and down the fields. I was able to enter my house and reach my bedroom unobserved. I wished to keep my secret from all; the two families were one, now, and the marriage would make us prosperous. I was the only witness, and without my testimony no harm would befal Brewster. It was a wicked thought, a wicked and selfish purpose, and God has justly called me to account for it. And how quickly! I am dying. I am making such reparation as I can; I repent me of my folly and sin; I beg the community to forgive me, remembering that in my long life this is the only deep fault that stains my good name, and that humbly and willingly I am paying for it the costliest price a man can pay. I throw myself upon the mercy of God, and leave my fate as a warning to any who would barter his soul's purity for the frail vanities of a perishable world.

Trial of the Squire

THIS FRAGMENT, a variant of the George Harrison story, was probably written in the summer of 1899. The story is presented "from the outside" in that the reader is not given George Harrison's thoughts as in "Which Was It?" Both the name of the squire—Baldwin rather than Brewster or Fairfax—and the time of the initial action—July rather than November—show that this is a quite early draft.

I T WAS a Saturday afternoon, in summer. About a mile outside the village four roads met. It was not the first time; they had always done it, as far back as the oldest resident of the region could remember; and so, if any one was ever surprised at it you could know him for a stranger by that sign. The blacksmith shop was there; also a solitary vast live-oak, which stretched its limbs straight out fifty feet, and no matter how many of the outlying farmers gathered there to wait while their horses were shod, they did not need to wait in the sun, there was shade enough and to spare. They were always coming and going, Saturday afternoons, but they did not hurry their going, for that was the central gossip-exchange for a wide stretch of country round about, and in that old simple day supplied the place of the lacking newspaper.

Several farmers were lolling in the shade on this particular afternoon, talking, and smoking their cob pipes. Ordinarily they would have been discussing the weather and the crops, then last

571

Sunday's sermon; afterward the gossip-mill would begin to grind; but now there was only one topic. A great and unusual event had occurred, and it had paled all other interests. Walter Baldwin had been horse-whipping Jake Bleeker. What for, nobody knew. Bleeker refused to say, and no one had inquired of Baldwin. Baldwin was the most respected man in those parts, a man of fine character and reputation, a good man; but the people stood in some little awe of him, for in mind and education he was rather their superior, and although he was friendly and courteous with all, he was a little reserved in his ways, and not really familiar with any. Everybody liked him, everybody was glad to talk with him and visit him and be visited by him, and everybody privately regarded his friendship as an honor; but no one of them all would have thought of asking him why he had horse-whipped Jake Bleeker. All wondered, with a strenuous and persecuting curiosity, what it could possibly have been that had carried his temper so far, for it had been many years since he had allowed it to get the best of him —not, indeed, since he was a young bachelor and once in a sudden rage had come near killing a man. He was in liquor at the time, and from that day forth had wholly ceased from drinking and had kept a stern guard over his hot disposition. He was getting toward fifty, now. He was a widower, with no family except two daughters, aged eighteen and twenty respectively. He loved them deeply, and they loved him—under limitations. In one regard he failed of their approval: he was not strongly interested in religious matters, and did not go to church, whereas religion was not merely an interest with them, it was a passion; their mother had had it before them.

Baldwin had not an enemy. George Harrison disliked him, but he was not an enemy. The dislike dated back to a time when the two were boys together, and if it had ever had a special origin, neither of them would now have been able to recall what it was.

Jake Bleeker worked in George Harrison's grist mill, and was a German. He had a wife, but no children living. He had been in America many years, and spoke good enough English. He always spoke it, except when angry or startled; then he was apt to revert to his mother tongue. On those occasions he was unintelligible to everybody except George Harrison, his employer, who, in the course of years, had gathered from him a smattering of his language. Harrison was a favorite. He was a good-hearted man, clean and upright, blithe and cheery, and conspicuously kind and compassionate and humane. He was possessed of a peculiarly nice sense of honor, and it was said of him that he could neither be persuaded nor driven to do a thing which he thought wrong.

The men under the live-oak talked the horse-whipping over at great length, and all kinds of guesses were made as to the nature of the provocation that had brought it about, but no satisfactory result was reached, of course. In the course of the talk it came out that there was a report that Baldwin was under the influence of liquor when he did the cowhiding. That piece of news made a great stir. But was it believable? Could it really be true?

"Burt will know," said Reuben Hoskins; "I'll go and ask him."

That was Burt Higgins, the blacksmith. Hoskins was soon back, and said—

"It's so; he was under the influence; Jake told Burt so."

It was decided, all around, that this detail was exceedingly important.

"It's twenty-two years since he touched a drop or lost his grip on his temper," said Park Robinson. "Why, it must have been something awful to stir him up like that, and knock all his props out from under him at one slam."

"I wonder what his girls think of the business?" said Sam Griswold.

"Think of it?" said Hoskins; "Burt says they're clean killed, and ashamed to look anybody in the face; he says they packed right up and left for their aunt Mary's, in the village, and ain't coming back till they've cried it out."

There was a general hum, but whether it signified approval, or pity, or what, was not determinable. The afternoon was far spent. The men unhitched their horses and prepared to ride. As they mounted, the blacksmith appeared at his door, untying his leather apron and delivering his good-byes, and the men asked him how Jake Bleeker was feeling about the matter.

"How does he take it?"

"Jake? Well, the way he carries on, you never see anything like it. But he's so raging mad you can't make much out of it, because he does the most of it in Dutch, the way he always does when his temper's up. Says he'll get even, if it's the last act; says he'll play him a trick, first thing he knows, that'll make him ashamed he was born; that he won't forget for *one* spell, anyway. Keeps saying that, then he goes off into Dutch again."

II

A COUPLE of days passed by. Rumors flew that Baldwin was still drinking. Then, on Tuesday morning, came dreadful news— Baldwin had murdered Jake Bleeker! He had been caught red-handed, and jailed. As for particulars, none were to be had. The murderer was the only witness of the act itself; only he and his legal counsel knew how the crime had come about, and they were not ready to talk yet. At the inquest the murderer said nothing. By and by the grand jury indicted him for murder in the first degree, but what they had learned about the case they kept to themselves, of course. The trial would take place in December; meantime the people could guess, and talk; and that is what they most diligently did. At first they were sorry for the prisoner, but that did not last. The thing was horrible; killings were not customary there; this was the first one that had happened in a generation; it had put a blot upon the region. As time went on, opinion grew bitter against the accused, and steadily more and more bitter, more and more hostile; and at the same time, opinion was changing regarding the murdered man. At first he had not seemed much of a loss, but gradually his value increased, and in the end reached an unreckonable preciousness. The gallows must avenge his taking off, nothing else would satisfy the community.

III

Five months drifted by.

When the case came up in court at last, in December, everybody was there to see. There was some difficulty in getting a jury, because nearly everybody had formed an unalterable opinion prejudicial to the prisoner because the prejudice against the prisoner was so general. Before the panel had been secured, the peremptory challenges had been exhausted on both sides. George Harrison was among the chosen. Neither side objected to him. He acknowledged that he disliked the accused, but said that that would be no bar to his bringing in a verdict in straight and honest accordance with the evidence. No one doubted that. His acceptance by the defence was a high tribute to his character, but an earned one. Sam Griswold was the first witness called.

Evidence of Samuel Griswold.—"On the 17th of July last, about eleven at night, I was coming along the old stage road with Nicholas Hyatt and Henry Joyce, and we heard a yell, like as if somebody was in trouble, and it seemed to come from prisoner's house, which was sixty yards off—it's been measured since. We rushed there, and up through the front yard, and found the door open; and inside, in the bedroom on the right, we found the prisoner struggling up off of the floor, and he was all bloody; and just inside the door a man was stretched on his back, with his arms spread out; and he was gasping, and his head was a sight to see. It was Jake Bleeker. So then—"

Prosecution. "Was there a light burning in the room?"

"No, but Joyce had a lantern."

"Do you recognize this stick—this club?"

"Yes; it was lying on the floor."

"Had you ever seen it before?"

"Yes; often."

"Where?"

"Prisoner often carried it."

"Go on."

"Prisoner had a dazed look, and was unsteady on his legs. We judged he had been drinking. We stood a minute, looking, then Bleeker gave a gasp, and was dead."

"Had he said anything?"

"Only moaned, and muttered something we didn't understand. Dutch, we reckoned."

"Go on."

"Joyce asked prisoner how it happened, but he only shook his head kind of slow and wondering, and said, 'It's an awful business —oh, my God!'" (*Sensation.*)

"Go on."

"Then I asked him if he was willing to go with us, and he said he was; so we went; and on the way to the village I was going to ask him some more questions, but Hyatt said maybe we best not—"

The Court. "And quite right."

"—so I didn't ask him and he never said anything more."

Joyce and Hyatt corroborated this testimony. The three witnesses were cross-examined, then they were followed by witnesses who testified to the horse-whipping, but did not know how it had come about. On cross-examination two of these deposed to having heard Bleeker threaten that he would "get even" with the prisoner; and one of them (Burt Higgins) added that deceased had said he would play a trick on [prisoner] that he "wouldn't forget for *one* spell."

Then Bridget Finnigan Bleeker was called.

A buzz of interest swept the house, and all eyes were centred upon the widow as she rose and kissed the book. She was in deep black. She was very pale, and her face was set, and hard, and unforgiving. After the usual perfunctory questions—

Prosecution. "Do you recognize the prisoner at the bar?"

Witness bent a vengeful gaze upon the prisoner for a moment, and said she recognised him—"to her sorrow."

Prosecution. "Where were you about nine o'clock of the evening of the 17th July last?"

"In the mill."

"How did you come to be there?"

"My husband had went over there after supper about something or other, and there was a message for him and I went with the nigger to find him and give him the note, which was from the murderer there—"

The Court. "Stop! You must not use language like that. Say prisoner."

"But he is a murderer, your honor, and the blackest one th—"

Prosecution. "Be quiet, and do as the Court tells you! Go on."

"Well, then, it was from *him,* and said he was sorry and ashamed he done it, and would my husband come over and let him tell him with his own mouth, he was sick and it would comfort him; and my husband went, though I begged him not to, and told him it was a trap—and the scoundrel murdered him."

The Court. "Witness!—"

Prosecution. "Do try and behave yourself!"

The Defence. "Your honor, I must protest. I beg your honor to instruct the jury to pay no attention to this evidence. It is pure hearsay. The note has not been produced here—"

Witness. "Because my husband had it with him, and any fool knows that that blackguard stole it off of the corpse and burnt it." (*Sobbing.*) "And I hope the everlasting fires of—"

The Court. "Shut up, will you!"

The Defence. "Your honor, the evidence is pure hearsay, and profoundly unfair to my client; it is unlawful and inadmissible. The whole community knows it is claimed that the messenger was a negro, the slave of my client and one of his servants. Right in the face of the law that negro slave is actually testifying in this court, by proxy, in a matter which wholly concerns a white man. It is monstrous—it is inhuman—it is unchristian! It is not provable here that the negro ever carried any note—"

A Voice. "*Says* he did, anyhow!"

Defence. "Yes—and is *paid* to say it! There is no evidence here, your honor."

The Court. "On the contrary. There is evidence that a note was sent; there is evidence showing what its contents were. How or by whom the note was conveyed is immaterial. Take your seat."

Witness. "There, now, how do you like the taste of that, you spalpeen!"

The Court. "Silence, woman!"

Prosecution. "Why did the prisoner cowhide your husband?"

Witness. "My Jake told me that the way of it—"

The Defence. "More hearsay! Your honor surely will not—"

The court silenced the witness. After a few tentative questions had been asked, it was clear that the witness had but a confused notion of the cause of quarrel; therefore the matter was dropped. The cross-examination accomplished little; and when it was finished the house was in no friendly mood toward the prisoner. It had long ago heard about the negro and the note, and the note's contents; these things had now been verified by sworn testimony; how the prisoner came to kill the [other man] was still a mystery, but the thing had a very bad look; for even if murder had not been originally intended but had resulted from a new quarrel, an advantage had been taken, for the prisoner was armed and the other man defenceless. The deceased was his guest, and entitled to fair play. The prisoner might be able to show that the killing was unavoidable and excusable, and of course he would do his best in that direction; it would be an able effort, for his intellectual equipment was good. No one knew his side of the case except himself and his counsel. His statement would be fresh, new, unstaled by previous handling and discussion, and there were advantages in that. He was now placed in the witness-box by the defence and sworn.

His long imprisonment and his sense of the disgrace that had come upon him had told upon him and he looked worn and old, and depressed. He let his eyes wander slowly about, as if he were vaguely hoping for the help of a friendly face; then dropped them, as one who is disappointed, and began his story. His voice was low, but audible, for a breathless hush of expectancy reigned in the place.

"I was alone in the house. I had given the servants passes, and they were away at a frolic." (*Murmur of low voices:"Um—carrying messages!"*) "I had taken to drinking again, and had been drinking now. I was in my room up stairs. I was sitting at my table, and I think I must have been half asleep; for when I started up I was in the dark; the candle had burned out. I was roused by a shout down stairs. There were no closed doors between, and I distinguished the words. They were, 'You godless villain!' The voice was Bleeker's. They were followed by a wild cry or yell, and a heavy fall. I groped my way to the door and to the stairs, and went stumbling down and into the room which has been described here already, and there at the threshold I fell over an obstruction. I was getting up when Joyce and the others entered with the lantern. The obstruction—but you know what it was."

Defence. "Had you sent for deceased?"

"No."

"Written him a note?"

"No."

"Were you expecting him?"

"No."

"Take the witness."

The house was astonished. So this lame tale was all he had to offer! This was the able and elaborate and convincing statement they had been waiting all these months to hear! A plain, straight, impudent pretence that he hadn't even quarreled with the man, let alone killed him! In its amazement and disgust it hardly knew which to do—swear or laugh.

Prosecution. "The servants were out, you say?"

"Yes."

"The jury will please take note that he ad—"

The Court. "Leave that. We cannot call the servants."

Prosecution. "You had recently had a misadventure with Jacob Bleeker, I believe?"

"Yes."

"State the origin of it."

"It was a thing of no consequence. I had been drinking; it would not have occurred, else. Since my wife died, two years ago, I have not been a happy man. And in my moral strength I have been losing ground. It was by her strength and her support that I had for twenty-two years forborne to drink and quarrel. I have said I was not happy. In a mood of despondency I tasted liquor again. That was fatal; the habit returned at once, and I shall be its servant till the end. That man provoked me, the drink inflamed my passion and I used my whip on him."

"What was it he did? what was it he said?"

"As I have said, it was a trifle. I will not particularize."

"A *trifle*. Do you resent trifles in such a violent way?"

"I have explained what influence I was under."

"You were under the like influence on the night of the 17th July, I believe?"

The prisoner nodded his head.

"And therefore in the proper condition to resent trifles again?"

The prisoner was silent. (Murmurs of "Prosecution scored on him *that* time!")

"Tell me. Did your feeling of resentment pass away with the horse-whipping? *Did* it? Answer me! Did it?"

The prisoner hesitated; started to speak; hesitated again, then remained silent.

"Answer the question!" thundered the lawyer.

"I think—think—"

"I ask you, did it pass *away!*"

"N-no—not wholly."

"Ah—not wholly. We are making progress. Pay attention, now; remember, you are on oath. Was something of that feeling still left on the night of the 17th of July?"

The prisoner tried to speak; he swallowed several times, as if his throat were dry—

"Answer!"

"Y-yes."

A deep murmur swelled through the house.

"Very well. Very *well*. Something of it was still remaining. Now then—do you recognise this stick—this club—with the hair and the black stains on it?"

"Yes."

"Is it yours?"

"Yes."

"How did it come to be on that floor by the side of that slaughtered man, that night?"

"I—I—give you my honor I am not able to explain it."

"Are you sure you did not take it there yourself?"

"I do not think I did."

"You do not *think* you did. It seems you are not certain. Do you swear you did not take it there?"

"I—well, I cannot swear, but I know I have no recollection of it."

"You had been drinking; you were not clearly at yourself; is it not presumable that you gathered it up and took it there without being conscious of it?"

"Y-es—I suppose it could happen."

"Very well. You suppose it could happen. The jury will take note of that. I will now ask you about another matter. You were roused out of a semi-conscious state that night by a shout, and you quoted the words. What did you say those words were?"

"You godless villain."

"You are certain those were the words?"

"Yes—quite certain."

"And the voice Bleeker's?"

"Yes."

"You are perfectly sure it was Bleeker's?"

"Perfectly."

"Those words were—say them again."

"You godless villain."

"Ah—you always say them the same way: I see you have your lesson well."

The house smiled, and a dim flush appeared for a moment in the prisoner's cheeks. The lawyer paused some moments, after the manner of his kind when an effect is preparing. Then—

"The idea which you wish to convey is sufficiently clear: that there was *another person* down there; that the words were shouted at that person; which gives us the opportunity to infer that *that person was quarreling with Jacob Bleeker, and killed him.* The idea is well enough—in the absence of a better; it has been used before, in fact is the usual thing; *but*—this time it has a defect." He paused again, to give the general curiosity a chance to work, and grow, then he said, as if to himself, slowly, meditatively, and as if he were carefully computing the weight and dimensions of each word—

"*You—godless—villain.* It is lofty—it is stately—it is theatrical —it is melodramatic." Then suddenly, with a shout which made the house jump, "Shakspeare could have built the phrase, but that ignorant German low-wage mill-hand *never* did!"

The effect was stunning. "By George, it's so!—I never thought of that!" That was the substance of a hundred ejaculations that burst out all over the house. And Ben Thurlow said to Park Robinson, "Why, Park, I never noticed it, but just think of poor Dutchy trying to get off such a swell thing as that; blame it, even the parson couldn't a done it."

"No, sir-ee," responded Robinson, "there ain't *any* man could a done it but the Squire himself."

The lawyer was happy, and looked it; one could imagine him purring inside.

"It may be that the jury will agree with me that there is one man among us, and only one, whose reading, whose cultivation, and whose habit of mind and speech have made it easy and natural for him to put words together in that large and uncommon way—and that man is the prisoner himself." (Robinson to Thurlow, with pride, "The very thing *I* said!") "I am afraid we shall have to doubt that that fine speech establishes the presence of a third person in that house on the fatal night. Now then, I wish to call attention to what seems to me to be a very curious thing. We know it to be unusual for a person to take note of the exact wording of a chance remark and keep it in his memory. We are accustomed to say, 'The *substance* is clear in my memory, but I do not feel quite able to swear to the precise wording of it;' but here we have a witness who remembers the exact wording of a chance remark, and reproduces it again and again in just the same form—powerful evidence of unembarrassed consciousness and a clear head at the time he heard it—and in the face of this he asks us to believe that not two minutes afterward he is in the presence of so tremendous a combination as a murdered man and a gory club and yet can't remember with certainty whether *he* carried that club thither or didn't—merely remarks that he *could* have done it. It seems quite likely! This is indeed a curious memory, a picturesque memory! It takes an iron grip upon the *absolutely impossible,* and wavers and is unsure about the *almost certain!*" (Murmurs of "He's *got* him—he's got him, sure!") "I am done. It is not my privilege, under the law, to go further. The matter stands thus: there is evidence—uncorroborated—that you sent for that man to come to you at dead of night, your family and servants being absent at the time and you alone in the house; there is unassailable evidence that you were embittered against him at the time; there is evidence that this weapon, so fatally used, is your property, and that you are not sure you did not take it there, and yet are positively sure as to the exact wording of a melodramatic and manifestly imaginary speech which you think you heard not two minutes before you were discovered, all drenched with blood, in the presence of that accusing weapon and its awful work. I am not permitted to ask you if there was a quarrel and if the man fell by your hand. The law mercifully shields you from these questions, and I proceed no further. Your counsel will defend you as well as he may; I shall make no plea; the jury will know its duty, and will perform it."

Counsel for the defence rose, but the prisoner motioned him to his seat again, and rose himself, and said, with dignity and a certain impressiveness:

"Nothing can avail, and it is not worth while. I know what the verdict will be, for I know the force of unchallenged evidence, and how to estimate it. I do not welcome that verdict, but I do not appeal against it. I should render it myself, in the jury's place. A word more. There comes a time in the lives of some men when rest from life is better than anything that life itself can offer. That time had come for me, even before this trouble. Nothing that I could say here could alter the impending verdict, and I will hold my peace; but I will leave behind me in writing—"

He broke off, moved his lips a moment or two, as if trying to continue, then made a wandering gesture with his hand and sat down.

There was a volleying discharge of whispers, all about the house: "It's a confession!—it's a confession!" "I *said* he was guilty, from the start!" "So did I!" "I said it, too!" "And I!" "And I!"

The jury retired.

Five minutes passed—they did not return. Ten minutes—fifteen —still they did not return. What could the matter be? Half an hour passed. An hour. Everybody was astonished. The judge began to look irritated. The afternoon sun was getting low. Two hours, and still no jury. Three hours. The audience still sat waiting—and stupefied with surprise. Evening was come.

A constable appeared, with a message:

"The foreman's compliments, your honor, and begs a dis-charge."

"A what!"

"The jury can't agree."

"Can't—a—gree! In-credible!"

"It is what he said, your honor."

"It is the most amazing thing—the most preposterous thing—the most—the—the—tell the sheriff to lock them up and keep them till they *do* agree! The sitting is closed."

The house and court and lawyers rose in a body and went swarming out, excitedly discussing the unheard-of and thitherto unthinkable and impossible incident—a man with not a word of evidence in his favor, and a perfect landslide of evidence against him, as good as confesses his guilt and the jury can't agree!

The prisoner sat with his head bowed. What he thought of the strange episode was not apparent.

IN THE JURY ROOM.

"NOW THEN, gentlemen," said Denison, the foreman, preparing to poll his men, "for one, I'm not sorry our melancholy job is over. Adams!"

"Guilty!"

"Conrad!"

"Guilty!"

"Cook!"

"Guilty!"
"Deming!"
"Guilty!"
"Myself! Same verdict. Denison!" [1]
"The same—guilty!"
"Fargo!"
"Guilty!"
"Jackson!"
"Guilty!"
"Johnson!"
"Guilty!"
"Peters!"
"Guilty!"
"Sexton!"
"Guilty!"
"Well, gentlemen, it's a verdict. Now—"
"Wait—you've skipped Harrison."
"Why, it's so—I beg pardon. Harrison!"
"Not guilty."
"What! Not g—oh, come, you don't mean it."
"Not guilty. It's what I said."

The eleven were speechless; they could only gasp and gaze. Then the foreman said—

"Well, it clean bangs *me*, I *must* say. You are the very *last* man. Why, Harrison—oh, great Scott! I can't understand it at all. Come —what is your reason? what's the difficulty?"

"It's very simple. I think his guilt is not proven."

The eleven threw up their hands and exclaimed in dazed and astonished unison, "Not proven!" Fargo added—

"How in the world *do* you make that out? Harrison, don't forget that you swore to bring in a verdict according to the evidence and your conscience."

"I'm not forgetting it, Henry. I'm sticking to the oath—letter and spirit. Answer me—if there's a doubt isn't the accused entitled to the benefit of it?"

"Certainly."

---

[1] Mark Twain used the same name for two jurors.

"The evidence leaves me in doubt. Now then, what is my duty? State it yourself."

"Well—er—*of course* if there's a doubt—but where in the nation do you find it? That is what puzzles *us.*"

"I don't mind admitting that I don't know, myself, what it is that gives me the doubt, but there it is, and I can't get rid of it. The evidence is sound, straight, looks all right, and I know it ought to convince me; and the fact is it *does* convince my head, but not the rest of me. The rest of me—that is my conscience, I suppose. It keeps warning me that nobody *saw* the Squire kill the man, and then it shoves in the doubt. It's not very much of a doubt, maybe, but it's a doubt. I can't bring him in guilty in the face of that."

"Well, upon my soul! George Harrison, you take the rag! I've seen a many exhibition consciences in my time, but I'm blamed if yourn ain't a long sight the thinskindest one I've ever struck yet. *I* think you ought to keep it done up in something, it's likely to catch its death in *this* climate."

"Delicate?" sniffed Hank Jackson; "land, it ain't any name for it!"

As time wore along, persuasions were tried—arguments were tried—beseechings, implorings, supplications were tried. All in vain. The man stood his ground. By request, the sheriff sent a message to the judge—the jury couldn't agree; he got his answer. Night fell at last; candles were lit; supper was brought; the meal was eaten; the reasonings, persuasions, beseechings, were resumed. There was no result. By midnight the men were tired out; and one by one they stretched themselves out, cocooned in blankets, on the floor around the roaring stove, and listened to the wintry gale shrieking outside, and lulled themselves to sleep with cursings of their brother's inconvenient conscience.

The morning came—dreary, cold, snowy, miserable. The men were worn, seedy, lame in all their joints, irritable. They ate their breakfast in moody silence. At intervals, during the day, the old subject was brought up, and in each case it got but a little way before the sheriff had to interfere to stop a row. The man with the conscience steadfastly refused to give in. Messengers went to the judge from time to time, but he would not discharge the jury.

Night came—and no supper! The judge said, "Starve them into a verdict."

The sheriff added three constables to his force, and he needed them. About midnight, the men sitting angry and still around the stove, there came a break after a long silence. It was Sexton who spoke:

"George Harrison, how much do you owe Squire Baldwin?"

The men pricked up their ears.

"Who says I owe him anything?"

"*I* say it. And I know how it happened, too. You owed four hundred and eighty dollars to his sister, widow Hooker—borrowed money. For years—three at least—ain't that so?"

"Oh, that! That's no news; everybody knows it. What of it?"

"Yes, everybody knows it, but there's something else that everybody *don't* know—but I know it. I just happen to."

"Well, what do you know?"

"I know this: that the Squire bought that note last summer. And I know this, too: that he was going to put the law on you and sell your mill. You were in an awful sweat and in a mighty close place. He was going to do it on the 19th of July—you know it well—but he got into jail on the 17th!"

All the men jumped up and began to shout at once:

"*That's* what's the matter with his conscience!"

"It's perfectly plain: if we hang the murderer, the estate'll sell the mill!"

"And if Harrison hangs the jury the debt's forgiven!"

"He's sold himself! sold himself for four hundred and eighty dollars and interest!"

"Worked like a dog to get on the jury—*now* we know why!"

"*Conscience* a-working him—oh, hell!"

"Go on—say what you want to. I never got on the jury to sell myself. But now that I am on it, I'll stand by my conscience. The judge says he'll starve a verdict out of us. Let him do it, if he thinks he can. I reckon you know me. Starve? I'll stay right here till I *rot,* and *then* I won't give in, you damned cabbages!"

The sheriff and his four constables took a hand, now, and at the end of ten minutes peace reigned once more and there was opportunity to gather up the rags and buttons.

The jury starved all through the next day and night, and then the morning of Christmas Eve dawned, and the famished men listened to the clamor of the joy-bells and groaned in spirit. The judge opened court at nine in the morning and sent to the jury-room for news. The same tiresome answer came back:

"The jury can't agree."

The judge pondered a moment, then said—

"Call them in."

They came in, and the foreman made his report. The judge looked the poor frowsy and ragged group over with a stern and reproachful eye, and said—

"If it was any day but this, I—you are discharged! Sheriff, set the prisoner free!"